PIEZOELECTRICITY

An Introduction to the Theory and
Applications of Electromechanical
Phenomena in Crystals

by WALTER GUYTON CADY, Ph.D., Sc.D.

Professor of Physics Emeritus, Wesleyan University

in two volumes

Volume Two

DOVER PUBLICATIONS, INC.
New York

CONTENTS TO VOLUME TWO

TABLES IN VOLUME TWO

SYMBOLS AND ABBREVIATIONS

References are given to sections in which the symbols are defined or first used.

A	Amplitude of vibration, real or complex, §56.
a	Coefficient of linear thermal expansion, §§20, 516.
a_{mh}, b_{mh}	Piezoelectric stress and strain constants used in the polarization theory, §188.
a, b, c	Crystallographic axes, §4.
a, b, c	Intercepts of the unit face on the a-, b-, c-axes, §4.
B	Dielectric saturation coefficient, §§449, 452.
b	Breadth of a bar or plate; electric susceptance (application to the resonator in §269).
C	Electric capacitance; for resonator, see R, L, C, C_1 below; specific heat, §23.
C_2	Capacitance of gap between crystal and electrodes, §284.
c	Wave velocity, §55; generalized symbol for an elastic stress coefficient, §201.
c_{hk}	Elastic stiffness coefficient, §26; superscripts E, P, D, and * denote the values at constant electric field, constant polarization, constant total displacement, and constant normal displacement, respectively, as explained in Chap. XII.
D	Electric displacement.
d_{mh}	Piezoelectric strain constant, §§23, 124.
E	Electric field strength, §20.
e	Thickness of a plate or bar.
e'	Electric spacing $= e + kw$, §110.
e_r'	Effective electric spacing of a resonator, §§229, 249.
e_{mh}	Piezoelectric stress constant, §§23, 124.
F	Frictional factor, §56; internal field strength, §§113, 485.
f	Frequency; $f_0 = \omega_0/2\pi =$ fundamental frequency, §58.
f_s, f_p	Frequencies at series and parallel resonance, §276.
f_m, f_n	Frequencies for maximum and minimum admittance, §279.
f_R, f_A	Frequencies at resonance and antiresonance, §306a.
G	Equivalent stiffness, §62.
g	Electric conductance (application to a resonator in §269).
H	Magnetic field strength; wave constant $= fl$, §362.
h	Order of harmonic, §55; ratio of any frequency f to the fundamental frequency f_0, §61.
I	Electric current; moment of inertia, §74; magnetic polarization, §548.
J	Mechanical equivalent of heat, §23.
j	$(-1)^{\frac{1}{2}}$.
K	The Boltzmann constant, §114.
k	Wave-number constant, §56; dielectric constant $=$ permittivity, §103; electromechanical coupling factor, §568.
k_l	Effective dielectric constant for lengthwise vibrations, §229.
k_m	Dielectric constant for field in any direction m; other special suffixes are explained in §§105, 107, 430.

k', k''	Dielectric constants, respectively, of a crystal free and clamped, §§104, 124, 204.
kc/sec	Kilocycles per second; occasionally, when there is no ambiguity, the term is abbreviated to kc.
L	The Langevin function, §§114, 548; self-inductance (for self-inductance of a resonator see R, L, C, C_1 below).
l	Length.
l, m, n	Direction cosines.
M	Equivalent mass of a resonator, §62.
ma	Milliamperes.
mc/sec	Megacycles per second; occasionally, when there is no ambiguity, the symbol is abbreviated to mc.
mf, mmf	microfarad, micromicrofarad.
N	Number of molecules per unit volume, §113; dynamic torsional stiffness, §74.
N_s	Static torsional stiffness, §35.
n	shear modulus, §24; measure of dissonance ($n = \omega_0 - \omega$), §58.
P	Electric polarization.
P^0	Spontaneous polarization.
p	Pyroelectric constant, §§20, 516; coefficient of the generalized Langevin function, §§114, 552.
ppm	Parts per million.
Q	Quantity of heat, §20; torque, §35; electric charge; quality factor $= \pi/\delta = \omega L/R$, §§56, 269.
Q_h	Quality factor at harmonic h, §232.
q	Electrocaloric constant, §523; coefficient of the generalized Langevin function, §§114, 552; general stiffness factor in vibrational equations, §55; thermoelastic coefficient, §§20, 23.
q', q_0	Stiffness factors with and without a gap, respectively.
R, L, C, C_1	Equivalent electric constants of a resonator, §232.
R', L', C', C_1'	Same for a resonator with gap, §232.
R_h', L_h', C_h'	Equivalent constants for overtone of order h, §232.
R_s, X_s, C_s	Equivalent series constants, §271.
R_p, X_p, C_p	Equivalent parallel constants, §273.
r	Electromechanical ratio, §233.
s	Generalized symbol for an elastic compliance coefficient, §§20, 201.
s_{hk}	Elastic compliance coefficient, §26; special superscripts same as for c_{hk}.
s_y	Scale value for admittances on the resonance circle, §266.
s_z	Scale value for impedances on the resonance circle, §270.
T	Absolute temperature; torsional compliance, §35.
t	Time; temperature in degrees centigrade.
U	Constant of the gap effect, §237.
u, v, w	Components of displacement of a particle, §26
V	Potential; potential difference.
v	Velocity of a particle in vibration, §58.
W	Equivalent frictional coefficient of a resonator, §62.
w	Total gap between crystal and electrodes, §110.
X	Generalized symbol for a stress, §§20, 201; electric reactance (for reactance of a resonator see §232).
X_h	A component of stress, §25.
X, Y, Z	Orthogonal axes, §5.
X', Y', Z'	Rotated orthogonal axes, §38

$(X_n)_d$	Driving stress, with orientation indicated by n, in resonator theory, §228.
x	Generalized symbol for a strain, §20.
x_h	A component of strain, §26.
x, y, z	Coordinates in space.
Y	Young's modulus, §24; electric admittance (for admittance of a resonator see §§ 232, 265, 269, 279).
Z	Electric impedance (for impedance of a resonator see §§232, 265, 269, 279).
α	Damping factor or attenuation constant, §56; molecular polarizability, §113; temperature coefficient (usually with a subscript), §§85, 357.
α, β, γ	Direction cosines.
γ	Internal field constant, §§113, 484; parameter in theory of forced vibrations, §57; of thickness vibrations, §250.
δ	Logarithmic decrement per cycle, §56.
δ, ϵ	Generalized symbols for piezoelectric constants d_{mh} and e_{mh}, used when it is desirable to omit suffixes, §§20, 201, 228, 246.
ζ	Second thermodynamic potential, §23.
η	Dielectric susceptibility, §104; special suffixes and superscripts are in general the same as for k; but see also §§449, 450, 454.
η_1	Clamped susceptibility of Rochelle salt, §450.
Θ	Angular parameter for expressing general orientation of a plate, §52.
θ	Angle of rotation, §§38, 51; phase angle, §234.
$\theta_{,h}$	Coefficients of dielectric impermeability, §106.
θ_u, θ_l	Upper and lower Curie temperatures.
ϑ	A small departure of temperature from a standard value, §20.
κ	Volume elasticity, §24.
λ	Wavelength; Lamé coefficient, §31.
μ	Moment of a dipole, §113.
ξ	First thermodynamic potential, §23; vibrational displacement of a particle, §56.
ρ	Density; radius of resonance circle, §266.
$\sum\limits_{m}^{h}$	Summation over integral values of m from 1 to h.
σ	Surface density of electric charge; Poisson's ratio, §24; scale value for frequency, §267.
σ'	Scale value for frequency, §268.
τ	Torsional strain, §35.
Φ	Force acting on the equivalent mass M of a resonator, §62.
ϕ	Angle of azimuth, §51.
χ	Reciprocal susceptibility, §106; special suffixes and superscripts same as for η.
ψ	Angle of skew used in expressing the general orientation of a plate, §52.
$\omega = 2\pi f$	Angular velocity or pulsatance; special subscripts same as for f.
$\sim$	Cycles; cycles per second; order of magnitude.

Some of the foregoing symbols, as well as others not listed, are used locally for special purposes. In such cases they are suitably defined.

PIEZOELECTRICITY

CHAPTER XVI

PROPERTIES AND TECHNIQUE OF QUARTZ

Marmoreum ne sperne globum. Spectacula transit
regia, nec rubro vilior iste mari.
informis glacies, saxum rude, nulla figurae
gratia: sed raras inter habetur opes.

—CLAUDIUS CLAUDIANUS.

Because of its physical stability and its superior elastic properties, quartz is the only piezoelectric crystal that has found important applications as a resonator. Its behavior as a resonator will be treated in the next chapter. For the present we shall be concerned first with the conventions respecting axes and angles and with those physical properties that are not treated in Chaps. II, VI, IX, XXX, and XXXI. Later in the chapter will be found a description of methods for orienting raw crystals, cutting and finishing of plates, and mounting in holders.

326. Axes and Angles for Right- and Left-quartz. Through the voluminous literature on the properties of quartz crystals there runs, like a crack in an otherwise clear crystal, an amazing ambiguity concerning the distinction between right- and left-quartz, the positive sense of the directions of the X- and Y-axes, and the positive sense of angles of rotation. This subject has been discussed at some length in two recent papers[110,558], and a committee of the I.R.E. has agreed upon a system of conventions to be recommended for general adoption.* The recommendations of this committee concerning the three matters named above are in agreement with the suggestions in the paper by Van Dyke and the author,[110] and they are followed in this book.

The distinction between right and left (dextro- and levogyrate) crystals has been pointed out in §7. The ambiguity in definition had its origin in the writings of Herschel and Biot, who used opposite definitions of the sense of rotation of a beam of plane-polarized light.† The convention now adopted is that of Biot, according to which a crystal is called *right when the direction of rotation appears clockwise to an observer looking back through the analyzer toward the source of light* (see also §538). This definition has the advantage that if a given crystal is "right"

---

* The report of this committee was approved by the directors of the institute on June 7, 1944. For later I.R.E. Standards see §558.

† SOSMAN, ref. B47, p. 649.

crystallographically, as judged by the s- and x-faces shown in Fig. 5 or Fig. 76, it is also "right" optically.

In all that has to do with the making of oblique cuts of quartz for special purposes or with the study of physical properties in oblique directions, the distinction between right and left specimens must be clearly borne in mind. Failure to do so will almost inevitably lead to false results. In many situations the difference between right and left is equivalent to that between right and *wrong*.

327. The I.R.E. Axial System. Until recently most writers, including Voigt, have used a right-handed orthogonal system of axes for both forms of quartz. This practice has the serious disadvantage of requiring, on passing from a right- to a left-crystal, a change in sign of all piezoelectric constants and of certain terms in the equations for transformed axes. These annoyances and possible sources of error are completely avoided by the adoption of a *right-handed axial system for right-quartz, left-handed for left-quartz*.

The advantages of such an arrangement were pointed out by Koga as early as 1929.* A similar proposal was made later by Mason and Willard† and independently by Cady and Van Dyke.[110]‡ This system of axes was also used by Builder and Benson[82] in 1938.

The convention by which right-handed and left-handed frames of reference are used, respectively, for right- and left-quartz will be referred to as the *I.R.E. system*. Under this system, all equations, together with all direction cosines, are exactly the same for both forms of quartz. In general, it is sufficient in diagrams, etc., to represent a right-handed system of axes, as for right-quartz. Not until the time comes to lay off angles on an actual specimen is it necessary to give heed to the question of enantiomorphism. Then, if the specimen is left-handed, one need only reverse the direction of the X-axis and observe the rule given below for the positive sense of angles.

The change in axes from right- to left-handed on passing from a right- to a left-quartz is a logical accompaniment to the corresponding change in the external appearance and physical properties of the crystal. If a photograph were taken of a right-quartz crystal showing the right-handed XYZ-axial system together with all equations, curves, polar diagrams, and models illustrating its physical properties including elastic and piezoelectric, then the mirror image of this picture, obtained, for example, by making a photographic print with the film reversed, would be an exact reproduction of a left-quartz together with its physical properties.

---

* KOGA, I., *Jour. Inst. Elec. Engrs. Japan*, July, 1929, pp. 49–92; *Electrotech. Jour. (Japan)*, 1938, pp. 287–289.

† W. P. MASON and G. W. WILLARD, *Proc. I.R.E.*, vol. 28, p. 428, 1940.

‡ This paper was written in 1939, but publication was delayed.

These considerations are made clear in Fig. 76, which shows an end view and also a cross section in the YZ-plane, for both right- and left-quartz. In the upper diagram the positive direction of the Z-axis, in the lower diagram the positive direction of the X-axis, points toward the observer.

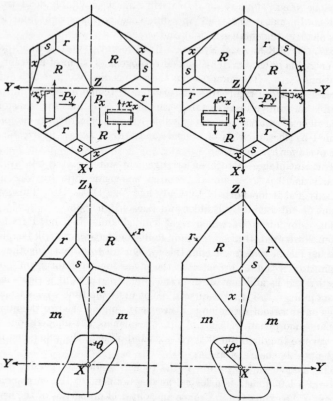

Fig. 76.—Left- and right-quartz, showing strains x_x and x_y, with accompanying polarizations P_x and P_y, also showing the positive sense of the angle of rotation θ.

The Y- and Z-axes have already been defined in §5. As may be seen from Fig. 76, *the positive end of an X-axis emerges from the crystal at each of the three prismatic edges where s- and x-faces may be found.* This is the end at which a positive charge appears when the x_x-strain is positive, *i.e.*, when the specimen is *stretched* in the X-direction. These statements hold for both right- and left-quartz.

Figure 76 shows an X-cut being stretched so that there is an extensional strain in the X-direction and accompanying contraction in the Y-direction. The arrow P_z indicates the positive direction of the ensuing electric polarization, in conformity with the statement above that a positive strain is associated with a positive charge at the positive end of the X-axis. *Compressional strains and stresses do not change sign in the mirror image.*

Positive Sense of Rotation for Quartz Axes. The general definition of positive and negative angles given in §38 is, according to the convention here adopted, to be applied to right-quartz. For a *left*-quartz the angle of rotation is to be considered as positive when *clockwise* as seen by an observer looking back toward the origin from the positive end of the axis of rotation.

These statements may be combined in the following single rule, applicable to both types of quartz crystals:

The angle of rotation is to be called positive when the sense of rotation is from $+X$ to $+Y$, from $+Y$ to $+Z$, or from $+Z$ to $+X$. In the I.R.E. system this definition is valid for both right- and left-quartz. An equivalent statement, following the usual convention for rotational vectors, is that a positive angle of rotation is related to the positive sense of the axis of rotation as the direction of twist of a screw is related to the direction of advance, the screw being right-handed for a right-quartz, left-handed for a left-quartz.

As an illustration of the rule for rotated axes there are shown in Fig. 76 polar diagrams of the distribution of Young's modulus in the YZ-plane. This quantity is the reciprocal of the compliance coefficient s'_{33} obtained by rotating the Y- and Z-axes through various angles θ about the X-axis. The maximum value is in the direction approximately perpendicular to an r-face, and the corresponding angle θ, according to the I.R.E. system, is about $+48°$ for both right- and left-quartz (§96).

In the upper portion of Fig. 76 is a section of a Y-cut plate undergoing a positive shearing strain x_y, together with the associated electric polarization P_y. Tangential forces are indicated by arrows. From the equation $P_y = e_{26}x_y = -e_{11}x_y$ and the sign of e_{11} as given below, it is seen that P_y is negative. The piezoelectric shear x_y produced by a field E_y in the positive direction of the Y-axis has the same sign for left- as for right-quartz. A similar statement applies also to all other piezoelectric shears.

The Signs of Elastic and Piezoelectric Constants. According to Voigt's notation, all elastic coefficients have the same signs for left- as for right-quartz, but the signs of all piezoelectric constants change in passing from right to left. Under the I.R.E. system, Voigt's notation for the elastic coefficients remains unchanged.

Voigt assigns negative numerical values to the constants d_{11}, e_{11}, and e_{14} for left-quartz and a positive value to d_{14}. These signs are with respect to a right-handed axial system. While other observers have obtained values differing in magnitude from Voigt's, there has been no disagreement as to sign. For a right-quartz the signs, according to Voigt, are reversed, *viz.*, d_{11^+}, e_{11^+}, d_{14^-}, e_{14^+}. According to the I.R.E. convention, adopted in this book, the signs of the piezoelectric constants for *both types of quartz* are those which Voigt would have assigned to a *right*-quartz; they are opposite to those commonly quoted. Voigt's statement that his observations were made on a left-quartz is so inconspicuous* as to be easily overlooked, and those who made later determinations seem to have been more interested in numerical magnitudes than in signs.

328. Some Physical Properties of Quartz.† Little is known concerning the effects of traces of impurity and of previous treatment on the physical properties. At all events, such effects are probably slight, except in the case of the electrical resistivity. Nevertheless, the discrepancies between the results of different observers may have been due in part to real differences between the various specimens used.

The *hardness* of quartz is 7 on the Mohs scale. Ichikawa‡ states that a surface cut normal to the optic axis is much softer than the natural faces. The *crushing strength* has been found by Bridgman§ to vary from 33,000 to 40,000 kg/cm², depending on the confining pressure. When the crushing stress was reached, the crystal specimen became reduced to a fine powder. Sosman[B47] states that at atmospheric pressure the crushing strength is around 24,000 kg/cm² and also that for small specimens a tensile strength of about 1,000 kg/cm² may be expected.‖ The tensile strength is slightly greater parallel than perpendicular to the optic axis.

Fracture. The atoms of quartz are so closely bound together in all directions that there are no planes of easy cleavage. There are, however, two tendencies that can often be observed. The first is a peculiar shell-like curved portion of the broken surface, called *conchoidal fracture.* The second is fracture approximately parallel to one of the faces of the major rhombohedron or, to a smaller extent, the minor rhombohedron.¶ This type of fracture is sometimes encountered on heating or when plates vibrated piezoelectrically are shattered by the application of too high a voltage. The author first observed this latter effect in 1920. Since then it has been recorded by others, for example Wright and Stuart,[594] Seidl,[455]

* "Lehrbuch," p. 861.

† All data are for *α-quartz* unless otherwise noted. Certain data on the β-modification (at temperatures above 573°C) will be found elsewhere in this book. For a full discussion of β-quartz see Sosman.[B47]

‡ S. Ichikawa, *Am. Jour. Sci.*, vol. 39, pp. 455–473, 1915.

§ P. W. Bridgman, *Jour. Applied Phys.*, vol. 12, pp. 461–469, 1941.

‖ From this figure and the elastic compliance of quartz the breaking extensional *strain* for a quartz bar is found to be of the order of 0.001.

¶ See H. W. Fairbairn, *American Mineralogist*, vol. 24, pp. 351–368, 1939.

Booth,[69] Gramont,[B21] Van Dyke,[555] Sanders,[446] Shubnikov,[463] and, especially, Straubel.[488] Gibbs and Tsien[159] observed a *spiral* fracture in the case of a torsionally vibrating hollow quartz cylinder with length parallel to the optic axis. Rivlin* found that, after a Z-cut plate had been suitably rough-ground, it showed a hexagonal pattern when held close to the eye while the observer viewed a point source of light. He attributed the effect to comparatively easy fracture in planes belonging to zones $\{10 \cdot l\}$ and suggested it as a means for locating the X-axes. Rivlin's pattern can be seen easily with the aid of the rodoscope described in §339. The grinding on the Z-surface should be done by hand, using very coarse carborundum (45 to 60 mesh) and water, and applying rather heavy pressure in short, curving strokes in random directions. In 1930 Shubnikov had already observed the formation of small triangular pits when a Z-surface had been struck with a sharp steel point. He found that subsequent etching with H_2F_2 made the outlines more distinct. A similar effect produced by dropping a steel ball on to the Z-surface is mentioned by Hawk.†

Luminescence is observed when prismatic edges of two quartz crystals are struck together in a dark room. The effect is not as bright as with sugar crystals.

329. The physical properties of quartz have been discussed very exhaustively by Sosman.[B47] A few of the data from his book, for *density*, *thermal conductivity*, and *specific heat*, are assembled in Table XXV.

TABLE XXV.—DENSITY ρ IN GM CM^{-3}, THERMAL CONDUCTIVITY IN 10^{-3} CAL CM^{-1} SEC^{-1} DEG^{-1}, AND SPECIFIC HEAT IN CAL GM^{-1} DEG^{-1}, FOR α-QUARTZ, AT VARIOUS TEMPERATURES

Temperature, deg. C	ρ	Thermal conductivity		Specific heat
		$\|Z$	$\perp Z$	
−50	2.655	40	20.5	0.1412
0	2.651	32	17.0	0.1664
50	2.646	25.5	14.9	0.1870
100	2.641	21	13.1	0.2043

The symmetry of quartz is such that the thermal and electrical conductivities have only two principal values, parallel and perpendicular to the Z-axis, just as is the case with the dielectric and optical constants. For oblique directions the values vary ellipsoidally between the two principal values.

* R. S. RIVLIN, *Nature*, vol. 146, pp. 806–807, 1940.
† H. W. N. HAWK, U. S. patent 2,264,380, 1941.

As the best mean value at 20°C Sosman adopts $\rho = 2.649 \pm 0.2$. Recently Miller and Du Mond* have found $\rho = 2.64822 \pm 0.00005$ at 25°. For most calculations it suffices to call $\rho = 2.65$ at ordinary temperatures.

The temperature coefficient of density $(\partial\rho/\partial t)/\rho$ as calculated by Mason and Sykes[343] is $-36.4(10^{-6})$.

For β-quartz, $\rho = 2.518$ at 600°C.†

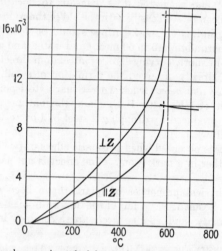

Fig. 77.—Thermal expansion of alpha- and beta-quartz, from Jay. Upper curve $\perp Z$-axis, lower curve $\|Z$-axis. Ordinates indicate expansion per unit length, starting at 18°C.

The *coefficient of thermal expansion* has been thoroughly investigated by Jay,‡ by an X-ray method, over a wide range of temperature. His results, shown in Fig. 77, include data on β-quartz. His values are in general agreement with those obtained by optical methods. In the neighborhood of room temperature the coefficients of expansion parallel and perpendicular to the optic axis are found from Jay's results to be 9.0 (10^{-6}) and 14.8 (10^{-6}) per degree, respectively.

More recently, the thermal expansion perpendicular to the optic axis has been measured by Nix and MacNair§ by means of their "inter-

* P. H. MILLER, JR., and J. W. M. DU MOND, *Phys. Rev.*, vol. 57, pp. 198–206, 1940.

† A. L. DAY, R. B. SOSMAN, and J. C. HOSTETTER, *Am. Jour. Sci.*, vol. 37, pp. 1–39, 1914.

‡ A. H. JAY, *Proc. Roy. Soc. (London) (A)*, vol. 142, pp. 237–247, 1933.

§ F. C. NIX and D. MACNAIR, *Rev. Sci. Instruments*, vol. 12, pp. 66–70, 1941. The dilatometer described in this paper should prove useful for measuring piezoelectric as well as thermal dilatations at all temperatures.

ferometric dilatometer." Their results are in substantial agreement with Jay's.

330. Electrical Properties of Quartz. Quartz is an excellent insulator, except at high temperatures. Such *electrical conductivity* as it has is much greater parallel than perpendicular to the optic axis. Parallel to the optic axis the conductivity is largely electrolytic at high temperatures, owing to traces of impurities. The data in the following table are from Sosman;[B47] they indicate only the order of magnitude. Observations of conductivity at various temperatures and under various voltages

TABLE XXVI.—RESISTIVITY OF QUARTZ AT VARIOUS TEMPERATURES
In ohm cm^{-1}

Temperature, deg C	Resistivity	
	$\|Z$	$\perp Z$
20	10^{14}	$200(10^{14})$
100	$8(10^{11})$	
1000	$5(10^4)$	$10(10^4)$

have been made more recently by Altheim.* Joffé[B30] found that exposure of a specimen to the radiations from radium caused a gradual increase in conductivity, so that after "many days" the initial value was exceeded many times.

The *electric strength* of quartz parallel to the optic axis is given by Austen and Whitehead† as $6.7(10^6)$ volts/cm. This value agrees well with the observations of von Hippel and Maurer,‡ who find that the electric strength increases almost linearly from about $4(10)^6$ volts/cm at $-80°C$ to $7(10^6)$ at $+60°C$. The value is slightly greater parallel than perpendicular to the optic axis.

331. The recorded measurements of the *dielectric constant* of quartz show a spread of several per cent. It is not yet known to how great an extent this may be due to actual differences between individual speci-

---

* OLGA G. VON ALTHEIM, *An. Phk.*, vol. 35, pp. 417–444, 1939. For further investigations on the conductivity of quartz see E. Darmois and R. Radmanèche, *Jour. phys. rad.*, vol. 7, pp. 16S, 17S, 1936; N. G. Rahimi, *Jour. phys. rad.*, vol. 9, pp. 291–296, 1938; E. G. Rochow, *J. Applied Phys.*, vol. 9, pp. 664–669, 1938; H. Saegusa and T. Matsumoto, *Japan Jour. Phys.*, vol. 11, p. 61, 1936; H. Saegusa and K. Saeki, *Sci. Repts. Tohoku Univ.*, vol. 18, pp. 231–244, 1929; H. Saegusa and S. Shimizu, *Elec. Rev. (Japan)*, vol. 18, pp. 69f., 1930; H. Saegusa and S. Shimizu, *Sci. Repts. Tohoku Univ.*, vol. 20, pp. 1–35, 1931; Seidl;[456] S. Shimizu, *Phil. Mag.*, vol. 13, pp. 907–934, 1932.

† A. E. W. AUSTEN and S. WHITEHEAD, *Proc. Roy. Soc. (London)* (A), vol. 176, pp. 33–50, 1940.

‡ A. VON HIPPEL and R. J. MAURER, *Phys. Rev.*, vol. 59, pp. 820–823, 1941.

mens. At least it can be said that the constant is slightly greater parallel to the optic axis than perpendicular to it and that there is no great change with frequency outside the experimental errors. Jaeger's values[*] were slightly greater at high than at low frequency. On the other hand, Doborzynski,[†] whose paper contains a comparison of the results of many observers, found from his own measurements at 50 cycles/sec that $k_\parallel = 4.66$, $k_\perp = 4.55$. At $5(10^6)$ cycles/sec he found $k_\parallel = 4.58$, $k_\perp = 4.41$. All things considered, we are inclined to accept the "most probable" values recommended by Sosman, viz.,

$$k_\parallel = 4.6 \qquad k_\perp = 4.5 \tag{472}$$

The value of $k_\parallel$ is independent of strain. 4.5 is the value of $k_\perp$ for a *free* crystal.

To calculate the *clamped dielectric constant* $k''_\perp$ of quartz for a field perpendicular to the optic axis we specialize Eq. (265) in §204. Using the values of the piezoelectric constants given in §156, we obtain

$$k'_\perp = k''_\perp + 4\pi(2e_{11}d_{11} + e_{14}d_{14}) = k''_\perp + 0.087 \tag{473}$$

Calling $k'_\perp = 4.5$, we thus have

$$k''_\perp = 4.41 \tag{474}$$

For lengthwise vibrations of an X-cut quartz bar with length parallel to the Y-axis, the effective dielectric constant k_l is derived from Eq. (311) in §229, using for s^E_{nn}, from §90, $s^E_{nn} = s^E_{22} = s^E_{11} = 1.269(10^{-12})$:

$$k_l = 4.5 - 0.047 = 4.45 \tag{474a}$$

The dielectric constant for a field in any oblique direction N having the direction cosines l, m, n is given in §108, Eq. (157):

$$k_N = l^2 k_{11} + m^2 k_{22} + n^2 k_{33}$$

For quartz, $k_{11} = k_{22} = k_\perp$, $k_{33} = k_\parallel$. Hence one can write, setting $n = \cos\theta$ according to Fig. 17, p. 81,

$$k_N = (1 - n^2)k_\perp + n^2 k_\parallel = k_\perp + (k_\parallel - k_\perp)\cos^2\theta \tag{474b}$$

For the free crystal this expression becomes

$$k'_N = 4.5 + 0.1\cos^2\theta \tag{474c}$$

The dielectric constant is the same in all azimuths; the only variation is with the angle of altitude.

[*] SOSMAN.[B57]

[†] D. DOBORZYNSKI, *Bull. Intern. Acad. Polon. Sci. Lettres*, ser. A, no. 6-8A, pp. 320–349, 1937.

Dependence of the Dielectric Constant on Temperature. Parallel to the optic axis the constant hardly changes from 0°C to about 100°C, after which it increases, slowly at first and then more rapidly, until at 300° the value is about 13. From here on up to 750°C there is practically no further change.

Perpendicular to the axis the constant is unchanged up to 300°, with a very slight increase from 300° to about 500°, where a rather sharp upward turn takes place until at 800° the value is about 12.*

Dependence of the Dielectric Constant on the Electric Field Strength. The results obtained by Saegusa and Nakamura† are as follows: $k_{\parallel}$ is independent of the field strength up to 2,000 volts/cm, showing an increase from there on; $k_{\perp}$ shows no variation up to 12,000 volts/cm.

EXPERIMENTAL DETERMINATION OF THE AXES OF QUARTZ CRYSTALS

332. Under this heading are to be included the methods for distinguishing right- from left-crystals and for locating twinned regions, as well as the use of polarized light, etching, and X-rays for determining the axial directions.

For both experimental research and industrial uses it is important to know the orientation of the preparation, whether bar, rectangular plate, or some other form, with respect to the crystallographic axes. The allowable tolerance depends, of course, on the purpose in hand. For demonstrations, qualitative tests, and the construction of piezo oscillators when the demand for precision is modest, results may be satisfactory if the orientation is in error by several degrees. The specimens used in the pioneer work on resonators were far from being accurately oriented.

The demand for greater constancy of frequency in radio transmitters that arose in the 1920's led first to thermostatic control of temperature of the X- and Y-cuts of quartz crystals that were then employed and later to the use of various oblique cuts. Such cuts can now be made with a vibrational frequency almost independent of temperature, although for some purposes temperature control is still used. The orientation of plates with zero temperature coefficient is quite critical; in some cases the tolerance is no more than a few minutes of arc.

In the past, quartz crystals were available that were developed with enough perfection to enable plates to be cut with good precision by reference to the natural faces. Even then, however, it was necessary to use optical tests for twinned regions and often also in order to know

---

* Sosman, ref., B47 p. 524.

† H. Saegusa and K. Nakamura, *Sci. Repts. Tohoku Univ.*, vol. 21, pp.411–438, 1932.

whether a crystal was right or left.   Entirely untwinned specimens have always been rare.

The demand for quartz crystals has now become so great that much of the raw material consists of poorly faced specimens, broken fragments devoid of natural faces, or "river quartz," which, while it may be of good quality inside, looks externally like a rounded cobblestone, with an almost opaque exterior.

Many techniques have been developed for determining the directions of the crystallographic axes without making use of natural faces.   The following data are sought:

1. The direction of the optic (Z-) axis.
2. The hand of the crystal, whether right or left.
3. The positive direction of either the X- or the Y-axis.

Usually it is most convenient to obtain the first two data by an optical method.   When once the optic axis has been determined within a few degrees, the etch method offers a quick and simple means for a more precise orientation; it indicates also whether the crystal is right or left, reveals twinned regions on the etched surface, and shows the positive directions of the transverse axes.   For highest precision, X-rays are used.

Piezoelectric or pyroelectric tests have often been used for finding the locations and positive ends of the X-axes.*

Such methods are useful mainly in making very rough preliminary orientations of raw crystals after the direction of the optic axis has been approximately found.   They cannot be included among the methods of precision.

333. Optical Tests of Quartz.   The effects employed are chiefly extinction and optical activity, both of which are described in Chap. XXX.   The optical constants of quartz are given in §534.

Immersion Liquids.   Polished plane-parallel plates can, of course, be tested without immersion.   If a specimen is irregular and unpolished, the light is refracted and scattered on entering and leaving the crystal unless the latter is immersed in a transparent liquid having at least approximately the same refractive index as quartz. For precise work in which the optic axis is to be parallel to the light beam, the index of the liquid should approximate closely to that of the ordinary ray, *viz.*, 1.544, and the liquid should be in a tank with parallel sides of plane strain-free glass.   For approximate tests one need not be quite so particular.   A clear lubricating oil is often sufficient.

The ideal immersion liquid would be transparent, colorless, non-volatile, non-inflammable, non-corrosive, and non-toxic, with the desired refractive index.   No available liquid has all these virtues.   Nitrobenzene makes a fair match but is toxic. Monobrombenzene is somewhat better, as is also a mixture of nitrobenzene with carbon tetrachloride, or of carbon disulphide with benzene.   Tetralin is sometimes used, and also methyl salicylate or cedar oil.   Very satisfactory results are obtained

---

*See, for example, L. H. Dawson.[121]

with tricresyl phosphate.* Recently a special liquid with refractive index 1.541 to 1.547 has become available.†

Preliminary Inspection. This step may be combined with the next following. The specimen is examined for cracks, phantom growths, "feathers," and inclusions, in a strong beam of transverse light, preferably with the crystal in the immersion liquid. Portions containing more than minute traces of imperfection should be rejected, since imperfections may make the finished plate more fragile and may also distort the elastic waves when the resonator vibrates. There appears to be no objection to the use of smoky quartz or of crystals that are otherwise tinted with impurities. With river quartz it may be necessary to grind or cut "windows" at various points before the preliminary inspection can be made.

Rough Determination of the Optic Axis and Detection of Optical Twinning. The crystal is immersed and examined between crossed polaroids in a beam of diffuse light, which may be white.‡ Rotating the crystal about the beam as axis will cause the transmitted light to change from light to dark four times in a complete rotation, owing to extinction, until an orientation is found for which the field remains bright on rotation. The optic axis is then approximately parallel to the beam. Extinction begins to be less complete when the optic axis is within 20° of the beam.§

When the crystal is thus viewed in plane-polarized light in a direction sufficiently close to that of the optic axis, if there is no twinning the field looks nearly uniform, except for differences in color or brightness due to differences in optical path through various portions of the crystal. If

* Sold under the trade name of Lindol. It is clear, colorless, and neither volatile nor inflammable. The refractive index is about 1.561 at 11.5°C and 1.555 at 25°C. To some individuals it is said to be a skin irritant. In any case, the liquid should be free from the ortho form, which is toxic. Tricresyl phosphate has been used in Scott Laboratory for quartz testing for many months without ill effects.

† Obtainable from the Socony Vacuum Oil Company. See also the list of liquids given by W. L. Bond.[66]

‡ If the ends have already been cut off with fairly plane surfaces approximately normal to the optic axis, as can be done if the crystal has natural faces, the examination for twinning can be made without complete immersion. A piece of ordinary glass can be placed in contact with each cut surface, with a smear of the immersion liquid between.

§ An instrument devised in this laboratory for the approximate determination of the optic axis without the necessity of dipping the hands in the immersion liquid is the *flicker polariscope.* The crystal is clamped in a holder that can be rotated about horizontal axes by rods extending down into the immersion liquid. The light beam passes vertically upward through the bottom of the glass jar containing the liquid. Above and below the jar are crossed polaroids, mounted in disks that are rotated synchronously by a chain drive about once per second. Periodic flashes of light are seen when the quartz is in place, which become a steady glow when the optic axis is parallel to the beam. A precision of 2 or 3° is easily obtained. With certain refinements settings can be made closer than 1°.

optical twinning is present, it is revealed by a sharply defined pattern, usually in the form of many triangles crowded together or streaks parallel to the X-axes, showing brilliant colors if the light source is white. The twinned regions are seen more often around the edges than in the center of the field. Their depth in the crystal can sometimes be estimated by tilting. Stereoscopic devices have also been used for the localization of twinned regions.

The approximate locations of twinned regions can be marked on the crystal and such portions discarded when the crystal is cut. Some crystals show a boundary separating the right from the left form. The boundary can be marked and the two regions utilized separately.

River quartz can usually be cleaned sufficiently by scouring to allow the optic axis to be found approximately by the method just described. A cut roughly normal to the optic axis is then made at each end, after which the crystal can be immersed again and examined for twinning.

There are also methods for finding the approximate direction of the optic axis by orienting the crystal for *maximum* extinction, instead of absence of extinction.

If the crystal is not more than about 3 cm in length parallel to the optic axis and is placed between polaroids in diffuse light, as described above, traces of the rings mentioned in the next section are usually visible to the eye placed close to the crystal.

334. *Determining the "Hand" of a Quartz Crystal in Convergent Polarized Light.* The apparatus is very simple and need not be of high optical quality. White light may be used, with or without a color filter, although with large crystals a mercury or sodium arc is to be preferred.

By means of a lens somewhat wider than the crystal, the light is converged to a cone of which the apex falls in the crystal, the outermost rays making an angle of 15° or so with the optic axis of the system. Unless the crystal is a polished Z-cut slab, which is usually not the case, it must be immersed. For large crystals the focal length of the lens may be from 5 to 10 in.; a condenser lens of the sort used in theater spotlights is suitable. A polarizer is placed between the light source and the crystal.

An observer looking at the quartz through an analyzer sees a system of more or less concentric rings. With an accurate Z-cut plate of any thickness greater than 0.5 mm, plane-parallel and untwinned, the rings are concentric circles centered on the beam if the optic axis is parallel to the beam. The rings are distorted if the crystal is irregular, and they are broken in outline, with abrupt changes in color or brightness, if there is twinning.

If now the analyzer is rotated, the rings either expand or contract according to the "hand" of the quartz. The rule is as follows:

When the analyzer is turned clockwise, if the rings expand, the quartz *is right; if they contract, the quartz is left.*   The clockwise rotation is from the viewpoint of an observer looking back toward the source of light.*

If the crystal is twinned, some segments of the rings may expand while others contract.

If white light is used and if the crystal is not more than about 2 cm thick parallel to the optic axis, the hand of the quartz can also be judged by observing the succession of colors in the clear field inside the circles, as the analyzer is turned.   On clockwise rotation of the analyzer, a right-quartz shows a gradual change from red through yellow and green to violet.   With a left-quartz the succession is reversed.   This method can be used with plates that are too thin to show the expansion of the rings.

Finding the Orientation of the Optic Axis by Convergent Light.   The apparatus is similar in principle to that just described but is constructed with more precision and with the addition of a lens and eyepiece between the analyzer and the eye.   Means must be provided for a fine angular adjustment of the crystal until the ring pattern is symmetrical and for correlating its position with the axis of the optical system.   A precision of 1 min of arc has been claimed for this method.†   A refinement of the method, in which use is made of Airy's spirals, has been described by Booth.[69]

335. Etching Tests of Quartz.   The solvent commonly used is hydro-fluoric acid, H_2F_2, since most other solvents, for example hot alkalis, act very slowly and there is no evidence that they produce better etch figures.‡   For most purposes commercial 48 per cent acid at room temperature is suitable, although in some cases, as will be seen, greater dilution gives better results.   The time of etching may vary from half an hour to several hours, depending on the orientation of the surface to be etched and on the manner of examining the result.

Among common materials attacked but little, if at all, by H_2F_2 are paraffin, rubber, lead, and copper.   Small-scale etching is conveniently carried on in a dish or tray lined with paraffin or in an old rubber battery

---

* The hand of a Z-cut slab of any thickness up to at least 2 cm can be determined with no apparatus beyond two small pieces of polaroid.   If the faces of the slab are unpolished, they can usually be made sufficiently transparent by merely moistening. The crystal is held close to the eye, with a polaroid on each side, in light from the sky or from any bright diffuse source.   A portion, at least, of the system of colored rings can be seen, and their expansion or contraction on rotating the analyzing polaroid can be observed.   Moreover, by making use of the partly polarized light from the sky, the polarizer can be dispensed with.   By a little juggling one can even contrive to use a piece of glass, for example a spectacle lens, as analyzer.

† A. Biot, *Ann. Soc. sci. Bruxelles*, vol. 58, pp. 98–100, 1938.

‡ Recently a new etch solvent for quartz, free from the more objectionable properties of H_2F_2, has become available under the name of Quartz-Etch, the base of which is said to be ammonium bifluoride.   Preliminary tests in this laboratory indicate that the etch figures and refraction images are inferior to those obtained with H_2F_2.

jar.   Copper implements and racks are useful for holding and handling crystals.   Most uniform results are attained by rocking the container during etching; a motor drive is easily contrived and greatly to be recommended.   The acid loses strength both by evaporation and use and has to be renewed rather frequently.   There is also some evidence that acid containing considerable amounts of the products of solution does not make as good etch patterns as freshly prepared acid.

Provision should be made for drawing off the vapor from the acid and for neutralizing it if necessary.   Every possible precaution must be taken to guard against even slight contact of the acid with the skin, since hydrofluoric acid burns are very serious.

Etching takes place most rapidly on surfaces normal to the Z-axis, less rapidly at the ends of a Y-axis (prismatic faces) and the positive ends of the X-axes, and very slowly at the negative ends of the X-axes.

Etching tests are useful for determining whether a crystal is right or left; for locating, on the etched surface, regions of optical and electrical twinning; and for determining approximately the orientation of any specimen or cut with respect to the crystallographic axes.   Several techniques are available: (*a*) microscopic examination; (*b*) production of large-scale patterns on a quartz sphere; (*c*) light reflection; (*d*) light refraction.*

336. *a. Microscopic Examination of Etched Surfaces.*†   We consider first the etch figures on surfaces normal to the X-, Y-, and Z-axes and their relation to the hand of the crystal and to optical and electrical twinning. Although the figures usually observed differ widely in size and in degree of perfection, still certain characteristic forms can be recognized.   These forms appear best after etching for an entire day and require no special preliminary treatment of the surface beyond enough lapping to remove gross roughness.

As illustrated in Fig. 78, at the positive end of the X-axis the figures resemble narrow hysteresis loops, which merge to form closely packed grooves parallel to the Z-axis.   At the negative end are parallelograms with one pair of sides parallel to Z.   The polar character of the X-axis is here clearly in evidence.   The Y-axis is not polar, and the figures at its ends, for crystals of the same hand, are alike except for orientation; this difference can be traced to the polarity of the X-axis.   The same remarks apply to the figures on faces normal to the Z-axis.   In each of

* A technique for making replicas of etched surfaces, suitable for microscope slides, has been described by V. J. Schaefer, *Phys. Rev.*, vol. 62, pp. 495–496, 1942.

† Perplexing discrepancies are found in the literature.   The outlines of etch figures on the *m*-faces (Y-cuts) in Groth (ref. B22, Table III) do not agree with those shown by O. Meyer and S. L. Penfield in *Trans. Conn. Acad. Arts Sci.*, vol. 8, pp. 158–165, 1889, and both are at variance with the results of very careful tests made in this laboratory.

the six diagrams the etch figures at the right and left of the vertical axis illustrate *optical* twinning.

The figures at the ends of the Z-axis (*i.e.*, on Z-cut surfaces) are due to minute pyramids or pits with triangular bases (see Plate 6 in the paper by Booth[69]). They vary greatly in appearance with time of etching, illumination, and microscope focus. On prolonged etching they undergo characteristic changes.[*]

If electrical twinning (§15) is present, some regions of the same hand are rotated 180° about the Z-axis with respect to the rest of the crystal. For example, a left-quartz may show etch figures like a_1 and a_2 on the same X-surface, b_1 and b_2 on the same Y-surface, and c_1 and c_2 on the same

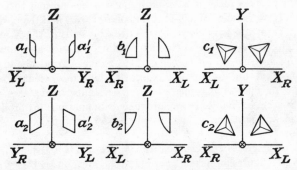

Fig. 78.—Typical idealized microscopic etch figures for right- and left-quartz, on surfaces normal to the X-, Y-, and Z-axes. Upper row is for surfaces from which the positive end of one axis points toward the observer. In the lower row the positive end points away from the observer. Figures for left-quartz are to the left of the vertical axis in each case, for right-quartz to the right. The symbol Y_L indicates the positive direction of the Y-axis for left-quartz, etc. The magnification is of the order of 200 diameters. The patterns are shown in their actual orientation on the crystal surface, and not as they appear under the microscope.

Z-surface. Electrically twinned regions are generally bordered by irregular lines. Both elastic and piezoelectric properties are different on opposite sides of the border; hence, electrically twinned plates are not suitable for resonators.

In *optical twins* there are two different possibilities, according to whether the two components have the positive ends of the X-axes or of the Y-axes pointing the same way (see Fig. 76). In the former case, a surface normal to X may show a_1 and a_1' on different areas, while the corresponding surface on the other side of the crystal shows a_2 and a_2'. If the Y-axes point the same way, a_1 and a_2 may be seen on one side of the crystal, a_1' and a_2' on the other. Analogous remarks may be made concerning the figures on Y-surfaces. As to the Z-surfaces, if the X-axes (or Y-axes) point the same way, the figures are always mirror

[*] HONESS, ref. *B*26.

images with respect to X (or Y). It seems to be a common convention to call the type of twinning when the Y-axes point the same way simply "optical twinning," while the term "combined optical and electrical twinning" is used in the other case.

If the X-axes point the same way in an optically twinned crystal, the piezoelectric properties are the same on both sides of the boundary, but not the elastic properties. If the X-axes are oppositely oriented (in which case the Y-axes are similarly oriented), the elastic properties, but not the piezoelectric, are the same on both sides of the boundary. In either case optical twinning beyond a very small amount makes a specimen undesirable for resonators.

(a)   (b)

FIG. 79.—Etch pattern on a 50-mm sphere of left-quartz, from Van Dyke. (a) View toward an m-face, with an R-face above it; (b) view along the optic axis.

Etched surfaces in other orientations show a great variety of characteristic figures, often very difficult to identify under the microscope. In practical cases it is much better to identify cuts and axes by reflected or refracted light rather than microscopically. The advantage thus gained is that the effects of multitudes of etch facets become integrated, yielding more dependable results than is possible from the examination of individual etch figures.*

337. *b. Large-scale etch patterns on a quartz sphere* have recently been described by Van Dyke.[558]† Figure 79, taken from his paper, shows the appearance of an initially polished sphere after several hours of etching in H_2F_2. The entire surface has been more or less attacked, but certain

---

* Excellent microphotographs of etch figures on quartz surfaces in many orientations appear in a paper by Bond.[63]

† References to the literature on the subject are given in this paper.

areas, notably near the negative ends of the X-axes, are so little etched that the formation of etch facets can be detected only by the "sheen" in light reflected at the proper angle.   On the other hand, the roughening of the surface marked out by the "tripus" in Fig. 79b is quite conspicuous. In general, the outlines of the pattern are determined not so much by marked differences in amount of etching as by changes in the sheen, indicating that the orientations of the facets formed in the process of etching, as well as the speed of solution, are strongly dependent on the angle at which the sphere cuts across the lattice structure.

When viewed by reflected light, five well-defined areas can be distinguished.   Most prominent is the tripus at each end of the optic axis.

 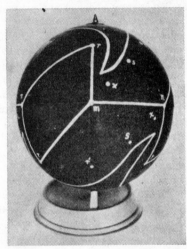

Fig. 80.—Models of left- and right-quartz showing outlines of etch patterns and the poles of various faces, from Van Dyke.   Left-quartz is at the left.   The optic axis is vertical.

The other three areas are parallelograms uniformly spaced around the equator.   These parallelograms are linked by etched "bars," which are broadest midway between the parallelograms.   The center of each bar marks the pole on the sphere of the positive end of an X-axis; the negative ends of the X-axes are at the centers of the parallelograms.

When the fine structure is examined under a microscope, at the ends of the axes characteristic figures, more or less like those in Fig. 78, can be recognized.   It is from the facets forming these figures that the sheen originates.   It is significant that the small-scale parallelograms in Fig. 78 are seen over the region outlined by the large-scale parallelograms, while the trigonal markings for Z-cuts are present on the trigonal tripus.

By means of a reflection goniometer or a rodometer, the characteristics of the etch pattern on any part of the sphere can be investigated quantitatively according to methods *c* and *d*.

Van Dyke has constructed models, illustrated in Fig. 80, in which are marked the outlines of the principal etched areas. One sees that the *s*-faces come above and below the middle of a bar ($+X$-axis) and that the four corners of the parallelograms are the poles of *m*- and *R*-faces. The long sides of the parallelograms are arcs of great circles on which the poles of all faces lie. Portions of the tripus at each end of the *Z*-axis can be seen. The tips of the tripus curl clockwise or counterclockwise according to whether the crystal is right or left.

338. c. Reflection Methods for the Examination of Etched Surfaces. An etched surface shows a characteristic sheen in reflected light when the beam strikes it in certain particular directions. By the use of a suitable reflection goniometer the orientations of the various groups of etch facets with respect to the specimen can be determined. This method has been used for determining the axes of quartz from etched surfaces.*

339. d. Refraction Methods. The first to observe refraction patterns from etched quartz crystals seems to have been Nacken.[387] Later Herlinger[220] developed a "photogoniometer" for studying both reflection and refraction patterns, and still later the refraction patterns were investigated by Gramont, who introduced some novel techniques. Although Gramont's theory is at some points open to criticism, his work pointed the way to methods of considerable usefulness for determining the axial directions and the hand of unfaced quartz crystals.

Refraction patterns present a wide diversity of form, depending on the direction of the emergent beam with respect to the crystal axes. For any given orientation, the pattern is the result of rays from facets of different inclinations and azimuths. Some of the facets are not plane, but have a characteristic curvature (or possibly a set of nearly parallel etch surfaces), producing streaks or brushes of refracted light; reflection effects may also play a part in the formation of the observed refraction pattern.

Refraction patterns may be seen with little or no apparatus. An etched plate or slab cut in any orientation is simply held close to the eye, and a point source of light (a frosted lamp a few meters away will do) is viewed through it. The etched surface may face either toward or away from the eye. If the opposite surface is not polished, it can be covered with a piece of glass with a drop of immersion liquid between.

An improvement on this method consists in placing the crystal, with the etched surface horizontal, between the eye and a point source of light located a few millimeters below the crystal. A pinhole over a

---

* See, for example, Gaudefroy,[154] Herlinger,[220] and Willard;[586] also P. D. Gerber, U. S. patent 2,218,489.

frosted light bulb can be used.   If the crystal is in the form of a flat plate, the lower surface, if not polished, can be laid on a piece of glass with a drop of immersion liquid between.   Large specimens can be supported with the lower portion immersed in the liquid.   A diverging cone of light traverses the crystal, and the rays reaching the eye from any point on the etched surface come from those facets located at this point which have the right orientation.   The greater the divergence of the rays from the source and the larger the etched surface, the less necessary it is to place the eye close to the crystal.   The focal plane of the observed pattern appears to lie a centimeter or so below the etched surface, as can be shown by a simple construction according to geometrical optics.*

A very sharp and bright pattern is seen when the point of light is produced by letting the rays from an automobile headlight bulb pass upward into the open end of a microscope objective of focal length around 2 mm.   From the focal point just above the objective lens the rays diverge in a wide cone.   Crystals several centimeters thick, placed just above the focal point, can be examined by this means.   The eye can be at any distance above the crystal, but with thick crystals the head must be moved from side to side in order to see the complete pattern. A device of this sort is called a *rodoscope* (from the Latin *rodere*, to eat away).

340.   A more precise means for examining refraction patterns is the use of a narrow beam of parallel rays instead of a diverging cone.   The beam passes vertically upward through the crystal, emerging from a surface that has been suitably ground and etched.   To prevent refraction and scattering of light where the beam enters the crystal, the lower portion of the latter is placed in an immersion liquid.   The light is refracted by etch facets on the small area of the surface through which the beam emerges, producing a pattern that can be photographed or examined visually on a translucent screen.   This pattern is determined by the orientation of the crystallographic axes with respect to the beam and is practically independent of the inclination of the etched surface. Hence, by tilting the crystal about horizontal axes and rotating it about the vertical axis, until certain well-defined features of the pattern conform exactly to a previously determined standard, the directions of all three axes with respect to the framework of the instrument become known.

This procedure is best carried out with a specimen on which an etched surface has been prepared that is normal to the optic axis within 10° or so.   When the optic axis is parallel to the beam, the refraction pattern has the appearance of a three-pointed star, which varies greatly

---

* Refraction patterns according to the method just described are discussed by R. S. Rivlin, *Proc. Phys. Soc. (London)*, vol. 53, pp. 409–412, 1941, and also by G. W. Willard.[586]

with time of etching, together with three characteristic *spots*.* After the etching has progressed far enough to make these spots visible, their positions remain practically unchanged over long periods of etching. Although they were observed long ago by Nacken,[387] their importance has only recently been appreciated. When the optic axis is parallel to the beam of light, the three spots fall at the vertices of an equilateral triangle, and from their positions the X- and Y-axes, with their positive directions, are determined. The pattern is similar to that seen in the rodoscope, but rotated by 180°.

An instrument for orienting crystals by this method has been called a *rodometer*.† By its use the crystallographic axes of any specimen of quartz can be determined easily and quickly within a degree, and in trained hands settings can be reproduced within +15 min of arc. At the same time the refraction pattern indicates the hand of the crystal, locates twinned regions on the crystal surface, and tells whether the twinning is optical or electrical.

341. Orientation of Quartz Crystals and Plates by X-rays. As we have seen, it is possible with apparatus of high quality to determine the optic axis within a few minutes of arc by purely optical methods. Such methods, however, cannot determine the X- and Y-axes. For approximate orientations of these axes it is most convenient to use a beam of light reflected or refracted at an etched surface. By the use of the rodometer all three axes can quickly be determined with a single setting. Nevertheless, no etch method can provide as accurate an orientation as is required for precise investigations in the laboratory or for meeting modern commercial demands. It is here that X-rays are indispensable, since by their use complete orientations, precise within a few minutes of arc, can be made very quickly. An accuracy of $\pm 1'$ can be attained with X-ray apparatus of high precision.

But little use has been made of the Laue method for quartz crystals, since it is applicable only to thin cuts. Koga and Tatibana‡ have used this method; in their paper are a list of atomic planes and two photographs of Laue patterns. The back-reflection method§ has been used to a limited extent. The Bragg reflection method is chiefly employed, with K_α-rays

* Before etching, the surface should be ground with carborundum (grain about 100), with random strokes in all directions. To bring out the spots most distinctly it has been found best to mix three parts commercial (about 50 per cent) hydrofluoric acid with one part water and to etch for 2 to 3 hr.

† W. G. CADY, *Proc. I.R.E.*, vol. 28, p. 144, 1940 (abst.); H. H. HUBBELL, JR., *Phys. Rev.*, vol. 59, p. 473 (abst.). The use of the spots for the orientation of quartz, as well as many features in the technique, were introduced by G. J. Holton (distinction thesis, Wesleyan University, 1941). A more complete account of the construction and use of the rodometer is given by Holton.[233]

‡ I. KOGA and M. TATIBANA, *Electrotech. Jour. (Japan)*, vol. 3, pp. 38–39, 1939.

§ A. B. GRENINGER, *Z. Krist.*, vol. 91, pp. 424–432, 1935.

from a copper target.   The choice of atomic plane in the crystal depends
on the orientation of the surface to be tested, whether normal to X, Y,
or Z or in some oblique direction.   "Glancing" angles up to 30° or more
are used.   The specimen under investigation is tilted until a response is
observed in a meter actuated by an ionization chamber or Geiger counter.
A full description of the method has been given by Bond and Armstrong.[68]

342. Cutting and Finishing of Quartz Plates.   Formerly muck saws
were used for cutting quartz, in which a rotating disk of copper or soft
steel dipped into wet carborundum powder.   At present diamond-
charged disks are preferred, the cutting edge being kept wet by kerosene
or a special coolant.   In the laboratory quartz cutting can be done with
such a disk mounted on the arbor of a milling machine.   For small work,
the author has had good success with a very thin carborundum grinding
wheel mounted in a lathe.

Omitting the various details of quantity production, we pass at once
to the "blank" as it comes from the saw, in approximately the right
orientation but slightly oversize.   It is good practice at this stage to
test the blank for twinning, if this test has not already been carried out
on the thin "wafer" from which, in some cases, the individual blanks are
cut.   The blank is lightly etched and examined by reflected light.
Twinned regions are revealed by differences in the sheen.

The blank must next be lapped to the desired dimensions (or frequency) and to precise orientation, with occasional X-ray tests.   For
l-f crystals (lengthwise or contour vibrations), the length and breadth
are of chief importance.

For *thickness modes* the thickness of the plate is the determining factor,
and the plate must be of uniform thickness, usually within 0.0005 mm.
Plates as thin as 0.2 mm are in practical use.   For best performance, the
four narrow peripheral faces have to be carefully lapped; they are sometimes also slightly beveled at the edges.   Owing to coupling between
different modes, a very slight change in length or breadth of the plate
may affect the activity very greatly.   The final contour lapping is a
matter of trial and error, except in the case of certain cuts for which the
optimal contour can be predetermined.

Lapping machines are of various types, some of which lap one side
only of a "nest" of several plates, while others lap both sides at once.
A drill press is easily converted into a machine for lapping one side at a
time; in this case the plate or plates to be lapped are cemented to a flat
metal plate.   Small-scale lapping can be done by hand on a slab of plate
glass or, better, on a trued cast-iron surface.   The fluid may be water,
soap and water, or a special oil.   The process is carried out in several
stages, depending on how much the crystal has to be reduced.   Usually
carborundum is used, of successive degrees of fineness down to 600.

The final fine lapping is done with emery or aluminum oxide. Polishing is, as a rule, neither necessary nor desirable. The finishing touches are usually performed by hand. Etching is also often employed to bring the crystal to exactly the desired vibrational frequency. Etching also removes loose particles of quartz and decreases the damping.[188]

The removal of a single layer of silicon atoms (§540) from a 1,000,000-cycle X-cut quartz plate 3 mm thick would increase the frequency by about 0.1 cycle/sec, an amount that is significant in precision oscillators. One of the fortunate characteristics of quartz is that the atoms are so well bonded as not to be easily removed.

343. Resonator Mountings and Holders. Since nearly all piezo resonators are of quartz, the subject of mountings, including the types

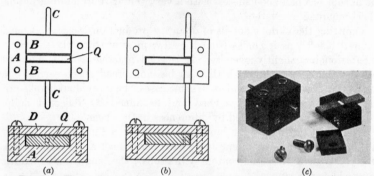

Fig. 81.—The earliest mountings for quartz resonators. The bars Q were all X-cut, length parallel to Y. The housings A and covers D were of hard rubber or bakelite, with brass electrodes B. (a) Full-length electrodes. (b) Short electrodes, for excitation of the fundamental and of both even and odd overtones. (c) Two small resonators, for frequencies 757 and 860 kc/sec. The cover is removed from the one at the right, exposing the quartz bar, about 3.2 mm long, between two large electrodes.

used for piezo oscillators, is considered here. The guiding principles are the same whatever piezoelectric substance may be used.

In the author's earliest experiments with resonators, bars of quartz or Rochelle salt were used, with tinfoil coatings cemented to the sides. The bars were laid flat on the table, suspended from fine wires, or placed on soft pads of cotton. It was soon found that resonance was much sharper when the tinfoil coatings were removed and the crystal stood on edge between rigid brass electrodes, with a small air gap on each side. In some cases the bars were held by silk threads tied around them at the center, in order to leave them more free to vibrate in the gap between the electrodes. Some of the quartz bars used in the early 1920's, together with typical holders, are illustrated in Fig. 81. At that time, since it was not foreseen that quartz plates could be made to resonate in thickness vibration, only lengthwise vibrations of bars were investigated. In order to push the frequency as high as possible, some of the bars were only a millimeter long.

Some of the resonators used by the author in 1923 for comparisons with standard frequency meters in government laboratories in the United

(a)

(b)

Fig. 82.—Early types of piezo-resonators.   (a) Four X-cut quartz bars, lengths 1.76, 3.60, 12.02, and 30.3 mm, parallel to Y.   Frequencies 1.523, 762.0, 235.9, and 91.66 kc/sec, respectively, in a common holder.   (b) Two steel bars, 180 and 90.5 mm long, 9.8 × 3.2 mm in cross section, each driven by a pair of small X-cut quartz plates.   Frequencies 14.43 and 28.94 kc/sec.   See description in §383.

States, Italy, France, and England are shown in Fig. 82.   These were the first international frequency comparisons to be made by means of crystal standards.   Since then, a number of such comparisons have been carried out, with improved resonators and higher precision (see the references at the end of Chap. XIX).   In the primitive mountings used in 1923, the quartz bars lay loosely in the bottoms of pockets between the electrodes. The damping was relatively high, and the frequency varied with slight displacements of the crystal. Moreover, there was no control of the temperature. The precision was about 0.1 per cent; today the minimum requirement is at least ten times better than this.

With increasing demands for constancy of frequency, the development of crystal holders has kept pace with that of crystals and circuits. In technical journals and patent literature can be found enough material for a treatise on mountings and holders alone. We can do no more here than discuss some of the principal features, especially of the more recent types. A few references on the subject will be found at the end of the chapter.

Crystal mountings and holders may be classified according to whether they are designed for use in oscillator circuits, stationary or portable; or for use as filters, including receiving sets; or as frequency standards. They differ also according to the mode of vibration of the crystal. Mountings of special types, as for flexural vibrations, luminous resonators, and ring-shaped crystals for quartz clocks, will be considered in later sections, with references to the original papers for details.

Of the four parameters R, L, C, and C_1 of the equivalent network, L and C are affected only to a minute extent by the character of the mounting. In recent years, through various improvements in the construction of holders, R has been greatly reduced in value and made practically free from variation due to mechanical shock and other service conditions. The effects of stray capacitances on C_1 have been reduced. At the same time, the newer holders are not less rugged and portable than the earlier types.

For the controlling crystals in *oscillator circuits*, the main requirements are constancy of frequency, ruggedness, and ability to stand fairly high voltage. Constancy of frequency demands, of course, a high Q and, in the case of portable sets, immunity against vibration. Variations in temperature are compensated in various ways. In the first place, the use of cuts having a low temperature coefficient of frequency (§357) has become almost univeral, making the use of temperature control unnecessary for most practical purposes. When such control is needed, for example to prevent condensation of moisture or to compensate for extreme variations in ambient temperature, small thermostats and heaters are sometimes built into the holder. For still more precise control, in transmitting stations and especially for frequency standards, the holder may be mounted in a special thermostatically controlled oven.

344. *Holders for Crystals in Thickness Vibration.* The crystal plates are usually square, rectangular, or circular. In the earlier types the crystal lay loosely on one electrode, held down by gravity, either with a small gap between it and the upper plane electrode, or else subjected to slight pressure from the upper electrode, the gap being eliminated. While such mountings are most convenient for laboratory experiments, they have proved to be unsuited to modern service conditions, owing to variations in frequency and damping when the plate moves about in the holder and also because of a tendency for metal to rub off onto the crystal.

A typical holder of more modern design uses the *pressure mounting.* It has a horizontal carefully lapped electrode upon which the crystal rests.   In one type the other electrode, which presses on the crystal, is slightly recessed on its lower face, so as to clamp the crystal at its four corners or around its circumference if it is circular, leaving a gap of the order of 0.2 mm between crystal and upper electrode.   For frequencies above 10 megacycles, it has been found feasible to clamp the crystal, for example by bolts passing through holes at the four corners.   An advantage in corner clamping is that it suppresses flexural modes.   The smaller the gap, the greater the power that can be controlled in the crystal circuit, but the more sensitive the frequency to minute variations in gap width.

In another type the gap is eliminated, and the upper electrode is pressed against the crystal by a spring.   The damping is greater in such mountings than when there is a gap; but even in gap mountings the damping due to contact with the lower electrode is great enough to be objectionable in precise work.   The pressure can, however, be surprisingly great without preventing the crystal from vibrating.   For example, Booth and Dixon[70] state that a piezo oscillator with area about 6 cm^2 (either X-cut or Y-cut) will function despite a force as great as 1.6 kg on the upper electrode.   The damping caused by pressure is less noticeable with shear vibrations than in the case of X-cuts, where the thickness vibrations are compressional.

In mountings of the type just described, especially when the upper electrode presses against the crystal, a "threshold effect" has sometimes been observed; *i.e.,* the crystal fails to oscillate until the voltage reaches a critical value depending on the friction to be overcome.   In mountings for resonators and filters, this effect must be avoided as far as possible. It is less objectionable in the case of oscillators.

Other types of gap mounting have been devised.   For example, the electrodes are sometimes held at the desired distance apart by spacers of insulating material with low coefficient of expansion, as fused silica or pyrex glass; crystalline quartz has also been used.[358]   Three separate spacers may be used, or a continuous ring of the proper thickness inside which the crystal is laid.   *Adjustable gaps* have also been employed,* one or both of the electrodes being held by a micrometer screw.   The advantage in this arrangement is the possibility of varying the frequency at will over a range of one-tenth of 1 per cent or so.   For laboratory

* For a recent form, see ref. 43.

purposes, the author has, for many years, found this device very useful. On the other hand, it is not now generally considered desirable for constant-frequency circuits, since the desired frequency can be attained with a fixed gap by suitable dimensioning of the crystal, the frequency then being more stable. Moreover, the mounting with adjustable electrodes has more stray capacitance and is bulkier.

For greater constancy of frequency as well as smaller damping, the crystal plate, if not too thin, is sometimes clamped at three or more points at its outer edges.* Three minute cavities are drilled in the plate edgewise—two on one side and one on the other if the plate is rectangular—and in these cavities are seated the pointed ends of spurs that extend inward from the housing. The plate is thus held only at points in the nodal plane and does not touch either electrode. Bechmann[43,†] describes mountings in which the quartz plates, oriented for zero temperature coefficient, are of circular form, beveled outward to a sharp edge all around the circumference. The edge lies in the nodal plane and fits into notches in three short rods, two of which are fixed while the other is pressed against the crystal by a spring. Each electrode is adjustable; but when the proper adjustment has been made, the entire mounting can be sealed in an evacuated holder. Mountings of this type are made for frequencies of 250 to 10,000 kc/sec.

Modern mountings usually have electrodes of some such material as monel metal, stainless steel, or duralumin. The housing is tightly sealed and waterproof.

345. In recent years the tendency to employ *plated crystals*‡ has been increasing, involving a special type of mounting, with metallic electrodes evaporated onto the crystal surfaces, specially designed lead wires, and hermetically sealed housings, either evacuated or filled with dry air.§ The metallic deposits on the crystal are usually of aluminum, silver, or gold, about 0.0005 mm thick. The crystal surfaces should first be etched to remove loose material left after lapping. By a special process, the ends of the phosphor-bronze lead wires, which also sustain the weight of the crystal, are attached firmly to the centers of the electrodes. The size and shape of these wires are predetermined and carefully adjusted, so that the wires will have the proper compliance for protecting the crystal against shocks, while at the same time not absorbing appreciable energy from the h-f vibrations of the crystal. The frequency is thus

* See, for example, L. Essen.[135]

† See also Heaton and Lapham.[212] Quartz plates with beveled edges, supported at points in the nodal plane, were used in this laboratory by K. S. Van Dyke in 1925.

‡ The first to use thin metallic films on the crystal were the Curie brothers. In some of their early devices they employed silver electrodes, deposited chemically.

§ See, for example, A. W. Ziegler, U. S. patents 2,218,735, Oct. 22, 1940, and 2,275,122, Mar. 3, 1942.

made more stable, while damping and stray capacitances are reduced to a minimum. The assembly of crystal and leads is mounted in a tube of glass or metal, with a standard plug-in base. In some forms the tube contains also a small thermostat and heater.

346. *Special Mountings for Low-frequency Crystals.* We are concerned here with bars in lengthwise vibration, and broad rectangular plates vibrating in a l-f mode. The general requirements and basic construction are similar to those for thickness vibrations. The crystal is now usually plated on both sides, thus eliminating the gap. Since a lengthwise-vibrating bar has a nodal region at the center, it can be firmly clamped here without too much damping. Until recently the commonest method in commercial mountings has been the use of a pair of metal knife-edges to clamp the crystal, one on each side extending in the direction of the breadth. For greater security each side is sometimes supported by two knife-edges close together. Still another method of clamping, designed especially for filters, consists in having two small metallic hemispheres pressed by springs against the crystal on each side.

In order to prevent possible displacement of the crystal, a type of mounting has been devised[69] in which a shallow groove is cut across the crystal on one side, into which a knife-edge fits, while a point contact presses against a countersunk hole on the other side. In a modification of this method two small steel balls press against conical holes in the bar on one side and one similar ball on the other.

Knife-edge mountings are applicable to bars down to about a centimeter in length (frequency around 300 kc).

In the case of broad plates vibrating in l-f shear modes, knife-edges interfere with the freedom of vibration. The plate is therefore supported by one or more pairs of pressure pins on each side.

Most recent of all is the *wire-supported type* of mounting,[188] in which the plated crystal is held by specially designed wires soldered to its surfaces, as described in §345. Crystals so mounted and properly aged are said to hold their frequency constant within 2 or 3 parts per million.

347. The Aging of Quartz Resonators. Soon after quartz began to be used as a precise standard of frequency, it was observed that for some weeks or even months after a plate had received its final lapping and was mounted in its holder the resonant frequency underwent a slow drift. It is well established that this drift persists after all possibility of change in the position of the electrodes has been removed and that it is due to the surface layers of the finished plate. A final etching of the surfaces has been found beneficial. Bechmann[44] found that aging can be hastened by repeated heating. It has now become standard practice to put the finished plate through several cycles of heating and cooling, for example between 25 and 115°C.[188]

REFERENCES

PHYSICAL PROPERTIES OF QUARTZ

DAKE, FLEENER, and WILSON, [B12] GRAMONT,[B21] SCHEIBE,[B45] SOSMAN,[B47] VIGOUR-EUX,[B50,B51] VOIGT,[B52] BALDWIN[16,17] (popular accounts), BOND and ARMSTRONG,[68] WILLARD.[584,585]

HUND, A.: "Phenomena in High-frequency Systems," McGraw-Hill Book Company, Inc., New York, 1936.

TESTING, PREPARATION, AND MOUNTING OF PLATES

BECKERATH,[47] BOKOVOY,[62] BOND,[67] DRUESNE,[126] GREENIDGE,[188] SHORE,[462] SYKES,[499] THURSTON,[519] TOLANSKY,[521] VENKOV.[564]

ELBL, L. A.: Crystal Holder Design, *Electronics*, vol. 16, pp. 134–138, October, 1943; Quartz Crystal Finishing, *Electronics*, vol. 17, pp. 122–125, 288, 290, January, 1944; Crystal Testing Techniques, *Electronics*, vol. 17, pp. 120–123, 380–382, August, 1944.

FLORISSON, C.: Improvements in Frequency-Stabilizers, L'Onde élec., vol. 10, pp. 131–135, 1931.

SCHAFFERS, T. W. M.: The Q-Lap, *Communications*, vol. 24, pp. 40–42, 80, Apr., 1944.

OPTICAL PROPERTIES AND OPTICAL METHODS OF TESTING

MYERS,[B38] SOSMAN,[B47] TUTTON,[B48] WOOD,[B55] ARNULF,[9] BIOT,[54] BOOTH,[69] BUISSON,[85] KAO,[253] MODRAK,[371] VAN DYKE.[558]

References on the etching of crystals are given at the end of Chap. II.

QUARTZ OSCILLATOR-PLATES

Symposium on Quartz Oscillator-plates, *American Mineralogist*, vol. 30, pp. 205–468, May-June, 1945. This symposium comprises the following papers:

FRONDEL, CLIFFORD: "History of the Quartz Oscillator-plate Industry," 1941–1944, pp. 205–213.

VAN DYKE, KARL S.: The Piezoelectric Quartz Resonator, pp. 214–244.

STOIBER, RICHARD E., CARL TOLMAN, and ROBERT D. BUTLER: Geology of Quartz Crystal Deposits, pp. 245–268.

GORDON, SAMUEL G.: The Inspection and Grading of Quartz, pp. 269–290.

LUKESH, JOSEPH S.: The Effect of Imperfections on the Usability of Quartz for Oscillator-plates, pp. 291–295.

PARRISH, WILLIAM, and SAMUEL G. GORDON: Orientation Techniques for the Manufacture of Quartz Oscillator-plates, pp. 296–325.

PARRISH, WILLIAM, and SAMUEL G. GORDON: Precise Angular Control of Quartz-cutting by X-rays, pp. 326–346.

GORDON, SAMUEL G., and WILLIAM PARRISH: Cutting Schemes for Quartz Crystals, pp. 347–370.

PARRISH, WILLIAM: Methods and Equipment for Sawing Quartz Crystals, pp. 371–388.

PARRISH, WILLIAM: Machine Lapping of Quartz Oscillator-plates, pp. 389–415.

FRONDEL, CLIFFORD: Final Frequency Adjustment of Quartz Oscillator-plates, pp. 416–431.

FRONDEL, CLIFFORD: Effect of Radiation on the Elasticity of Quartz, pp. 432–446.

FRONDEL, CLIFFORD: Secondary Dauphiné Twinning in Quartz, pp. 447–460.

Glossary of Terms Used in the Quartz Oscillator-plate Industry, pp. 461–468.

CHAPTER XVII

THE QUARTZ RESONATOR

. . . this electric force, that keeps
A thousand pulses dancing. . . .
—TENNYSON.

The earliest resonators, crudely cut and crudely mounted, could be depended on for a precision in frequency of about 0.1 per cent. This precision was much higher than that of most wavemeters of two decades ago. Soon, however, there came an increasing demand for constancy of frequency in radio transmitters. This demand was met by the introduction of the piezo oscillator, together with temperature control of the crystal and improvements in its preparation and mounting. In 1929 the first quartz resonators of low temperature coefficient appeared. Since then, the intensive study of the elastic and thermal properties of quartz has led to the discovery or predetermination of many useful cuts for all radio frequencies, and with resonant frequencies so little dependent on temperature that thermostatic control is unnecessary.

In the present chapter the principal cuts and their properties and uses are described, with illustrative numerical data.

Excitation of the Simpler Modes of Vibration in Quartz. We shall here apply the rules outlined in Chap. X to quartz, in order to ascertain how an electric field may be applied to preparations of various forms and orientations, for the excitation of lengthwise, thickness, flexural, and torsional vibrations.

I. LENGTHWISE COMPRESSIONAL VIBRATIONS OF BARS

348. The earliest resonators were in the form of bars, using compressional lengthwise vibrations. Since the author's first experiments, which were made with bars of both Rochelle salt and quartz, it has been recognized that this type of piezo resonator offers the advantage of well-defined response frequencies, free from the effects of undesired vibrational modes. The simplest example is that of an X-cut bar with length parallel to Y, as used statically by the Curie brothers and dynamically by many others. Here the strain of primary importance is $y_y = d_{12}E_x$.

If l is parallel to X, lengthwise excitation can be brought about by placing electrodes at the ends of the bar or by applying a field parallel to X over a portion of the bar, as was done by Giebe and Scheibe (§349). For intermediate orientations of l in the XY-plane this excitation can

435

also be used, or the field may be applied across the bar in the XY-plane so that it has a component in the X-direction.

A bar with length parallel to Z cannot be *directly* excited in lengthwise vibration; such vibrations are, however, possible through elastic coupling, by applying an alternating field of the right frequency parallel to X. This experiment does not seem to have been performed with a thin bar, but the principle was verified by Hund,[238] who observed compressional vibrations in the Z-direction in a rectangular plate in which the applied field was parallel to X.

For a bar in any arbitrary orientation, the effective piezoelectric constant has a different value according to whether the vibrations are excited by a field *parallel* or *perpendicular* to the length. We shall dispose of the former and less usual case first. Here the shape and orientation of the cross section are of no consequence. Although no complete theory for this type of excitation has been developed, still one knows at least that the piezoelectric constant must be of the type d'_{33}, if the length of the bar is taken as parallel to the rotated Z'-axis. Equation (219) for d'_{33} shows that this constant involves d_{11} alone. It vanishes only when $\varphi = \pm 30°$ or $\pm 90°$ (projection of l on the XY-plane parallel to a Y-axis) or when $\theta = 0°$ (l parallel to Z).

In the usual case the exciting field is *perpendicular to l*, and the orientation of the cross section must be considered. Since no general equations for d'_{hk} in all orientations are available, we shall consider each of the principal planes separately. The problem is analogous to that of producing lengthwise vibrations in oblique bars of Rochelle salt (§371).

There is always an optimum orientation for E and hence for e. *If l lies in the YZ-plane*, the only possible excitation is by E_z, and X-cuts rotated about the X-axis must be used. If l is taken as parallel to the Y'-axis, making the angle θ with the Y-axis, the strain characteristic of this type of vibration is $y'_y = d'_{12}E_z$, where, by Eqs. (221),

$$d'_{12} = -c^2 d_{11} + scd_{14} \qquad (475)$$

When $\theta = 0$, $d'_{12} = -d_{11} = d_{12}$ and we have the ordinary case of a bar parallel to Y. When $\theta = 90°$, $d'_{12} = 0$ and no direct excitation is possible ($l \parallel Z$). Otherwise, both d_{11} and d_{14} contribute to d'_{12}.

If l lies in the ZX-plane, one can in general let the thickness e, parallel to which the field is to be applied, have such an orientation that the field will be E_y, or a component of E_x, or a resultant of the two. A simple case is that of a rotated Y-cut, analogous to the rotated X-cut mentioned above: if l is parallel to Z', making the angle θ with Z, the strain equation is $z'_z = d'_{23}E_y$, where, by Eqs. (222), p. 213,

$$d'_{23} = -csd_{14} \qquad (476)$$

Lengthwise excitation by a field parallel to Y is therefore possible except when l is parallel to Z or X. When $\theta = 45°$, $d'_{23} = -d_{14}/2$ and the excitation is of exactly the same nature as for an X-cut 45° Rochelle-salt bar [Eq. (203)]. No observations seem to have been made on bars with l inclined obliquely in the ZX-plane, but compressional vibrations of this type have been observed by Wright and Stuart[594] in circular Y-cut plates and discussed by Bechmann.[36]

If l lies in the XY-plane, we may let l and e be parallel to Y' and X', respectively, so that

$$y'_y = d'_{12}E'_x = -d_{11}E'_x \cos 3\theta \qquad (477)$$

by Eqs. (223), where θ is the angle between Y' and Y. When $\theta = 0$, we have the X-cut with l parallel to Y. Lengthwise vibrations can be excited at all angles in the XY-plane except when l is parallel to X, making $\cos 3\theta = 0$.

The elastic stiffness calculated from observations of the frequency of a narrow bar of known length is the isagric Young's modulus, provided that the gap is zero. Consideration of the depolarizing effect of the electric field and of the value of the effective piezoelectric constant is needed only when there is a gap, according to Eq. (330). As long as the dimensions of the cross section are not over one-tenth of the length, the correction for finite cross section is inappreciable.[340] Bechmann's derivation of Young's modulus for various orientations from observations with narrow quartz bars has been mentioned in §96.

One other quantity occurring in the equations for vibrations of bars is the effective dielectric constant k_l, given by Eq. (311). This quantity is a little smaller than the free dielectric constant k'_i. The difference, at least for quartz, is slight and has been ignored by some writers. For any arbitrary orientation, k'_i is the same as k'_N in Eq. (474c). A rough approximation to the values of d_{in} and s^E_{nn} for the orientation in question is usually sufficient. The value of k_l for an X-cut quartz bar with length parallel to Y is given by Eq. (474a).

A full discussion of coupling effects between different modes lies outside the scope of this book. Some of the more important references on the subject are given at the end of this chapter.

349. Experimental Results with Lengthwise Vibrations. Working with rectangular quartz bars with lengths parallel to X or Y, Giebe and his associates[162,169,171] investigated the dependence of frequency upon cross section, for the fundamental and various overtones.* They derived formulas for frequency and for the departure of overtone frequencies

---

* We have discussed the excitation of overtones in bars in §238. The theory is treated further by Sokolov.[473]

from harmonic relations.   Their theory involves coupling effects, Poisson's ratio, and the piezoelectric correction to the stiffness.   Their electrodes were very small, since the bars were intended to show the luminous effects described in §365.   For the bars with length parallel to Y, the small electrodes were placed at the center, so that the field was in the X-direction.   When the length was parallel to X, two pairs of electrodes were used, as illustrated in Fig. 88B, giving rise to a field parallel to X at the center of the bar.   Giebe and Blechschmidt[162] observed frequencies at different temperatures and calculated from them the temperature coefficients of s_{11} and s_{44}.   The principal results of all these investigations are given in more detail by Scheibe.[B45]

Frequencies of thin rods in many orientations and at different temperatures have been observed by Bechmann.[32]   From his results, already

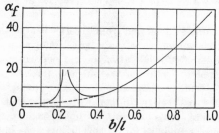

Fig. 83.—Dependence of the temperature coefficient α_f of an X-cut bar (length parallel to Y) on the ratio b/l, from Mason.   For this bar $e = 0.05\ l$.   Abscissas represent b/l; ordinates are in parts per million per degree centigrade.

referred to in §96, one can find the dynamic value of Young's modulus for any orientation in space, together with its temperature coefficient (summary in Scheibe[B45]).

All quartz bars or plates in lengthwise vibration, whatever the orientation may be, have negative temperature coefficients of frequency (see §357), the value becoming zero in certain special cases.   For an X-cut bar with length parallel to Y, the first recorded value was that of Powers,[431] who found $\alpha_f = -5(10^{-6})$.   Considering that Powers' bar had a b/l ratio of about 0.17, his α_f fits satisfactorily on the curve in Fig. 83, which represents the dependence of α_f on b/l, as found by Mason.[332]   The anomaly between 0.15 and 0.4 is due, according to Mason, to coupling with the second flexural mode in the YZ-plane. α_f is smallest for very narrow plates; it is smaller for thick than for thin plates (X-direction).   If the cross section is square ($e = b$), $\alpha_f = 0$ when $b/l = 0.272$.   Qualitative agreement with Mason's results will be found in Table 13 in Scheibe's book.[B45]   Booth[69] agrees with Mason in finding $\alpha_f = -2(10^{-6})$ for very narrow bars with length parallel to Y.

The *dependence of frequency on the gap width w*, for a bar at room tem-perature, has been investigated* by Dye[127] and the author.[107]   According to Eq. (336b) there should be a linear relation between w and the relative change in frequency witn gap, the coefficient U being the same for all gaps.   The experiments yield a value of U about 15 per cent smaller than that predicted by theory and also a progressive decrease in U with increasing gap.   Possible explanations of the discrepancy are discussed in the author's paper.   The observed frequency increases by about one-half of 1 per cent as the gap is increased from zero to a very large value.

Lengthwise vibrations of quartz plates having a breadth b comparable with the length l have been studied by Petrzilka,[417,418] Bechmann,[36,41,42,44] and Mason.[332,340] Petrzilka used both rectangular and circular Z-cut plates, with electrodes so placed as to provide a driving field perpendicular to Z.   His paper contains photographs of the wave patterns obtained. He identified, at suitable frequencies, the three vibrational modes pre-dicted by theory and from his results calculated the elastic modulus and Poisson's ratio.†

Mason measured the variation in frequency of an X-cut 18.5° rectangular plate (see Table XXIX) as the ratio b/l was increased from 0.1 to 1.   There was a general decrease of about 12 per cent, due to coupling with a flexural mode and with compression parallel to b. An anomaly occurred for values of b/l from 0.2 to 0.3, owing to close coupling with the flexural mode.   Mason points out that the Rayleigh correction for cross section (§65) is incomplete when applied to quartz, since it does not take account of the coupled modes.‡

The problem was also analyzed by Bechmann, who derived, for a rectangular plate in any orientation, a cubic equation of which the roots give the three fundamental frequencies: compressional vibrations parallel to l and b, and a shearing mode.   His theory does not include flexural vibrations and coupling between modes, but his experimental results reveal the presence of these effects, for various cuts.   They show a general agreement with the work of Mason mentioned above.

350. *Unsymmetrical Effects with Lengthwise Vibrations.*   From Figs. 31 (curve C), 33 (curve C), and 38, it is clear that in quartz Young's modulus $Y = 1/s'_{33}$ varies greatly with orientation.   For any given polar angle θ except 0° and $\pm 90°$, Y varies with the azimuth φ.   For all values of φ, Y varies with θ.   In particular, in the YZ-plane, $Y(10^{-10})$ varies from 130.2 at $\theta = 48°36'$ to 70.3 at $\theta = -71°4'$.

* Among other papers in which the gap effect in bars is treated are those by Koga,[268] Watanabe,[581] and Grossmann and Wien,[189] but the data are either insufficient or taken with the crystal in the generating circuit.   Results obtained by the latter method are not characteristic of the crystal alone.

† For a critical study of Petrzilka's values see Lonn[319] and Ekstein.[131]

‡ See also Scheibe, ref. B45, p. 92, and Giebe and Blechschmidt, ref. 161.

Through the combined effects of the fundamental elastic constants that occur in Eq. (55) for Young's modulus,* the wave pattern for length-wise vibrations is such that, at the fundamental frequency, the nodal plane crosses the center of the bar at right angles only when the bar is very narrow or, if it has an appreciable breadth b, only when the length lies in the direction of maximum or minimum Y. In a broad plate the nodal line, revealed for example by lycopodium powder, may make a very pronounced angle with the b-direction. Meissner, who first observed this effect,[361] found that in an X-cut circular disk there were two direc-tions along which compressional waves were propagated. These direc-tions made angles $\theta = 48°$ and $-71°$, corresponding to the directions of maximum and minimum Young's modulus. In a rectangular plate with length in the direction $\theta = -71°$ Straubel[488] found the nodal line to be parallel to the breadth.

It is only when the length of the plate is parallel to the direction of maximum or minimum Y that the amplitude of vibration is the same at all portions of the end faces. This fact was ascertained by Meissner[359] by means of lycopodium powder, and by Bücks and Müller,[79] who made a vibrational survey of X-surfaces of plates both with length parallel to Y and at $\theta = -71°$, by observing under a microscope the movements of small specks on the silvered quartz.†

The asymmetry in the wave pattern is further revealed by another effect discovered by Meissner[359] and by Tawil.[506] This effect is an *air blast* directed outward from certain regions at the boundary of the plate, chiefly at the ends. The simple harmonic motion at the ends has a rectifying effect on the air molecules, drawing them in tangentially when the end surfaces recede and expelling them normally when the same sur-faces advance—an effect already known in hydrodynamics. Meissner found the blast strong enough to blow out a candle and turn a pinwheel. The air blasts have been discussed further by Bücks and Müller,[79] Harding and White,[204] Hight,[225] Straubel,[485] Wachsmuth and Auer,[577] and Wright and Stuart.[594] Some very interesting photographs are shown in Straubel's paper.

---

* The constant chiefly responsible for the obliquity of the nodal plane is s_{44}. It tends to produce a contour shear mode, as described in §359. The 18.5° cut mentioned in §357 was designed to eliminate this shear mode.

† The microscopic method has been employed in this laboratory by G. W. Scott, Jr. (distinction thesis, 1934), R. L. Brown (M. A. thesis, 1936) and R. I. Hulsizer (M. A. thesis, 1942). The latter measured the vibrational directions and amplitudes at a large number of points, thus finding the distribution of strain and of piezoelectric polarization. From the integrated polarization a value of the electric current was derived, of the same order of magnitude as the observed value. He used X-cut plates with $\theta = 0°$ and $-71°$, also a GT-cut, recording especially the evidences of coupling between different vibrational modes.

The air blast issues symmetrically from the ends of the plate only when the length is in the direction of maximum or minimum Young's modulus. Otherwise, and especially when l is parallel to the Y-axis and of about the same magnitude as b, the blast is very unsymmetrical, as indicated by Fig. 84.

In order to demonstrate the effect of these unsymmetrical air currents Meissner[359] constructed a "quartz motor," consisting of a plate like that shown in Fig. 84, pivoted at the center so as to rotate in its own plane. A similar device is described by Tawil.[506] In this connection may be mentioned the rotation of a quartz sphere 4 cm in diameter observed by Van Dyke.[548,549,556] The sphere rested on the periphery of a 3-mm hole in a brass plate, which served as the lower electrode. When excited at the frequencies of certain vibrational modes, the sphere turned so as to select

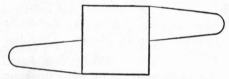

FIG. 84.—Air blasts from an X-cut quartz plate.

a vertical axis about which it then rotated. Since the effect took place also in vacuum, it must have been due to a frictional creeping where the quartz touched the brass. This fact, together with Gramont's observation[181] that a plate mounted according to Meissner rotated better in vacuum than in air, indicates that Meissner's rotation was due at least in part to a periodic frictional effect at the pivot rather than to reaction from the air. Gramont describes still other forms of quartz motor.

Van Dyke[549] found that his quartz sphere could also be made to slide along a straight track or to travel continuously along a circular track. These motions were due chiefly to reaction from the surrounding air. He found the principal resonant frequencies to be in the ratios 1, 1.47, 1.61, 1.83, 2.12, 2.18, 4.12, where the lowest frequency was approximately that of a bar parallel to Y with length equal to the diameter of the sphere, having a wave constant $H \approx 2,780$ kc sec^{-1} mm. At reduced pressures he observed and photographed characteristic luminous patterns (§365) at the various frequencies, and made a motion-picture record of the changes in pattern as the frequency was varied.

The rotational and translational effects mentioned above are doubtless related to the tendency of an X-cut quartz plate, whether in lengthwise or thickness vibration, to slide in one direction or another on the horizontal surface on which it rests. A motion of this sort was noted in unpublished observations by the author as early as 1923; in some cases at a critical frequency the quartz slid completely out from the space between the fixed electrodes. Many others have since then observed the effect.*

This ease in sliding on the part of a vibrating quartz plate points to a decrease in friction (§364) between the crystal and other surfaces in contact with it.

Hirschhorn† observed a motion of translation in an X-cut quartz bar suspended by a thread between electrodes. Here it was not a question of friction against a solid surface; it is not certain how much of the effect was due to the piezoelectric field surrounding the crystal and how much to the effort of the quartz, like any other dielectric, to move into the strong part of the field between the electrodes.

Instead of observing the air-blast given off from a vibrating crystal, N. H. Williams,[587] used the opposite procedure: he set a quartz bar into vibration by means of the ultrasonic air waves from a jet of air through a nozzle. The ultrasonic "noise" excited many overtones as well as the fundamental vibration in a bar with length parallel to Y. Short electrodes and also multiple electrodes like those described in §239 were connected to an amplifier.

II. PIEZOELECTRIC EXCITATION OF THICKNESS VIBRATIONS

351. Vibrations of at least one of the three types described in §§66, 93, and 245 can be excited in a quartz plate in any orientation. In a Z-cut the field must be applied edgewise, parallel to X or Y, the strains being $y_z = d_{14}E_x$ or $z_x = d_{25}E_y$. Such vibrations in a Z-cut have been observed by Atanasoff and Hart.[12] For all other orientations the field can be parallel to the thickness. Equation (344) for the effective piezo-electric constant ϵ (applicable when the field is parallel to the thickness), when specialized for quartz, becomes

$$\epsilon = \alpha(e_{11}l^2 + e_{26}m^2 + e_{25}mn) + \beta[e_{14}nl + (e_{12} + e_{26})lm] + \gamma(e_{14} + e_{25})lm \tag{478}$$

When $m = n = 0$, we have an X-cut with $\alpha = 1$ (compressional mode parallel to X), and $\epsilon = e_{11}$. When $l = n = 0$, the plate is a Y-cut, with $\alpha = 1$ (vibration direction parallel to X, hence a shear mode[98]), and $\epsilon = e_{26} = -e_{11}$. A Z-cut corresponds to $l = m = 0$, in which case $\epsilon = 0$, showing that thickness vibrations cannot be generated with the field in the thickness direction.

The effective stiffness is given by Eq. (355). For the clamped dielectric constant we have, in the XY-plane, from Eq. (474), $k''_\perp = 4.41$ and, from Eq. (472), parallel to Z, $k''_\parallel = k_\parallel = 4.6$. When the field is oblique, in the N-direction, the rotated k''_N is calculated from an equation similar

---

* See, for example, Shaw's observations.[461]
† S. I. Hirschhorn, *Z. Physik*, vol. 44, pp. 223–225, 1927.

to Eq. (474c),

$$k_N'' = 4.41 + 0.19 \cos^2 \theta \qquad (479)$$

where θ is the angle between N and Z.

352. Some Experimental Results with Thickness Vibrations. With bars in lengthwise vibration it is not difficult, by proper dimensioning, to avoid coupling with other modes. Modes of lower frequency (flexural or torsional) are usually not troublesome, while all others have too high frequencies to introduce undesired resonances. The situation is very different with thickness vibrations, since even with careful dimensioning of the contour it is difficult to avoid coupling with *overtones* of various l-f modes. This fact is notoriously true of the X-cut.

The elimination of disturbing frequencies is the most difficult problem in the design and construction of thickness-mode resonators. The

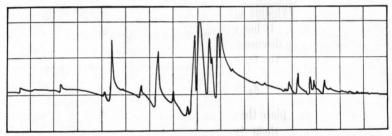

Fig. 85.—Resonance curve for an X-cut 1,500 kc/sec quartz plate in thickness vibration, from Bechmann,[37] showing many resonant frequencies over a range of about 30 kc/sec.

undesired modes, if close to that for which the resonator is designed, can cause serious disagreement between theoretical and experimental values of frequency and its temperature coefficient. By accurate lapping, dimensioning, and edge grinding it is possible to obtain a strong response frequency, corresponding to a vibrational mode that is sufficiently removed from adjacent modes so that it will control the frequency of an oscillator over the desired range of temperature (see §244). The oblique cuts that are most used on account of their low temperature coefficients of frequency are also largely free from the coupling effects that are responsible for the disturbing frequencies.

An example of the complicated frequency spectrum encountered with an X-cut plate is seen in Fig. 85.

The X-cut was first used for thickness vibrations by Pierce. The strain equation is $x_x = d_{11}E_x$. When tested as a resonator, it usually has a large number of response frequencies, strong and weak, in the neighborhood of the calculated value. As an oscillator it selects some one of these frequencies but tends on slight provocation to shift to a different frequency. By any one of the methods described in §366 it can, when vibrating at any resonant frequency, be shown to have a very complicated wave pattern, due to coupling with overtones of modes of lower frequency. Thus, while the mode of vibration is nominally compressional, many parts of the surface have vibration directions with tangential components; and they may also be out of phase with the true compressional vibration. Nevertheless, as a whole the motion of the major faces is in the direction of the thickness. It is for this reason that X-cuts are usually employed as ultrasonic emitters. Owing to the disadvantages just mentioned and to their larger temperature coefficient of frequency, X-cuts are now but little used in piezo oscillators. The value of α_f is usually given as between $-20(10^{-6})$ and $-22(10^{-6})$.

When there is a gap between an X-cut quartz plate and either electrode, stationary air waves are produced when the gap is an integral multiple of the acoustic half wavelength. This effect is the basis of the ultrasonic interferometer (§510). The influence of the gap on the performance of resonators has been investigated by Dye,[127] Koga,[268] Vigoureux,[B50,B51] and others. The loss of energy at the critical gap values is serious, and the coupling of the crystal to the air waves reacts on the frequency. This dynamic effect of the air gap of course vanishes in vacuum mountings. It has nothing to do with the characteristic effect of gap on frequency discussed below.

For a *Y-cut* with the field parallel to Y, the strain equation is

$$x_y = d_{26}E_y = -2d_{11}E_y$$

In a relatively thin plate the vibration direction is parallel to X, and the vibration is of the shear type.[98] Since there is little or no motion normal to the surface, the plate (as with all shear-type plates) can be more firmly clamped than an X-cut without stopping the vibration.* For the same reason there is less trouble from stationary air waves in the gap. Clamping also helps eliminate coupled vibrations of the type $z_x = d_{25}E_2$. Still, as with the X-cut, troublesome couplings are present, and the plate when used as an oscillator tends to jump from one frequency to another closely adjacent. Moreover, the temperature coefficient of frequency is even greater than for the X-cut; values have been observed from $+60$ to $+90(10^{-6})$, depending on dimensions and coupling with other modes.

It was this large temperature coefficient which led several investigators to experiment with *oblique* cuts, culminating in cuts of the types

---

* Using the interferometer method described in §313, Straubel[490] found that there was a slight movement normal to the surface of a Y-cut plate in thickness vibration. This effect was presumably due to coupling with other modes, which it should be possible to eliminate by proper dimensioning.

described in §§357–361. Like the Y-cut, these newer cuts vibrate in a shear mode. Oblique cuts now in common use have almost exactly constant frequency over a considerable range of temperature, while at the same time the coupling effects are reduced.

353. *Effect of the Gap Width on Frequency.* One method for varying the frequency of a piezo oscillator is to vary the gap. A variation of a few tenths of 1 per cent can thus be brought about, most of which takes place while the gap is very small. Equation (370) shows that an approximately linear relation should hold between the relative change in frequency and $w/(e + k''w)$, the coefficient U being a constant. The author's experiments[107,*] indicate that, as in the case of the lengthwise vibrations mentioned above, U decreases as the gap increases. The departure of U from the theoretical value appears to be least with plates which are good resonators and with those which are relatively free from coupling, as, for example, the BT- and AC-cuts; for these cuts almost the exact theoretical value was found at small gaps, although at large gaps the discrepancy amounted to as much as 30 per cent. The observed U was far below the theoretical value for the two X-cut plates employed, both of which were rather poor resonators. For Y-cut plates the deficiency in U was of the order of 20 per cent.

In Eq. (355) it is seen that three terms are necessary in general to express the effective stiffness for thickness vibrations. As an illustration of the relative magnitudes of these terms we may consider the Y-cut, for which it is shown in §351 that $\epsilon = -e_{11} = -5.2(10^4)$, while from Eq. (474) $k'' = 4.41$. The isagric stiffness coefficient is

$$q^E = c_{66}^E \approx 40(10^{10})$$

Hence, for zero gap Eq. (355) becomes, for a Y-cut plate,

$$q' = \left(40 + 0.77 - \frac{0.62}{h^2}\right)10^{10}$$

The second term is here 1.9 per cent of q^E. At the fundamental frequency, $h = 1$, and the third term is 1.5 per cent of q^E. At the fifth "harmonic," $h = 5$, and the third term is only 0.06 per cent of q^E.

The presence of a gap decreases the third term, which vanishes at infinite gap.

It was pointed out in §250 in connection with Eqs. (350) and (350a) that, as the order h of the overtones of thickness vibrations increases, the theoretical relation between the overtone frequencies becomes

---

* Further data were also obtained by Booth and Dixon,[70] Dye,[127] Koga,[268,274,276] Matsumura and Hatakeyama,[344] Namba and Matsumura,[388] and Vigoureux.[B51] As far as they go, they corroborate the present statements.

more nearly harmonic. This has been confirmed in the case of quartz
by Atanasoff and Hart (§90) and also by Bergmann.[53]

For thickness vibrations in special cuts see §358. The use of thickness vibrations in ultrasonics is described in §507.

III. PIEZOELECTRIC EXCITATION OF FLEXURAL VIBRATIONS

354. According to §179, a state of flexure can be produced by applying an electric field in such a way as to cause the portion *ABFE* of the
bar shown in Fig. 86 to expand in the direction *AB* while the portion
EFCD contracts. The same result is reached by applying fields to the
right and left portions of the bar so as to cause opposite *shears* in *AGHD*
and *GBCH*. In either case, if the field alternates with the proper frequency, flexural vibrations result.

With suitable arrangements of electrodes, overtone frequencies can
also be excited. For example, Fig. 87 shows the state of deformation

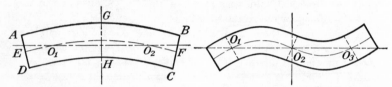

FIG. 86.—First flexural mode. The
nodes O_1 and O_2 are 0.224 of the length from
each end.

FIG. 87.—Second flexural mode. Node
O_2 is at the center. Nodes O_1 and O_3 are
0.132 of the length from each end.

for the second mode (first overtone), in which, instead of two nodes O_1
and O_2 as in Fig. 86, there are three nodes O_1, O_2, O_3. However many
nodes there may be, the extensional strain at any instant has the same
sign in either half of the bar (lower or upper in the figure) from one *node*
to the next, while the shear has the same sign from one *loop* to the next.
At the ends, the extension has the same sign as the adjacent interval
between nodes. Appreciation of these facts is essential in the proper
placing of electrodes.

For best results the bar should be supported at one or more nodes.
It will respond as a resonator even if the field is applied to only a small
part of the bar, as long as this part lies entirely, or chiefly, in a region
where the instantaneous strain has the same sign. For an oscillator the
electrodes, preferably plated, must of course be relatively large, and for
very low decrement the bar should be mounted in vacuum, since the
loss of energy to the surrounding air is considerable.

With quartz crystals both constants $d_{11}(= -d_{12} = -d_{26})$ and
$d_{14}(= -d_{25})$ can be used in obtaining the extensional or shearing stresses
needed for exciting flexural vibrations. An even greater choice of excita-
tions is possible when the bar or plate is cut obliquely. An idea of the

different possibilities can be gained from Fig. 88. Electrodes of opposite sign are distinguished by heavy and light lines. Electrodes of the same sign are usually connected in parallel. Field directions are indicated by arrows. The end view in each case shows the cross section in the form of a square, with the thickness e equal to the breadth b. *The plane of flexure, in which vibration takes place, is always le.* The greater the ratio

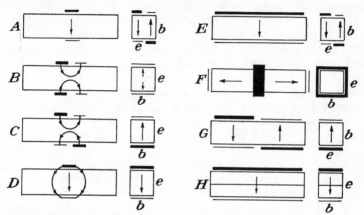

Fig. 88.—Locations of electrodes for exciting flexural vibrations. In the elongated rectangles motion takes place in the plane of the paper in all cases except A, E, and G, where it is perpendicular to the paper.

l/e, the lower the frequency. The breadth b has no appreciable effect on the frequency. Experiment shows that flexural vibrations can still be obtained even when e is as great as l, although when e is relatively large a special form of theory is required, as indicated in §73. From the figure and Table XXVII it is evident that in some cases the same bar or plate can be used for flexure in more than one plane, according to the

TABLE XXVII

Fig.	Direction of length	Direction of field	Plane of flexure	Number of nodes	Strain equation
A	Y	X	YZ	Even	$y_y = d_{12}E_x$
B	Y	X	XY	Odd	$y_y = d_{12}E_x$
C	X	X	ZX or XY	Even	$x_x = d_{11}E_x$
D	X	X	XY	Odd	$x_x = d_{11}E_x$
E	Y	X	YZ	2	$y_y = d_{12}E_x$
F	Y	Y	XY	2	$x_y = d_{26}E_y$
G	$\{X$ or Z	Y	ZX	2	$z_x = d_{25}E_y$
	$\ Y$ or Z	X	YZ	2	$y_z = d_{14}E_x$
H	Y	X	YZ	2	$y_y = d_{12}E_x$

arrangement of the electrodes. The nature of the piezoelectric excitation in each case is shown in this table.

In Fig. 88, A, B, C, and D represent resonators described by Giebe and Scheibe.[166-170] The electrodes are very short, in order to show the luminous effect at resonance in various overtones when the resonators are used as frequency standards. The field parallel to X needed for excitation in B, C, and D is the X-component of the stray field indicated by the curved arrows. Such excitation is necessarily weak.

E is Harrison's arrangement,[205] which is similar to Giebe and Scheibe's device A and was discovered independently and published in the same year. Harrison used two pairs of full-length electrodes for more efficient excitation of the first flexural mode. By using four pairs of electrodes (each set of two pairs covering approximately half the length of the resonator), he excited the second mode. When observing the first mode at reduced air pressure he found a series of luminous striations crossing the exposed surface of the bar near the center (see also Harrison and Hooper[208]).

F and G in Fig. 88 represent modes that have been observed by the author. They include flexure in all three principal planes. As may be seen from Table XXVII these arrangements make use of the shearing piezoelectric effect rather than compression. In F the central electrode is a girdle surrounding the bar, and from it the field in the quartz extends in both directions to electrodes (connected in parallel) opposite the ends. While this excitation is comparatively weak, that in G is much stronger, since the field is normal to the plane of flexure instead of parallel to the length of the bar.

Figure 88H represents a "Curie strip," consisting of two X-cut quartz plates cemented together with polarities opposing. When the field E_x is applied, one plate expands lengthwise while the other contracts. The resonator vibrates flexurally as a unit. With two plates, each 4 by 1 by 0.05 cm, cemented with Canada balsam, the author in 1927 found resonance at a frequency of about 400 cycles/sec. Resonance was indicated by lycopodium powder, by an audible note, and by response in the anode circuit of a tube to the input of which the resonator was connected. The use of the Curie strip in a piezo oscillator is mentioned in §396. The static theory is treated by Voigt.*

355. The excitation of flexural vibrations of low frequency is most efficient when the field is parallel to the thickness e, since this is the dimension which must be made small if the frequency is to be low. The breadth b can then be made large, permitting the use of electrodes of large area. This case can be realized by a modification of Fig. 88C, as illustrated in Fig. 89. The driving field is no longer the stray field parallel to X, but

* "Lehrbuch," p. 906.

the relatively strong field parallel to Y.   Each half of the plate is subject
to a shearing stress $X_y = -e_{26}E_y$; and since these stresses have opposite
signs, a state of flexure results.   With $l = 7.4$ cm, $e = 0.1$ cm, $b = 2$ cm,
the author has observed a resonant frequency of 1,050 cycles/sec.   This
seems to be the lowest recorded frequency for a bar of uniform cross
section with the field in the thickness direction.   Still lower frequencies
were obtained by Gruetzmacher,[191] but in his resonator the quartz was
left very thick at the ends, having the form of a thin strip only in the
central portion.   This was therefore not a "bar" in the ordinary sense.

With the cut shown in Fig. 89, *even* modes of flexural vibration can
be excited by full-sized electrodes covering the entire *lb*-faces.   This is
because the bar is then divided into an *odd* number of segments, sheared
alternately in opposite senses.

Flexural quartz resonators can be used for controlling the frequency
in a piezo-oscillator circuit.   For example, a circuit like that in Fig. 99
was made to oscillate at crystal frequency with the Y-cut 1,050-cycle
bar described above.

Fig. 89.—Y-cut quartz plate for low-frequency flexural vibrations.   The length l is parallel
to X, and the thickness e is parallel to Y.   The plane of flexure is XY.

The same principles that have been described for quartz can, of course,
be applied to other piezoelectric crystals.   As long as the ratio l/e is
large, frequencies can be calculated by Eq. (128), p. 112.

References on flexure and flexural vibrations are given at the end
of the chapter.   Some of the applications are treated in §§368 and 396.
Theory and application of static flexure are considered by Voigt* and by
Voigt and Fréedericksz;[576] vibrational theory will be found in the papers
by Doerffler,[124] Mason,[333] Thomson,[518] and Tykocinski-Tykociner and
Woodruff.[537]

Flexural resonators have been proposed by Giebe and Scheibe [B45] as
standards of frequency from 1 to 20 kc.

IV. PIEZOELECTRIC EXCITATION OF TORSIONAL VIBRATIONS

356. According to §180, the torsion of a cylinder or prism involves
opposite shears on opposite sides of the axis, the plane of shear containing
the axial direction.   In quartz, torsional vibrations have been produced
with the axis of the specimen parallel to X, Y, or Z.   Oblique directions
could, of course, also be chosen.   The same arrangements of electrodes
may be used as in Fig. 88; we can therefore indicate the methods of
excitation by reference to that figure and Table XXVIII.

* "Lehrbuch," 1928 ed., p. 965; also ref. 573.

TABLE XXVIII

Method	Fig. 88	Direction of length	Direction of field	Number of nodes	Strain Equation
I	A	X	Y	Odd	$x_y = d_{26}E_y$
II	A	Y	Y	Even	$x_y = d_{26}E_y$
III	C	Y	Y	Odd	$x_y = d_{26}E_y$
IV	F	Z	X and Y	Odd	$\begin{cases} y_z = d_{14}E_x \\ z_x = d_{25}E_y \end{cases}$
V	F	Y	X	Odd	$y_z = d_{14}E_x$
VI	F	X	Y	Odd	$z_x = d_{25}E_y$

Methods I, II, and III were devised by Giebe and Scheibe.[169]* In method II it is the stray fields extending to right and left along the length of the bar (parallel to Y) that are effective.

Method IV is described by Hund and Wright,[242] who used a circular cylinder with length parallel to Z. The field entering the quartz from the girdling electrode had components $\pm E_x$ and $\pm E_y$, which produced in the adjacent regions the shears requisite for torsion. In some of their experiments they used, in place of electrodes at the ends, girdles surrounding the cylinder spaced at a certain distance from the center.

Method V was realized experimentally in this laboratory in 1931. The piezoelectric excitation is due to the component of field parallel to X entering the bar from the girdling electrode on opposite sides in opposite directions, according to $y_z = d_{14}E_x$. Instead of a girdling electrode, two small plane electrodes could be used, one at each end of the X-axis. Evidence of the torsional mode was provided, not only by agreement between observed and calculated frequencies, but also by the fact that fine sand sprinkled on the vibrating bar formed a lengthwise nodal line along the center.

Method VI, which has not yet been tried, is similar to method V.

Of all the methods for producing torsional vibrations in a bar, the most effective is method I in Table XXVIII, especially if the electrodes extend the full length of the bar, as in Fig. 88E. If the bar has a rectangular cross section, the field should be parallel to the smallest dimension e (the field direction is shown parallel to b in Fig. 88E). In order that this arrangement shall produce torsion, the crystal cut must be such that the field parallel to e will cause a shear in the el-plane with respect to axes parallel to e and l. With quartz, oblique cuts (the possibilities of which have not yet been explored) being excluded, the only torsional excitation by this method is with the length l parallel to X. In a crystal such as Rochelle salt, in which d_{14}, d_{25}, and d_{36} are all present, torsional

* See also Giebe and Blechschmidt.[162] In the latter paper the theory is discussed as well as the effect of temperature on frequency.

vibrations should be very efficiently producible in a bar with two pairs of electrodes as described above, the length of the bar being parallel to one of the crystal axes and the breadth and thickness making angles of 45° with the other two axes.

Any bar cut so that it responded torsionally with electrodes divided along the length, as in Fig. 88E, would also respond flexurally if the electrodes were divided transversely as in Fig. 88G.

Method I has been applied by Giebe and Scheibe to circular cylinders. As a more efficient means of excitation they employed four concave electrodes running parallel to the axis. An analogous arrangement for a rectangular bar is described by Giebe and Blechschmidt.[162]

Experiments with hollow quartz cylinders (axes parallel to Z) have been described by Tawil, by Tsi-Ze and Tsien, and by Zacek and Petrzilka, using a combination of inner and outer electrodes. It was in the course of these experiments that Tawil observed an effect which he attributed to "strephoelectricity," later shown by Langevin and Solomon to be completely explained in terms of d_{14}. Tsi-Ze and his associates also used their resonator as an oscillator in a Pierce circuit. Experiments on various modes of vibration of quartz cylinders, both solid and hollow, are described by Benoit; the cylinders were used in piezo-oscillator circuits.

Torsional resonators may be supported at a node or nodes, or, according to Giebe and Blechschmidt,[162] the bar or cylinder may be held by a pointed rod at each end, fitting into a small conical cavity at the center of the section. As with flexural resonators, it is not always necessary to provide the full quota of electrodes or to place them exactly as shown in Fig. 88. Local excitation over any region where the strain is all of the same nature should be enough to produce a response, although in some cases a strong alternating field may be required.

General formulas for the calculation of frequency are given in §74. Special formulas for quartz will be found in Giebe and Blechschmidt.[162]

357. Quartz Resonators of Special Cuts and Shapes. The resonators now to be described were designed to reduce the effect of temperature on frequency or to reduce coupling with undesired vibrational modes. In some cases both aims can be attained satisfactorily in the same device. Out of the large number of solutions of the problem, the choice of resonator depends on the frequency, the capacitance ratio, the extent to which the effective piezoelectric constant is diminished by rotation, the tolerance with respect to temperature effects, and the use to which the resonator is to be put—frequency standard, power oscillator, filter, etc.

Temperature changes affect the frequency, not only by causing small alterations in density and dimensions of the resonator, but also, and chiefly, by changing the values of the various elastic constants that determine the vibration. All the quartz compliance constants of type

L or S in Fig. 15, except s_{66}, have positive temperature coefficients, while the cross constants s_{12} and s_{13} have negative coefficients. By the use of oblique cuts (Chap. VI), and in some cases by taking advantage also of the coupling between different modes, it is possible to have negative and positive temperature coefficients neutralize one another in such a way as to reduce the effective coefficient to zero. This reduction can be accomplished in many ways, for various vibrational modes and various ranges of frequency.

Unfortunately, the various temperature coefficients present in the frequency formulas usually lead to an expression for the temperature coefficient of frequency containing the square and higher powers of the temperature difference. As a consequence, the temperature coefficient can, by varying the orientation, be made strictly zero only at one particular frequency, if at all. It is only by finding an orientation such that the coefficient of the square term vanishes (terms of higher order being relatively small) that the frequency can be made practically independent of temperature over a considerable range of temperatures. This end has been attained in the GT-cut mentioned below.

We use the abbreviation α for temperature coefficient, with a designating subscript when necessary. Thus the temperature coefficient of s_{11} may be written $\alpha_{s_{11}} = (1/s_{11}) \, \partial s_{11}/\partial t$, or that of frequency $\alpha_f = (1/f) \, \partial f/\partial t$ s_{11} and f being taken at some standard temperature. The curve relating f to t can be expressed by an equation that usually contains both the first and higher powers of t. $\alpha_f = 0$ wherever the curve is parallel to the axis of temperatures. If the flat portion of the curve is narrow, it may be necessary for sufficiently constant frequency outside a very small temperature range to use a thermostat. The broader the flat portion, the less important is thermostatic control.

Both the original X-cut and the Y-cut that began to compete with it about 1927 have large temperature coefficients and give much trouble from the tendency to jump from one frequency to another. The era of resonators with low α_f began in 1929. In that year Marrison[330] described a piezo oscillator of high precision containing a Y-cut ring-shaped crystal vibrating at 100 kc, with $\alpha_f < 10^{-6}$. The use of a ring had already been introduced by Giebe.[160,167,168]

Essen[137,138,139] later used a quartz ring as a frequency standard, his ring having its axis parallel to Z. A compressional circumferential mode was used, with three complete wavelengths spaced around the mean circumference. A proper ratio of inner to outer diameter reduced α_f to 10^{-6} or less over a range of 30°C. The frequency was 100 kc.

It was also in 1929 that Lack[298] described a specially dimensioned Y-cut devised by R. A. Heising, in which the shear mode with its positive α_f was coupled to a flexural overtone mode with negative α_f in such a way as to give a zero coefficient at a certain temperature.

In 1932 and 1933 Matsumura and Kanzaki[351,352] showed that a value of α_f approaching zero for lengthwise vibrations in an X-cut bar could be reached by inclining the length l of the bar at the angle $\varphi = -20°$ to the Y-axis and at the same time giving the ratio b/l an optimal value of about 0.5. Their critical angle $\varphi = -20°$ corresponds to $\theta = +110°$ for $1/s'_{33}$ in curve C, Fig. 31, or to $\theta = +20°$ for $1/s'_{22}$ in curve B; it is practically the angle for minimal Young's modulus. This angle is so close to that for the so-called 18.5° cut that they may be credited with having first appreciated the advantage of this cut.

The 18.5° cut was first described in 1934 by Mason.[332,340] It is an X-cut rectangular plate with length making an angle of 18.5° with the Y-axis, this angle being measured in the direction from $+Y$ toward $+Z$, as shown in Fig. 92. At this angle the coupling between the lengthwise and shear modes (§349), which would otherwise be troublesome in a plate that did not have a very small b/l ratio, disappears.* The b/l ratio chosen for use as a filter is not such as to make α_f approach zero. The plate vibrates in a compressional mode parallel to one of the longer dimensions.

Somewhat similar characteristics are possessed by Mason's $-5°$ plate,[343] illustrated in Fig. 92. Of all the series of X-cut bars with lengths in the YZ-plane it has the lowest temperature coefficient of frequency. This fact, together with its low C_1/C ratio and the fact that it can serve either as a lengthwise or flexural resonator, makes it useful as a filter crystal.

All the resonators so far described are for relatively low frequencies, of the order of 60 to 200 kc.

358. In the development of resonators for higher frequencies, for which thickness vibrations are used, notable innovations were made in 1934. By one of the coincidences that are so frequent in scientific and technological history, there appeared independently, from four widely separated sources, papers on the temperature characteristics of thickness vibrations in quartz plates containing the X-axis, the normals to the plates

---

* The angles $+18.5°$ and $-5°$ for these two cuts are expressed in conformity with the rule stated in §51 for rotation about a single axis. In the earlier publications of the Bell Laboratories they were given as $-18.5°$ and $+5°$. The signs of θ for the AT-, BT-, CT-, DT-, GT-, MT-, and NT-cuts, as given in this book, likewise conform to §51.

The nature of the coupling mentioned above is indicated by the expression $y'_y = -s'_{24}Y'_z$, the length, breadth, and thickness of the plate being parallel, respectively, to Y', Z', and X. The compliance s'_{24}, which represents the coupling between the y'_y- and y'_z-strains, contains s_{44} as a chief constituent. It is the vanishing of s'_{24} at 18.5° (see curve L in Fig. 31) that characterizes this cut.

lying in the YZ-plane at various angles θ with the Y-axis.* All these investigators—Koga[272] in Japan, Bechmann[32] and Straubel[491,492,493] in Germany, and Lack, Willard and Fair[299] in New York—showed that $\alpha_f = 0$ when θ is approximately $-35°$ or $+49°$ (see Fig. 92, p. 459).

Previously to his work cited above, Koga[270] had experimented with his R- and R'-cuts in thickness vibration. These cuts are parallel to the R- and r-faces of the crystal (Fig. 76) and are not very far removed from the AT- and BT-orientations mentioned below. Bechmann considered the effect of the b/l ratio on α_f; he also found that α_f had a zero value for X-cuts rotated about the Y-axis by an angle somewhere between 50 and 70°. Lack, Willard, and Fair investigated the discontinuities in frequency of thickness vibrations in a Y-cut with changing temperature. They found the discontinuities to be due to coupling between the x_y-strain, which is the essential one for thickness vibrations in this cut, and overtones of the z_x-strain. The stress-equation is $X_y = c_{66}x_y + c_{56}z_x$, c_{56} being a measure of the coupling. When the plate is rotated about X by the angle θ, the expression becomes $X'_y = c'_{66}x'_y + c'_{56}z'_x$. Lack, Willard, and Fair found that when $\theta \approx -31°$ or $+60°$ the coefficient c'_{56} vanishes. Plates of these orientations vibrate in a very pure x'_y-shear mode free from anomalies as the temperature changes. Owing to the freedom from parasitic vibrations, local stresses are reduced to a minimum, so that higher voltages can be applied without danger of fracture. Lack, Willard, and Fair called these cuts the AC and BC, respectively.

Although the temperature coefficients of the AC- and BC-cuts are low, they do not vanish. At $\theta = -35°15'$, however, α_f vanishes at 45°C, changing from negative to positive at this temperature (see Fig. 90). Following Lack, Willard, and Fair, this is now commonly called the AT-cut (see Fig. 92). At $\theta = +49°$, α_f vanishes when the temperature is 25°C, changing from positive to negative at this temperature (the BT-cut.) The AT and BT have orientations so close to those of the AC and BC that they partake of the advantages of the latter to a large extent and are commonly used.

All four of the cuts just mentioned are examples of "rotated Y-cuts" or "Y'-cuts." In each case the electric field is parallel to the thickness

* The symbol θ has been used very loosely in the literature, to signify rotation about any axis, in either sense, and measured from any fiducial direction according to some convention adopted, and not always clearly specified, by each individual writer. In this book we use θ for a single rotation about any one of the three crystallographic axes X, Y, or Z, according to the definition in §51. In the present discussion θ is the angle between the Y-axis and the normal to the plate, positive when the rotation is about the X-axis from $+Y$ toward $+Z$. For the most general rotation, in which three angles must be specified, we use φ, Θ, and ψ, where Θ is the angle about the Y_1-axis in §52. The conventions used by various writers are shown in a comparative table in ref. 110.

and makes the angle θ with the Y-axis. The axes of the rotated plate are X, Y', and Z', with Y' parallel to the thickness and X and Z' parallel to l and b (or b and l). The effective piezoelectric constant ϵ of §246 becomes e'_{26} [Eq. (221)], and the driving stress is $X'_y = e'_{26}E'_2$, where E'_2 is the instantaneous driving field. With increasing θ, e'_{26} diminishes; hence the capacitance ratio, given by the reciprocal of Eq. (414), also diminishes.

The AT-cut has a higher capacitance ratio than the BT-cut (normal to the surface is closer to the Y-axis, so that e'_{26} is greater), but the BT-cut has a higher frequency for the same thickness. Both the AT- and BT-cuts are subject to coupling between odd shear and even flexural modes in the XY'-plane.*

It is commonly found that plates are most active when their surfaces are plane or very slightly convex. The slightest concavity lowers the activity and makes the frequency spectrum more complex. As an example may be mentioned an experiment by Koga and Tatibana,[283] who explored the surface of a BT-cut in a piezo-oscillator circuit by having one of the electrodes of small size and moving it to various parts of the surface. Finding the frequency to be somewhat higher near the edges, they prepared a plate with a concave surface, hoping thereby to make all parts vibrate in more exact synchronism. The result was failure to oscillate at all.

359. Low-frequency Resonators in the Form of Broad Plates. Some of the types to be considered make use of compressional vibrations parallel to l or b, as in the case of thin rods. Other types involve shears in the plane of the plate, the frequency depending on both b and l. Such modes of vibration are often called "contour modes" or "face shear modes" (see §71). Owing to the large b/l ratio various coupling effects have to be considered.†

The CT- and DT-cuts, due to Hight and Willard,[227] are the l-f counterparts of the AT- and BT-cuts. The piezoelectric excitation is of the type $z'_x = d'_{25}E'_y$. The vibration is essentially of a shear mode in the

---

* By an "odd shear mode" is meant a thickness mode in which the major surfaces do not move to and fro as units in the X-direction but are divided into an odd number of segments, adjacent segments being joined by lines parallel to Z'. For example, the frequency might be that of three plates, each of dimensions b parallel to Z' and approximately $l/3$ in the X-direction. As with lengthwise vibrations of bars at odd harmonic frequencies (§238), these odd shear modes can be excited with electrodes covering the entire crystal, only in this case, since the frequency depends primarily on the thickness, the odd modes differ but little in frequency from the fundamental thickness shear. As to the "even flexural modes," they have been described in §355, where it was shown that they can be excited by full-sized electrodes. It is the similarity in strain distribution of these shear and flexural modes that accounts for the coupling between them. The coupling can be suppressed by suitable dimensioning.

† Various contour modes in Y-cut plates are discussed by Builder and Benson.[83]

plane of the plate, and the frequency depends on the contour (usually rectangular) rather than the thickness. The edge dimensions are parallel to X and Z'. The fundamental elastic equation is $z'_x = -s'_{55}Z'_x$. For the CT- and DT-cuts the angles θ for zero α_f are $-38°$ at $41°C$ and $+52°$ at $50°C$ respectively (see Table XXIX). These angles are within a few degrees of those for the AT- and BT-cuts. The CT-cut has a better capacitance ratio than the DT-cut and is usually preferred. Both cuts have good freedom from coupling with undesired modes; their frequencies are constant to within 1 part per million from 20 to 30°C.

The GT-cut. The most remarkable of the cuts with low temperature coefficient is the GT-cut, introduced in 1940 by Mason.[336] Without thermostatic control the frequency remains constant within 1 ppm from 0 to 100°C. This cut may be thought of as a CT-cut with the angle θ (for definition of θ see §361) increased from $-38°$ to approximately $-51°$, followed by a rotation of the rectangular plate in its own plane until the edges make angles of $\pm45°$ with the X- and Z'-axes. Its vibrational mode is best understood, however, by starting with a narrow Y-cut 45° bar, the length of which bisects the angle between the X- and Z-axes. The piezoelectric lengthwise strain is $z'_z = d'_{23}E'_y$ analogous to the 45° Y-cut bar in Rochelle salt. The elastic equation is $z'_z = -s'_{33}Z'_z$. Since from Fig. 33 the s'_{33}-curve is symmetrical about the Z- and X-axes, the 45° angle may be taken in either sense. Such a bar has a negative α_f. If now the breadth b is progressively increased, the b-and l-compressional modes become more and more closely coupled. At the same time α_f diminishes in magnitude, becoming positive at sufficiently large b. Mason found not only that there is a certain b/l ratio for which $\alpha_f = 0$, but that, at a certain value of θ, α_f remains approximately equal to zero over a very wide range of temperature. When $\theta = -51°7.5'$ and $b/l = 0.859$, the center of the flat region falls at 25°C. By edge grinding, both frequency and α_f can be adjusted independently, and by slight variation of θ the center of the flat portion of the frequency: temperature curve can be varied. A suitable value of thickness is chosen in order to avoid coupling with a flexural mode. In vacuum this cut has Q up to 330,000. It is used for frequency standards, filters, and receivers.

The MT- and NT-cuts of Mason and Sykes[343] are l-f rectangular plates used in filters and oscillators. Their orientations can be explained by considering first an X-cut plate with its *length* at an angle θ (see explanation of Table XXIX) $-8.5°$ from $+Y$. We may call the direction of length the Y'-axis, the breadth b being parallel to Z'. The plate is now to be rotated through an angle A about Y' so that the positive end of the Z'-axis moves toward $+X$. For the MT- and NT-cuts the angle A

has the values 40° and 50°, respectively.*   These orientations permit the
MT-cut to vibrate in its lengthwise mode, with low α_f, while the NT-cut
has low α_f when vibrating flexurally, according to Harrison's arrangement
shown in Fig. 88E.   Depending on the dimensions, the MT-cut is used
at frequencies from 50 to 100 kc/sec, and the NT-cut from 4 to 50 kc/sec.
When the NT-cut is used as an oscillator, as for example in frequency
modulation, at these low frequencies, a circuit similar to that in Fig. 99
is employed.

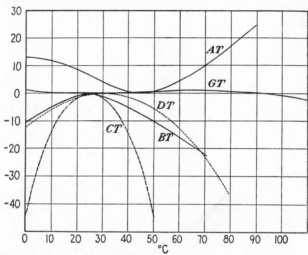

Fig. 90.—Dependence of the temperature coefficient α_f upon frequency, for some cuts of low
α_f, from Mason, ref. 340.   Ordinates are frequency changes in ppm.

Still other cuts of low temperature coefficient have been described,
for example the ET- and FT-cuts of Hight, described by Mason,[337] and
the YT-cut of Yoda,[595,596] which is similar to the BT-cut.   Yoda states
that he experimented with a plate so thin that its fundamental thickness
mode gave a wavelength of only 4.7 m (64 megacycles/sec.).

The MT- and NT-cuts described above are examples of cuts obtained
by a *general rotation*, in which the normal to the plate makes oblique
angles with all three crystallographic axes.   The general rotation has
been treated by Bechmann[35] and Mason.[337]   Further examples are the
V-cuts of Bokovoy and Baldwin.†   These are similar to the AT- and
BT-cuts, but rotated 5° around the Z-axis.

* In their paper, Mason and Sykes describe the properties of the set of cuts that
they call the "MT series," in which θ lies between 0° and −8.5° and A between 34°
and 50°.

† S. A. Bokovoy and C. F. Baldwin, Australian patent 21,959, 1935, and British
patent 457,342, 1936.   See also Builder[80] and Baldwin and Bokovoy.[18]

The temperature coefficients of frequency of some of the more important cuts are shown in Fig. 90. For all cuts except the GT the coefficient vanishes or has a low value only when the temperature is held
close to a certain value. For example, with the AT-cut this value* is
45°C. The GT-cut has a very low coefficient over the entire temperature
range; *i.e.*, the second derivative of frequency with respect to temperature
is nearly zero over the whole range.

360. *The Straubel Contour and Quartz Spheres.* A circular X-cut
plate excited in compressional vibration along a diameter gives a complex
frequency-spectrum. Straubel[484,486,488] conceived the idea of shaping

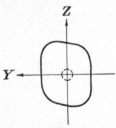

an X-cut plate so that the radius in any direction
in the plane of the plate is proportional to the
square root of Young's modulus in that direction.
The result is the contour illustrated in Fig. 91. A
compressional wave starting at the center reaches
all points on the circumference at the same instant.
Such radial waves can be excited by electrodes
covering the major surfaces in the usual way.
Straubel found a single well-marked resonant
frequency, free from disturbing modes; the
lycopodium test (§366) showed a single nodal spot

Fig. 91.—The Straubel
contour.

at the center. Even with thickness vibrations a plate of this shape is somewhat freer from multiple frequencies than round or rectangular plates.

Quartz spheres have been experimented with as resonators. The
modern crystal gazer, instead of trying to divine the future, observes
modes of vibration. We have already referred in §350 to the experiments
of Van Dyke. Kamienski[250] has also examined various vibrational modes
and measured the temperature coefficient of frequency. The modes are
too complex and the labor in fashioning a sphere of quartz too great for
this type of resonator to offer promise of practical applications.

361. Table XXIX gives the orientations of some typical cuts,
together with the wave constant H, the effective piezoelectric constant ϵ, and the frequency range within which each cut is commonly used.
The data are taken chiefly from Mason[340] and Bond.[66] For the cuts from
AT to GT, θ is the angle between the Y-axis and the normal to the plate,
positive when measured from $+Y$ toward $+Z$; it is also the angle between
the Z-axis and the *plane* of the plate, positive when laid off from $+Z$
toward $-Y$, as indicated in Fig. 92. For the MT-, NT-, 18.5°, and $-5°$
cuts, θ is the angle between the *length* of the plate and the Y-axis, measured from $+Y$ toward $+Z$, as in Fig. 92.

The angles φ, Θ, and ψ in the table specify the orientations according
to the I.R.E. 1945 Standard (see p. 82). With respect to the rotated

* By a slight change in angle this critical temperature can be altered.

axial system the length, breadth, and thickness in each case are parallel to X', Y', and Z', respectively.

For the X-cut in Table XXIX, the first line is for a broad plate in compressional thickness vibration, the second line for a narrow bar in

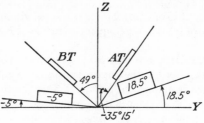

Fig. 92.—Angular orientations of some oblique cuts of quartz.

lengthwise vibration. Similarly, the first line for Y is for the shear thickness mode, and the second for the l-f shear mode in the plane of the plate. Through the process of rotation these two modes become the thickness mode of the AT- and BT-cuts and the contour mode of the CT- and DT-cuts.

TABLE XXIX.—SUMMARY OF DATA FOR VARIOUS CUTS

Cut	Mode	θ	φ	Θ	ψ	H kc sec^{-1} mm	ϵ	Range kc sec^{-1}
X	x_x	....	$0°$	$90°$	$90°$	$2,870$	$e_{11} = 5.2(10^4)$	
X	y_y	....	$0°$	$90°$	$90°$	$2,700$	$\dfrac{d_{11}}{s_{11}^E} = 5.4(10^4)$	
Y	x_y	....	$90°$	$90°$	$90°$	$1,954$	$e_{11} = 5.2(10^4)$	
Y	z_x	....	$90°$	$90°$	$90°$	......	$e_{14} = 1.2(10^4)$	
AT	x_y'	$-35°15'$	$-90°$	$54°45'$	$90°$	$1,662$	$e_{26}' = 2.9(10^4)$	$1,000$–$5,000$
BT	x_y'	$+49°$	$90°$	$41°$	$90°$	$2,549$	$e_{26}' = 2.8(10^4)$	$2,000$– $>13,000$
CT	z_x'	$-38°$	$-90°$	$52°$	$90°$	$3,080$	$e_{25}' = 3.0(10^4)$	100–$1,000$
DT	z_x'	$+52°$	$-90°$	$-38°$	$90°$	$2,060$	$e_{25}' = 1.8(10^4)$	70–500
GT	z_z'	$-51°8'$	$-90°$	$38°52'$	$\pm45°$	$3,292$	....	100–$1,000$
MT	y_y'	$-8.5°$	$6°40'$	$50°28'$	$79°36'$	......	....	50–500
NT	y_y'	$-8.5°$	$9°25'$	$40°40'$	$77°40'$	......	....	4–50
$18.5°$	y_y'	$+18.5°$	$0°$	$90°$	$108°$	$2,554$	$d_{12}' = 7.0(10^{-8})$	Filter
$-5°$	y_y'	$-5°$	$0°$	$90°$	$85°$	......	....	Filter

A word must be added concerning the piezoelectric constants for rotated plates in Table XXIX. The subscripts attached to these constants are applicable as long as the plates are considered as Y'-cuts with the electric field parallel to Y'. In terms of the I.R.E. notation the thickness is parallel to Z' for all cuts; in order to be consistent with this system the piezoelectric constants would have to have different subscripts. For example, the constant for the AT- and BT-cuts would be written e'_{35}, with analogous changes in all the other constants, including also those for the X- and Y-cuts. The numerical values would of course remain unchanged.

By making use of high overtones of thickness vibration, as described in §397, the range of practicable frequencies for the AT-cut is extended to 150,000 kc.

362. Numerical Data on Quartz Resonators. Experimental data from various sources, for bars in lengthwise vibration and plates in thickness vibration, are assembled in Table XXX. The fundamental mode was excited in each case. Quantities in parentheses are calculated by the author from the published data. The wave constant H is defined as $H = fl$ for bars and as $H = fe$ for plates, where f is in kilocycles per second and l and e are in millimeters. The number of meters, h, per millimeter can be calculated from the equation $h = 300,000/H$. In all cases the gap was zero, or close to zero, so that q_0 is the effective stiffness at zero gap.

In the table, Nos. 1, 8, 9, and 10 are from Vigoureux.[B51] Number 2 is the bar discussed in §298; the large R and low Q are due to frictional losses in the primitive form of holder in which the bar was mounted. Numbers 3 to 7 are from Mason.[B35,340] The angles specified give the deviation θ of the length l from the Y-axis, as indicated in Fig. 92 for the $-5°$ and 18.5° cuts.* These five examples illustrate the wide variations in H and q_0 for bars in different orientations.

Numbers 11 to 14 are from Bechmann.[37] The high values of Q are evidence of the excellent mounting of these plates. The value of C_1/C is calculated from the theoretical formula (414a) in §280, in which it is assumed that $C_1 = kA/4\pi e$ esu. From C_1/C and Bechmann's values of C, C_1 is calculated.

In No. 4, C_1/C is the value given by Mason.[340] The same value can be derived from Eq. (414a) using his data. The very large values of C_1/C occurring in the table are probably due to low effective values of the piezoelectric constant.

For *flexural resonators*, values of R, L, C and $\delta = \pi/Q$ are given by Rohde and Handrek,[438] whose paper must be consulted for details. They find that, for resonators of frequencies of 1,000 to 60,000 cycles/sec, R ranges from $22(10^5)$ to $1.6(10^5)$ ohms, C from 0.005 to 0.0027 mmf, L from 500 (10^4) to $0.26(10^4)$ henrys, δ from 0.00022 to 0.00034. Some of these resonators have two nodes, others three.

* For these five cuts the I.R.E. orientation angles (§52) are $\varphi = 0$, $\Theta = 90°$, $\psi = 90° + \theta$.

TABLE XXX.—THE CONSTANTS OF SOME TYPICAL QUARTZ RESONATORS

No.	Cut	l mm	b mm	e mm	f_0 kc/sec	R ohms	L henrys	C mmf	C_1 mmf	$\frac{C_1}{C}$	Q	H kc sec^{-1} mm	q_0 dyne cm^{-2} × 10^{-10}
1	X-bar	62.2∥Y	7.5	1.5	44	1,640	(216)	0.06	8.7	145	(37,000)	(2,740)	(79.6)
2	X-bar	30.7∥Y	4.1	1.4	89.9	15,000	137	0.0205	3.54	173	5,150	2,750	80.6
3	X-bar 79.5°	24.03	2.5	0.502	130.7	—	—	—	—	—	—	3,141	(105)
4	X-bar 18.5°	20.0	2.5	0.502	127.7	—	—	—	—	137	—	2,554	(69.2)
5	X-bar 0.9°	19.97	2.99	0.502	135.2	—	—	—	—	—	—	2,705	(77.5)
6	-18°	20.02	2.95	0.50	155.4	—	—	—	—	—	—	3,111	(102.5)
7	X-bar -42.6°	20.0	2.95	0.50	174.8	—	—	—	—	—	—	3,495	(129.5)
8	X-plate	16.40∥Y	15.64∥Z	6.15	472	2,100	(28.2)	0.004	1.93	460	(40,000)	(2,900)	(89.0)
9	X-plate	Disk, diam.	48.5 mm	7.52	389	400	(9.25)	0.018	9.6	530	(57,000)	(2,920)	(90.8)
10	X-plate	Disk, diam.	9.43 mm	0.58	4,980	4.6	(0.00725)	0.14	26.3	190	(50,000)	(2,880)	(88.5)
11	X-plate	Disk, diam.	25.0 mm	1.89	1,500	12.7	0.181	0.0622	(10.2)	(164)	(134,000)	2,838	85.46
12	Y-plate	Disk, diam.	25.0 mm	1.28	1,500	8.4	0.056	0.2011	(15.0)	(75)	(63,000)	1,919	39.10
13	BT	Disk, diam.	25.0 mm	1.66	1,500	35.0	0.391	0.0288	(11.9)	(413)	(105,000)	2,492	65.99
14	AT	Disk, diam.	25.0 mm	1.10	1,500	24.2	0.119	0.0945	(17.9)	(189)	(46,500)	1,657	29.23

363. *The High Q of Quartz.* It is well known that the energy losses in quartz resonators are due, as a rule, chiefly to friction and air waves in the mounting and to vibrations imparted by the crystal to its supports. It has been shown by Van Dyke[554] that a considerable amount of damping is also caused by losses at the surfaces of the crystal, when these surfaces have simply been ground or lapped smooth, owing to microscopic cracks and other imperfections. If the surfaces are etched before mounting, these losses are greatly reduced, while a final polishing causes a still further diminution. Van Dyke's results obtained with an X-cut bar (frequency 67.5 kc/sec) are given below. The bar was silvered and suspended by a fine wire attached exactly at the center, serving also as a lead to the silver coating.

With surfaces ground, in air at atmospheric pressure, $Q = 25,000$; in hydrogen at atmospheric pressure, $Q = 101,000$; in vacuum,

$$Q = 180,000 \text{ to } 290,000.$$

With surfaces etched, in vacuum, $Q = 490,000$; etched and polished, in vacuum, $Q = 580,000$, corresponding to a logarithmic decrement of $5.4(10^{-6})$.

For a quartz bar in the primary frequency standard at the Reichsanstalt (§399), Scheibe* found the decrement to be from $13(10^{-6})$ to $18(10^{-6})$.

These decrement values for quartz are lower than the smallest value that we find recorded for a gravity pendulum.†

If compressional waves of frequency 67.5 kc/sec were impressed on the end of a quartz bar of indefinite length, for which the logarithmic decrement was $5.4(10^{-6})$, they would travel about 70 km before the amplitude was reduced to 1 per cent of that at the source.

For some of the vibrational modes of a Y-cut quartz *ring* Van Dyke[557] found values of Q of over a million (see also §565).

The highest Q that we find recorded for a tuning fork is about 500,000, for a 480-cycle fork.‡

364. *Reduction in Friction at the Surface of a Vibrating Crystal.* When an X-cut quartz plate vibrates near resonance, the friction between it and the surface of a solid with which it is in contact is greatly reduced. This effect was described by Straubel[486] in 1931. In the same year frictional experiments were carried out in this laboratory by Hagen,§ based on earlier unpublished observations by Van Dyke. Hagen used

---

* A. Scheibe and E. v. Ferroni, *Physik. Z.*, vol. 39, pp. 257–258, 1938.

† H. Gockel and M. Schuler (*Z. Physik*, vol. 109, pp. 433–458, 1938) give $19.1(10^{-6})$ for the logarithmic decrement per cycle of a Schuler pendulum.

‡ E. Norrman, *Proc. I.R.E.*, vol. 20, pp. 1715–1731, 1932.

§ J. P. Hagen, M.A. thesis, Wesleyan University, 1931.

several different methods, including the measurement of the drag exerted on the quartz by a rotating brass disk on which it rested and also the effect of vibration on the angle of repose when the quartz rested on an inclined plane. When Hagen's experiments were performed in air, the friction was reduced to about half the normal value. In vacuum the effect almost disappeared, indicating that a layer of air between the surfaces was a necessary condition for the reduction in friction. On the other hand, Hagen found that the friction of a *pivot* supported by a bearing that rested on the vibrating quartz was reduced by about one-half even in vacuum.

365. Luminous Resonators. In a well-mounted resonator, driving voltages of only a few volts can cause local strains so great that the accompanying piezoelectric polarization gives rise to a charge density on the surface large enough to produce close to the surface a field sufficiently strong to ionize the air. The result is a visible glow. This effect was observed at atmospheric pressure in this laboratory in the course of the early experiments, but the results were not published. Since then, many others have also encountered it.

In 1925 Giebe and Scheibe[163] published the first of a series of papers on the luminous resonator. With rods parallel to X or Y, using very short electrodes according to §349, they were able to obtain luminosity at the fundamental lengthwise frequency and odd overtones up to the 33d order. The order can be determined by counting the number of luminous regions. Thus a single rod can serve as a frequency standard for a large number of frequencies. By proper placing of the electrodes even orders can also be excited. For the lower range of frequencies, 1,000 to 20,000, they used flexural modes, according to §354.

As standards of frequency, a precision as high as 1 part in 10^6 is claimed for the luminous resonators. The crystals are mounted in bulbs containing air or, for brighter effects, a mixture of Ne and He, at a pressure of a few millimeters.

The luminous resonator is connected in series with a pickup coil coupled to a generator of finely controllable frequency. The right setting of the generator is first found approximately with fairly close coupling. For the final precise adjustment the coupling is made as loose as possible.

366. Wave Patterns on Quartz Resonators. A vibrational survey of a resonator can be made by the use of probes, polarized light, or optical interference or by observing the movements of a liquid or of solid particles in contact with the surface.

The probe method consists in touching the resonator lightly at various points with a slender rod, to locate the nodal regions. Vibrations are suppressed least when contact is at the nodes. This method, much used by the author from the first, is described by Wright and Stuart. Its use can go a long way in helping to avoid false conclusions as to modes of vibration.

In 1922 the use of *lycopodium powder* on quartz resonators was first described.[93] When this powder is dusted onto the surface, it tends to be shaken away from loops of motion and to collect at the nodes. Fine sand or other pulverized material can also be used. In some cases the powder is seen to move in small vortices or whirls, or to be projected violently from the surface. Wachsmuth and Auer[577] describe an experiment in which they found lycopodium to be projected as much as 50 cm. In this connection may be mentioned the experiments of Bücks and

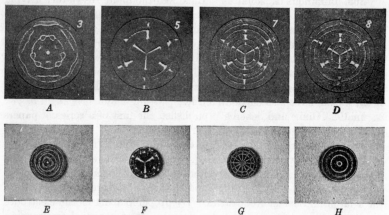

Fig. 93.—Lycopodium patterns on Z-cut disks vibrating in various modes, from Petrzilka. *A, B, C, D,* quartz. *E, F, G, H,* tourmaline.

Müller,[79] who observed the projection of smoke from the vibrating surface.

Many papers have appeared on the study of vibrational patterns of quartz by the use of lycopodium. Some of them contain very beautiful photographs of the lycopodium figures, examples of which are shown in Fig. 93, from Petrzilka.[417] Patterns *A, B, C, D* are from circular Z-cut quartz plates, excited by electrodes arranged around the circumference. For comparison, some of Petrzilka's patterns obtained with Z-cut tourmaline plates are also shown[415] (see §382). From the similarity in the elastic properties of quartz and tourmaline one would expect a similarity in the wave patterns, as is indeed made evident to some extent in the figures.* For a discussion of these and many other patterns, which were

---

* In comparing the patterns it must be understood that the vibrational modes are not necessarily the same in each quartz pattern as in the tourmaline pattern below it The pictures were selected solely because of superficial similarities.

obtained in a test of Love's theory of radial and circumferential waves, Petrzilka's original papers must be consulted.

Complex patterns, such as those on the surface of an X-cut in thickness vibration, can be observed by *covering the surface with oil* or immersing the crystal in a shallow bath of oil. When viewed in a beam of reflected light, the oil surface is seen to be covered with minute irregularities. Crossley[116] found water on the surface to be quickly vaporized and that a ferroferricyanide solution left a sediment with a distinct pattern.* The oil method has been used by Tawil.[515] Bücks and Müller found that a drop of alcohol placed on the surface was shot off in a fine spray, forming striations between the vibrating surface and the plane electrode.

367. *The interference method* was introduced in 1927 by Dye and later applied by many others.† Dye produced a set of interference fringes between the non-vibrating polished quartz surface and a glass plate just above it. When the plate vibrated, the fringes were distorted, and from their appearance one could judge the quality of the resonator and the amplitude of vibration (normal to the surface) at different points. By an ingenious stroboscopic arrangement, using a synchronously flashing helium lamp, clear images of the distorted fringes were obtained, free from blurring.

Dye's method has been modified by Strong[497] and by Straubel,[490,491] whose optical system was so arranged that the entire field remained dark when the plate was not vibrating. Osterberg[398–402] describes interferometric methods, based on Dye's work, for studying various types of vibration. Osterberg and Cookson devised a "multiple interferometer"[407] for observing the vibrational patterns on all six faces of a rectangular parallelepiped. They used this method (see §313), applied to a quartz plate undergoing forced vibrations at 60 cycles/sec, for obtaining, by the converse effect, the values of d_{11} and d_{14} given in Table XVIII.

Mention may be made here also of the use of the "schlieren" method by Petrzilka and Zachoval[421] and by Schaaffs.[450]

368. *The polarized light method* was first used by Tawil[505,507,509–511] and later by several others.‡ Tawil placed his vibrating quartz plate, along with a second compensating quartz plate, between a crossed polarizer and analyzer, so that the field was dark except when the resonator vibrated. Vibrations caused certain portions of the field to be

---

* See also Sanders.[447]

† References at the end of this chapter. An account of Dye's work, with illustrations, is given by Rayner.

‡ K. Eichhorn, *Z. tech. Physik*, vol. 17, pp. 276–279, 1936 (he used a synchronized Kerr cell and calculated the stresses in flexural vibrations); P. T. Kao,[253] R. Moens and J. E. Verschaffelt, *Compt. rend.*, vol. 185, pp. 1034–1036, 1927; K. Grant,[187] Petrzilka,[414] Wachsmuth and Auer,[577] L. Bruninghaus, *Jour. phys. rad.*, vol. 6, pp. 159–167, 1935.

illuminated, leaving the nodal regions dark. The effect arises from the rotation of the plane of polarization by the stressed quartz, as explained in §538. Tawil and his followers investigated various vibrational modes by this method.

Many of the recorded wave patterns are so complex as to defy analysis. Compressional, shear, flexural, and torsional modes or certain of their overtones may be inextricably coupled at any given resonant frequency. It is only by a careful study of the resulting nodal patterns that conclusions—mostly qualitative—can be drawn concerning the contributing modes and their coupling.

Finally, brief mention may be made of the fact that the distribution of vibrational amplitude in quartz plates can be studied by the observation of air blasts, as described in §350, and also by means of ultrasonic waves.[B5,B24,422]

369. Beta-quartz Resonators. Increase in temperature past the transformation point at 573°C deprives quartz of all piezoelectric coefficients except d_{14}, $d_{25} = -d_{14}$, e_{14}, and $e_{25} = -e_{14}$. The possible piezoelectric stresses, as given in §168, are therefore $Y_z = -e_{14}E_x$ and $Z_x = e_{14}E_y$. The cuts and modes of excitation are similar to those for Rochelle salt or for the CT- and DT-cuts in quartz described in §359.

Such resonators have been investigated by Osterberg and Cookson.[404] Their use by these workers and also by Atanasoff and Hart, Atanasoff and Kammer, and Lawson, for the determination of elastic constants of quartz at high temperatures, is described in §§90, 92, and 101.

Osterberg and Cookson succeeded in making plates of β-quartz operate as piezo oscillators.

REFERENCES

OBLIQUE CUTS AND TEMPERATURE COEFFICIENTS, SIMPLE MODES

General. SCHEIBE,[B45] VIGOUREUX,[B50,B51] BECHMANN,[32,39,44] BROWN and HARRIS,[71] BUILDER,[80] GIEBE and SCHEIBE,[167,170] GRAMONT and BÉRETZKI,[183] KOGA,[272–274,276] MASON,[332,337,340] NAMBA and MATSUMURA,[389] SANDERS,[447] STRAUBEL,[491–493] SYKES,[498] VECCHIACCHI.[560]

Lengthwise Vibrations. GRAMONT,[B21] SCHEIBE,[B45] VIGOUREUX,[B50,B51] BECHMANN,[42,44] BUNING,[86] DYE,[127] GIEBE and BLECHSCHMIDT,[162] GIEBE and SCHEIBE,[167,172] MATSUMURA and KANZAKI,[350–352] MEISSNER,[359] NAMBA and MATSUMURA,[388] POWERS,[431] SANDERS.[447] A. HUND, "Phenomena in High-frequency Systems," McGraw-Hill Book Company, Inc., New York, 1936.

Thickness Vibrations. SCHEIBE,[B45] VIGOUREUX,[B50,B51] BECHMANN,[32,36,43,44] GERTH and ROCHOW,[156] GIBBS and THATTE,[158] HATAKEYAMA,[209] KOGA,[272] LACK,[298] NAMBA and MATSUMURA,[388] TSI-ZE and KENG-YI.[526]

AT-cut, BT-cut. LACK, WILLARD, and FAIR,[299] MASON,[337,340] MASON and SYKES,[343] SANDERS,[447] YODA.[595,596]

CT-cut, DT-cut. HIGHT,[226] HIGHT and WILLARD,[227] MASON and SYKES.[343]

GT-cut. MASON.[336,340]

V-cut. BALDWIN and BOKOVOY,[18] BENSON,[51] BUILDER,[80] SANDERS.[447]

Ring-shaped Resonators. ESSEN,[137] GIEBE and SCHEIBE,[167,168] MARRISON,[330,331] VAN DYKE.[557]

COUPLING EFFECTS BETWEEN DIFFERENT MODES

BALDWIN,[16] BECHMANN,[43,44] BUILDER and BENSON,[84] EKSTEIN,[131] GIEBE and BLECHSCHMIDT,[162] GIEBE and SCHEIBE,[165] HITCHCOCK,[230] LACK,[298] LACK, WILLARD, and FAIR,[299] LISSÜTIN,[317] MASON,[332,340] MATSUMURA and HATAKEYAMA,[345-347] NAMBA and MATSUMURA,[388] SANDERS,[447] SCHIFFERMÜLLER,[452] SYKES.[498]

CONTOUR MODES AND OTHER COMPLEX MODES

BECHMANN,[36] BUILDER and BENSON,[84] EKSTEIN,[131] FOX and HUTTON,[144] GIEBE and SCHEIRE,[166,169,171] KOGA and SHOYAMA,[281] LONN,[319] PETRZILKA,[414,417,418] SYKES.[498]

LUMINOUS RESONATORS

GRAMONT,[B21] SCHEIBE,[B45] VIGOUREUX,[B50,B51] GALOTTI,[153] GIEBE,[160] GIEBE and SCHEIBE,[163,165,170,172] HARRISON and HOOPER,[208] HEHLGANS,[217] JIMBO,[248] MITSUI,[370] MÖGEL,[373,374] NAMBA and MATSUMURA,[388] SKELLETT,[470,471] VAN DYKE,[556] WRIGHT and STUART,[594] ZAKS and UFTIUJANINOV.[599]

FLEXURAL VIBRATIONS

Theory. DOERFFLER,[124] MASON,[333] OSTERBERG and COOKSON,[405] SYKES,[498] THOMSON,[518] TYKOCINSKI-TYKOCINER and WOODRUFF,[537] VOIGT and FRÉEDERICKSZ.[576]

Equivalent Electric Constants. ROHDE,[437] ROHDE and HANDREK.[438]

Temperature Coefficients. ROHDE,[437] ROHDE and HANDREK.[438]

Use as Frequency Standard. SCHEIBE.[B45]

Use in Filters. ROHDE,[437] ROHDE and HANDREK.[438]

Use in Oscillators. ROHDE,[437] ROHDE and HANDREK.[438]

Luminous Resonator. ZAKS and UFTIUJANINOV.[599]

Curie Strip. GRAMONT and BÉRETZKI (frequencies down to 50$\sim$).[185]

Miscellaneous Experiments. DOERFFLER,[124] EICHHORN,[130] GIEBE and SCHEIBE,[166-170] GRUETZMACHER,[191] HARRISON,[205] HARRISON and HOOPER,[208] JIMBO,[248] KRISTA,[290] NAMBA and MATSUMURA,[388] OSTERBERG,[399,400] TAWIL,[512] TYKOCINSKI-TYKOCINER and WOODRUFF.[537]

TORSIONAL VIBRATIONS AND STATIC TORSIONAL EFFECTS

Theory. GIEBE and BLECHSCHMIDT,[162] LANGEVIN and SOLOMON,[307] VOIGT and FRÉEDERICKSZ,[576] ZACEK and PETRZILKA.[598]

Use in Oscillators. BENOIT,[49] HUND and WRIGHT,[242] TSI-ZE and MING-SAN,[527] TSI-ZE and TSIEN,[530] TSI-ZE, TSIEN, and SUN-HUNG.[536]

Miscellaneous Experiments. BENOIT,[49] GIBBS and TSIEN,[159] GIEBE and BLECHSCHMIDT,[162] GIEBE and SCHEIBE,[166,167,169,170] HUND and WRIGHT,[242] TAWIL,[515] TSI-ZE and SUN-HUNG,[528,529] TSI-ZE and TSIEN,[533] ZACEK and PETRZILKA,[598] A. HUND, "Phenomena in High-frequency Systems," McGraw-Hill Book Co., Inc., New York, 1936.

Static Effects. TAWIL,[508,513,514] TSI-ZE and TSIEN.[531,532,534, 535]

Hollow Cylinders. BENOIT,[49] TSI-ZE,[525] TSI-ZE and MING-SAN,[527] TSI-ZE and SUN-HUNG,[528,529] TSI-ZE and TSIEN,[530-535] TSI-ZE, TSIEN, and SUN-HUNG,[536] ZACEK and PETRZILKA.[598]

Resonator Experiments with Polarized Light

Cady,[104] Kao,[253] Moens and Verschaffelt,[372] Petrzilka,[414] Tawil,[505,507,509,510] Tsi-Ze and Tsien,[530,533] Tsi-Ze, Tsien, and Sun-Hung,[536] Wachsmuth and Auer.[577]

Examination of Vibrating Plates with the Optical Interferometer

Scheibe,[B45] Vigoureux,[B51] Dye,[128] Kotlyarevski and Pumper,[289] Osterberg,[398–402] Petrzilka and Zachoval,[421] Rayner,[433] Schaaffs,[450] Schumacher,[453] Straubel,[490,491] Strong,[497] Wataghin and Sacerdote.[580]

CHAPTER XVIII

RESONATORS FROM OTHER CRYSTALS, AND COMPOSITE RESONATORS

For they marueyle that annye men be soo folyshe as to haue delyte and pleasure in the glysterynge of a lytyll tryfelynge stone, whyche maye beholde annye of the starres, or elles the soone yt selfe.—SIR THOMAS MORE.

Although quartz is almost the only material used at present for piezo resonators, much experimental work has been done with resonators from Rochelle salt and tourmaline. The former of these two has found some application in filters, and the latter in piezo oscillators of very high frequency. The phosphates and arsenates mentioned in Chap. XXVII have properties that recommend them as resonators; concerning them, however, judgment must be withheld until more data are available.

After a discussion of the effect of the anomalies of Rochelle salt upon its usefulness as a resonator, the resonator equations for lengthwise vibrations of 45° bars will be given. The discussion is confined to the case in which the driving field is small, since only then are the various stress-strain relations linear. The behavior of Rochelle-salt resonators with varying gap and also at very high frequencies is considered. Some experimental results are discussed, not only for lengthwise vibrations, but for other modes as well.

The resonating properties of a few other crystals are described, with special reference to tourmaline. Lastly, an account is given of the composite type of resonator, which consists most commonly of a metallic bar vibrated by having a bar of piezoelectric crystal attached to it.

370. The Rochelle-salt Resonator. Rochelle salt offers a very wide range of choice in orientations, shapes, and vibrational modes for resonators. The mechanical and thermal limitations of this crystal have restricted its practical application as a resonator. On the other hand, the experimental study of resonators has contributed greatly to our knowledge of the physical properties of Rochelle salt. Moreover, Rochelle-salt resonators are easily constructed and operated, affording some striking and instructive demonstrations.

Since the only piezoelectric strain coefficients are d_{14}, d_{25}, and d_{36}, it is impossible to obtain by direct piezoelectric excitation lengthwise vibrations parallel to the X-, Y-, or Z-crystallographic axes or thickness vibrations in plates normal to these axes.* In general, however, both

---

* We are here leaving out of account the possibility of exciting feeble compressional vibrations of type x_x, y_y, or z_z, through the quadratic effect discussed in §464.

types of vibration are possible in any *oblique* cut, since with respect to obliquely rotated axes the necessary piezoelectric coefficients are always present except in certain special cases. The formulas for the rotated coefficients are given in §§139 and 140. Flexural and torsional vibrations can be excited in practically any cut.

The anomalies of Rochelle salt, summarized in §402, are present only in the X-cut or in any cut in which the electric field has a component parallel to X. As long as the field is normal to X, which usually means a Y-cut or a Z-cut, there is no appreciable trouble from variability of the elastic, piezoelectric, and dielectric constants with field and stress. The change in elastic properties with temperature, while causing a rather large temperature coefficient of frequency, is fairly uniform. Although the decrements are an order of magnitude greater than in quartz, still for these cuts the equations and approximations given in Chap. XIII are usually entirely applicable.

It is when the field in the resonator has a component parallel to X, and of course most of all in the X-cut, that the anomalies have their field day, at least between the Curie temperatures and in the regions just outside of them. Some of the anomalies, however, can be avoided even between the Curie points when the field strength is restricted to a few volts per centimeter; most of the experimental work has been done with weak fields. As long as the field is weak, the dependence of strain and polarization upon the field is very nearly linear, so that the elastic and piezoelectric coefficients can be treated as constants. According to the domain theory we may define a "weak" field as one too weak to cause reversals of domains. As will be seen in §434, reversals of domains, as indicated by the beginning of the steep part of the polarization curve, do not take place as long as the field strength does not exceed 50 volts/cm, except close to the Curie points, where it rapidly sinks to a value which theoretically is zero. Between the Curie points it is best to keep the peak value of the driving field below 10 volts/cm, especially when there is a gap between crystal and electrodes, since near resonance the field in the crystal may be very greatly in excess of the driving field. At temperatures well outside the Curie points all relations are linear, so that the limitation to weak fields is removed—except for the danger of overheating or fracturing the crystal.

Between the Curie points, if the field is allowed to become so great that the relations are not linear, the elastic, dielectric, and piezoelectric constants vary in the course of each cycle (see also §426). The mechanical driving stress is then no longer proportional to the field. Even if the applied voltage is strictly sinusoidal, overtone vibrations will be present. This non-linear effect has been proposed by Wologdin[590] for application in a Rochelle-salt frequency multiplier. The analysis of results obtained with Rochelle-salt resonators in large fields would be very difficult, and it does not seem to have been attempted.

Between the Curie points, when the vibrations are sufficiently vigorous, reversals of the spontaneous polarization in each half cycle may take place, especially in regions where the strain is greatest. The electric and elastic behavior are affected thereby, so that an anomaly in the frequency is to be expected, as well as pronounced damping. As was shown first by Mueller[380] and later in greater detail by Matthias,[353] the frequency of any mode involving s_{44}, in a plate with zero gap, is increased by application of a steady biasing field parallel to X, approaching a constant value when the biasing field is around 1,500 volts/cm. At the same time, as shown by Matthias, the damping is greatly reduced. These effects are attributable to the fact that the biasing field tends to prevent the reversals of the spontaneous polarization. Unfortunately, the crystal breaks or melts before a field can be applied great enough to prevent the reversals entirely. Matthias's work is treated further in §376.

Even in weak fields the Rochelle-salt resonator is not free from anomalies. Especially is this true when the electrodes are in contact with the crystal, since the elastic compliance then has its isagric value, which is extremely dependent on temperature.* It is only with large gaps that the X-cut resonator is nearly free from dependence on temperature.

A complication in the Rochelle-salt resonator to which attention should be given in future is the phenomenon of lag discussed in §427. From an inspection of the oscillographic data in Chap. XXII as well as Fig. 117 and the table on page 553 it appears that from about 500 cycles/sec upward the polarization is reduced by the lag, the effect increasing with rising frequency. One would expect the amplitude, and perhaps other properties, to be affected thereby. A start at the theoretical solution of this problem has been made by Mason.[338]

371. Resonator Equations for Rochelle-salt X-cut 45° Bars. Most of the experimental work with Rochelle-salt resonators has been done with lengthwise vibrations in bars. Other orientations and vibrational modes will be considered later. The present section is written in the notation for X-cut 45° bars. For other orientations all that is necessary is to make suitable changes in the coefficients. The gap is here assumed to be zero; its effect is treated in §377. Although a complete theory would include dielectric losses and the non-linear effects mentioned above, we shall here assume the field strength to be low enough for all effects to be linear. The parallel capacitance C_1 can then be regarded as free from dielectric loss; *i.e.*, the only resistance in the resonator is in the RLC-branch.

---

* See §§79, 200, 211, and 466 for the isagric coefficients and their relation to the constant-displacement and constant-polarization values.

The symbols d_{14} and e_{14} signify the *initial* piezoelectric coefficients, denoted in §§459 and 460 by $(d_{14})_0$ and $(e_{14})_0$ or, between the Curie points, by $(d_{14})_0^s$ and $(e_{14})_0^s$. The following equations hold at all temperatures, though the parameters vary greatly with temperature.

Since we are dealing only with X-cuts, the subscript x can be omitted from symbols for electrical quantities without confusion. And since the gap is zero, it is to be understood that all elastic quantities have their *isagric* values, unless otherwise specified.

The general equations for Rochelle-salt X-cut 45° bars are derived from Equations on pp. 183 and 203. When the strain and field are prescribed,

$$\left. \begin{array}{l} Y'_y = \quad c'_{22}y'_y - e'_{12}E = c'_{22}y'_y - e_{14}E \\ Z'_z = \quad c'_{33}z'_z - e'_{13}E = \quad c'_{33}z'_z + e_{14}E \\ P = \eta''E + e'_{12}y'_y + e'_{13}z'_z = \eta''E + e_{14}(y'_y - z'_z) \end{array} \right\} \quad (480)$$

When stress and field are prescribed,

$$\left. \begin{array}{l} y'_y = s'_{22}Y'_y + d'_{12}E = s'_{22}Y'_y + \tfrac{1}{2}d_{14}E \\ z'_z = s'_{33}Z'_z + d'_{13}E = s'_{33}Z'_z - \tfrac{1}{2}d_{14}E \\ P = \eta'E + d'_{12}Y'_y + d'_{13}Z'_z = \eta'E + \tfrac{1}{2}d_{14}(Y'_y - Z'_z) \end{array} \right\} \quad (480a)$$

η'' and η' are the clamped and free susceptibilities as defined in §450.*
Strictly, Eqs. (480) and (480a) are for *static* conditions. Equation (480) expresses the basic relations on which the theory of thickness vibrations rests, and also the special case treated in §372. Equations (480a) correspond to the case of lengthwise vibrations in a free bar, with which we are concerned in the present section.

We seek first the expression for the effective piezoelectric stress coefficient ϵ, from Eq. (307). Taking the length of the bar parallel to the Y'-axis, 45° from the Y-axis, we have, for the longitudinal isagric compliance, s'_{22} (p. 75). The only fundamental piezoelectric coefficients to consider when the field is parallel to X are d_{14}, and $e_{14} = d_{14}/s_{44}$. With respect to the transformed axes the coefficients are, from p. 203,

$$d'_{12} = \frac{d_{14}}{2} \qquad d'_{13} = -\frac{d_{14}}{2} \qquad e'_{12} = e_{14} \qquad e'_{13} = -e_{14}$$

In Eq. (307) we set $n = 2$, $i = 1$, $h = 2$ and 3, obtaining, with the aid of Eqs. 43, p. 75,

$$\epsilon = \frac{d_{14}}{2s'_{22}} \quad (481)$$

* Outside the Curie points, η'' and η' are the same as η_1 and η'. Between these points $\eta'' \equiv \eta''_s$ and $\eta' \equiv \eta'_s$ [Eqs. (499) and (504a)]. No thought need be given to these distinctions in the present section, since the equations are equally valid at all temperatures.

An estimate of the numerical value of ϵ is given in §416a.

By the method used on p. 293 the current to the bar is found to be

$$I = j\omega V\left[\frac{bl}{4\pi e}\left(k' - \frac{\pi d_{14}^2}{s_{22}'}\right) + \frac{bd_{14}^2}{2\gamma e s_{22}'}\tanh\frac{\gamma l}{2}\right] \qquad (482)$$

This expression is valid at all frequencies. The effective dielectric constant is

$$k_l = k' - \frac{\pi d_{14}^2}{s_{22}'} \qquad (483)$$

whence the effective susceptibility is found to be

$$\eta_l = \eta' - \frac{d_{14}^2}{4s_{22}'} \qquad (483a)$$

Anticipating the results of the polarization theory as given in Eqs. (495b) and (522c), we find from Eq. (483a) that the reciprocal susceptibility, in terms of the *polarization theory*, is given by

$$\chi_l = \frac{1}{\eta_l} = \chi' + \frac{b_{14}^2}{4s_{22}'^P} = \chi' + \frac{a_{14}^2}{4s_{22}'^P c_{44}^{P\,2}} \qquad (483b)$$

This equation shows that $\chi_l - \chi'$, like $\chi_1 - \chi'$ in Eq. 497, is a constant independent of temperature, insofar as a_{14} is temperature-independent.

Equation (483b) offers the advantage of having all quantities except χ' practically independent of temperature and stress. χ_l can be proved identical with Mason's[338] χ_{LC}, which he calls the value for "longitudinal clamping." This quantity can be measured by Mason's ingenious expedient of using the double frequency, as may be seen by writing $\omega = 2\pi(2f_0)$ and $c = 2f_0 l$ in Eq. (74) for γ and substituting this γ in Eq. (315). The last term vanishes, and the current is the same as if the crystal were a simple condenser with a dielectric constant k_l given by Eq. (483). The constant k_l is the same as Mueller's[380] ϵ_H.

At frequencies not too close to resonance, the damping can usually be ignored. With sufficient precision the electrical admittance Y_1' for longitudinal vibrations at the fundamental frequency is then, from Eq. (316),

$$Y_1' = j\omega\left(\frac{blk_l}{4\pi e} + \frac{bld_{14}^2 f_0}{2\pi f e^2 s_{22}'}\tan\frac{\pi f}{2f_0}\right) \qquad (484)$$

In the resonance range we specialize Eq. (319) for the present case and find for the admittance

$$Y_1' = \frac{bd_{14}^2}{\rho l e (s_{22}')^2 (n^2 + \alpha^2)}(\alpha + jn) + j\omega\frac{blk_l}{4\pi e} \qquad (484a)$$

where $\alpha = \pi f/Q = f\delta$ and $n = \omega_0 - \omega$.

The equivalent electric constants are

$$
\left.
\begin{aligned}
L &= \frac{\rho l e (s'_{22})^2}{2 b d_{14}^2} \\[6pt]
C &= \frac{2 d_{14}^2 b l}{\pi^2 e s'_{22}} \\[6pt]
R &= \frac{\rho \alpha l e (s'_{22})^2}{d_{14}^2 b} \\[6pt]
C_1 &= \frac{b l k_l}{4 \pi e} \\[6pt]
X &= \omega L - \frac{1}{\omega C} = \frac{\rho l e (s'_{22})^2 n}{\pi d_{14}^2}
\end{aligned}
\right\}
\qquad (485)
$$

Values of η_l, η'', and k'' for a few temperatures, with the electric field in the X-direction, are given in Table XXXI; they are derived from the same data as Figs. 145 and 146. The values of $k'' = 1 + 4\pi\eta''$ fit in fairly well with the h-f values of k_x in Table XXXIV (page 572). Outside the Curie points $\eta'' \equiv \eta_1$; between them, $\eta'' \equiv \eta''_s$. k'' is the dielectric constant to use in the equations for thickness vibrations (§378).

TABLE XXXI

t, deg C	η_l	η''	k''
5	9.6	8.2	104
24.7	30	22	280
31.0	13	11	140
47.5	5.3	4.9	62

372. Rochelle-salt X-cut 45° Bar with Lateral Clamping. If the bar could be so clamped that all motion in the Z'-direction was prevented (clamping parallel to X is not essential), while freedom to vibrate in the Y'-direction was still allowed, its behavior would be described by the following equations. In some forms of mounting this condition may be approximated. If there is any lateral constraint at all, the solution may be expected to lie between the condition of complete lateral constraint and that of complete freedom postulated in the preceding equations.

Since the only permitted strain is y'_y, the appropriate elastic coefficient is c'^E_{22} rather than s'^E_{22}, just as in the case of thickness vibrations of a plate of large area. The following substitutions are to be made in the general equations in §§228 to 237: $q = c'^E_{22}$, $\epsilon = e'_{12} = e_{14}$, $(X_n)_d = (Y'_y)_d = -e_{14}E$.

In order to find the effective dielectric constant for lateral clamping we proceed as in the derivation of η_l in Eq. (310). The subscript i, which now denotes the X-direction, will be dropped. For ϵ and x^E_n we write e_{14} and $(y'_y)^E$. Since the strain z'_z is prohibited, the polarization component $e'_{13}(z_z)^E$ as well as $e_{14}(y'_y)^E$ must be subtracted from the polarization $\eta'E$ of the unclamped crystal, where $(z'_z)^E$ is $d'_{13}E$, the static strain due to the instantaneous impressed field E. Since the only strain is y'_y, we have $(y'_y)^E = -(Y'_y)_d/c'_{22} = e_{14}E/c'_{22}$, so that, in place of Eq. (310), the expression for polarization becomes

$$P^E = \left(\eta' - \frac{e_{14}^2}{c_{22}'} - e_{13}'d_{13}'\right)E \equiv |\eta_l|E$$

The bars indicate lateral clamping. On substituting $e_{14}d_{14}/2$ for $e_{13}'d_{13}'$, $d_{14}c_{44}$ for e_{14}, and making use of the equation $\eta' = \eta'' + e_{14}d_{14}$ and of the expressions for c_{22}' and c_{23}' in Eqs. (44), one finds for the laterally clamped susceptibility

$$|\eta_l| = \eta'' + d_{14}^2 c_{44}\left(\frac{c_{22}' - 2c_{44}}{2c_{22}'}\right) = \eta'' + d_{14}^2 \frac{c_{44}c_{23}'}{2c_{22}'} \tag{486}$$

The laterally clamped dielectric constant is

$$|k_l| = 1 + 4\pi|\eta_l| \tag{486a}$$

The equation for the current to the resonator is found from Eq. (315), on substituting e_{14}, $|k_l|$, c_{22}', and e, for ϵ, k_l, q', and e', respectively:

$$I = j\omega V\left(\frac{bl}{4\pi e}|k_l| + \frac{2e_{14}^2 b}{\gamma e c_{22}'}\tanh\frac{\gamma l}{2}\right) \tag{486b}$$

Outside the resonant range the admittance is approximately

$$Y_1' = \frac{j\omega bl}{4\pi e}|k_l| + \frac{2e_{14}^2 blf_0}{\pi e f c_{22}'}\tan\frac{\pi f}{2f_0} \tag{486c}$$

At frequencies close to resonance, as in Eq. (319), p. 295,

$$Y_1' = \frac{A\alpha}{n^2 + \alpha^2} + j\frac{An}{n^2 + \alpha^2} + j\omega\frac{bl|k_l|}{4\pi e} \tag{486d}$$

where $A = 4be_{14}^2/\rho le$.

The equivalent electric constants are

$$\left.\begin{array}{ll} L = \dfrac{\rho le}{8be_{14}^2} & C = \dfrac{8e_{14}^2 bl}{\pi^2 e c_{22}'^E} \\[2ex] R = \dfrac{\rho\alpha le}{4e_{14}^2 b} & C_1 = \dfrac{bl|k_l|}{4\pi e} \\[2ex] X \approx -\dfrac{n}{A} = -\dfrac{\rho len}{4be_{14}^2} \end{array}\right\} \tag{486e}$$

373. Equivalent Mechanical Constants of 45° Bars. Whether there is lateral clamping or not, the equivalent mechanical constants can be found from Eqs. (104) to (107). The equivalent mass is $M = \rho ble/2$; the mechanical resistance is $W = 2M\alpha = 2MAR$ [A as in Eq. (486d)]; the mechanical reactance is $X_c = -2Mn = 2MAX$; mechanical stiffness factor $G = 2MA/C$; mechanical impedance $Z_c = 2MAZ$. The constant $2MA$ is the reciprocal of the electromechanical ratio r (page 297).

Comparison of the Driving Stresses. As we have seen, the driving stress for the free bar is $(Y_y')_d = d_{14}E/2s_{22}'$, and for lateral clamping it is $(Y_y')_d = e_{14}E$. The ratio of these is $s_{44}^E/2s_{22}'^E$, the value of which for temperatures around 20°C is about 1.6, approaching a value of about 2 at the Curie point. Hence the driving stress is considerably greater in the case of the free bar.

Comparison of the stiffness factors shows that the resonant frequency for lateral clamping should be nearly twice as great as that of the free bar.

374. Rochelle Salt at Very High Frequencies. As we have seen, the Rochelle-salt X-cut 45° bar has the two piezoelectric constants d'_{12} and d'_{13}. As long as *only lengthwise modes* are considered, the contribution made by d'_{13} to the dielectric constant, at any instantaneous field strength, is the same as if the field were static, and the effective susceptibility η_l of the resonator is given by Eq. (483a). With increasing frequency, vibrational effects become more and more nearly negligible, so that the observed impedance approaches that due to η_l alone.

When the frequency rises to the region where lateral resonances involving d'_{13} appear, the observed susceptibility approaches the clamped value, as explained in §260. For Rochelle salt between the Curie points this is the value η''_s for monoclinic clamping, which can either be derived from observations at very high frequency or calculated from vibrational data at the fundamental lengthwise frequency. The latter process was carried out in determining $\chi''_s = 1/\eta''_s$ for Fig. 145. In that figure it is seen that at about 5°C χ''_s has a maximum of about 0.128, whence η''_s has a minimum value of about 7.8 at this temperature, yielding a dielectric constant in the neighborhood of 100. This value is in good agreement with the results of h-f measurements described in §442, and with Mueller's estimate, which he reaches by a somewhat different route on page 573 of his paper III.[380]

Experimental Results with Rochelle-salt Resonators. Most investigations have had the purpose of determining elastic constants and temperature coefficients, for which only observations of resonant frequencies are needed. In much of the earlier work the importance of special precautions in the treatment of crystals and the placing of electrodes was not understood, and the failure to mention these details makes the quantitative results of comparatively little value.

375. Lengthwise Vibrations. Almost all the recorded resonator experiments have been with 45° bars. The elastic constants thus determined by Cady, Davies, Hiltscher, Mason, Mattiat, and Mikhailov are given in Table VI (page 125). Hiltscher[228] observed at both fundamental and overtone lengthwise frequencies.

Mattiat[355] observed the dependence of the frequency of Y-cut bars on the ratio b/l of breadth to length and also the dependence of the frequency constants of X- and Y-cut bars on the angle between l and the Z-axis, obtaining approximate agreement with the values calculated from Mandell's elastic constants as given in Table IV or Fig. 26.

Mikhailov[367] measured d_{14} and k_l (§229) at temperatures from 0 to 40°C, by methods a and c, §310, using three X45° bars. He found the expected parallelism between the curves for d_{14} and k_l as functions of temperature. His results with d_{14} are mentioned in §474.

Reference has already been made in Chaps. VI, IX, and XXIV to Mason's observations of lengthwise vibrations in Rochelle-salt bars, which are the most complete and accurate to be found. The use that we have made of his results with bars in different orientations, for determining the "best" values of the elastic constants of Rochelle salt, has been described in §79. The present section has to do with his observa-

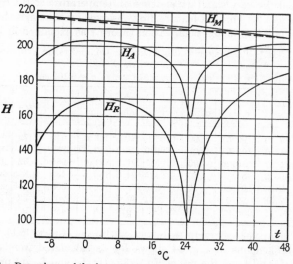

FIG. 94.—Dependence of the frequency-constant H on temperature, for a Rochelle salt X45° bar, from Mason. H is in kc sec^{-1} cm. The curves marked H_R and H_A are for resonance and antiresonance when $w = 0$. H_M is for the response frequency when $w = \infty$.

tions at the fundamental lengthwise frequency on a single X45°-bar, from which much information can be gained concerning the behavior of Rochelle salt at different temperatures. The bar had dimensions $l = 2.014$ cm, $b = 0.418$ cm, $e = 0.104$ cm. The electrodes were of gold, evaporated onto the surfaces in vacuum, so that the gap was strictly zero. The exciting field was restricted to a few volts per centimeter, so that only the initial values of the elastic and electric coefficients came into play; non-linear effects were not investigated. As stated in §474, these observations were used in preparing the data for Fig. 146. In Mason's paper[338] on hysteresis phenomena is a tabulation, for temperatures from $-12°$ to 47.5°C, of the resonant and antiresonant frequencies f_R and f_A (our f_s and f_p, which, when the damping is small, are seen from Table XXIII to be very nearly the same as f_m and f_n); also the frequency-constant H_M for the same bar with infinite gap; and $q = \omega_s L/R$ (our Q).

By multiplying f_R and f_A (expressed in kilocycles per second) by the length l in centimeters one obtains the frequency constants H_R and H_A in kc sec^{-1} cm. Their values, together with H_m for the special case in which the gap is infinite, are shown in Fig. 94. Most noticeable are the low minima in frequency at the upper Curie point, the wide differences between the resonant and antiresonant frequencies when $w = 0$ (owing to the low capacitance ratio C_1/C, which in turn is due to the large value of d_{14}), and the very small dependence on temperature of the frequency at infinite gap.* This last feature, first observed by Mason, is the experimental foundation of the polarization theory,† as explained in §189.

TABLE XXXII.*—FREQUENCIES AND ELECTRIC CONSTANTS OF A ROCHELLE-SALT
$X45°$-BAR

$l = 2.014$ cm $b = 0.418$ cm $e = 0.104$ cm

Temp. °C	f_R kc/sec^{-1}	f_A kc/sec^{-1}	R ohms	L henrys	C mmf	C_1 mmf	R_0 ohms	C_1/C	k_l	Q
−9.0	79.10	99.51	1300	0.066	61.5	106.0	649	1.72	148.0	25
+5.0	84.20	100.63	2600	0.0939	38.2	89.2	1850	2.34	124.8	19
20.5	71.82	95.20	900	0.0537	91.8	121.0	985	1.32	169.0	27
23.7	56.12	84.13	200	0.0415	194.0	156.5	430	0.805	219.0	73
24.7	52.00	81.60	60	0.0345	271.0	186.0	308	0.685	260.0	188
31.0	82.55	99.00	65	0.0934	40.0	93.0	209	2.32	130.0	745
47.5	94.15	100.90	2250	0.425	6.8	46.5	1480	6.9	65.0	112

* The values from the fourth column on are from recent data kindly furnished by Dr. Mason.

The broken line in Fig. 94 shows H_M as calculated from observed values of f_R and f_A by the use of Eq. (335) (f_R, f_A, and f_M are practically identical with f_0, f_p, and f_∞). The agreement with the observed H_M is excellent.

In Table XXXII are shown some of Mason's numerical results with this crystal. The values of the equivalent electric constants should be compared with those of quartz in Table XXX, due allowance being

* Mueller[381] has expressed the view that the slight slope and the kink in the curve for H_M may be due to the morphic effects described in §464.

† This constancy of frequency implies that the elastic constant s_{44}, which by Eqs. (43) occurs in the expression for s'_{22}, is nearly independent of temperature. When the gap is infinite, the elastic constants are those at constant normal electric displacement. It is shown in §§207 and 211 that for a Rochelle-salt X-cut bar the value s^*_{44} at constant normal displacement is, within the limits of experimental error, identical with s^D_{44}, the value at constant total displacement, and with s^P_{44}, the value at constant polarization. Thus the conclusion is reached that s^P_{44} is nearly independent of temperature and that c^P_{44} (the reciprocal of s^P_{44}) is to be taken as the "true" stiffness coefficient of Rochelle salt rather than c^E_{44}.

made for differences in dimensions. Outstanding are the much lower values of C_1/C and of Q in Rochelle salt. Close to the Curie point, C becomes greater than C_1. Rochelle salt evidently functions best as a resonator in the neighborhood of 30°C, where Q is largest. Above this temperature the low Q and high R and R_0 are due to increasing electrical conductivity.

R_0 is a resistance that according to Mason's theory* of hysteresis in Rochelle salt[338] is a property of the dielectric, distinct from the resistance R that corresponds to the vibrational losses. The variation of R_0 with temperature is similar to that of R. Curves with R_0 and k_l plotted against temperature are in Fig. 6 of Mason's paper.† R_0 has a broad maximum at about 5°, sinking to a flat minimum around 30°C.

The reason for the wide spread of values of f_R, f_A, and f_M for Rochelle salt has already been given in §295. The variation of these quantities with temperature should be compared with the general properties of this crystal, as set forth in Chaps. XX to XXV.

We return for a moment to the consideration of the low values of Q, and correspondingly large R in Table XXXII. Although these values of R were not great enough to affect perceptibly the frequencies and the elastic constants deduced therefrom, still it should be pointed out that not all observers have found so low a Q. For example, Mattiat,[355] in a table containing values of R, L, C, C_1, and Q for a number of X- and Y-cut 45° Rochelle-salt bars of different sizes, records Q from 1,300 to 3,600. Gockel's results[173] (see also §381) give $Q = 7,300$ for an $X45°$-bar. Unpublished observations in this laboratory by Van Dyke gave $Q = 2,200$ for an $X45°$-bar 21.3 by 5.6 by 2.1 mm, at 55 kc/sec. Both Mattiat and Van Dyke observed at room temperature.

Mason's results led him to the conclusion that "practically all hysteresis and dissipation effects are associated with the clamped dielectric properties of the crystal." This view is substantially in agreement with Mueller's, as stated in §468, that the anomalies in Rochelle salt lie in the properties of the clamped crystal.

376. The contrast between the variability of frequency, together with high energy losses, in the case of vibrational modes involving s_{44}, and the freedom from these troublesome characteristics with those modes from which this compliance coefficient is absent has recently been pointed out by Matthias.[353] By tests with an optical lever, luminous effects in partial vacuum, photoelastic effects in polarized light, and lycopodium particles, he found relatively flat resonance and small increase in amplitude at resonance for the "temperature-dependent" modes (i.e., those

---

* Reference to this theory is made in §428.

† The numerical data in Mason's Fig. 6 differ somewhat from his more recent values in Table XXXII.

involving s_{44}). He showed that an X-cut 45° bar with zero gap (silver electrodes deposited in vacuum) had a much lower decrement and a frequency much higher and less dependent on temperature when a steady biasing field of 1,500 volts/cm was superposed on the driving voltage, as already stated in §370. Without a biasing field the decrement for temperatures between the Curie points was relatively low with small driving voltage, reached a maximum at a voltage corresponding to the steep portion of the polarization curve, and at high voltages approached the value recorded above the upper Curie point. For the details of these experiments, together with the theory, Matthias's paper should be consulted. In agreement with Mason[338] he attributes the damping in X-cuts chiefly to dielectric rather than to mechanical losses.

377. *The Gap Effect in Rochelle Salt.* Owing to the large size of the dielectric constant, the frequency increases at a much greater rate than with quartz resonators, as the gap increases from zero. The value for infinite gap is closely approximated even while the gap is less than the thickness of the plate. Calling f_w and f_∞ the frequencies corresponding to gaps w and ∞ and letting α represent a number small in comparison with unity, one can prove from Eq. (336) that $f_w = (1 - \alpha)f_\infty$ when

$$\frac{w}{e} \approx \frac{2\pi d_{in}^2}{s_{nn}^\infty k'^2 \alpha} \tag{487}$$

When this is applied to an X-cut 45° bar at 20°C, one has $d_{12}' = d_{14}/2 = 1.25(10^{-5})$; $s_{22}'^\infty = 3.16(10^{-12})$; $k' = 500$ (p. 530). Then $w/e = 0.0012/\alpha$; and if $\alpha = 0.01$, $w/e \approx 0.12$. That is, at this temperature the frequency is within 1 per cent of the value for infinite gap when the gap width is only one-eighth of the thickness of the bar.

A *visible glow* analogous to that for quartz described in §365 has been observed with Rochelle-salt X-cut 45° bars by Hiltscher.[228] His bars had electrodes of small area, so that most of the crystal surface was exposed. At both fundamental and overtone lengthwise frequencies the glow was observed when the bar was driven as a resonator, in air at a pressure of 0.3 to 0.6 mm.

378. Thickness Vibrations of Rochelle-salt Plates. The special equations for plates of Rochelle salt can be adapted from the theory in Chap. V. Rochelle-salt plates cut normal to the crystallographic axes cannot be piezoelectrically excited in thickness vibration. Theoretically, this type of vibration, both shear and compressional, can be excited in practically all *oblique* cuts. The activity of the resonator depends on the cut, being very low for small angles of rotation. The Christoffel theory has been applied to Rochelle salt by Mason[335],* and by Takagi and Miyake.[501] The latter

---

* Also U. S. patents 2,178,146 (1939) and 2,303,375 (1942). Reference to Mason's experimental results with shear thickness vibrations has been made in §77.

investigators give experimental results on shear vibrations in a plate with normal perpendicular to a (110) face of the crystal.

Compressional thickness vibrations can also be generated in oblique plates. The only record of such vibrations is that of the author,[108] obtained with the *L*-cut described in §140.

379. Contour Modes in Rochelle-salt Plates. In vibrations of this type the exciting field normal to the plate causes a shearing stress in the plane of the plate, like the "contour modes" in quartz described in §359. Most experimenters have used relatively thin rectangular or square plates with edges parallel to the crystallographic axes. According to the axis selected for the normal to the major surfaces, the piezoelectric stress is of the type $Y_z = -e_{14}E_x$, $Z_x = -d_{25}E_y$, or $X_y = -e_{36}E_z$. The frequency depends essentially only on the major dimensions a and b, not on the thickness, and is given by Eq. (122). For the *X*-, *Y*-, and *Z*-cuts the reciprocal stiffness $1/q$ is s_{44}, s_{55}, or s_{66}, respectively. If there is no gap, the isagric values are to be used. The piezoelectric contribution to the stiffness when there is a gap has not been formulated, but the presence of a gap must certainly cause an increase in effective stiffness and hence in frequency.

Vibrations of this type have been described by Busch,[87] Mikhailov,[367] Mueller,[379,382] N. Takagi and associates,* and Taschek and Osterberg.[504] The pronounced change in frequency of *X*-cut plates near the upper Curie point, common to all vibrational modes in Rochelle salt in which the compliance s_{44} plays a part, was first observed by Busch in contour vibrations.

Observations in this laboratory on many rectangular plates of all three cuts have yielded results in agreement with Eq. (122). The plates were in a secondary circuit, and resonant frequencies were observed. The largest of these plates had dimensions *X* 0.485, *Y* 7.8, *Z* 12.0 cm, with a fundamental contour frequency of 22.6 kc/sec.† As a further test of the formula some of the plates were progressively reduced in length or breadth, with results in agreement with theory. From the dimensions and frequencies the compliance constants were calculated. Approximate agreement with the accepted values was found, but the results are not considered sufficiently precise for inclusion here.

In the experiments just described, as well as in those discussed in the next section, it was found highly important to apply to the crystal a voltage in the form of a pure sine wave. Harmonic frequencies were almost certain to excite undesired vibrational modes and cause misleading

---

* *Electrotech. Jour. (Japan)*, vol. 4, pp. 95–96, 186, 232–233, 1940.

† These observations and those recorded below on flexural and torsional vibrations were made by P. D. Zottu at intervals from 1928 to 1932. The author's thanks are due the Brush Development Company for the Rochelle-salt plates.

responses. For this reason, in all the later work the supply from the tube oscillator was carefully filtered. For identifying vibrational modes,

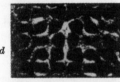

reliance was not placed on agreement between observed and calculated frequencies alone. In most cases the wave patterns were examined directly. For this purpose the plate lay horizontally on the lower electrode, usually with a few grains of sand between to provide a sort of roller bearing and diminish the friction. Nodal patterns were formed by lycopodium powder or fine sand sprinkled on the top of the plate. The upper electrode was then adjusted closely above the powder. By the use of a gauze electrode or an electrode of relatively small size, the formation of the patterns could be observed.

When the supply was not filtered the patterns were very complex; some of them are shown in Fig. 95. With a well-filtered supply voltage, the pure contour shear mode described above gave rise to a more or less irregular nodal region in the center of the plate, such movements as the particles exhibited being chiefly in the plane of the plate. A pure flexural mode was recognized by two or more transverse nodal bands extending across the plate, and a torsional mode by a nodal line running lengthwise, midway between the lateral edges.

When the finger was touched to a vigorously vibrating portion of the surface, the crystal felt exceedingly slippery, and a sensation of warmth was felt at the finger tip.

380. Flexural and Torsional Modes in Rochelle-salt Plates. *Flexural vibrations* are easily excited, either in 45° bars or in rectangular plates with edges parallel to the crystal axes, using any one of the three cuts. The 45° bars are provided with electrodes as in Fig. 88E, the length l and breadth b being at 45° with two axes and the thickness e parallel to the third axis. Flexure takes place in the le

Fig. 95.—Dust patterns on X-cut Rochelle salt plates vibrating in complex modes. a, b, c, and d are from a plate X 0.48 cm, Y 7.8 cm, Z 12.0 cm. The frequencies are a, 27,300; b and c, close to 37,000; d, 54,300 cycles/sec. e has dimensions X 0.485 cm, Y 6.60 cm, Z 12.0 cm, frequency 27,500 cycles/sec. In some cases the dust particles moved in whirls or vortices, which persisted as long as the vibration continued.

plane. Piezoelectric excitation is through the transformed constants d'_{12}, d'_{23}, or d'_{31}, corresponding to an l-axis in the direction of Y', Z', or X',

respectively.   Vibrations of plates in all these orientations have been
observed by the author.

For plates cut according to the second method mentioned above, the
electrodes are placed as shown in Fig. 89.   In the case of quartz (if the
edges of the plate are parallel to the crystal axes), there is but one
orientation yielding flexural vibrations by this type of excitation.   In
Rochelle salt, l may be parallel to X, Y, or Z, the field being applied in
the b-direction, with opposite senses in the two halves of the plate.
Flexure takes place in the le-plane.   When l is parallel to one axis, e may
be parallel to either of the other two axes, giving in all six different possibilities.   Depending on the cut, the driving stress is $Y_z = -e_{14}E_x$,
$Z_x = -e_{25}E_y$, or $X_y = -e_{36}E_z$.   With plates of various sizes, measurements of flexural vibrations have been made in this laboratory with all
six arrangements.   In each case the electrodes were separated from the
crystal by small gaps.   Plated electrodes could of course be used.

Torsional vibrations have been observed in this laboratory with bars
parallel to X, Y, and Z.   In each case a girdling electrode surrounded the
bar at its center, as in Fig. 88F.   As explained in §356 for quartz, the
effective field components are those which enter the crystal from the
girdle in a direction perpendicular to the length.

As stated in §356, more effective torsional excitation should be possible in a bar with length l parallel to one of the crystallographic axes, but
with a rectangular cross section rotated 45° about this axis.   The electrodes should be disposed as in Fig. 88E.

381. Resonator Results with Other Crystals.   By the method mentioned in §320 Gockel measured at room temperature the logarithmic
decrements of resonators prepared from the following crystals (the numbers in parentheses are logarithmic decrements in units of 10^{-4}): quartz
(0.53), tourmaline (1.69), asparagine (1.63), urotropine (1.80), rhamnose
(2.62), Rochelle salt (4.30).   These values were obtained with the specimens mounted in vacuum.   For the cuts employed and for further details
the original paper should be consulted.   The recorded decrements are
almost unbelievably low, except for quartz and tourmaline.

Pavlik[411] has derived equations for the purpose of orienting plates
from crystals in the two monoclinic piezoelectric classes so as to avoid the
piezoelectric excitation of shearing stresses with respect to the axes of the
plates.   He describes resonator experiments with plates cut from crystals
of beet sugar.   Those who use his results should not forget that shearing
effects can arise through elastic coupling even if they are not directly
excited by the applied electric field.

Mandell[329] measured the frequencies of $X45°$, $Y45°$, and $Z45°$ bars
of sodium-ammonium tartrate in lengthwise vibration.   The bars served
as piezo oscillators in a Pierce circuit.   Discrepancies with the calculated

values amounted to as much as 5 per cent in some cases.   This fact is not surprising, since there must have been at least a small effective air gap (the electrodes made only light contact with the crystal surfaces); moreover, the vibrational frequencies of the bars in the Pierce circuit, owing to the large piezoelectric constants and consequent large differences between resonant and antiresonant frequencies, were probably considerably above the true resonance values.   Experiments with resonators made from certain phosphates and arsenates are mentioned in §499.

382. *Tourmaline Resonators.* * The density of tourmaline varies from 2.94 to 3.24 gm/cm³, depending on the composition of the specimen. A fair average value is 3.1.   Parallel to the Z-axis the dielectric constant of the unconstrained crystal is 7.1; perpendicular to Z it is 6.3 ± 0.2.†

The eight piezoelectric constants offer a wider variety of direct excitation than do the five constants of quartz.   The largest is $d_{15} = d_{24}$, which is almost twice as great in magnitude as d_{11} in quartz.   By means of the excitation represented by $z_x = d_{15}E_x$, it should be possible to excite shear thickness vibrations in an X-cut plate.‡   The only tourmaline resonators that have been used extensively are of the Z-cut, in which compressional thickness vibrations are produced in accordance with $Z_z = -e_{33}E_z$.   As has been pointed out by Giebe and Blechschmidt,[162] the relatively low values of the elastic cross constants responsible for coupling effects give to tourmaline resonators comparative freedom from undesired vibrational modes.

Tourmaline resonators were introduced in 1928 by Henderson.[219] Their use as piezo oscillators is described in §400, where further numerical data and references to the literature will be found.   Various vibrational modes have been investigated by Petrzilka[415,416,419],§ with the aid of lycopodium patterns and the luminous effects at low pressure, as well as by frequency measurements.   His papers contain many excellent photographs of nodal patterns, some of which are reproduced in Fig. 93.   Further experiments with tourmaline resonators are described by Straubel,[490] Osterberg and Cookson,[406] Modrak,[371] and Khol.[258,259]

383. Composite Resonators.   Among the earliest experiments with piezo resonators were tests made with metal bars excited in longitudinal vibration by means of crystals.‖   At first a single X-cut 45° Rochelle-salt

---

* For other properties of tourmaline see pages 30, 227, 228, 506, and 702.

† "International Critical Tables," vol. 6, 1926.   The measurements were made at audio frequency.

‡ See the calculations in Koga.[270]   In this paper Koga derives the equations for thickness vibrations of tourmaline plates.

§ See also the discussion of his results by E. Lonn.[319]

‖ Master's theses by G. W. Bain, 1922, and H. C. Palmer, 1925, Wesleyan University; W. G. Cady, *Phys. Rev.*, vol. 21, pp. 371–372, 1923 (abst.).   See also refs. 96

bar 1 to 2 cm in length was cemented endwise to a steel rod about 15 cm long. When the current from a tube oscillator was supplied to the crystal and tuned to the longitudinal frequency of the rod, the latter vibrated as a resonator, with energy derived from the reaction of the crystal. The successful results obtained with this device encouraged further investigation. It was soon found that a flat steel bar from 10 to 20 cm in length could be driven by means of a pair of quartz plates cemented on opposite sides at the center. Two such resonators are shown in Fig. 82; the construction is seen in outline in Fig. 96.

Resonators like that in Fig. 96 have been used in this laboratory with bars of various metals, glass, and fused silica, for obtaining dynamic values of Young's modulus for these materials. A quartz-steel resonator of this type has been made to serve as a piezo oscillator when provided with two pairs of quartz plates, the pairs connected, respectively, to the input and output of an amplifier.

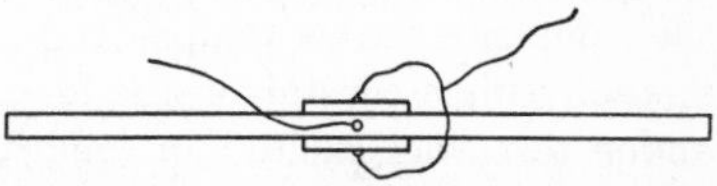

FIG. 96.—Quartz-steel resonator, 1923. The quartz plates are cemented to the flat sides of the steel bar; their outer tin-foil coatings are connected in parallel. The hook from which the bar is suspended serves as one terminal.

By the use of Rochelle-salt plates instead of quartz, a steel bar over a meter long has been driven as a resonator at its natural frequency, giving a loud musical note. A brass tube about a meter long, with four X-cut 45° Rochelle-salt bars at its center, clamped between two metal rings surrounding the bar, has been found to be especially useful as an acoustic generator with a frequency of 2,150 cycles/sec, for experiments with Kundt's tubes. The sound is emitted from a brass disk soldered across one end of the brass tube. The tin-foil coatings of two oppositely situated crystal bars are connected to the input of an amplifier, while the amplifier output is connected through a step-up transformer to the other pair of bars, the latter thus being the ones that drive the brass tube.†

In the composite resonators described above the size of the crystal element is made relatively small in order that the frequency and damping may be as nearly as possible characteristic of the vibrator to which the crystal is attached. Although this arrangement provides rugged and efficient resonators, the attachment of the crystal at a point of maximum stress is not well adapted to the precise measurement of the characteristics of the material of the bar.

---

and 97. The earliest of all piezoelectric devices that can be called "resonators" was Langevin's quartz-steel "sandwich" mentioned in §§224 and 506. References on composite resonators will be found at the end of this chapter.

† A device similar to this is described in R. M. Sutton's "Demonstration Experiments in Physics," New York, 1938.

384. The first step toward using the composite resonator for a more precise measurement of the elastic constants of various solids was taken in 1925 by Quimby, who developed the theory of vibrations in a solid bar driven by a quartz bar cemented to it at one end. The length of the quartz bar was parallel to Y, with the driving field parallel to X. His immediate object was a determination of the viscosity in rods of aluminum, copper, and glass. In his method there was no special relation between the lengths of the two components of the resonator.

The advantage gained by having the cement joint come at a node of stress was pointed out by Balamuth in 1934. Balamuth's technique has been followed by numerous other investigators (see references at end of chapter). The results have yielded data on the elastic constants, and their dependence on temperature, of a large number of solids, including metallic single crystals in the form of bars. In most cases the specimen under test was excited in lengthwise compressional vibrations by an X-cut quartz bar. On the other hand, Brown, Good, Rose, and in some of their observations Hunter and Siegel used torsional vibrations; the quartz was in the form of a cylinder with length parallel to X, provided with four electrodes according to the method of Giebe and Scheibe, as described in §356. Grime and Eaton (using flexural vibrations) and Schenk (using longitudinal vibrations) employed the quartz only as a detector, not as a driver. Boyle and Sproule examined the dust patterns on the end of a relatively thick vibrating bar, finding a configuration similar to the well-known Chladni figures. Their work makes it clear that false conclusions respecting the elastic constants of a bar may be drawn unless the bar is sufficiently thin.

In Mason's book the theory of the composite resonator, considered as an electromechanical transducer, is developed with reference to both longitudinal and torsional vibrations. Original data on the elastic properties of various materials are also presented. Some of these materials are plastics of high viscosity, for the measurement of which a special arrangement of crystals and circuit is described.

385. *Crystal-driven Tuning Forks.* The author has maintained a 2,048-cycle tuning fork in vibration by the use of X-cut 45° Rochelle-salt bars and an amplifying circuit.[95] Several different arrangements were used. In the first, a bar of size 4.6 by 1.5 by 0.4 cm was cemented endwise between the stem of the fork and a rigid base. The bar had two pairs of tin-foil coatings, connected to the input and output of a four-stage untuned resistance-coupled amplifier. When the fork was once started, it continued to vibrate with energy supplied by the amplifier at twice the fork frequency. In the second method each prong of the fork had cemented to it near the tip the end of a crystal bar with a single pair of coatings, the bars extending outward in the plane of the fork. One bar was connected to the amplifier input, while the other, which supplied energy to the fork, was connected to the amplifier output. Here again the fork continued to vibrate after being lightly struck. The driving force was supplied by the inertial reaction of the bars. Third, a "cartridge" consisting of the crystal bar mentioned above with two pairs of coatings in a small holder, connected to the amplifier, maintained the fork in vibration when merely held in contact with one prong.

Although not a composite resonator, the quartz tuning fork of Koga[267] may be mentioned at this point. This was a 1,000-cycle fork fashioned from a single crystal and maintained in vibration piezoelectrically with the aid of suitable electrodes and an amplifier.

386. A Quartz-Liquid Resonator. Fox and Rock[147] cemented an X-cut quartz plate to the bottom of a cylindrical jar of water. By means of thickness vibrations at about 2.5 megacycles/sec stationary waves were produced between the quartz and a reflecting piston, and the characteristics of the resulting composite resonator were measured. With 200 stationary waves present, a value of $Q = 3,680$ was observed, whereas for the quartz in air Q was only 418. In comment, it may be said that the low Q in air was undoubtedly due to the cement and that, while the resonance of the water column greatly reduced the decrement, still 3,680 is too low a value of Q to warrant the expectation of practical applications. The attempts of these investigators to make a resonator of variable frequency by this method did not lead to promising results, since the response became relatively weak when the frequency departed appreciably from the natural frequency of the quartz.

REFERENCES

ROCHELLE-SALT RESONATORS

Most of the papers on this subject have already been mentioned in the text. To them may be added the following references: MASON,[B35,335] CADY,[103,108] STAMFORD.[475]

COMPOSITE RESONATORS

MASON,[B35] BROWN,[78] FOX and ROCK.[147]

BALAMUTH, L.: A New Method for Measuring Elastic Moduli and the Variation with Temperature of the Principal Young's Modulus of Rocksalt between 78°K and 273°K, *Phys. Rev.*, vol. 45, pp. 715–720, 1934.

BALLOU, J. W., and S. SILVERMAN: Young's Modulus of Elasticity of Fibers and Films by Sound Velocity Measurements, *Jour. Acous. Soc. Am.*, vol. 16, pp. 113–119, 1944.

BOYLE, R. W., and D. O. SPROULE: Oscillation in Ultrasonic Generators and Velocity of Longitudinal Vibrations in Solids at High Frequencies, *Nature*, vol. 123, p. 13, Jan. 5, 1929.

COOKE, W. T.: The Variation of the Internal Friction and Elastic Constants with Magnetization in Iron, Part I, *Phys. Rev.*, vol. 50, pp. 1158–1164, 1936.

GOOD, W. A.: Rigidity Modulus of Beta-brass Single Crystals. *Phys. Rev.*, vol. 60, pp. 605–609, 1941.

GRIME, G., and J. E. EATON: Determination of Young's Modulus by Flexural Vibrations, *Phil. Mag.*, vol. 23, pp. 96–99, 1937.

HUNTER, L., and S. SIEGEL: The Variation with Temperature of the Principal Elastic Moduli of NaCl near the Melting Point, *Phys. Rev.*, vol. 61, pp. 84–90, 1942.

IDE, J. M.: Some Dynamic Methods for Determination of Young's Modulus, *Rev. Sci. Instruments*, vol. 6, pp. 296–298, 1935.

QUIMBY, S. L.: On the Experimental Determination of the Viscosity of Vibrating Solids, *Phys. Rev.*, vol. 25, p. 558, 1925.

QUIMBY, S. L.: New Experimental Methods in Ferromagnetism, (abstr.) *Phys. Rev.*, vol. 39, pp. 345–353, 1932.

QUIMBY, S. L., and S. SIEGEL: The Variation of the Elastic Constants of Crystalline Sodium with Temperature between 80°K and 210°K, *Phys. Rev.*, vol. 54, pp. 293–299, 1938.

READ, T. A.: The Internal Friction of Single Metal Crystals, *Phys. Rev.*, vol. 58, pp. 371–380, 1940.

RINEHART, J. S.: Temperature Dependence of Young's Modulus and Internal Friction of Lucite and Karolith, *Jour. Applied Phys.*, vol. 12, pp. 811–816, 1941.

ROSE, F. C.: The Variation of the Adiabatic Elastic Moduli of Rocksalt with Temperature between 80°K and 270°K, *Phys. Rev.*, vol. 49, pp. 50–54; 1936.

SCHENK, D.: Measurement of the Damping in Vibrating Steel Rods, *Z. Physik*, vol. 72, pp. 54–67, 1931.

SHEAR, S. K., and A. B. FOCKE: The Dispersion of Supersonic Waves in Cylindrical Rods of Polycrystalline Silver, Nickel and Magnesium, *Phys. Rev.*, vol. 57, pp. 532–537, 1940.

SIEGEL, S., and S. L. QUIMBY: The Variation of Young's Modulus with Magnetization and Temperature in Nickel, *Phys. Rev.*, vol. 49, pp. 663–670, 1936.

ZACHARIAS, J.: The Temperature Dependence of Young's Modulus for Nickel, *Phys. Rev.*, vol. 44, pp. 116–122, 1933.

CHAPTER XIX

THE PIEZO OSCILLATOR

Over earth and ocean, with gentle motion,
This pilot is guiding me.

—SHELLEY.

The stabilizing effect of a crystal on a circuit that is already oscillating will be considered first. This effect will lead naturally to the principle of the piezo oscillator, in which the crystal not only controls the frequency but is also an essential element in the maintenance of oscillations. Several types of piezo oscillator are described, with chief emphasis on the Pierce and Pierce-Miller circuits and some of their modifications.

By far the most important crystal for piezo oscillators is quartz, and most of the data on circuits, tubes, etc., are based on the assumption that quartz will be used. In §400, Rochelle-salt and tourmaline oscillators are treated. The chapter closes with a brief reference to the literature on the mathematical theory of the piezo oscillator.

387. Crystal Stabilizers. Any piezo resonator connected to an oscillating circuit tends to control the frequency. Having made this rather strong statement, we must state its limitations. In the first place, the controlling action is negligible except in the neighborhood of frequencies corresponding to natural modes of vibration of the crystal. If a tube circuit oscillating at frequency f contains a crystal, say in parallel with the tuning condenser, and if the crystal is clamped so that it cannot vibrate, the only effect is to add a little to the total capacitance; the amount added is substantially the parallel capacitance C_1 of the equivalent network shown in Fig. 50.

When the crystal is unclamped, the alternating potential makes it vibrate mechanically. If f is far from any characteristic frequency of the resonator, the amplitude is practically imperceptible. Nevertheless, the phase of the vibration and the consequent piezoelectric reaction of the crystal on the circuit are always such as to make the variation of frequency with change in tuning capacitance, or in any other circuit parameter, less than it would be in absence of the crystal. This fact is a sort of Lenz's law for the crystal-controlled oscillator.

As the oscillating frequency approaches one of the characteristic frequencies of the resonator, the vibrational amplitude and the electric reaction increase to a certain maximum; and on the other side of crystal

489

resonance the reaction diminishes approximately to the previous low value. As a measure of the reaction we take the equivalent parallel capacitance $C_p = - 1/\omega X_p$, §273. As may be seen from the curve for X_p in Fig. 66, p. 374, C_p has a maximum at point P_1 (Fig. 67), a minimum (negative maximum) at P_2, and is zero at P_3 and P_4. The stabilizing effect increases with C_p, which in turn increases with the size of the resonator. A very small crystal has a maximum C_p so small that the stabilization is imperceptible. Thus a crystal bar 1.5 by 0.5 by 0.2 mm, although it resonates very nicely for lengthwise vibrations at a frequency around 2,000 kc, would make a poor showing if placed in control of a power oscillator.

In the foregoing statements we have made use of the concept of the equivalent network. With most resonators the parameters of the network are practically constant, and the electric behavior of the resonator can be fully described in terms of the network, whether the resonator is used as an oscillator or filter or for any other purpose. The crystal does nothing that could not be accomplished by an actual network containing a resistance, inductance coil, and condensers having the same values as the equivalent network. It is the impossibility of constructing such a physical network, not to mention having it stay constant if it could be constructed, that puts the crystal into a position of unique usefulness. Numerical data for quartz resonators will be found in §362.

It must be remembered that the network has different constants for each vibrational mode and that for any given mode it is applicable only over a range of frequencies undisturbed by other modes. It would be a superhuman task to derive a single equivalent network applicable to all modes.

Thus far we have discussed chiefly the stabilizing effect of a resonator in a circuit that oscillates independently of the presence of the resonator. Such a circuit, as has been stated in §223, is said to be *crystal stabilized*, and a resonator when so employed is called a *stabilizer*. The action of the stabilizer will now be explained more fully.

388. Only the case need be considered in which the crystal is in parallel with the tuning condenser of a tube oscillator, as shown in Fig. 97. The experiment is instructive and easily performed. The oscillator shown here is of the simple magnetically coupled type with tuned grid circuit, though other types may be used equally well; L_2 and C_2 must be such that the circuit can be tuned through the frequency f_0 of one of the crystal modes. Variations in frequency are observed by listening to the beat note between this circuit and a constant-frequency oscillator very loosely coupled to it.

The relation between the frequency f of the oscillator and the setting of C_2 is shown qualitatively in Fig. 98. The total capacitance

$C_t = C_2 + C_p$ (the effective parallel resistance R_p can here be ignored) is related to f by a continuous curve.* As C_2 is decreased, the frequency rises, rapidly at first and then more slowly as f_0 is approached, becoming almost constant in the neighborhood of the point A. At A comes a sudden break, the frequency jumping abruptly to point B. From there on the frequency is related to C_2 by the line BD. On increasing C_2, the path $DBEF$ is followed, with another region of stabilization in the neighborhood of E.

The explanation may be expressed either in terms of the equivalent network $RLCC_1$ or of the effective parallel parameters C_p and R_p. In

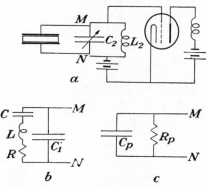

FIG. 97.—Circuit for showing the stabilizing effect of a crystal in parallel with the tuning condenser C_2 of an oscillating circuit. b is the customary equivalent network of the crystal, and c represents the crystal as a capacitance and resistance in parallel.

the former case we regard the network $RLCC_1$ as coupled to the tuning circuit C_2L_2; if the network has small damping, it tends to pull the circuit into step with its own frequency of series resonance f_0. The theory has been treated by Watanabe,[581] who showed that the coefficient of coupling between the two tuned circuits is approximately $C/(C_2 + C_1)$ and that, from observations of stabilization, the values of both C and R of the equivalent network can be calculated. The results are not very precise, owing to various effects of the tube circuit.

As we have stated in §387, the stabilizing effect is explained most simply in terms of C_p. This quantity varies with frequency in the manner indicated in Fig. 98. The maximum and minimum are higher and sharper the smaller the value of R and the greater the value of C (i.e., the greater the size of the resonator). The frequencies at these two extreme values of C_p come at the quadrantal points P_1 and P_2 on the resonance circle,

* The symbol C_2 in Figs. 97 and 98 must not be confused with the C_2 denoting the capacitance of the gap that may be present between crystal and electrodes. When a gap is present, its effect is to be regarded as included in the values of R, L, C, and C_1.

as shown in Fig. 61 or 67. When C_2 is decreased to the point A, C_p cannot become any greater, the crystal loses control, and the frequency springs from A to B, and similarly at E. No oscillations are possible between P_1 and P_2.

Using the crystal $N2$ mentioned in §298, the author has found that close to the points A and E in Fig. 98 the variation in frequency for a

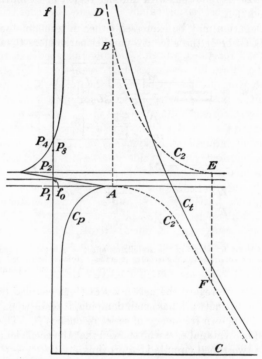

Fig. 98.—Stabilizing action of a resonator as the tuning capacitance C_2 is varied.

small change in C_2 (or in filament current or any other variable) was only one-thirtieth as great as when the crystal was absent.

The crystal-stabilized circuit was first arrived at in 1920 as one stage in the search for a crystal-controlled oscillator. While the stabilizer has found some application,* its usefulness is far less than that of the piezo oscillator, to which we now turn.

389. The Crystal-controlled Oscillator. Although the circuits described in the following sections may be used with any piezoelectric crystal, particular reference is made to quartz, as this is the only

* See, for example, Heegner,[214] Handel, Krüger, and Plendl,[202] Kusunose and Ishikawa,[297] Watanabe.[581]

material in common use for the purpose. The various cuts of quartz and their properties have been discussed in Chap. XVI.

The piezo oscillator may be considered as evolved out of the stabilizing circuit just described. The tuning circuit C_2L_2 in Fig. 97 is transferred to the anode circuit of the tube, replacing the tickler coil and becoming the tank circuit, as shown in Fig. 100a. The only reactance connected to the grid is that of C_p, the equivalent parallel capacitance of the resonator. If the oscillating circuit is regarded as consisting of C_p in series with the grid-anode capacitance and the impedance Z_2 of the anode circuit, oscillations will be generated if C_p can assume a value that makes the total reactance vanish. Usually this condition requires that the crystal be vibrating near a resonant frequency. For stable oscillations the operating point must be on a region of the C_p-curve in Fig. 98 where $\partial C_p/\partial f$ is positive, since otherwise an increase in f will not be neutralized by a corresponding increase in C_p. At first sight it might appear that the tube would oscillate with a frequency slightly below that at P_1 if Z_2 had an inductive value lying between certain limits. Actually, this is impossible, since on the l-f side of resonance the crystal is vibrating in the wrong phase. On the h-f side, however, just above P_2 (between P_2 and the frequency for antiresonance) stable oscillations can occur if Z_2 is inductive. C_p is here negative, and the crystal operates as an inductance, automatically selecting that point on the curve which makes the total circuit reactance zero. Z_2 must of course lie between certain inductive limits, but a good resonator has such a wide range of values of negative C_p that the tolerance in Z_2 is very wide. Usually a tank circuit is employed, tuned to the optimum inductive reactance.

In terms of the equivalent series reactance X_s, the condition for stable oscillations is that $\partial X_s/\partial f$ shall be positive and that the frequency shall come between resonance and antiresonance. This consideration restricts the operating range to a region on the l-f side of point P_8, Figs. 66 and 67, between P_8 and P_2. We return to this subject in §392.

It is shown by Hight and Willard, according to Llewellyn's theory and confirmed by their experiments, that the frequency is most nearly independent of small changes in the circuit reactances, plate voltage, and change of tube when the reactance of the tank circuit is numerically equal to the tube resistance R_p between cathode and plate and at the same time $R_p = (\mu + 1)R_g$, where μ is the amplification factor and R_g the cathode-grid resistance. At the optimal setting of C_2 the frequency is a maximum. A further improvement in stability is brought about by tuning a small variable condenser between grid and anode to secure an additional adjustment to maximal frequency.

390. Some Early Types of Piezo Oscillator. One of the earliest circuits, devised by the author in 1921, operates by means of piezoelectric feedback. It is essentially an amplifier with input and output coupled through a crystal with two pairs of electrodes, as shown in Fig. 99. In the earliest form a three-stage resistance-coupled amplifier was used, but it was found by Van Dyke in 1922 that a single tube was quite sufficient.* The original crystal was an X-cut quartz bar, of size X0.15, Y3.9, Z0.7 cm, having a fundamental lengthwise frequency of about 70 kc. With two pairs of electrodes suitably connected, the circuit oscillated at the first overtone, approximately twice the funda-

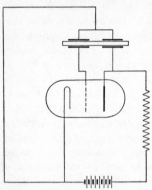

FIG. 99.—The earliest type of crystal-controlled oscillator consisting of an amplifier with input and output coupled through a crystal.

mental frequency. Neither coil nor condenser was necessary: the anode circuit contained only a resistance of 12,000 ohms and was slightly capacitive from stray effects. Reversing one pair of electrodes caused the oscillations to take place at the fundamental frequency. Watanabe[581] has made a theoretical study of this type of oscillator; his results are in agreement with the foregoing statements and prove moreover that when the anode circuit is made *inductive* the connections in Fig. 99 give rise to the *fundamental* frequency, while reversing one pair of electrodes gives rise to the first overtone. His investigation shows also on which side of resonance the oscillating frequencies lie.

In another type of oscillator first described by the author, a tuned grid circuit was used, the coil in the grid circuit being very loosely coupled to a coil in the anode circuit. The crystal replaced the blocking condenser between the tuning element and the grid. A modification of this arrangement has been used by Horton and Marrison.[234]

The author has also used the piezoelectric feedback for driving metal rods at audio frequencies (§383). The same principle is used in oscillators described by Rohde,[436] Rohde and Handrek,[438] and Mason and Sykes.[343]

391. The Pierce and Pierce-Miller Circuits. These two circuits, especially the latter, are in very wide use. In the Pierce circuit the crystal is between grid and anode of a vacuum tube, while in the Pierce-Miller circuit it is between grid and filament.† In simple form, without

---

* See also Mallet and Terry.[325]

† G. W. PIERCE, U. S. patent 1,789,496, application Feb. 25, 1924, issued Jan. 20, 1931; J. M. MILLER, U. S. patent 1,756,000, application Sept. 10, 1925, issued Apr. 22, 1930. Pierce's paper[423] describes only the grid-anode connection, for which the reactance in the anode circuit has to be capacitive, as explained in §394. Hence the

the modifications to which reference will be made later, it is illustrated in Fig. 100. In a the crystal is between grid and filament. The action of the crystal in controlling the frequency has already been explained in §389, in terms of the equivalent parallel capacitance C_p. In principle, the device is a tuned-grid tuned-plate circuit with the crystal replacing the tuning elements in the grid branch. Feedback takes place through the capacitance between grid and plate, shown by dotted lines. The alternating potential on the grid comes from the charges liberated piezo-electrically by the vibrating plate.

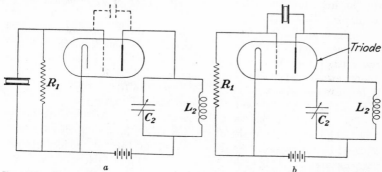

FIG. 100.—Piezo-oscillator circuits. a, the Pierce-Miller circuit; b, the Pierce circuit.

The tank circuit $L_2 C_2$ should be tunable over a considerable range on either side of the crystal frequency. A high L_2/C_2-ratio gives a large harmonic content, which for some purposes is advantageous. If one starts with C_2 at its setting for lowest capacitance (Fig. 100a), the circuit usually does not oscillate and the anode direct current is large. As C_2 is increased, oscillations set in at a certain point and the direct current diminishes. The oscillation current increases with C_2, until a critical value is reached at which oscillations cease.

In the Pierce-Miller circuit just described, the crystal vibrates at a frequency slightly below its antiresonant frequency, according to the

---

coil used by Pierce in his anode circuit must have had enough distributed capacitance to make this circuit act like a condenser. J. M. Miller first recognized this fact. He also—independently of Pierce—made a circuit oscillate with the crystal between grid and filament, and he introduced the tunable element in the anode circuit ($L_2 C_2$ in Fig. 100a), with a tap to L_2 to increase the output current.[115,369,461]

Although a recent legal decision has awarded to Pierce the priority for the grid-filament connection, it can hardly be denied that Miller deserves at least to share in the credit. In the literature both circuits of the types shown in Fig. 100 are commonly called "Pierce circuits." In this book, also, this term is sometimes applied generically to circuits of either type, but when special mention of the grid-filament connection is made we refer to the "Pierce-Miller circuit."

statement in §389. Strictly, the antiresonant frequency in question is
that of the crystal and all associated capacitances, including those contributed by the tube itself. For satisfactory operation the impedance
of this combination at antiresonance should be as high as possible, a
condition which requires that the Q of the crystal shall be as large as
possible. When oscillating, the tube provides the negative resistance
necessary to neutralize the positive resistance component of the imped-.
ance. The smaller the associated capacitances, the greater is the antiresonant impedance and the better the oscillator. The magnitude of
this antiresonant impedance is a useful *index of performance* for the
oscillator.

Instead of the Q of the RLC-branch of the crystal network, use is
sometimes made of the antiresonant Q_a, which is the ratio of the inductive
reactance to the effective resistance of the crystal and associated capacitances at the frequency of antiresonance. This Q_a is much smaller than
Q: for example, with a BT-cut of quartz for 5 to 10 megacycles, Q may be
of the order of 500,000, while Q_a is only around 10,000.

The circuit with the crystal *between grid and plate* is shown in Fig.
100b. This circuit is of the ultraudion type, the tuning element being
replaced by the crystal. Feedback takes place through the crystal itself,
the tank circuit serving to determine the optimum (capacitive) reactance.

392. Without reference to the equivalent network, the action of the vibrating
crystal in maintaining the oscillations may be explained as follows: Let it be assumed
that the crystal is connected as in Fig. 100a or b but not vibrating. There is then an
unvarying electron current through the tube, with a fixed positive static charge on
the anode and a negative charge on the grid. Owing to the potential difference
between grid and filament (or between grid and anode), the crystal is statically
deformed to a slight extent through the converse piezoelectric effect. If now any
small momentary disturbance occurs, causing the grid to become more negative, the
deformation increases. The crystal has in effect received a shock excitation, which
makes it vibrate;* by the direct piezoelectric effect it impresses an alternating voltage
on the grid, which soon dies down if nothing occurs to maintain it. But this alternating voltage on the grid causes a variation in the anode current at the same frequency, thereby varying the anode potential by an amount and phase angle depending
on the impedance in the plate circuit. If this impedance lies within a certain range
of values, the effect becomes cumulative. At each surge of current to the grid, the
anode changes its potential in such a way as to increase the intensity of the surge, thus
compensating for the energy losses in the crystal and in the grid circuit and causing the
amplitude of vibration to build up instead of decrease. This continues until a balance
is reached, just as in any other oscillating device. Part of the energy of the anode
supply has become converted into a-c energy through the medium of the crystal
vibrations. Unless the crystal vibrates, the circuit will not oscillate.

Owing to the high Q of the crystal, its resonating range is very narrow. Hence
the generator, when once started, will hold its frequency extremely constant. Within

* The mechanical inertia of the resonator plays a part strictly analogous to the
electromagnetic inertia, or self-inductance, of the equivalent circuit.

wide limits, any change in circuit conditions, as for example a variation in C_2, filament temperature, or anode voltage, can affect the frequency only to the extent of causing the crystal to vibrate at a different point on its resonance curve. An equivalent statement is that the L of the resonator is so extremely great and its C so extremely small, in comparison with the effective inductance and capacitance of the rest of the circuit, that under no conditions can the frequency depart far from $(1/2\pi)(LC)^{-\frac{1}{2}}$.

393. *The Minimum Size of Crystal for a Piezo Oscillator.* For a given frequency, the length of a bar or the thickness of a plate may be considered as fixed. The question is then how narrow the bar can be, or how small the area of the plate, and still control the frequency in a Pierce circuit. In either case, it becomes a question of minimum size of electrodes, the latter being assumed to cover the entire crystal surface. Since a resonator, however small, has an inductive reactance over a certain frequency

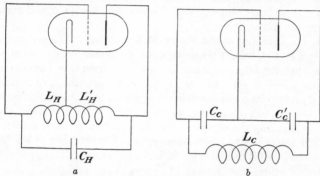

FIG. 101.—*a*, Hartley oscillator; *b*, Colpitts oscillator.

range as long as the damping is sufficiently low, there is no theoretical reason why it should not control the frequency in a Pierce circuit. There are, however, two very practical reasons for a lower limit. The first is the difficulty in mounting an extremely small resonator so as to have a sufficiently high Q. The second reason is that a minimum oscillating grid current is necessary; and if the electrode area were very small, too high a voltage would be required across the crystal. The relation of crystal resistance to the condition for oscillations is discussed by Watanabe[581] and Vigoureux.[B50,B51]

394. A piezo-oscillator circuit may be shown to function as either a Hartley or a Colpitts oscillator, depending on the location of the crystal. These two general types of oscillator are shown schematically in Fig. 101, in which *a* corresponds to Fig. 100*a*: when the crystal is between grid and filament, it vibrates on the h-f side of resonance and therefore has an inductive reactance. The crystal corresponds to L_H, and the inductively tuned tank circuit to L'_H, while the grid-plate capacitance corresponds to C_H.

With the crystal between grid and anode we have in effect a Colpitts circuit. If the grid circuit is capacitive (in practice a condenser is often connected across R_1), corresponding to C_C, and if the tank circuit is also capacitive, corresponding to C_C', oscillations can take place on the h-f side of crystal resonance. The crystal now replaces L_C.

For the higher range of frequencies, for which thickness vibrations are chiefly employed, the grid-filament connection seen in Fig. 100a is chiefly used. The same circuit can of course be employed also for low frequencies, though for this purpose the grid-plate connection is often preferred.

In the simple Pierce-Miller circuit, as in all crystal-controlled oscillators, best results are obtained with tubes of high amplification. The 801 triode is suitable, with the plate voltage held to 300 volts or less, in order not to endanger the crystal. The maximum safe crystal current is considered in §257.

395. Modifications of the Pierce-Miller Circuit. The simple circuits shown in Fig. 100, using a triode tube, have a rather low output of power, and the frequency is not sufficiently constant to meet the exacting requirements of practical service. As in all oscillators, the power increases with the plate voltage, as does also the current to the crystal. Since the crystal current is proportional to the amplitude of vibration, there is danger of breaking the crystal if the plate voltage is much greater than about 250 volts. As to the frequency, any slow drift or sudden fluctuation in circuit conditions, due, for example, to variations in supply voltages or in temperature, may change the value of the grid-plate capacitance or of the anode impedance and thus force the crystal to operate at a different frequency in order to satisfy the condition for oscillations. Moreover, unless the resonator has zero temperature coefficient, the resonant frequency of the crystal itself will vary with changes in the current flowing to it. Best frequency stability in this simple circuit is obtained by the use of a relatively low ratio of L_2 to C_2 in the tank circuit, especially for the higher frequencies.

The power output can be increased to several watts by substituting a r-f choke and biasing battery for the resistance R_1 in Fig. 100a.* A proper choice of bias on the control grid is important, since the current to the crystal increases with the amount of bias. As an alternative to the biasing of the grid by R_1 alone, the "cathode bias" illustrated in Fig. 102 has been introduced, by which the potential between grid and filament is controlled by the d-c potential drop through a resistance R_2 in series with the (indirectly heated) cathode. This arrangement, which may be used without R_1 but with a choke in parallel with the crystal, is found to make

---

* A. CROSSLEY, U. S. patent 1,696,626, (1928), also ref. 115. Crossley has obtained as much as 100 watts output from a single tube at frequencies from 3,000 to 4,000 kc.

the crystal start oscillating more easily. A combination of grid-leak
bias with cathode bias is often employed, at least with triodes. The
cathode bias alone is recommended for frequencies over 1,500 kc.

The criteria in the selection of tubes are high amplification, low grid-
anode capacitance, small current to the crystal, and sufficient power
output.

Among the various present-day piezo-oscillator circuits, which for
the most part are of the Pierce-Miller type, we illustrate only one, in
Fig. 102. This circuit is widely used in amateur transmission and is
well suited to general laboratory use. The tube may be either a tetrode
(in which case the suppressor grid in the figure is omitted) or a pentode.

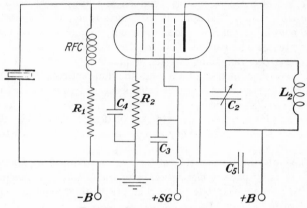

Fig. 102.—Pentode piezo-oscillator.

The advantages offered by these tubes are high amplification, greater
power without fracturing the crystal, and higher frequency stability from
the action of the screen grid. With a high L_2/C_2 ratio the harmonics
are very pronounced. When a pentode is used, the suppressor grid may
be grounded, or for greater power it may be given a small positive
potential.* As represented in the figure, both grid-leak and cathode
bias are used. If the grid-plate capacitance provides insufficient feedback, a very small auxiliary condenser may be connected between grid
and plate. To safeguard the crystal, such capacitance should be as small
as possible. The L_2/C_2 ratio is usually greater than in triode circuits.

Push-pull piezo oscillators have been used with both triodes and

* Suitable pentodes are the 41, 42, 6F6, and 802 or the beam types 6L6 and 807.
With maximum plate voltage on the latter, the output should be at least 10 watts for
frequencies over 1,500 kc/sec. The following typical values of circuit elements
shown in Fig. 102 are taken from the "Radio Amateur's Handbook": C_2, maximum
100 mmf, with L_2 designed for the frequency used; C_3 and C_5, 1,000 mmf or more; C_4,
0.01 mf; R_1, 10,000 to 50,000 ohms; R_2, 250 to 400 ohms.

tetrodes.* In some of his experiments Harrison used crystals with four electrodes, oscillations taking place through piezoelectric feedback as described in §390. In other cases, the crystals had two electrodes, and oscillations were maintained as in the Pierce-Miller circuit. Harrison's oscillators seem especially well suited to l-f oscillations, including those controlled by plates vibrating flexurally. He was able to obtain an output of 5 watts at 50 kc/sec, with a flexural resonator. The power derived from two tubes in push-pull may be as much as $1\frac{1}{2}$ times that from a single tube. It is a characteristic of push-pull circuits that all *even* harmonics are eliminated.

396. Low-frequency Piezo Oscillators. For crystal control, any of the l-f types of piezo resonator described in Chaps. XVII and XVIII can be used. In practical applications quartz is employed almost exclusively; the usefulness of Rochelle salt is mainly for experimental work and demonstration. The various types may be classified as follows:

1. Lengthwise vibrations of bars or plates. Owing to the scarcity and cost of large quartz plates and the impracticability of making oscillators with very short bars, the usual limits of frequency for this type are from 80 to 300 kc/sec.

2. Broad plates, usually a rotated cut as described in §358, vibrating in a contour shear mode. They can be used from about 70 to 1,000 kc/sec.

3. Flexural vibrations, either of the type introduced by Harrison,[205] with two or more pairs of electrodes, or of one of the types described in §354, with a single electrode pair. The practicable range in frequency is from 1 to 100 kc/sec.

4. Torsional vibrations. The frequency range is about the same as for flexure. No practical application of this mode seems to have been made.

5. Flexural vibrations of a Curie double strip, in which two very thin quartz bars are cemented together, as described in §354. By this method Gramont and Béretzki[185,186] have obtained oscillations at frequencies down to 50 cycles/sec.†

6. Beats between two h-f piezo oscillators, using two different crystals or a single crystal with two regions of different thickness, according to Hund.[238-241] This method seems to have been used mainly in experimentation‡ rather than in routine practice.

*Push-pull piezo oscillators have been described, for example, by Harrison[207] and Koga.[266] See also I. F. Byrnes, British patent 277,008 (1927) and U.S. patent 1,722,196 (1929).

† An interesting demonstration of the acoustic waves from these oscillators was a feature in the French building at the New York World's Fair in 1939.

‡ The first suggestion leading to method 6 was made by Pierce.[423] See also Koga

Other l-f quartz cuts for piezo oscillators are described in §§357 and 359.

Whatever form of oscillating circuit is employed, it must be remembered that the l-f crystals have relatively large mass and rather low activity and are easily broken by overvoltage. Good practice calls for the use of low-power tubes, high L/C ratio in the anode circuit, and a high grid-leak resistance.

Among the available circuits, the Pierce form is commonest, though the "tritet" (see reference to Lamb[300,301] at end of chapter) and bridge circuits can also be used. Gramont and Béretzki mention the use of a relaxation circuit for their very low frequencies.* The mechanically tuned feedback has been employed by Harrison[207] for his flexural oscillators and by Rohde[437] for lengthwise vibrations.

Piezo oscillators employing torsional vibrations are described by Tsi-Ze and Tsien,[530] Tsi-Ze, Tsien, and Sun-Hung,[536] and Hund and Wright.[242]

397. High-frequency Piezo Oscillators. For this purpose only thickness vibrations are used, generally of the shear type, cut at an angle for low temperature coefficient. For the same cut, the fundamental frequency varies inversely as the thickness.

In recent years attempts to increase the frequency have been stimulated partly by the demand for shorter waves in communication and partly by the success of Straubel in 1931 in obtaining very high frequencies from tourmaline oscillators (§400). In the years following Straubel's investigations the experimental work of Fox and Underwood,[148] Osterberg and Cookson,[403] Yoda,[596] Gramont and Béretzki,[186] Koga,[278] as well as Uda and Watanabe,[538] offered convincing evidence that quartz plates could be made to oscillate at frequencies practically as high as tourmaline. This fact, together with the high cost of even small tourmaline plates and their relatively high temperature coefficient of frequency, has practically ruled tourmaline out of consideration for generating short waves in radio.

In some of the experiments just referred to, the quartz plate was less than 0.1 mm thick. Kamayachi and Watanabe report results with a plate only 0.015 mm thick, the wavelength being 1.8 m. Gramont and

---

and Yamamoto;[284] Gramont and Béretzki;[184] A. Wertli, A Quartz-controlled Heterodyne Note Generator, *Helv. Phys. Acta*, vol. 6, p. 495, 1933; and Gramont.[182] Cases have been recorded in which a plate of uniform thickness vibrated simultaneously with two modes of nearly the same frequency, causing two separate output frequencies, which could be detected as a beat note. See, for example, F. Bedeau and J. de Mare, *Compt. rend.*, vol. 185, pp. 1591–1593, 1927; Sabbatini,[444] and Vigoureux.[568]

* On the use of relaxation oscillators, see also Hund,[239] Eccles and Leyshon,[129] and Kao.[252]

Béretzki have pointed out that, in order to match the input impedance of the tube, a very thin plate should have a small area. They recommend a ratio of diameter to thickness between 30 and 40.

On the whole it has not been found practicable to use quartz plates of a thickness smaller than about 0.2 mm, corresponding to 15 megacycles for the fundamental frequency. For still higher frequencies it has been customary to use frequency-multiplying circuits, the fundamental frequency being controlled by a quartz plate of convenient thickness, for example 1 mm.

The complication of frequency-multiplying circuits can be avoided by causing the crystal itself to vibrate at a high "harmonic" frequency. Crystal control of this type with a relatively low order of harmonics was achieved by some of the investigators named above. Nevertheless, in the past there has been the difficulty that the order of harmonics, at least so far as the ordinary Pierce-Miller circuit is concerned, is strictly limited by the considerations in §296. Very recently these obstacles have been surmounted by Mason and Fair,[141,341] who placed a quartz plate (AT or BT) in a capacity bridge* between grid and ground. By this means the harmful effect of the parallel capacitance C_1 was eliminated. For further details of the circuit the original papers must be consulted. By using the 23d harmonic of an AT-cut a frequency of 197 megacycles/sec was obtained by Mason and Fair; and by doubling the frequency they could go as high as 300 megacycles (1-m waves).

398. Other Crystal-controlled Circuits. Many circuits have been described, mostly modifications of the Pierce-Miller circuit. They include transmitter circuits of various powers and frequencies, primary and secondary standards of frequency, monitors, multivibrators, frequency multipliers and dividers, and receiving circuits. Some involve the attempt at making the crystal vibrate at its resonant frequency instead of on the inductive side of the resonance curve.† At the end of the chapter are a few references selected from the very extensive literature.

Two forms of piezo oscillator use other than purely electromechanical means for coupling the crystal to the oscillating circuit. One employs a beam of sound, the other a beam of light. Wheeler and Bower[583] described a circuit in which the controlling crystal is a large quartz bar in flexural vibration, the vibrations being maintained by acoustic waves from a telephone membrane, which in turn is vibrated by the output current from the amplifier to which the crystal is connected. The light-beam method, devised by the author,[104] makes use of an X-cut quartz bar in lengthwise vibration, through which a beam of polarized light

---

* Bridge methods for balancing out the parallel capacitance C_1 have long been known, especially for receiving circuits; see also Builder and Benson.[82]

† See, for example, the papers by Heegner[216] and Boella.[58]

passes parallel to the Z-axis. The light, modulated by the periodic strains in the crystal, falls on a photoelectric cell, the current from which is amplified and connected to the resonator electrodes.*

In two-way telegraphic communication, the detector at the receiving end can have coupled to it a low-power piezo oscillator, controlled by a crystal having a frequency differing by, say, 1,000 cycles/sec from that at the sending end. A heterodyne note of great purity is thus produced.

Special mention should be made of a "bridge-stabilized" piezo oscillator of very high constancy,† described by Meacham.[357] The crystal forms one arm of a bridge, of which the other three arms are resistances. One diagonal of the bridge is coupled inductively to the input of an amplifying tube, the other to the output. Meacham's analysis shows that the crystal vibrates at its resonant frequency, acting as a filter. The circuit is stabilized against all fluctuations by having one of the resistance arms of the bridge thermally controlled. Over a period of several hours the change in frequency has been found to be less than ± 2 parts in 10^8. In addition to its commercial applications this circuit has proved itself superior to a chronometer when used as a time standard for gravity measurements.

399. Standard-frequency Piezo Oscillators and Quartz Clocks. Under this heading are included primary and secondary frequency standards, portable frequency monitors, and the quartz clock.

Our only concern here has to do with the crystals employed for these purposes. As a guide to the literature on circuits and temperature control, a list of references is given at the end of this chapter.

For all the purposes named above the chief requirements with respect to crystals are very low damping and small variation of frequency with temperature. Modes of vibration other than that selected for operation are not troublesome as long as they are not close to the latter. On the other hand, more attention must be paid to the mounting, especially in primary standards and quartz clocks, than in any other use to which crystals are put.

A primary frequency standard is a formidable and elaborate apparatus in a fixed location. It is essentially a crystal-controlled oscillator of highest precision, with amplifiers and circuits for multiplying and subdividing the crystal frequency. Usually the output at one of the lower

---

* In *Engineering* (London), vol. 124, p. 841, 1927, is an account of the measurement of the frequency of a vibrating quartz plate placed between crossed nicols in such a manner that a beam of light, modulated by the crystal, was reflected by a rotating mirror of known angular velocity.

† Oscillators of this type are now obtainable from the General Radio Company, Cambridge, Mass. A brief analysis of the theory is given in the *Gen. Radio Experimenter*, vol. 18, no. 2, pp. 6–8, May, 1944.

demultiplied frequencies—say 1,000 cycles/sec—drives a synchronous motor geared to a dial, so that time intervals can be precisely determined and comparisons made with other crystal-controlled standards and with pendulum clocks. Such a device is called a "crystal clock" or a "quartz clock."

It is now recognized that quartz clocks, at least over limited lengths of time, are more precise than the best astronomical pendulum clocks. Indeed, small variations in the rate of astronomical clocks, due to fluctuations in the earth's rotation, have been revealed by comparisons with quartz clocks.

Primary standards usually consist of three or more independent crystal-controlled oscillators. The advantages of this arrangement are continuity of service if one oscillator stops, as by the burning out of a tube; the possibility of detecting any irregularity in the performance of any one oscillator; and increased precision over long periods of time.*

A discussion of the methods and technique of making frequency comparisons with standards cannot be undertaken here.

The secondary standard is like the primary, except that it is usually of less high precision and that the clock feature may be omitted.

The crystal monitor is a small portable low-power secondary standard with a restricted range of frequencies. In some forms it has a scale to read frequencies directly.

At the National Bureau of Standards there are seven quartz-controlled primary standard oscillators, *viz.*, six with 100 kc/sec GT-cuts in bridge-stabilized circuits, and one with a special doughnut shape at 200 kc/sec in a modified Pierce circuit. The crystal in each unit is kept at constant pressure in a small sealed metal box, in a constant-temperature oven. For the better units the short-time variations under normal operating conditions are less than ± 2 parts in 10^9. The drift of frequency in a month is less than 2 parts in 10^9, with a daily drift of less than 10^{-10}.†

The crystal-controlled standard at the National Physical Laboratory in England, according to the most recent publication,[139,69,] contains a 100 kc/sec ring, as described in §357. In vacuum, at constant temperature, the stability is $\pm 4(10^{-10})$ during hourly periods and $1(10^{-8})$ during monthly periods. The "long-period stability" is stated by Essen‡ to be $2(10^{-8})$.

According to Scheibe[B45] the four quartz clocks at the Physikalisch-Technische Reichsanstalt make use of quartz bars with lengths parallel

---

* See E. W. Brown and D. Brouwer, Analysis of Records Made on the Loomis Chronograph by Three Shortt Clocks and a Crystal Oscillator, *Monthly Notices, Roy. Astron. Soc.*, vol. 91, pp. 575–591, 1931.

† For this information the author is indebted to Dr. J. H. Dellinger.

‡ Ref. 69, p. 131.

to X or Y (§349).   The frequency is 60 kc/sec.   The bars are separated from the electrodes by 1-mm gaps and are mounted in vacuum with thermal control.   For these clocks the daily variation is claimed to be less than $2(10^{-10})$, the monthly variation about $3(10^{-9})$.

In the primary standards of the General Radio Company* an X-cut 50-kc quartz bar with length parallel to Y is used, as illustrated in Fig. 103.   The dimensions are $X = 9.4$ mm, $Y = 54.4$ mm, $Z = 7.0$ mm, with R around 2,700 ohms and Q around 85,000.   The temperature coefficient of frequency is from $-0.7(10^{-6})$ to $-1.5(10^{-6})$.   The elec-trodes are of chemically deposited silver, protected by copper or gold plating or both.   In ordinary industrial service the short-period stability is of the order of 2 to 3 parts in 10^9.   After 3 to 4 weeks of initial drift period the oscillators settle down to a slow long-time drift, usually an increase in fre-quency of 1 or 2 parts in 10^6 for a year.   Crystals that have run for some years appear to have no systematic drift, but only fluctua-tions of unknown origin amount-ing to 1 or 2 parts in 10^7.

The General Radio monitors employ AT-cut plates in fre-quencies from 500 to 5,000 kc/sec.

FIG. 103.—X-cut quartz bar for primary standard of frequency.   The bar is clamped between two resilient pads at the mid-points of the YZ-surfaces.   A baffle at each end is adjusted for quarter-wave resonance, re-moving at least 90 per cent of the loss due to acoustic radiation from the ends of the bar. The radiation from the sides is negligible. (*Courtesy of the General Radio Company.*)

The plates are mounted in holders with adjustable gaps.   Electrodes are chromium plated.

400. Piezo Oscillators with Rochelle-salt and Tourmaline Crystals. Owing to the large piezoelectric constants of Rochelle salt, bars of this material, either X-, Y-, or Z-cuts, can easily be made to vibrate in a Pierce-Miller circuit.   Nevertheless, for mechanical and thermal reasons they are unsuitable for practical applications.   While much has been published on their performance as resonators, chiefly for the purpose of determining the dynamic elastic and piezoelectric constants, still the only mention we find in the literature on their use as piezo oscillators is in papers by Pierce[423] and Mikhailov.[366]

---

* This information was kindly furnished by Mr. J. K. Clapp.   He states also that X-cut bars inclined at $\theta = -18°$ and $+48°$ from the Y-axis have higher Q's, but also higher temperature coefficients.   At $\theta = +5°$ the temperature coefficient averages less than at $\theta = 0°$, but Q is quite low.   When a 50-kc bar with length parallel to Y operates at its second "harmonic" frequency, Q is considerably greater, and at 60°C the temperature coefficient is zero.

*Tourmaline oscillators** were introduced by Straubel in 1931, when he obtained an output of 5 watts at 7 m wavelength and succeeded in getting crystal control down to 2 m. In his second paper he reported direct control at 80 cm (thickness only 0.01 mm) but found it preferable to use crystal control at 2 m, followed by a threefold frequency multiplication. In his third paper he described the stabilization of a magnetron at 1.6 m.

Wavelengths around 1.6 m were also attained by Awender and Bussman and by Kühnhold.

Various circuits were used by the experimenters listed at the end of this chapter, including the Pierce, push-pull, and stabilizing circuits. Several determinations of temperature coefficient of frequency have been made, with an average of about $-40(10^{-6})$. For the same thickness, tourmaline gives a frequency about 35 per cent higher than quartz. The frequency constant is about 3,750 kc sec^{-1} mm.

Besides having a high temperature coefficient, tourmaline crystals rise considerably in temperature while vibrating. Heierle finds an increase of 10°C in temperature in 1 hr (see also Booth and Dixon). These facts do not favor the use of tourmaline as compared with quartz for high frequencies.

In all the foregoing experiments, Z-cuts of tourmaline were used, the plates being in the form of circular disks a few millimeters in diameter. The thickness vibrations were compressional, with a strain given by the equation $z_z = d_{33}E_z$. The outstanding advantage offered by tourmaline, emphasized by Straubel and by Petrzilka, is that since the elastic properties are symmetrical about the Z-axis, very pure compressional waves are propagated in the Z-direction. There is therefore less trouble from undesired vibrational modes and parasitic frequencies than in the case of quartz.

401. Theory of the Piezo Oscillator. The earliest attack on the problem of the crystal oscillator was made by Terry[517] in 1928, in a paper that had to do mainly with the conditions for stability of frequency. In this treatment, circuit resistances are included, but a linear tube characteristic is assumed. In the years that followed numerous other treatments of the theory appeared,† each containing certain simplifying assumptions. One of the most thorough was that of Vigoureux,[B50,B51,568] who derived formulas for frequency and current in terms of crystal, tube, and circuit parameters, in good agreement with experiment.

Special mention should also be made of Llewellyn's paper in 1931,[318] which contains an analysis of the Hartley, Colpitts, and other circuits,

---

* See list of references at end of chapter.

† A list of some of the more important contributions is given at the end of this chapter.

with special reference to the conditions for frequency stability. Application is made to crystal control.

Both Vigoureux's and Llewellyn's conclusions will be found helpful in understanding the functioning of the Pierce circuit and in predetermining the various constants.

In the papers by Watanabe and Usui are applications of the resonance circle to their analyses. Watanabe discusses at length the effect of a gap in series with the crystal.

REFERENCES

The classified lists below are a selection of representative papers through 1945. References to some of the more recent literature are given at the end of Appendix II.

PIEZO-OSCILLATOR THEORY

VIGOUREUX,[B51] BOELLA[56,57] HANDEL,[200,201] HEEGNER,[215,216] JEFFERSON,[247] KOGA,[268] PETRZILKA and FEHR,[420] SMIRNOV,[472] TERRY,[517] USUI,[540] VIGOUREUX,[568] WATANABE,[581] WHEELER,[582] WRIGHT.[593]

PIEZO-OSCILLATOR CIRCUITS

SCHEIBE,[B45] BECHMANN,[31,33,36,38,43] BENSON,[50] BOELLA,[58] BOOTH,[69] BORSARELLI,[72] BUILDER and BENSON,[82] CADY,[104] HARRISON,[206,207] HAYASI and AKASI,[211] HEEGNER,[216] HIGHT and WILLARD,[227] JACKSON,[244] KISHPAUGH and CORAM,[260] KOGA,[268,280] KOGA and YAMAMOTO,[284] KOGA, YAMAMOTO, NISIO, HARASIMA, and IKEZAWA,[285] KUSUNOSE and ISHIKAWA,[297] LACK,[298] LAMB,[300,301] [the "tritet" oscillator, for which see also I. Koga and W. Yamamoto, *Electrotech. Jour. (Japan)*, vol. 4, pp. 110–115, 1940] LAMB,[302] LLEWELLYN,[318] MacKINNON,[324] MEACHAM,[357] MEAHL,[358] NELSON,[390] PAVLIK[408] PINCIROLI,[425] PONTECORVO,[429] POPPELE, CUNNINGHAM, and KISHPAUGH,[430] SABAROFF,[443] TAKAGI and NAKASE,[502] VECCHIACCHI,[561] WHEELER and BOWER.[583]

PERFORMANCE OF PIEZO OSCILLATORS, DEPENDENCE OF FREQUENCY ON CIRCUIT CONDITIONS

HUND,[B27,B28] MOULLIN,[B37] SCHEIBE,[B45] VIGOUREUX,[B51] AMARI,[2] ANDERSON,[3] ANTSELIOVICH,[6,7] BOELLA,[56,57] BOOTH,[69] BOOTH and DIXON,[70] BORSARELLI,[72] BROWN and HARRIS,[77] BUILDER,[80] BUILDER and BENSON,[82] DYE,[127] GOODMAN,[179] HEEGNER,[215,216] HIGHT and WILLARD,[227] HOVGAARD,[235] KOGA,[268,274] KOGA and SHOYAMA,[282] LAMB,[302] MacKINNON,[324] NAMBA and MATSUMURA,[388] SABBATINI,[444] THURSTON,[520] VECCHIACCHI,[560,562] WATANABE.[581]

PIEZO OSCILLATORS FOR VERY HIGH FREQUENCIES

FAIR,[141] FOX and UNDERWOOD,[148] GRAMONT and BÉRETZKI,[186] KAMAYACHI and WATANABE,[249] KOGA,[278] MASON and FAIR,[341] OSTERBERG and COOKSON,[403] UDA, HONDA, and WATANABE.[538]

Frequency Standards and Quartz Clocks

Scheibe,[B45] Vigoureux,[B50,B51] Essen,[139] Gramont,[182] Jimbo,[248] Koga,[277] Marrison,[330,331] Mason,[336] Vecchiacchi.[562]

Adelsberger, U.: Equipment for Emission of Standard Frequencies from the German Transmitter, *Hochfrequenztech. Elektroakustik*, vol. 53, pp. 146–150, 1939.

Adelsberger, U.: Very Accurate Measurements of Time and Frequency, *Elek. Nachr.-Tech.*, vol. 12, pp. 83–91, 1935.

Clapp, J. K.: "Universal" Frequency Standardization from a Single Frequency Standard, *Jour. Optical Soc. Am.*, vol. 15, pp. 25–47, 1927.

Clapp, J. K., and J. D. Crawford: Frequency Standardization, *QST*, vol. 14, pp. 9–15, March, 1930.

Decaux, B.: Measurements of Frequency at the Laboratoire National de Radio-électricité, *L'Onde élec.*, vol. 15, pp. 411–439, 1936.

Dobberstein, H.: On the Performance of Two Commercial Quartz Clocks, *Z. Instrumentenk.*, vol. 61, pp. 188–191, 1941.

Dobberstein, H.: Small Quartz Clocks, *Z. Instrumentenk.*, vol. 62, pp. 296–301, 1942.

Essen, L.: International Frequency Comparisons by Means of Standard Radio-frequency Emissions, *Proc. Roy. Soc. (London)*, vol. 149, pp. 506–510, 1935.

George, W. D.: Production of Accurate One-second Time Intervals, *Jour. Research Nat. Bur. Standards*, vol. 21, pp. 367–373, 1938.

Hall, E. L., V. E. Heaton, and E. G. Lapham: The National Primary Standard of Radio Frequency, *Jour. Research Nat. Bur. Standards*, vol. 14, pp. 85–98, 1935.

Harnwell, G. P., and J. B. H. Kuper: A Laboratory Frequency Standard, *Rev. Sci. Instruments*, vol. 8, pp. 83–86, 1937.

Jatkar, S. K. K.: Absolute Frequency of Piezoelectric Quartz Oscillators, *Jour. Indian Inst. Sci.*, vol. 22A, pp. 1–17, 1939.

Loomis, A. L.: Precise Measurement of Time, *Monthly Notices Roy. Astron. Soc.*, vol. 91, pp. 569–575, 1931.

Loomis, A. L., and W. A. Marrison: Modern Developments in Precision Time-keepers, *Electrical Engineering*, vol. 51, pp. 542–549, 1932.

Meacham, L. A.: High-precision Frequency Comparisons, *Bridge of Eta Kappa Nu*, vol. 36, pp. 5–8, February–March, 1940.

Mickey, L., and A. D. Martin: Development of Standard Frequency Transmitting Sets, *Jour. Research Nat. Bur. Standards*, vol. 12, pp. 1–12, 1934.

Rohde, L., and R. Leonhardt: Quartz Clock and Standard Frequency Generator, *Elek. Nachr.-Tech.*, vol. 17, pp. 117–124, 1940.

Scheibe, A.: Quartz Clocks: Constructional Outline, Rate and Frequency, *Arch. f. tech. Messen*, part 122, sheets T114–115, 1941.

Scott, H. J.: A Precise Radio-frequency Generator, *Bell Labs. Record*, vol. 11, pp. 102–108, 1932.

Stansel, F. R.: A Secondary Frequency Standard Using Regenerative Frequency-dividing Circuits, *Proc. I.R.E.*, vol. 30, pp. 157–162, 1942.

Tomlinson, G. A.: Recent Developments in Precision Time-keeping, *Observatory*, vol. 57, pp. 189–195, 1934.

Vigoureux, J. E. P., and H. E. Stoakes: All-electric Clock, *Proc. Phys. Soc. (London)*, vol. 52, pp. 353–357, 1940 (discussion pp. 357–358).

Wheeler, L. P., and W. E. Bower: A New Type of Standard Frequency Piezo-electric Oscillator, *Proc. I.R.E.*, vol. 16, pp. 1035–1044, 1928.

CRYSTALS IN FREQUENCY MODULATION

DOHERTY,[125] KOGA,[284] MORRISON.[375]

TOURMALINE OSCILLATORS

AWENDER and BUSSMAN,[14] BOOTH and DIXON,[70] FOX and UNDERWOOD,[148] HEIERLE,[218] KÜHNHOLD,[291] LEITHAÜSER and PETRZILKA,[314] MATSUMURA and ISHIKAWA,[348] MATSUMURA, ISHIKAWA, and KANZAKI,[349] OSTERBERG and COOKSON,[403] PETRZILKA,[419] STRAUBEL.[487,489,494-496]

CHAPTER XX

ROCHELLE SALT: HISTORY, GENERAL PROPERTIES, AND TECHNIQUE

And thou, Rochelle, our own Rochelle, proud
  city of the waters,
Again let rapture light the eyes of all thy
  mourning daughters.
As thou wert constant in our ills, be joyous
  in our joy;
For cold, and stiff, and still are they who
  wrought thy walls annoy.

—MACAULAY.

402. Summary of Properties. Rochelle salt (*sel de Seignette*) is so important as a dielectric on both theoretical and technical grounds that it will be considered somewhat at length. Like quartz, Rochelle salt is enantiomorphous, but it is usually of the right-handed form, produced from the natural tartaric acid of grapes. Tartaric acid occurs chiefly in the dextro form, although the levo form as well as the optically inactive mesotartaric and racemic acids can be produced artificially. Together with a few other more or less related crystals Rochelle salt possesses properties so unique that they are sometimes given a special name, the *ferroelectrics* (the term "Seignette-electric" was used in the first edition of this book).

In this summary we shall consider only Rochelle salt itself. Its outstanding feature, which pointed the way to the discovery of other remarkable properties, is the huge piezoelectric effect, unapproached by any other known substance. Notwithstanding its rather poor mechanical strength and low temperature of disintegration (55°C), Rochelle salt finds important applications, especially in the field of acoustics. Of chief scientific interest are its electric anomalies.

These anomalies are confined to effects observed with fields in the X-direction and shearing stresses in the YZ-plane. The piezoelectric constants d_{25} and d_{36}, though larger than for most other crystals, exhibit no special peculiarities, nor do the dielectric constants for the Y- and Z-directions, both values of the latter being in the neighborhood of 10 and having small temperature coefficients.

For electric fields in the X-direction the dielectric properties of

510

Rochelle salt exhibit the much discussed *ferromagnetic analogy*. Just as iron and other ferromagnetics are characterized by maximum permeability at a certain temperature—the Curie point, above which the permeability decreases rapidly—so in Rochelle salt there is also a critical temperature, called by analogy the "Curie point,"* at which a similar change takes place in the dielectric constant k'_x of the free crystal. In iron the Curie point is around 770°C, while for Rochelle salt it is about 24°C, only slightly above room temperature. By analogy with the ferromagnetic and paramagnetic states of iron below and above 770°C, respectively, the terms "ferroelectric" (or "Rochelle-electric;" or "Seignette-electric")and "parelectric" are applied to the corresponding states in Rochelle salt. In contrast to iron, however, the ferroelectric state is confined to the region between approximately −18°C and +24°C. The lower critical temperature is called the "lower Curie point"; like the upper Curie point, it is characterized by a maximum in the dielectric constant k'_x of the free crystal.†

In the ferroelectric region the relation between polarization and field is non-linear, and the crystal shows dielectric hysteresis. The strictly parelectric state, in which hysteresis disappears and the polarization is proportional to the field, is found only above +32° and below −26°C. Between these temperatures and the Curie points the properties of the crystal are somewhat affected by the nearness of the ferroelectric region. We shall designate the upper and lower Curie points by θ_u and θ_l, respectively. It will be shown later that the values of these temperatures are changed by mechanical constraint and by the application of hydrostatic pressure.

403. Some of the principal features of the piezoelectric and dielectric properties will now be further summarized.

The Direct Piezoelectric Effect. By the static methods that have usually been employed, widely varying values of d_{14} have been observed, depending not only on temperature, but on the electrodes, surface impurities, previous history of the specimen, and certain effects of lag and fatigue as well. Between the Curie points the curve relating polarization with stress shows saturation at large stresses (the effective stress is Y_z, although by the usual technique this shearing stress is brought about by compression of the specimen in a direction bisecting the angle between the Y- and Z-axes). Near the Curie points, values of d_{14} as high as $26,000(10^{-8})$ have been reported.

The Converse Effect. Experimental data are more complete and con-

---

* The term "Curie point" was first used with reference to Rochelle salt by Valasek [542]

† As will be seen later, the maxima in k'_x at the Curie points are observed only with relatively weak fields.

sistent than with the direct effect. The curves relating strain with field between the Curie points are quite similar to the dielectric polarization and hysteresis curves. Outside the Curie points the strain: field relation is linear. In general, the values of d_{14} derived from the converse effect have been found to be several times greater than those from the direct effect.

Dielectric Properties. Between the Curie points, hysteresis is observed in the relation between P_x and E_x. Over most of this region the reversible portion (first, or initial, stage) extends to the order of ± 50 volts/cm, for frequencies from around 200 to 10,000 cycles/sec. In this initial stage the initial susceptibility $\eta_0 = P_x/E_x$ is practically independent of E_x, varying only with temperature.* As the amplitude of E_x is increased, the second stage enters in: domains tend to become polarized in the same direction, the virgin curve turns steeply upward, and the hysteresis loop has steeply sloping sides. It is here that the greatest values of the permittivity k_x are found (up to 200,000; what is observed is here the *differential* value k_d, §430). Then at $E_x \sim 150$ comes the knee of the polarization curve, followed by the region of saturation (third stage), in which the differential susceptibility is approximately the same as the initial η_0. Different specimens give different results at small E_x, perhaps owing to differences in domain structure, but they usually agree fairly well in the saturation region. The hysteresis loops are broadest in the neighborhood of 0°C, gradually becoming narrower and smaller as the Curie points are approached, where hysteresis disappears. For several degrees outside the Curie points, however, the $P:E$ relation remains non-linear. At very low frequencies, and especially under static fields, the second stage begins at smaller values of E_x. Under these conditions the effects of lag and fatigue are observed both in dielectric observations and in measurements of the converse piezoelectric effect, just as with the direct effect.

When observations, by bridge or oscillograph, are made at increasingly high frequencies, the dielectric constant is found to decrease progressively, with an anomaly at each resonant vibrational frequency of the crystal. The value at radio frequencies so high that the wavelength λ is small in comparison with the dimensions of the crystal can be taken as a measure of k_x'' for a clamped crystal; it is of the order of 100 except close to the Curie points, where it rises to a value around 230. The effects of periodic deformation of the crystal are then practically eliminated. For it must be remembered that at frequencies for which λ is of the order of the crystal dimensions, even when the crystal is not vibrating in resonance, it is still in a state of forced vibration, and the piezoelectric reaction increases the value of k_x above that for a clamped crystal. It is this piezo-

* For the sake of simplicity we here omit the subscript x from the symbol η.

electric reaction, for example, that accounts for the rapid increase in k_x with field along the sides of the hysteresis loop.

When the crystal specimen is more or less constrained, as by mechanical clamping, the values of d_{14} and of k_x are reduced. The hysteresis loop becomes smaller and is greatly deformed, the area of the loop finally vanishing when the clamping stress becomes sufficiently great. An interesting feature is that the slope of the *initial* part of the polarization curve is not altered by pressure, although it includes a wider range of field than when the crystal is free. It is also found that the more completely a crystal is clamped, the less are its electrical and elastic properties affected by temperature.

This last fact is of importance in connection with many technical applications of Rochelle-salt crystals, in which the freedom of the crystal to deform itself in the field is to some extent inhibited. The result of such constraint is to make the crystal less temperature sensitive; and although under such conditions the extremely high values of d_{14} of which Rochelle salt is capable cannot be realized, still they are large enough for practical purposes.

The thermal, optical, elastic, and electrical properties of Rochelle salt, especially at the Curie points, have been objects of much study and speculation. In the foregoing paragraphs we have touched only on some of the outstanding electric and piezoelectric features. In Chaps. XXIII and XXIV it will be seen that at the Curie points the piezoelectric constant d_{14}, the dielectric constant k'_x of the free crystal, and the elastic compliance s_{44} (all at small fields) become, theoretically, infinitely great.

The Domain Structure of Rochelle Salt. The best evidence indicates that a Rochelle-salt crystal, like iron, is made up of distinct domains, each of which possesses, between the Curie points, a *spontaneous electric polarization* having a flat maximum of about 740 esu at 5°C, diminishing to zero at θ_u and θ_l. Some of the domains are polarized in one direction, some in the other, along the X-axis. The domains appear to be of the order of a centimeter in size, enormously greater than those in iron. The spontaneous polarization is accompanied by a spontaneous strain.

In the following chapters the properties of Rochelle salt will be discussed in more detail, and an attempt will be made to correlate some of the chief results of various investigators. The theoretical aspects of the Seignette-electric crystals are summarized in §471.

404. Historical. There are perplexities in the history of Rochelle salt as well as in its physical properties. According to H. S. van Klooster in the *Journal of Chemical Education*, vol. 36, pp. 314–318, 1959, the first synthesis of this material was performed about 1655 by Élie Seignette, an apothecary in the city of La Rochelle. He was the father of Pierre de la Seignette, to whom credit has sometimes been given. From Macquer's "Dictionnaire de chymie," published in Paris in 1777, we learn that this substance came to be known as *sel de Seignette, sel polychreste, tartarus natronatus,* or *sel de la Rochelle.* The same source* tells us that

"Ce sel a été d'abord composé pour l'usage de la Médecine à l'imitation du tartre Soluble ordinaire ou sel végétal, par M. Saignette, Apothicaire de la Rochelle, qui l'a mis en grande vogue, & qui l'a tenu secret tant qu'il a pu."

While the medicinal virtues as well as the chemical properties of Rochelle salt became universally recognized, nothing remarkable in its physical properties seems to have been observed until 1880. In that year the Curie brothers included it in their first pioneer researches on the piezoelectric effect.

The first quantitative measurements of the piezoelectric effect in Rochelle salt were made in 1894 by Pockels; his results are not in bad agreement with those of later observers. In the course of his experiments, Pockels also discovered the Kerr effect in this crystal, as well as the anomalous dielectric behavior in the *a*-direction. Unfortunately, there had appeared previously a paper by Borel, giving low and quite normal values for all three dielectric constants, which seems to have held the question of the anomaly in abeyance for a quarter of a century.

Interest in the physical properties of Rochelle salt, from the standpoint of their application in h-f underwater signaling, was revived in 1917. Investigations in this country were made independently by J. A. Anderson, A. M. Nicolson and the author.

In the work of Anderson and the author, experiments were performed with tin-foil-coated *X*-cut 45° plates cut from crystals that were grown by R. W. Moore (§412). Each observed the deflection of a ballistic galvanometer as a function of applied electric and mechanical stresses, together with the fact that marked differences exist between individual plates, even from the same crystal. Anderson found the polarization to depend upon the sign of the applied voltage and also upon the sign of the mechanical stress. This was the first observation of what is now known as the unipolarity of Rochelle salt (§433). He also made the first record of hysteresis effects with Rochelle salt. Among his most significant results was the fact that the ballistic throw upon application of a given electric field was increased by mechanical pressure up to a certain value of the pressure and that above this point the throws, for the same field, diminished.

In this laboratory the wet-thread method was used for cutting Rochelle-salt crystal plates.† The author's chief experimental results were as follows: For the first time, Young's modulus was determined for stresses at 45° to the *Y*- and *Z*-axes, from observations on vibrating rods. The dielectric constant, for *X*-cut plates at

---

* Vol. 3, p. 122. See also §416*a*.

† The suggestion that led to this device, which has since been widely used, originated with one of the author's students, P. E. Eckstorm.

high frequency, was found to be around 80.   The importance was noted of having the electrodes closely adherent.   Piezoelectric fatigue caused by mechanical stress and recovery on application of an electric field or after baking at 55°C were observed. A decrease was found in the piezoelectric effect in the neighborhood of 23°C (first observation of the Curie point).   It was found that different plates under various conditions gave values of d_{14} from 3.4 (10^{-5}) to 40 (10^{-5}), thus foreshadowing the enormous values found by later observers.

The anomalous behavior of Rochelle salt as revealed in these two investigations is for the most part explained in the light of the investigations discussed in later chapters.

The first descriptions of technical applications of Rochelle-salt crystals, with information on the properties and methods of producing crystals, were published by A. M. Nicolson in 1919.   Nicolson's crystals were of the composite, or "hourglass," type, produced by the rapid cooling of a saturated solution.   His experiments were with entire crystals, and he laid great emphasis on treatment with alcohol and heat.   Although this type of crystal preparation is now obsolete, his papers are of interest insofar as they record some of the earliest observations of the electric response to various stresses and the converse; the dependence of the reactance of Rochelle-salt crystals on frequency; and the evidence of hysteresis.

These early investigations were followed a few years later by a series of important papers by J. Valasek, in which the characteristic dielectric and piezoelectric properties were quite thoroughly treated, although some of his conclusions have been subject to revision.   It was he who introduced the term "two Curie points" for Rochelle salt.   His most important contribution was the pioneer work on the analogy between the dielectric properties of Rochelle salt and ferromagnetism, an idea that seems to have been first conceived by W. F. G. Swann.

Widespread interest in the internal properties and structure theory of this substance began about the year 1929.   Initial impetus came from the Physical-Technical Institute in Leningrad, through the publications first of Shulvas-Sorokina, later of I. Kurchatov and his collaborators. This has been followed by many investigations, both theoretical and experimental, outstanding among which are those of Scherrer and his associates in Zurich, of Fowler in England, and of Mueller and Mason in this country.

Recently the investigations have been extended to "heavy-water" Rochelle-salt crystals containing deuterium oxide in place of ordinary water.

405. General Chemical and Physical Properties.   Rochelle salt, or sodium potassium tartrate tetrahydrate, is the sodium potassium salt of tartaric acid with four molecules of water of crystallization.   Its formula is $NaKC_4H_4O_6\cdot 4H_2O$.

$$\begin{array}{c}
KO \qquad O \\
\diagdown \; \diagup \\
C \\
| \\
H-C-OH \\
| \qquad\qquad 4H_2O \\
H-C-OH \\
| \\
C \\
\diagup \;\; \diagdown \\
O \qquad ONa
\end{array}$$

As the structural formula indicates, the molecule, and hence the crystal, is enantiomorphous. Since only the dextro form of tartaric acid occurs commonly in nature, it is in general true that all Rochelle salt crystals are right-handed. All data here presented refer, therefore, to the so-called "d-Rochelle salt" (dextro). Hence there is no twinning of the Brazil type (§15) in Rochelle-salt crystals, as is so often the case with quartz.

The molecular weight of Rochelle salt is 282.184; the density at 25°C is 1.775 ± 0.003 (W. P. Mason[335,*]). The solubility per liter of water at 0°C is 1.50 moles (420 g.); at 30°, it is 4.90 moles (1,390 g). It has been stated by Hedvall[†] that the velocity of solution undergoes an abrupt change at the upper Curie point. The growth of crystals from solution must take place at temperatures below 40°C, since above this temperature sodium tartrate is deposited. The crystal itself changes at 55.6° to a mixture of Na and K tartrates and their saturated solution, and at 58° these salts are completely dissolved in the water.[‡] This is what has commonly been referred to as the "melting" of the Rochelle-salt crystal. The process is irreversible.

For the axial ratio and structure of Rochelle salt, see §542.

406. Etch Figures on Rochelle Salt. The following account of tests made by the author may be helpful in determining the axial directions in plates cut from this crystal. Very characteristic figures are easily produced by lightly moistening a polished surface. After drying, a face normal to the X-axis is found to be covered with fine striations parallel to the Z-axis. On faces normal to the Y- and Z-axes minute rectangular pyramids ("etch hills"), sometimes truncated, extend upward from the surface. Some characteristic forms for the XY-plane are shown in Fig. 104, as seen from above. The X-axis bisects the projection on the XY-plane of the acute angle α, which has a value of roughly 60°. On a

---

* The estimate of precision was kindly furnished by Dr. Mason. Within the probable error the value given above holds from 15 to 35°C.

† In a discussion of P. Scherrer's paper.[451]

‡ J. Docters Van Leeuwen, Z. physik. chem., vol. 23, pp. 33–55, 1897; J. F. G. Hicks and J. G. Hooley, *J. Am. Chem. Soc.*, vol. 60, pp. 2994–2997, 1938.

face normal to the Y-axis the pyramids are of the same general nature as in Fig. 104, the longer dimensions of the base being in most cases parallel to the Z-axis.

Owing to the strong polarity in the X-direction, one might expect marked differences in the etch figures on opposite sides of an X-cut plate. On the contrary, the striations look just alike. It was hoped that the domain structure might be revealed by the arrangement of the etch figures, especially on the X-faces. All that can be said at present is that a cursory examination gives no indication of domains. It is possible that a minute inspection, perhaps with the aid of the rodometer, would yield positive results.

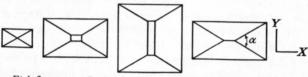

Fig. 104.—Etch figures on a Rochelle salt surface normal to the Z-axis. In each case the X-axis is horizontal, the Y-axis vertical.

407. *Thermal Expansion.* Observations by Vigness[566] indicate an almost exactly linear dependence of dimension upon temperature along each of the three crystallographic axes. The only peculiarity is a very slight bend at the upper Curie point for the Y- and Z-directions, for which there is no obvious explanation. Vigness's expansion coefficients have the following values: in the X-direction, 12 to 35°C, 58.3(10^{-6}); Y-direction, 12 to 24°C, 35.5(10^{-6}), 24 to 35°, 39.7(10^{-6}); Z-direction, 14 to 24°C, 42.1(10^{-6}), 24 to 35°, 43.6(10^{-6}). The coefficient of *volume* expansion calculated from these data is approximately 0.00014. Earlier observations by Valasek[543] are in fair agreement with those of Vigness.

On the other hand, Hablützel[198] does not find this normal behavior. In particular, he finds an anomaly in the direction bisecting the Y- and Z-axes, which, as will appear in §482, can be understood as a converse piezoelectric effect due to the spontaneous polarization.* Hablützel also recorded certain anomalies in the X-direction, a possible explanation of which will be found in §464.

To some degree these discrepancies may also be due to different electrical states of the crystals used by different observers in their measurements of thermal dilatations. According to §199, the value of the strain caused by a given stress depends on whether or not the electrodes attached to the crystal are short-circuited. Since a thermal strain may be regarded as the result of thermal stress, it follows that reproducible results can be

---

* This anomaly had been predicted by E. P. Harrison (*Nature*, vol. 120, p. 770, 1927).

attained only when the specimen is maintained in a definite electrical state. It can usually be assumed that thermal observations take place so slowly that the surface of the specimen is substantially equipotential at all times.

The *thermal conductivity* of Rochelle salt is several times lower than that of quartz.*

408. *The Dielectric Constants in the Y- and Z-directions.* According to Table XIV (page 162), crystals of the rhombic system have three principal dielectric susceptibilities η_{11}, η_{22}, η_{33}. Different values of the permittivities k_x, k_y, k_z along the crystallographic axes are therefore to be expected. k_x, the *enfant terrible*, will be dealt with in later sections. Concerning k_y and k_z the data are fairly consistent and indicate no anomalies. Mueller[376] recorded values of $k_y = 10$, $k_z = 9.6$, with temperature coefficients $+0.007$ for k_y, $+0.003$ for k_z. Measurements over a wide range of temperatures have been made by Hablützel.[199] He finds the values for ordinary and heavy-water Rochelle salt to be almost identical. From $-180°$ to $+40°C$ his value of k_y increases pretty uniformly from 6 to 10, with a flat region between the Curie points. Over the same temperature range k_z increases from about 5.3 to 10. At 20°C, $k_y \approx 9.4$ for both forms of Rochelle salt; the values of k_z are 9.5 and 9.8, respectively, for ordinary and heavy-water Rochelle salt. The temperature coefficients are of the same order of magnitude as those of Mueller.

Probably the best values at present are those of W. P. Mason,[B35] for which, unfortunately, the only datum concerning temperature is that the values "vary little with temperature."

Mason's values are to be recommended for use at ordinary temperatures.‡

$$k_y' = 9.8 \qquad k_z' = 9.2 \tag{488}$$

The primes indicate that these values are for *mechanically free* crystals. The corresponding susceptibilities from the equation $k' = 1 + 4\pi\eta'$ are

$$\eta_y' = 0.70 \qquad \eta_z' = 0.65 \tag{488a}$$

The susceptibilities η_y'' and η_z'' for *clamped* crystals are found from Eq. (262), together with values of d_{25}, d_{36}, e_{25}, and e_{36} from §141:

$$\eta_y'' = 0.63 \qquad \eta_z'' = 0.64 \tag{488b}$$

---

* From unpublished observations by Dr. H. Jaffe at the Brush Development Company.

‡ Since writing this section the author has been informed by Dr. Mason that his most recent determination of k_y' yields a value somewhat greater than the one quoted here. From observations of the frequency of a Y-cut 45° bar he finds for k_y' the value 11.1 from $-10°$ to $+24°C$, followed by a linear increase to 12.5 at 45°C.

409. *Anomaly in the Specific Heat.* Just as ferromagnetic theory led to the expectation of a sharp rise in the specific heat of iron at the upper Curie point (§556), which has been fully verified, so by the analogous argument several investigators have looked for a corresponding effect with Rochelle salt. It is easy to prove that, while an anomalous value of specific heat is to be expected in the neighborhood of either Curie point, the theoretical magnitude is extremely small. As in the case of ferromagnetism, the increase above the normal value of the specific heat c at the Curie point is

$$\Delta c = \frac{\gamma}{2} \frac{\partial P_0^2}{\partial T} \text{ erg cm}^{-3} \text{ deg}^{-1}$$

where γ is the internal field constant, P_0 the spontaneous polarization, and T the temperature. From his data on the variation of P_0 with T, Mueller[382] finds that this expression, for Rochelle salt at the upper Curie point, reduces to

$$\Delta c = 4.0\gamma(10^4) \text{ erg cm}^{-3} \text{ deg}^{-1} = 0.15\gamma \text{ cal mole}^{-1} \text{ deg}^{-1}$$

At the lower Curie point the theoretical value is a little greater, with sign reversed.

For any reasonable value of γ, these theoretical values are very small. This fact was confirmed by the very careful observations of A. J. C. Wilson,[588] who measured the specific heat of Rochelle salt from $-30°$ to $+30°$C. He found that this quantity could be well represented by the equation $c = 1.290 + 0.0031t$ joule g^{-1} deg^{-1} (t in degrees centigrade) for single crystals; the mean deviation of individual points was 0.3 per cent. At the lower Curie point a small anomaly in the right direction was found, the value of Δc amounting to somewhat less than 1 cal mole^{-1} deg^{-1}. No anomaly at the upper Curie point could be detected by the calorimetric method used; these observations indicate that if any exists it must be much smaller than 1 cal mole^{-1} deg^{-1}.* When these results are compared with Mueller's expression for Δc above, it appears that γ is of the order of magnitude of 1, and certainly not appreciably greater than the Lorentz factor $4\pi/3$.

As to the absolute value of c, Wilson's value is about 11 per cent smaller than that of Rusterholz,[441] but it agrees within one-half of 1 per cent with the value given by Kobeko and Nelidov.[264] The "International Critical Tables" give 1.37 joule g^{-1} deg^{-1} $\pm$ 2 per cent as the specific heat of Rochelle salt.

The specific heat of Rochelle salt from 15 to 340°K has been investi-

* Observations on the specific heat of Rochelle salt by Wildberger are in agreement with these findings (A. Wildberger, Diplomarbeit, Zurich, 1938; cited by P. Scherrer, *Z. Elektrochem.*, vol. 45, p. 173, 1939).

gated by Hicks and Hooley.* They find a sudden change at the decomposition point at 328.78°K (55.6°C, §405), but no anomaly at either Curie point.

410. *Electrical Conductivity and Dielectric Strength; Magnetic Properties.* The values of conductivity for the X-direction given in Table XXXIII were obtained by Valasek[542,543] using direct current. From $-65°$ to $+35°$, field strengths up to 10,000 volts/cm were used; the remaining data were obtained with a Wheatstone bridge at low voltage. After tin-foil electrodes had been attached with shellac to the well-dried crystal, the whole was coated with paraffin.

TABLE XXXIII

Temperature, Deg C	Conductivity, Mho cm^{-1}
-65	2.0×10^{-14}
-40	3.6×10^{-14}
-20	5.4×10^{-14}
0	9.0 and 5.0×10^{-14}
$+20$	22.0 and 11.0×10^{-14}
30	11×10^{-13}
35	1.0×10^{-11}
43	5.0×10^{-9}
47	3×10^{-8}
49	5×10^{-8}
51	5×10^{-7}
53	6×10^{-5}
54	1.7×10^{-4}
57 and over	5×10^{-4}

The two values at $0°$ and $+20°$ were obtained by reversing the emf and are related to the unipolarity of the crystal (prevalence of domains polarized in one direction: see §433). Somewhat higher values of conductivity were recorded by B. and I. Kurchatov[293]; from data in Oplatka's paper[397] it appears that his crystals had a conductivity thousands of times greater than Valasek's. Moisture on the surface can affect the apparent conductivity enormously. On the other hand, a dehydrated surface or a layer of cement between crystal and electrode may cause the observed conductivity to be much too low. This was probably not the case with Valasek's data in Table XXXIII, since his values agree approximately with those obtained at the Brush Laboratories.† Moreover, the anomalous values in the region of spontaneous polarization could hardly have been so pronounced if the high resistance had been due chiefly to the shellac. From Table XXXIII it follows that at room temperatures, with a dielectric constant of 10^3, several minutes would be required

---

* J. F. G. Hicks and J. G. Hooley, *J. Am. Chem. Soc.*, vol. 60, pp. 2994–2997, 1938.

† The author is indebted to the Brush Laboratories for this information.

for the charges to fall to half values if there were no other leakage than that through the body of the crystal.

It is probable that the data in Table XXXIII are not representative of Rochelle salt exposed to the air under ordinary conditions.

Between the Curie points, the observations of hysteresis may be complicated by conduction effects. If the humidity is excessive, both the height and the width of hysteresis loops are increased, and the tips of the loops tend to become rounded off. The latter effect can be detected on some of the oscillograms shown in later paragraphs. Observations of dielectric constant, coercive field, and dielectric losses can easily be somewhat falsified by the presence of leakage.

According to Vigness[566] exposure to X-rays causes a roughening of the surface as well as a yellow coloration.

Mueller finds that a properly annealed and dried crystal (§415) has a *dielectric strength* in air better than 20 kv/cm. No such value as this can be depended on for plates that are not carefully prepared. Naturally the danger of breakdown is very greatly increased if even the minutest flaws are present. According to Gorelik* a Rochelle-salt plate under oil at high hydrostatic pressure will withstand 600 kv/cm.

Magnetic Properties. Rochelle salt is diamagnetic. The only measurements appear to be those of Lane,[303] who finds the magnetic mass susceptibility to be $-0.54(10^{-6})$ in all directions, independently of temperature. This value does not vary more than 0.25 per cent between 10 and 30°C. Thus the "ferromagnetic analogy" of Rochelle salt does not involve any *magnetic* anomaly.

411. *Requirements for Reproducible Results.* Among the following, requirements 2 and 3 should always be observed. The others are important chiefly in measurements of precision.

1. Homogeneous crystal material. The crystal should be crystallographically and optically as perfect as possible, free from the flaws mentioned in §414.

2. Clean and smooth surfaces, well dried, yet with surface layers not deprived of their water of crystallization. The drying is of importance to avoid surface conduction; on the other hand, the material close to the surface should not become a dehydrated layer of relatively low dielectric constant. For example, if $k_x = 10,000$ for the crystal and if a dehydrated or otherwise damaged surface layer only 0.001 mm thick has $k_x = 10$, the thickness of the crystal being 10 mm, the measured value of k_x will be in error by 10 per cent.

3. From the foregoing paragraph it follows that the electrodes should make extremely close contact with the crystal in order that the applied

---

* B. Gorelik, Electric Breakdown in Rochelle Salt, *Jour. Tech. Phys.* (*U.S.S.R.*), vol. 10, pp. 369–375, 1940.

potential drop shall be impressed on the crystal, and not largely on the surface layers.

4. Freedom from mechanical stresses caused by electrodes or mounting. This requirement is due to the piezoelectric sensitiveness and to the close interaction between piezoelectric and dielectric effects.

5. Constant and uniform temperature. Rochelle salt is very sluggish in attaining equilibrium (§427) so that for reproducible results it may be necessary, after a change in temperature, to wait several hours before making observations.

The means of fulfilling these requirements as completely as possible, together with further technical details, will now be discussed. Their disregard undoubtedly accounts for many of the discrepancies between the results of the different observers.

412. *Production of Rochelle-salt Crystals.* Rochelle-salt crystals are always grown from a solution. Supersaturation may be caused by cooling or by evaporation. In the latter case, the solution may be either placed in a desiccator or subjected to reduced pressure. Although the cooling method is more commonly employed and seems to be the only one used on a commercial scale, nevertheless for scientific purposes the evaporation method is to be preferred, since the temperature may be held approximately constant, internal elastic stresses being thus avoided.

Crystallization by cooling. R. W. Moore* produced very beautiful and perfect Rochelle-salt crystals, measuring several centimeters in the smallest dimension, by suspending one or more minute Rochelle-salt-crystal "seeds" in a jar of solution, which in turn was placed in a larger jar of water provided with electric heater and thermostat. The temperature was allowed to drop 0.1°C per day at first, the rate increasing to 0.6° per day as the crystals grew. The same process is also described in detail by Schwartz.[454,†] For the suspension, silk threads have commonly been used, although Hiltscher[228] used a fine silver wire. Hiltscher also caused the seed to rotate slowly in the solution.

The largest and most flawless Rochelle-salt crystals hitherto recorded are produced by the Brush Development Company.‡ According to the patent specifications, seeds, often several centimeters long, are laid in a depression on the bottom of a tank of saturated solution, which is very slowly rocked about a horizontal axis. The solution is saturated at 35°C but is heated to a somewhat higher temperature before the cooling process commences. Crystallization is more rapid if a suitable hydrogen-

---

* R. W. Moore, *Jour. Am. Chem. Soc.*, vol. 41, p. 1060, 1919; U.S. patent 1,347,350.

† See also H. Hinz[229] and P. Vadilov (*Jour. Exptl. Theoret. Phys. U.S.S.R.*, vol. 6, pp. 496–500, 1936) for comparison of various methods.

‡ B. Kjellgren, U.S. patents 1,906,757 and 1,906,758 (also reissues 19,697 and 19,698).

ion concentration is maintained, for example, by the addition of KOH or of NaOH, corresponding to one-tenth normal solution. Sugar or formaldehyde is also sometimes added. It is found that growth takes place most rapidly in the direction of flow of the liquid, and the seed is also correspondingly oriented in order to have the long dimension of the finished crystal parallel to the desired axis. Seeds are usually placed with their X-axes vertical; each finished crystal is in the form of a long prism parallel to the Z-axis. The crystallizing process requires several days, the temperature being allowed to fall gradually and uniformly by thermostatic control. On being taken from the bath, the crystal may be rinsed with dilute alcohol and dried with a soft cloth. Single crystals weighing more than 2 kg have been grown by this method.

The method of Christopher* may also be mentioned, according to which a seed, suitably oriented, is placed in a Rochelle-salt solution between parallel glass plates, so that the finished crystal is in the form of a flat slab. For example, if a plate of large dimensions in the Y- and Z-directions is desired, the X-axis of the seed should be perpendicular to the glass plates.

The properties of the finished crystal are of course independent of its shape and of the orientation of the seed. A crystal plate cut in any particular orientation with respect to the crystal axes will theoretically— and so far as is known also experimentally—give the same results whatever may have been the shape of the crystal as determined by conditions of growth.

Crystallization by evaporation. Kurchatov[B32] places the solution, containing a seed, in a desiccator in the presence of concentrated H_2SO_4 or P_2O_5 at approximately constant temperature. In 5 to 6 days crystals weighing about 100 g are produced. The method of Busch[87] differs from this in that the solution, which is kept at a temperature constant to within 0.01°C by means of a thermostat, is connected to a trap immersed in CO_2 snow. The rate of evaporation is controlled by varying the pressure over the solution. An initial pressure of 50 mm Hg is recommended, changing to 25 mm toward the end of the process. Several 50-g crystals are produced from such a solution in 2 weeks.

Seidl and Huber[460] use a similar method, with liquid air instead of CO_2. The Moore patent mentioned above includes a description of crystallization at constant temperature by passing a current of dry air over the solution. For Stilwell's method see §478.

Further details on the process of crystallization of Rochelle salt and other Seignette-crystals may be found in papers by Bloomenthal,[55] Busch,[88] and Hinz.[229]

---

* J. H. CHRISTOPHER, U.S. patent 1,746,144 (1930).

413. *The Cutting of Rochelle-salt Crystals.* Mandell[326] finds it advisable not to cut the crystals until a month has elapsed after growth. Others do not appear to have observed this precaution. Most experimenters have used a wet thread or wet stretched rubber band. Details of this procedure are given by Busch,[87] David,[119] Staub,[478] and Hinz.[229] The author, who first used this method, has had good success with the apparatus shown in Fig. 105.

A stout endless linen thread is passed four times over a system of pulleys, so that from one to four cuts can be made at a time. The presence of a single large knot where the ends are joined is avoided by splaying the fibers at each end of the thread into three slender strands. These strands are tied separately with the knots staggered. The driving pulley, fixed to the shaft at A, has four grooves and is itself

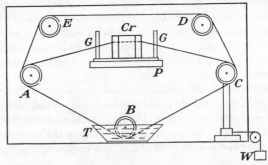

FIG. 105.—Machine for cutting Rochelle-salt crystals by means of a wet thread.

driven by a small motor at such a rate as to move the thread at a speed of about 15 cm/sec. The distance AC is about 40 cm   If fewer than four cuts are made, the unused turns pass over idler pulleys at D and E, which are simply glass tubes on brass rods. Pulley C is mounted on a post, the base of which fits on a track, so that the tension can be regulated by the weight W. The tension should be quite large to ensure an accurate cut. The lower part of the pulleys at B dips slightly into water in a flat tray T. Across the top of the tray is a strip of wood (not shown in the figure) carrying a piece of thick felt against which the threads rub in order to wipe off excess water. The crystal Cr is held in place by adjustable clamps on a brass plate P, fastened to the back of the apparatus, and the threads are guided by vertical brass rods GG. It is a wise precaution to give the crystal a waterproof coating, especially on the lower surface, before clamping it in place. About half an hour is required to make a cut of 5 by 5 cm. With some crystals there is a pernicious tendency for the thread to wander from the path prescribed by the guides, as if avoiding a hard or relatively insoluble region in the interior of the crystal. As was stated in §404, the electrical and elastic properties also have sometimes been found to depend on the région from which a specimen was cut.

Rochelle-salt crystals can also be cut with a suitably constructed saw. Ordinary hack saws, whether coarse or fine, are not suitable, since they produce large chips and cracks. However, for cutting small specimens, a jeweler's No. 6 hack saw, dry or moistened with water, is quite suitable. A band saw can also be used, if the teeth are sharp and well set, so as to make a cut somewhat wider than the thickness of the saw. An ordinary $\frac{1}{2}$-in. metal-cutting saw with 14 teeth per inch, having every tooth set, has been found in this laboratory to be entirely suitable; a woodcutting blade about $\frac{1}{4}$ in. wide also gives good results. In any case, all traces of salt should be removed from the teeth after use.*

414. *Flaws in Rochelle-salt Crystals.* When visible flaws are present in Rochelle-salt crystals, they may usually be attributed to too rapid cooling or non-uniform crystallization, to some disturbance in the course of the crystallizing process, or to impurities in the solution. Flaws may appear as fine streaks or as phantom planes within the crystal, parallel to one or more of the crystallographic faces. There are no well-defined cleavage planes. With the very flawless Brush crystals, such cleavage as there is seems to take place most easily in planes approximately perpendicular to the Z-axis. In less perfect crystals there sometimes seems to be a tendency for cracks to start most easily in planes *containing* the Z-axis, so that Z-cut plates are the most fragile.† This is especially the case when such plates contain phantom planes, for the latter, so far as the author's experience extends, are found mostly parallel to the Z-axis. There may be some relation between these facts and the observation made on one occasion while a cut was being made by the wet-thread method at an angle oblique to the Z-axis, when the thread tended very decidedly to follow a course parallel to this axis. Moreover, it has been found that fracture, at least along phantom planes, becomes very much easier with plates that have been kept in a desiccator long enough for a large amount of superficial dehydration to take place. This seems to indicate that dehydration and consequent weakening can take place along these almost invisible flaws.

In his experiments on Rochelle salt under hydrostatic pressure, Bancroft[20] found that a sudden change in pressure, even though small, almost invariably cracked the crystal.

It is not at all impossible that some of the erratic results that have been reported for Rochelle salt are due to the presence of minute cracks or other flaws originating in the growth or treatment of the crystal. Such imperfections may be expected to affect the elastic properties and thus the electric reactions; and insofar as they introduce local peculiari-

---

* For a description of the band-saw method used on a large scale by the Brush Development Company, see U.S. patent 1,764,088 by C. B. Sawyer (also Canadian pat. 302,528). For large crystals, the saw here described moves with a speed of 500 ft/min; a scraper removes excess material from the teeth. It is important that the saw be at approximately the same temperature as the crystal.

† The great fragility of Z-cut plates is also mentioned by Mandell (ref. 326, p. 632).

ties in the state of hydration, they may alter the dielectric properties as well. Variable behavior on the part of the same specimen may then be brought about by changes in temperature or humidity.

A special contributing cause of the fragility of Rochelle-salt crystals probably lies in the fact that they consist of domains of varying size and of opposite electric polarization. With changing temperature these domains tend to undergo opposite shearing strains, causing large stresses at the interfaces.

415. *Grinding and Finishing of Preparations.* After a plate has been cut from the parent crystal, it usually has to be reduced to a definite size and shape, with due regard to exactness of orientation. Large specimens should be handled carefully, since cases are on record in which cracks were started from the heat of the hand.

For demonstrations, qualitative tests, and many technical applications, a very small amount of smoothing and truing suffices. Any one of several techniques may be used, provided that care is always taken not to overstress or overheat the specimens. For example, preliminary grinding may be done with rather coarse garnet paper, followed by finer garnet- or sandpaper. It is an aid both to speed and to accuracy to have the grinding paper glued to a flat disk, which can be rotated by a motor or lathe at the rate of one or two turns per second. A method preferred in this laboratory consists in the use of a 12-in. curved-tooth flat file, of the type designed for filing soft metals. By this means the surfaces can easily be made so flat and true that, except when extreme accuracy is required, little or no subsequent treatment is needed, except the final polishing.

For the local truing of crystal surfaces a razor blade is also found useful. Hinz[229] describes a special form of plane in which the cutting edge is that of a razor blade. Some workers (Körner,[287] Vigness,[565] Busch[87]) have trued their plates by rubbing them on moist ground glass.

Many procedures have been used for lapping Rochelle-salt plates. The simplest is to rub the plate on a damp, thin silk cloth stretched on a plane surface; since this process leaves the surface covered with minute etch pits, it cannot be used for optical purposes.* Staub[478] lapped the surfaces with pumice powder, finally cleansing them with pure water (for X-ray reflections); Schwartz[454] used pumice powder mixed with saturated Rochelle-salt solution; Evans,[140] fine carborundum powder and paraffin. Stamford[475] recommends rubbing the plates on a ground-glass lap, using fine pumice powder and turpentine at first, followed by methylated spirit. Holden and Mason[231] lap the surface first with carborundum and machine oil; the resulting powdery surface is dissolved

---

* Prof. Hans Mueller informs the author that for optical work good results are obtained by polishing the surface with optical rouge in nujol.

off in the solution used for growing crystals and warmed above the saturation point, after which a fresh surface is crystallized on for about 5 min.

One important advantage in fine lapping is that it removes minute irregularities and broken fragments that would otherwise form an undesirable layer between crystal and electrodes.

For ordinary purposes no special aging process is necessary. Earlier workers advised treatment with alcohol; for example, Valasek[544] has stated that his crystals, after immersion in alcohol, showed a great increase both in piezoelectric activity and in dielectric constant. There is, however, no indication that these values were any greater than those obtained by other observers with normal crystals. If the surface layers are dehydrated or otherwise impaired, it seems possible that alcohol treatment may increase either the conductivity or the dielectric constant close to the surface, thus yielding values more nearly characteristic of the normal crystal.

Those who experiment with home-grown crystals containing visible flaws may also find protracted soaking of the crystal or plate in very pure alcohol helpful in removing water from the flaws, since the presence of water may render the crystal practically inactive. Accidental cracks can sometimes be healed—though perhaps not permanently—by prompt application of pressure.

In order to avoid dehydration of surface layers, preparations should not be kept long in a desiccator, nor at low pressure. Disregard of this consideration doubtless accounts for some of the discrepancies in published results. There is probably no better procedure in preparation for quantitative work than that of Mueller,[376] who annealed his preparations several hours at 45°C and then dried them for 20 min over phosphorus pentoxide. This dries the surface sufficiently without causing dehydration. But if there is any possibility that the surface is dehydrated, the outer layers should be washed off before this is done.

Under normal atmospheric conditions Rochelle-salt crystals are not deliquescent, nor do they desiccate. The reason is that at room temperature the vapor pressure is only about one-third of that of pure water, while the vapor pressure of the saturated solution is somewhat less than nine-tenths of that of water.* Nevertheless, the amount of H_2O present in the crystal is quite variable; according to Valasek[541] the weight of a crystal may vary with the humidity of the surrounding air by as much as 5 per cent. Crystals and plates cut from them that have stood unprotected on cabinet shelves in this laboratory for over twenty years show no loss in transparency or sharpness of outline. Such disintegration

* H. H. LOWRY and S. O. MORGAN, *Jour. Am. Chem. Soc.*, vol. 46, pp. 2192–2196, 1924.

as has been observed in certain cases is due either to extremely dry air or to chemical or electrolytic action caused by contact with other materials. Plates to which metallic coatings have been cemented seem to be subject to attack, as are also plates wrapped in ordinary paper or cheap cotton batting. Crystals are not permanently injured by moist air as long as the relative humidity is below 86 per cent.

If Rochelle-salt crystals or plates cut from them are to be preserved over long periods of time, it is advisable to wrap them in very clean, soft paper or paraffin paper. Ground surfaces had best be glazed over first by treatment with water as indicated above. Plates that are not intended for use as resonators may be coated with "ambroid," shellac, rubber cement, varnish, or paraffin.* Of these, the author prefers ambroid. Some such protection is especially desirable for plates to which metal coatings are attached, since when exposed to the atmosphere the coated plates seem to disintegrate more rapidly than if left uncoated.

If it is desired to keep otherwise unprotected plates under very constant conditions, they may be sealed in a jar containing saturated solution of Rochelle salt[477,565] or in a container in which the humidity is under control; Schwartz[454] uses slightly diluted sulphuric acid for this purpose. In all such cases due regard should be given to the dependence of vapor pressure upon temperature. In a paper giving many useful technical details Körner[287] states that he coats his plates with an alcohol-free cement immediately after they have been sufficiently dried in vacuum or in a desiccator.

416. *Electrodes for Rochelle-salt Plates.* The choice of electrodes depends on the use to which the plates are to be put. For quantitative observations of the properties of the crystal it is essential, as was pointed out in §111, that the electrodes make extremely close contact with the crystal surfaces and that at the same time the crystal be free from mechanical stresses. For crystals used in acoustic applications the former of these requirements is the more important. It is important to have the electrodes cover the entire face of the crystal, since otherwise the outlying portions diminish the piezoelectric strain. The following types of electrodes have been used by different observers:

1. Finely divided metal particles. This includes molten Wood's metal or Rose metal sprayed onto the crystal (Nicolson) and evaporated silver deposited on the crystal in vacuum (Valasek). Neither process has been widely used.

2. Liquid electrodes. Körner,[287] Goedecke,[174] Schwartz[454] and Hablützel,[199] have used mercury, while Kobeko and Kurchatov[263] and Errera[134] have used saturated Rochelle-salt solution. Although this

---

* Special treatment of Rochelle-salt plates with a waterproof coating is described by J. H. Ream in U.S. patent 2,324,024 (1943).

method removes the possibility of a layer of low dielectric constant between electrode and crystal, still the technique involves objectionable mechanical stresses.

3. Metal-foil electrodes are most commonly used. For precise measurements the foil must be exceedingly thin to avoid mechanical constraint. Cements containing alcohol should be avoided; most of the recent experimenters have used a dilute solution of Canada balsam in xylol. Sawyer and Tower[449] used beeswax in benzol with the addition of a little rosin. Sawyer (U.S. Patent 1,994,487) recommends the addition of powdered carbon to the Canada balsam–xylol cement, to render the layer of cement conductive; his procedure is to apply the electrode, rub it down into close contact, bake at a temperature well below 55°C, and then rub again with a warm pad. A layer of colloidal graphite on the crystal, covered with metal foil, is advocated by Kurchatov and by Seidl and Huber,[460] while Valasek[544] has used amalgamated tin "squeegeed" on to the polished surfaces.*

In this laboratory it was found several years ago that a very satisfactory material for electrodes is gold leaf. The polished crystal surface is lightly moistened by breathing upon it and then brought down carefully over a horizontal sheet of gold leaf, which adheres very smoothly and firmly. The same procedure was later described by Körner[287] and Busch.[88] Aluminum leaf 0.003 mm thick has been used by the Zurich school. Electric connection with the circuit is established in various ways, for example by having the connecting wires soldered to thin, flexible metal foil, which touches the electrode lightly. It has been found that delicate contact between the gold-leaf electrode and the hairspring from a clock serves excellently; it is especially useful in h-f resonator experiments. H. Mueller[376] states that "electrodes of conducting paint, graphite or metal foil were found equally suitable and gave the same results. The tinfoil electrode, provided it is properly attached, was found most convenient."

The newest method of all, and perhaps the best, is the use of gold electrodes evaporated onto the crystal surface in vacuum, as described in §444.

In order to avoid secondary effects from stresses near the boundaries of plates, in all work of precision the electrodes should cover the entire surface. An alternative method is that of David,[119] who secured a uniform electric field and at the same time immunity from edge effects by the use of a "guard ring" kept at the same potential as the electrode proper. To this end the inner portion of each electrode is separated from the outer by a gap 0.5 mm wide. David's comparative tests show

---

* "Graphoil" electrodes are described by A. L. Williams in U.S. patent 2,106,143 (1938).

this precaution to be of some importance. So far as securing a uniform field is concerned, the method is not needed, since owing to the large dielectric constant, at least in the X-direction, the field is sufficiently homogeneous if the electrodes cover the entire surface.*

Owing to the interaction of dielectric and piezoelectric effects, the mounting of the crystal should be so designed as to introduce no disturbing stresses either before or after the application of an electric field. This may be accomplished by suspending the plate freely or by letting it rest on supports so located as not to hamper the deformation of the plate.

In the case of plates that are not intended for precise measurements, many of the above precautions may obviously be disregarded.

While Rochelle-salt plates of various cuts function strongly as resonators and oscillators, still on mechanical and thermal grounds it seems unlikely that they will find applications as standards of frequency.

416a. *A Consistent Set of Rochelle Salt Constants at Room Temperature.* For cuts in which the electric field is parallel to the Y'- or Z'-axis there is no difficulty, since there are then no ferroelectric anomalies. Dielectric constants are given on p. 318, piezoelectric on p. 205. The elastic constants on p. 123 are for constant normal displacement. From them the isagric (constant field) values can be derived by use of equations on p. 271.

With the X-cuts it is impossible to assign to the elastic, dielectric, and piezoelectric "constants" values much better than the order of magnitude, owing to the very large dependence on temperature, field, and stress.

For a given crystal at a given temperature the following relationships must be satisfied: p. 268, Eq. (264); p. 273, Eq. (277); p. 274, Eq. (281); and p. 591, Eq. (495b). The only parameters that are fairly constant and trustworthy are $a_{14} = 7.4(10^4)$ on p. 207, and $s_{44}^P = s_{44}^* = 8.65(10^{-12})$ on p. 123. The clamped dielectric constant k_x'' lies between 100 and 200. In terms of these quantities, η', d_{14}, s_{44}^E, and e_{14} have been calculated from the equations above, for $k_x'' = 100$, 150, and 175. Of the three sets of values, those that agree best with experimental data from various sources are the ones for $k_x'' = 175$.

The rounded-off values thus calculated are:

$$k_x' = 500 \qquad d_{14} = 2.5(10^{-5}) \qquad s_{44}^E = 25(10^{-12}) \qquad e_{14} = 100(10^4)$$

These values are recommended as rough approximations for use in applications at ordinary temperatures, with low field strength and small stresses.

For the 45° X-cut plated bar (p. 472) a value is needed for Young's modulus $1/s_{22}'^E$, at room temperature. This quantity can be calculated from Eq. (43), p. 75, using the constants on p. 123 reduced to isagric values. When this is done we find $s_{22}'^E = 7.3(10^{-12})$. Another value can be derived from Fig. 94, p. 477, where at 20°C, $H_R = 145$ kc sec^{-1} cm. From this it follows that $s_{22}'^E \approx 6.8(10^{-12})$. As an average value we may take $s_{22}'^E \approx 7(10^{-12})$.

The effective piezoelectric stress-constant ϵ for the 45° bar can be calculated from Eq. (481), page 472. Using the values of d_{14} and $s_{22}'^E$ given above, we find $\epsilon \approx 180(10^4)$.

* The use of guard rings to prevent surface leakage is described by J. P. Arndt in U.S. patent 2,289,954.

CHAPTER XXI

ROCHELLE SALT: PIEZOELECTRIC OBSERVATIONS

Sel de Seignette.—La forme hémièdre la plus ordinaire est un tétraèdre $b^{\frac{1}{2}}$; les axes d'électricité polaire sont dirigés d'un sommet de ce tétraèdre à la base opposée; ils ne coïncident donc avec aucun des axes cristallographiques; quant à leur direction exacte, nous ne l'avons pas encore déterminée: la prévoir théoriquement ne nous a pas été possible, le tétraèdre étant irrégulier, et la trouver expérimentalement demanderait une série de mesures très délicates des quantités d'électricité développées suivant des directions voisines; du reste, cela n'a pas d'importance pour la question qui nous occupe; il suffit de savoir que l'axe va du sommet à un point de la base du tétraèdre; le pôle positif par contraction est situé vers le sommet.

—P. and J. Curie.

Piezoelectric observations fall into two general classes, according to whether they are made by means of the direct or the converse effect. The experimental investigations from various sources described in this chapter illustrate some of the anomalies of Rochelle salt and the general resemblance of piezoelectric to dielectric effects. In addition to the determinations, under various conditions, of the piezoelectric constant d_{14} recorded here, other determinations from observations with h-f vibrations will be given in later chapters.

THE DIRECT PIEZOELECTRIC EFFECT IN ROCHELLE SALT

In this chapter we are concerned mainly with stresses in the YZ-plane and polarizations in the X-direction.* So much of the published material is only qualitative, fragmentary, or obtained under questionable conditions, that reliable data with properly prepared specimens over wide ranges of stress and temperature are still lacking. From the close relationship between the piezoelectric and dielectric coefficients it is natural to anticipate a similarity between the curve of polarization vs. pressure and that of polarization vs. electric field, including the case in which the mechanical or electric stress is carried through a complete cycle. While the electrical case has been investigated with some thoroughness, surprisingly little attention has been paid to the mechanical.

417. *Methods of Measurement.* For static observations, both electrometer and ballistic galvanometer have been used. Dynamic measurements are described in §§310 and 375. For static measurements of d_{14}, d_{25}, and d_{36}, rectangular X-, Y-, or Z-cut 45° plates are used, and compressions are applied parallel to one pair of edges of the major surfaces,

* For d_{25} and d_{36} see §§141 and 418.

as explained in §184. For example, in the case of the X-cut, we may suppose the length l of the plate to be parallel to the Y'-axis, along which the stress $Y'_y = F/eb$ is applied, F being the force in dynes parallel to Y'; b and e are the breadth and thickness of the plate in centimeters. If Q (esu) is the total charge liberated, we have, for the piezoelectric polarization, $P = Q/bl = -d'_{12}Y'_y = -d'_{12}F/be$, whence $d'_{12} = -Qe/Fl$. Then, from Eqs. (203), $d_{14} = 2d'_{12} = -2Qe/Fl$. The same final equation holds also for d_{25} and d_{36}.

The galvanometer method is sufficiently sensitive and does not require a knowledge of the capacitance of the crystal specimen. This is a great advantage in view of the uncertainty in the dielectric constant and its variability with changing field. At temperatures high enough for electrical conductivity to be troublesome the galvanometer method has been found preferable. Schwartz[454] called attention to the importance of connecting a condenser of large capacitance in parallel with the crystal when the electrometer method was used. With this precaution he obtained identical results by the two methods. Mandell[328] corrected his electrometer readings for the error due to leakage by extrapolation to the value for zero time. No observations with such crystals as Rochelle salt should be made without due regard to these or equivalent precautions.

Pockels in his early investigations observed that upon compressing a 45° bar the polarization in the X-direction required a considerable time to reach its full value. According to Shulvas-Sorokina[465] from 3 to 4 min are required when the pressure is not over 1 kg/cm². With large pressures no such effect is observed. This piezoelectric lag is very like the dielectric effect described in §431 and suggests that the underlying cause may be the same (*cf.* also §84). Nevertheless, Schwartz,[454] whose observations of dielectric lag are shown in Fig. 117, does not appear to have found the effect in his piezoelectric measurements.

On the other hand, Pockels found the discharge upon removal of pressure to be *instantaneous*. In view of this, it is astonishing that all later observers made their measurements upon *application* of pressure.

418. *Dependence of the Direct Piezoelectric Effect upon Stress and Temperature.* Neither Pockels, Valasek, nor Mason, whose measurements of d_{25} and d_{36} are in fair agreement (§141), reported any dependence of these quantities upon stress. From the general absence of anomalies in the Y- and Z-directions none is to be expected. Nevertheless, Schwartz found d_{25} and d_{36} to *increase* as the compressional stress on 45° bars increased up to 6 kg/cm². Greater significance would be attached to this statement were it not that Schwartz's values of d_{25} and d_{36} are in very poor agreement with those of Pockels, Valasek, and Mason.

The dependence of d_{25} and d_{36} upon temperature is shown in Fig. 106, from Valasek.[545] The numerical data for d_{25} and d_{36} have already been given in §141. Valasek's curve for d_{14} (stress not specified) fails to show the expected maxima at the two critical temperatures, probably owing to the use of relatively large stresses (§480). These maxima have been observed by Schwartz,[454] who, like Valasek, fails to state the stress. Similar observations by Shulvas-Sorokina are discussed below.*

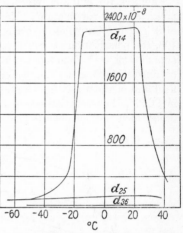

FIG. 106.—Dependence of piezoelectric strain coefficients of Rochelle salt upon temperature, from Valasek.

The earliest observation that the piezoelectric polarization is not a linear function of stress except outside the Curie points appears to have been made by Iseley,[243] as shown in Fig. 107. He applied compressional stresses Y'_y (§39) to an X-cut 45° bar and measured the piezoelectric charge with a ballistic galvanometer. The normal behavior of the crystal at the higher temperatures and the approach to saturation at temperatures between the Curie points are very evident. The greatest charge recorded was at 22.25°C (approximately the right temperature for the upper Curie point), with a stress of 2.225 kg/cm²,

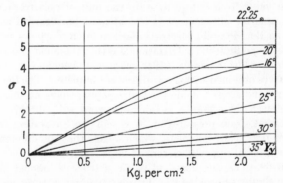

FIG. 107.—Curves relating charge-density σ in 10^{-8} coulombs/cm² with stress Y_y' in kilograms per square centimeter, for various temperatures, from Iseley.

beyond which the observations did not extend. From Fig. 107 the value of d_{14} under these conditions is found to be about $17,000(10^{-8})$. A still

* Using Schwartz's apparatus, Körner[288] measured d_{14}, d_{25}, and d_{36}, but the quantitative interpretation of his results is uncertain.

greater value would doubtless be found at smaller stresses. Iseley's elastic observations on the same crystal are discussed in §462.

Figures 107 and 108 represent almost all the published data on the polarization-stress relation. Mention should be made also of the work of Schwartz,[454] in whose paper is a curve in which, unlike Figs. 107 and 108, the polarization at 18.8°C has a very low value for pressures up to about 1 kg/cm², followed by a gradual rise. In view of the theory outlined in §480, as well as the form of the curves relating polarization to field and of those relating strain to field in the converse effect described in §422, this observation seems reasonable enough; it is unfortunate that others have not corroborated it. Figure 108,* from a paper by Shulvas-

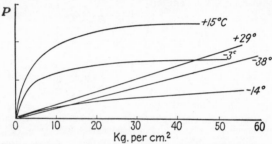

FIG. 108.—Polarization P_x as a function of pressure, at various temperatures, from Shulvas-Sorokina. Ordinates are in arbitrary units, not the same for all the curves.

Sorokina,[465] covers a wide range of stresses and temperatures, but it suffers in value from failure to state the unit of polarization, which is not the same for all curves. It can at least be regarded as definitely established that the piezoelectric polarization curve shows saturation in the range of spontaneous polarization and that there may be an inversion in the curve at low pressures. If this is true, the analogy with the polarization curves obtained with applied *field* is complete. The linear relation between P_x and stress outside the Curie points, changing to a saturation curve between these points, is fully in accord with theory. It will be observed that, from pressures of 50 kg/cm² on, saturation (rotation of dipoles) is practically complete, which means that the differential piezoelectric coefficient approaches zero at large stresses.

These relations are presented in an instructive manner in Fig. 109, also from Shulvas-Sorokina.[465] The outstanding features are the enormous value of d_{14} ($26,000 \times 10^{-8}$) between the critical temperatures *at small pressures*, the effects of saturation, and the low and uniform value of d_{14} outside the critical temperatures. The only unaccountable feature is the comparative flatness of the curves at the lower Curie point. From

* From Shulvas-Sorokina's data we have computed Y_x for Figs. 108 and 110 and d_{14} for Fig. 110.

Fig. 109 the saturation polarization is calculated as about 1,000 esu, of the same order, though nearly twice as great, as the dielectric saturation polarization discussed in §438. In collaboration with Posnov[469] the same author later finds the value to be 940 esu.

419. The value of $26,000(10^{-8})$ for d_{14} is the largest we find published as obtained by the direct effect, except that the author, from observations on an L-cut plate as described in §140, derived values as high as $32,500(10^{-8})$. The maximum observation by Shulvas-Sorokina, mentioned below, for which no numerical value is stated, may have been still higher. For the very large values obtained by the converse effect

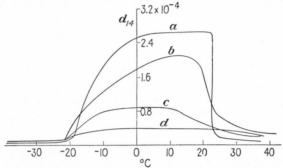

Fig. 109.—Dependence of d_{14} on temperature, from Shulvas-Sorokina. Stress Y_z for curve a is 0.5 kg/cm²; b, 4 kg/cm²; c, 15 kg/cm²; d, 25 kg/cm².

see §423. The value of $26,000(10^{-8})$ is ten times as great as Valasek's in Fig. 106. To account for such discrepancies one must take into account the variability of the piezoelectric constant with pressure, differences between different specimens, and such systematic sources of error as faulty mounting and depolarizing effect of surface layers. Since the various sources of error tend to make the observed value of d_{14} too small, it may be said that in general the highest recorded values are the most representative.

In a later paper[466] Shulvas-Sorokina reports that, by careful temperature regulation and application of pressures not exceeding 2 kg/cm², a very sharp and narrow maximum in d_{14} is found at 22.5°C. The height of the maximum is found to be less with thick than with thin crystal plates; this is attributed to lack of uniformity of temperature in the thick crystals. She finds the maximum in k_x to come at exactly the same temperature. At 38 kg/cm², however, there is no trace of a maximum at the Curie point. Correspondingly, the maximum in k_x disappears when the field strength exceeds 300 volts/cm. With pressures above 50 kg/cm² the piezoelectric properties were found to be the same at *all* temperatures.

The dependence of piezoelectric polarization upon stress is further shown in Fig. 110, from Shulvas-Sorokina.[465] The data are for 3°C, and they illustrate the importance of keeping the stress small if the greatest piezoelectric effect is to be realized. The sudden drop in d_{14} from the very large initial value of about $26(10^{-5})$ esu, shown at 2 kg/cm² in Fig. 110, does not seem to have been confirmed by other observers.

It was observed by Shulvas-Sorokina[467] that when a periodic mechanical stress was applied to a Rochelle-salt plate the value of d_{14} diminished rapidly as the frequency was increased from 10 cycles/sec. This observa-

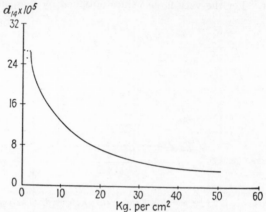

Fig. 110.—Dependence of d_{14} on pressure at 3°C, from Shulvas-Sorokina. Y_z is in kilograms per square centimeter.

tion can be correlated with the facts concerning "lag" discussed in §427. In a later paper[468] Shulvas-Sorokina describes experiments, with theoretical interpretation, in which periodic mechanical pressures up to 10 gm/cm² at frequencies from 3 to 3,000 $\sim$ were impressed.

420. The following early observations by Valasek[541] made at room temperature should be mentioned here, since they afford a qualitative confirmation of the theory discussed in §459. With a ballistic galvanometer he measured the charge Q liberated when a force $F = Y_y' be$ was applied to an X-cut 45° plate, according to §417. The distinguishing feature of these experiments was that the force was applied while the plate was in a known electric field. The total polarization is then $P^t = P^0 + P^E + P^F$, where P^0 is the spontaneous polarization and P^E and P^F are the contributions due to the field and to F. The results are shown in Fig. 111, in which the ordinates are $Q = blP^F$. It is seen that the maxima of P^F occur at certain negative values of E; that these negative values become greater with increasing stress; and that, for the same stress, P^F is greater for large negative values of E than for large positive values.   Either because a long time was allowed to elapse between successive observations or because E was not carried through a complete cycle, P^F appears in Fig. 111 (the dotted curve being disregarded) as a single-valued function of E.   In a later paper,[542] Valasek describes similar observations, made in rapid succession, in which E was varied through a complete cycle.   The result is illustrated qualitatively in Fig. 111 for the largest stress, the full line indicating the form of the curve for increasing E, while the dotted curve indicates the form for decreasing

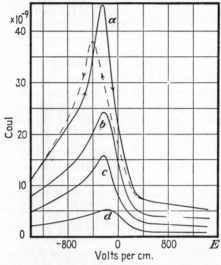

Fig. 111.—The direct effect in Rochelle salt. Piezoelectric response for various stresses with crystal in an electric field, from Valasek. Ordinates are in 10^{-9} coulomb, abscissas in volts per centimeter.   Curve a, force $F = 880$ g; b, 660 g; c, 350 g; d, 140 g.

E.*   This result, as well as the other features mentioned above, can be interpreted in the light of the discussion in §462 and by reference to Fig. 139, on the assumption that a stress Y_z is equivalent to a field strength $-E/b_{14}$.

421. *Unipolarity in the Direct Piezoelectric Effect.* Although the effect of unipolarity has recently been observed in connection with the *converse* effect (§422), little attention seems to have been given to its influence on the *direct* effect since the pioneer work of Anderson, to which reference was made in §404. Anderson used square X-cut plates with edges at 45° with the Y- and Z-axes. The sign of the strain y_z was

* This loop may be said to illustrate a sort of mixed piezoelectric and dielectric hysteresis. Piezoelectric hysteresis loops, by both the direct and the converse effect, are discussed in §§422 and 492.

reversed by changing the direction of pressure 90° in the YZ-plane, as explained in §184. He found that with some specimens the polarization was increased many times upon reversal of the sign of the stress. Later observations by Vigness are described in the next section. The explanation of the effect, in terms of the domain theory, will be found in §§462 and 477.

THE CONVERSE EFFECT

In the ferroelectrics there are anomalies in the converse effect similar to those in the direct effect previously discussed, demanding special experimental and theoretical investigation. We are here concerned chiefly with Rochelle-salt plates having the field in the X-direction. The theoretical discussion is reserved for §460.

For measuring the piezoelectric constants of crystals the converse effect offers the advantage that no correction need be made for leakage of charge through or over the surface of the specimen. As always, it is important that the electrodes lie in immediate contact with the crystal: no appreciable layer of impurities, cement, or, in the case of such crystals as Rochelle salt, dehydrated material must be allowed to intervene. In order to satisfy this condition without hindering the deformation of the crystal, very thin electrodes should be used, as for example of evaporated gold.

The principal experimental work is that of Sawyer and Tower,[449] Bloomenthal,[55] Vigness,[565,566] Norgorden,[393,394] and Hinz.[229] In broad outline it may be said that greater values of d_{14} have been observed than with the direct effect; that the mechanical strain produced by an applied field, like the electric strain (polarization), shows both saturation and hysteresis, and depends on temperature in a manner similar to the dielectric and the direct piezoelectric effects; and that the phenomena of fatigue and unipolarity are present. Bloomenthal and Hinz applied static fields, while the other observers measured maximum strains under alternating fields. In most cases the change in length Δl of 45° X-cut bars or plates was observed. The basic formula is

$$y_z = 2\frac{\Delta l}{l} = d_{14}E \tag{489}$$

422. *Static Fields.* Vigness's plates had the l-dimension normal to the (021) faces of the crystal, hence 40°53′ from the Z-axis. This is near enough to 45° to permit the substitution in Eq. (489) of Δl. Vigness calculated Δl from observations of X-ray reflections. This is almost the only case (see p. 330) in which X-rays have been used for the measurement of piezoelectric deformations. The method appears to be reliable, provided that one can be sufficiently certain as to the lattice planes from which reflections occur.   A drawback is the formation of superficial imperfections or disintegration of the crystal after some hours of exposure, which causes a broadening of the lines on the photographic plate.   Vigness found good agreement between the X-ray data and those obtained with a microscope.   His chief results are shown in Figs. 112 and 113.   The curves are of the same form as those shown in Fig. 118 for the dielectric effect and in Figs. 106 to 110 for the direct piezoelectric effect.   The conspicuous features are the characteristic behavior near the upper Curie point and the extremely large value of d_{14}—around ten

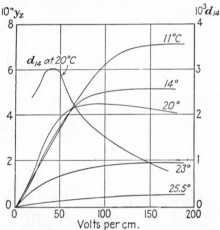

FIG. 112.—Converse piezoelectric effect in Rochelle salt, from Vigness.[565]   Dependence of strain, also of d_{14}, upon static field.   If $2\Delta r$ is the total change in length r of an X-cut plate observed on reversal of field, the mean strain corresponding to the field strength shown in the figure is $y_z = 2\Delta r/r$.

times as large as the values recorded for the direct effect.   Although Vigness's observations do not include the initial value of d_{14}, still it appears from the strain curve for 20°C in Fig. 112 that around this temperature the comparatively low initial value of d_{14} begins to increase at a field strength of the order of 10 volts/cm.   This increase at low fields, characteristic of *static* observations, is similar to that for the dielectric constant, as mentioned in §431.

The importance of a consideration of lag and fatigue (§427) in interpreting piezoelectric data is brought out in the following observations by Vigness.[565]   With small fields (27 volts/cm) deformation and recovery are slow, occupying several seconds.   With larger fields (165 volts/cm) the deformation is almost instantaneous up to nearly the full value, followed by a slow exponential creep that may last for hours.   After long application of a large field, recovery requires more than a minute.

After application of a field in one direction, a field in the opposite direction causes a greater deformation than if the first field had not been applied.

Vigness claims to have found experimental evidence for the existence of three different relaxation times in Rochelle salt: (1) a small fraction of a second, which makes possible the acoustic and h-f vibrations; (2) a relaxation time reaching a maximum of about 15 sec at 164 volts/cm, 7.5 sec at 27 volts/cm, a little above 0°C, falling to zero at each Curie point; (3) a longer relaxation time, lasting for minutes or hours (see also §427).

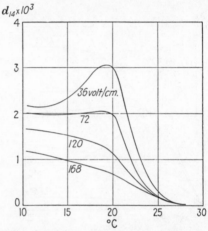

FIG. 113.—Converse effect in Rochelle salt, from Vigness.[565] Dependence of d_{14} upon temperature for various field strengths.

Mention is made in §§421 and 433 of the unipolar effect in the dielectric and the direct piezoelectric properties of Rochelle salt. It has been found by Vigness[566] that the magnitude of the strain in X-cut plates in the converse effect is not always the same upon reversal of sign of the electric field. It may be several times greater in one direction than in the other. This unipolarity with respect to strain in an electric field is analogous to the dielectric unipolarity discussed in §433. It was in effect an observation of the *spontaneous strain* and was used later by Jaffe (§482), in making the first calculation of the actual value of this quantity.

Bloomenthal used a combined optical and mechanical lever system for measuring the change in length of 45° X-cut bars of Rochelle salt containing 0.37 per cent of $C_4H_4O_6Tl\,Na\cdot4H_2O$. The field strength E was varied in steps through a cycle between -400 and $+400$ volts/cm. The plot of $y_z:E$ forms a hysteresis loop except at temperatures above the upper Curie point. The temperature range was from about 10 to 35°C.

The coefficient d_{14} at each temperature was computed from the maximum slope of a curve like that shown in Fig. 151.   The maximum value, which comes at 19°, is 70(10⁻⁵).   The time of recovery from the residual strain with field removed was not recorded.   For pure Rochelle salt, his values of d_{25} and d_{36}, and also of d_{14} for temperatures above 25°C, agree with those of Valasek shown in §418.

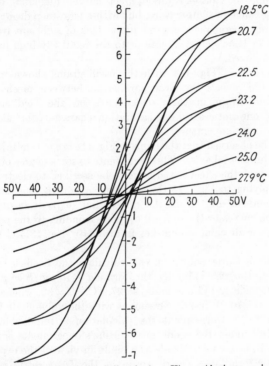

Fig. 114.—Converse effect in Rochelle salt, from Hinz.   Abscissas are in volts applied to the 45° X-cut plate.   Maximum field strength, for 50 volts, was 285 volts/cm.   Ordinates multiplied by 0.00145 give the elongation in mm; when multiplied by 4.35(10⁻⁵) they give the piezoelectric strain y_z.

Hysteresis loops for the converse effect have been obtained by Hinz,[229] who observed the change in length of an X-cut plate 40 by 15 by 1.75 mm, to which potential differences up to 50 volts (E to 285 volts/cm) were applied.   The potential was reversed after each step of 10 volts.   An optical lever with rotating mirror was used, as in the measurement of the elastic constants (§77).   The electrodes were of tin foil cemented on with "Acetonlack."   The results, shown in Fig. 114, are in general agreement with those of Vigness and Bloomenthal.   The observed elongations are proportional to the strain $y'_y = y_z/2 = d_{14}E/2 = b_{14}P^z/2$. From these relations, together with Eq. (500) or (512b), a theoretical explanation is found for the "saturation effect" made evident by these curves for temperatures between the Curie points. Hinz shows also a curve relating the change in length of plate at maximum field strength (ordinates of the tips of the loops in Fig. 114) with temperature; the form is somewhat similar to Valasek's direct-effect curve (Fig. 106) for the corresponding range in temperature, but with a less steep drop at the Curie point. This discrepancy may be due to lack of sufficient freedom from constraint in Hinz's crystal plate or to the relatively high field strength that he employed.

Comparison of Fig. 114 with the oscillograms shown in Figs. 123, 124, and 125 reveals the close parallelism between mechanical strain and electric strain in their dependence on the field strength. In particular, one notices similar saturation characteristics and a similar dependence on temperature.

It will be observed that the loops in Fig. 114 are not quite symmetrical about the horizontal axis. This fact points to some degree of unipolarity in the crystal—the effect is too large to be ascribed to electrostriction.

By applying to Fig. 114 the equation $y_z = d_{14}E$, one can calculate, at each temperature, either the differential $(d_{14})_d = dy_z/dE$ from the slope of the curves or the over-all d_{14} corresponding to the peak value of E. The over-all value diminishes from $36(10^{-5})$ at 18.5°C to $3.1(10^{-5})$ at 27.9°C.

Above the Curie point one can calculate the coefficient b_{14} of the polarization theory (§452) by the formula $b_{14} = y_z/P = y_z/\eta'E$. For example, from Fig. 145 one finds, at 27.9°C, $\eta' \approx 32$, whence from Fig. 114, $b_{14} = 6.5(10^{-7})$, in fair agreement with the value $6(10^{-7})$ from Fig. 146. Below the Curie point the calculation is impossible, since the susceptibility under the conditions of Hinz's experiments is not known. Moreover, if, as seems probable, especially in view of the experiments of Vigness,[565, 566] the piezoelectric strain in the ferroelectric region is as dependent on the specimen and on its mode of treatment as is the polarization when observed with static fields, one cannot expect the hysteresis loops in Fig. 114 to be generally reproducible.

For an estimate of the spontaneous strain y_z^0 from Fig. 114 see §482.

423. *Alternating Fields.* Sawyer and Tower[449] observed the shear in an X-cut plate with edges parallel to the Y- and Z-axes. A surface normal to the Z-axis was cemented to a metal block, and the maximum displacement of the opposite face in the Y-direction was observed with a microscope when a 60-cycle field was applied. The amplitude of shear y_z is the quotient of this displacement by the length of the plate in the Z-direction. The result is shown in Fig. 115. Especially noticeable is the fact that the converse effect fails to appear in this figure at field strengths below 50 volts/cm. The experiments of Norgorden, which will be considered presently, show that strains are indeed produced by fields below 50 volts/cm, although they are too small to have been made evident by the method of Sawyer and Tower. Except at low voltages there is fair agreement between Sawyer and Tower's a-c results and those of Vigness under static conditions.

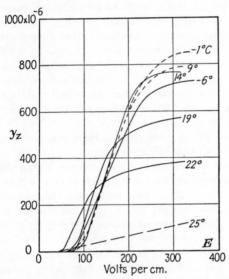

FIG. 115.—Dependence of strain upon field in an X-cut Rochelle-salt plate, for various temperatures (Sawyer and Tower). To avoid confusion, only the upper portion of the curve for $-1°C$ is shown.

The strain in Fig. 115 approaches saturation at a value between $4(10^{-4})$ and $9(10^{-4})$, depending on the temperature in the same manner as the dielectric constant shown in Fig. 123.

From the slopes of the curves in Fig. 115 the maximum differential values of d_{14} may be calculated. For example, at $14°$ it is found to be about $200(10^{-5})$, of the order given by the preceding authors. The maximum over-all value, obtained from the tangent drawn from the origin to the curve at $14°$, is about $100(10^{-5})$, four times as great as the maximum for the direct effect shown in Fig. 109.

424. With frequencies from 30 to 4,000 $\sim$ and maximum fields from 5 to 47 volts/cm, Norgorden[393,394] observed the maximum change in length of a $45°$ X-cut cube over a temperature range from 13 to $35°C$. The cube edge was 2 cm in length. Mueller's method (§§415,416) was followed for annealing the crystal and for attaching the electrodes to the faces normal to the X-axis. One of the 45° faces also carried an electrode which served as one plate of a condenser, the other plate being fixed in close proximity. These condenser plates, across which was a bias of 184.2 volts, were connected to an amplifier so that as the crystal vibrated the maximum strain could be calculated from the amplifier output. The circuits were carefully shielded electrically.

Norgorden's work is in effect a study of the *initial converse* $(d_{14})_0$, as defined in Eq. (512), p. 607. While his results are of value qualitatively, the numerical values of d_{14} are so low that they cannot be accepted as typical. In the first place, they are hundreds of times smaller than those of Vigness, a fact that can be only partly accounted for by the fact that Vigness used a static method. Second, these values are only about one-third as large as those shown in Fig. 146, with which they can fairly be compared in spite of the difference in method. If, notwithstanding Norgorden's precautions, surface layers of low dielectric constant were on his crystals, the recorded field strengths would be too high and the calculated d_{14} too low. Excessive mechanical constraint from cemented electrodes would also make d_{14} too small.

With this reservation, one may summarize Norgorden's results as follows: Like its analogue, the initial dielectric constant k_0 (§434), $(d_{14})_0$ is nearly constant up to at least 50 volts/cm. The relation between the reciprocal strain $1/y_z$ and the temperature interval $(T - \theta_u)$ is linear, at a given field strength, on both sides of the Curie point. We have here the first, and so far the only, confirmation of the Curie-Weiss law for the piezoelectric effect (see §467).

Norgorden's observations show also a tendency toward saturation in d_{14} with increasing field, as is to be expected from Eq. (512b) and from the analogy with the dielectric constant. He finds the strain to be nearly independent of frequency from 100 to 4,000 $\sim$.

COMPARISON OF THE DIRECT AND CONVERSE EFFECTS

425. Let us suppose that a stress Y_z is impressed on a Rochelle-salt crystal in zero electric field, at some temperature between the Curie points, causing a strain y_z and a polarization P. Then let a field E be applied of such magnitude as to bring the strain back to zero. We inquire first how the polarization P' due to E compares with P.

For the direct effect, $P = -d_{14}Y_z = d_{14}y_z/s_{44} = e_{14}y_z$. For the converse effect, we may write $y_z' = d_{14}'E$ and $P' = \eta E$, where the primes indicate the converse effect. The symbol d_{14}' allows for the possibility that the piezoelectric strain coefficient may have different values in the direct and converse effects. η is the effective susceptibility, which in ordinary piezoelectric crystals would be denoted by η' (constant stress) but which in Rochelle salt depends on both Y_z and E, and is usually less than η'. Then if $y'_z = -y_z$,

$$\frac{P}{P'} = -\frac{d_{14}d'_{14}}{\eta s_{44}} = -\frac{e_{14}d'_{14}}{\eta}$$

With *ordinary crystals* $\eta = \eta'$ and $d'_{14} = d_{14}$, whence

$$e_{14}d'_{14} = e_{14}d_{14} = \eta' - \eta''$$

by Eq. (516). Then $P/P' = -(\eta' - \eta'')/\eta'$; and since usually

$$(\eta' - \eta'') << 1$$

it follows that $P << P'$.

On the other hand, in Rochelle salt, owing to the large value of d_{14}, for certain ranges of temperature and of field, $\eta' >> \eta''$, so that P' can be nearly as large as P. That is, the same strain is then associated with nearly the same polarization in both the direct and converse effects.

It must be emphasized that equality in y_z in the two effects is defined in terms of the external configuration of the crystal (more properly, of the domain). Yet the fact that in the direct effect the field can be zero, which is not the case in the converse effect, indicates that the internal forces in the unit cell, and hence the arrangement of atoms in the cell, cannot be the same in the two cases. In terms of dipole theory one may say that in the direct effect the mechanical stress turns the dipoles, while in the converse effect the rotation of dipoles in the applied field deforms the lattice.

One would suppose that this disparity in lattice configuration in the two cases might make the process irreversible and explain the fact that the observed values of d_{14}, at least under static or l-f conditions, have usually been found greater in the converse than in the direct effect. Nevertheless, doubt is cast on this view by Vigness's observation of the same value of the strain whether the measurement was by X-rays or microscope. For by X-rays only strains in the primary lattice can be observed; and since the microscope, which yields the same y_z, measures the change in external configuration due to the field, one must conclude that approximately the same strain in the primary lattice is produced by the converse as by the direct effect. One can go no further at present than to say that the relatively large values of d_{14} by the converse effect *may* be found to be due entirely to the absence of some of the sources of error that tend to make the value by the direct effect too small. If after the elimination of all sources of error there is still found a disparity between the values of d_{14} in the two effects, one can only conclude that the piezoelectric process is thermodynamically irreversible.

A better comparison between the two effects would be possible if observations were made with the same specimen, leading to curves for

$P : Y_z$ and $y_z : E$ at various temperatures, especially between the Curie points; and it would be better yet if the $P : E$ curve were included, with P observed at the same time as y_z. For lack of any such comprehensive study as this, we can only summarize some of the fragmentary results recorded in this chapter. We note first that the piezoelectric strain in the converse effect, which as has been seen leads to a larger d_{14} than does the direct effect, also shows, like the polarization curve, three stages. In the first stage, up to fields of about 40 volts/cm or less, y_z is relatively small. Then, as is shown by Figs. 114 and 115, comes a rapid rise, followed by an approach to saturation. On the other hand, Figs. 107 and 108 for the direct effect show only a rapid rise in the piezoelectric polarization at small stresses, followed by saturation. Only the observations of Schwartz, mentioned in §418, indicate the existence of a first stage of low polarization.

426. *The Effective Value of d_{14} in Piezo Resonators.* At high frequency and in weak fields, very large values of d_{14}, such as those observed by Vigness, Bloomenthal, and Hinz in static fields or those of Sawyer and Tower at $60 \sim$ with fields above 50 volts/cm, are not to be expected. One would rather expect to find values of the order indicated in Fig. 146. It should be pointed out that the d_{14} derived from observations on resonators is due to the combined action of the direct and converse effect, as shown in §221.

Concerning the performance of resonators in strong fields very little is known. One may expect d_{14} in the ferroelectric region to vary throughout the cycle, somewhat as is suggested by the form of the curves in Fig. 114. The effect of this non-linearity on the resonator performance is mentioned further in §§370 and 480. The only practical application of strong fields in vibrating crystals is found in certain types of transducer, and here again next to nothing is known concerning the effect of the performance of mechanical work on the effective value of d_{14}.

427. Lag and Fatigue. The more important experimental results, some of which are recorded in §§417 to 424 and 431 to 437, will now be summarized.

The term *lag* refers to the slow development of electric or mechanical strain on the application of electric field or mechanical stress. It is somewhat dependent on the *fatigue*, which means the state of the crystal as a result of previous electrical or mechanical treatment. Both terms are used chiefly with respect to static observations.

Observations of Lag. (a). *In charging a Rochelle-salt condenser*, the amount of charge for a given field strength E_x is found to increase with the charging time t_c as long as t_c is only a few thousandths of a second. For values of t_c from a few seconds to several minutes the charge is the same, and on discharge the entire amount is given up rapidly enough to be observed with a ballistic galvanometer. With strong fields (over 400 volts/cm) the full charge is reached in about 0.01 sec, while with fields corresponding to the steep part of the polarization curve the growth of charge is more gradual.

With thick plates the saturation polarization has been found to be attained at smaller fields than with thin plates; but if fields lower than the saturation values are applied, the thick plates require a longer charging time than the thin (Kurchatov). The thick crystals also discharge more slowly.

b. *Lag in piezoelectric observations.* In the *direct effect* the full polarization P_x corresponding to a given stress Y_z may require several minutes to develop; on the other hand, the discharge is instantaneous (§417). In the *converse effect*, if the impressed field is small, both the piezoelectric deformation y_z and the recovery on removal of the field are slow. With large fields the deformation is almost instantaneous, but recovery may require more than a minute (§422).

c. *Lag in elastic observations.* Iseley[243] found that, on the application of compression to a 45° X-cut bar, as much as 30 sec. was required for the full attainment of the strain. Mandell[326] records a similar experience.

Observations of Fatigue. Both dielectric and piezoelectric fatigue (§404) have been observed, though the latter has been but little investigated. Dielectric fatigue consists in a reduction in the discharge after prolonged application of a field. Recovery is very slow, but it can be hastened by application of an opposing field. It is also stated that fatigue can be avoided by the use of "solution" electrodes; if this turns out to be generally true, it must point to conditions at the surface rather than in the interior of the crystal as the seat of the fatigue effect.

In his measurements of the elastic constants of Rochelle salt and of ammonium–sodium tartrate crystals (§§78, 88), Mandell encountered elastic fatigue; unfortunately, quantitative particulars are lacking.

Observations in Alternating Fields. Corresponding to the increase in polarization with longer application of a field is the observed diminution when an alternating field is used. Up to about 50 or 100 cycles per second there is a transition state, beyond which the results are not very different up to 10,000 cycles per second (see §§432, 436, 438). Similar results are found with the converse piezoelectric effect (§422).

428. Relaxation Times. It is probable that in most if not all of the observations on lag and fatigue the electrodes were separated from the normal Rochelle-salt structure by cement or dehydrated layers. Not only is the field in the crystal reduced thereby (§411), but in such layers there may also be depolarizing effects that affect the observations. For example, the wide discrepancy between Kurchatov's and Schwartz's results, as shown in Fig. 117, does not strengthen the view that the lag effect is a property inherent entirely in the crystal.

The slow adjustments due to surface layers are not the only effects present in Rochelle salt that must be taken into consideration before one can begin explaining anomalies by the theory of relaxation times in the Debye sense.   Non-linearity in the $P_x:E_x$ relation; interaction effects (§448); hysteresis, with attendant readjustments of boundaries between domains*—all these may depend upon time in ways that can fully account for most of the observed effects of lag and fatigue.   Mueller[380] goes so far as to assert that "the existence of a relaxation time longer than 10^{-6} second is not justified by any experiment."

As instances of attempts to throw the responsibility for observed effects onto relaxation times may be mentioned certain conclusions of Vigness[565,566] (§422), Norgorden (§424), Staub,[477] Shulvas-Sorokina and Posnov (§437), Shulvas-Sorokina,[467] and Goedecke.[174,†]   The last two of these papers contain a mathematical treatment of the problem.

In an alternating field, Rochelle salt reacts like a capacitance associated with a resistance.   The power factor may be affected by any or all of the following: (1) true relaxation times; (2) energy required to reverse domains; (3) shifting of the boundaries of domains; (4) leakage of charge through or over the surface of the crystal; (5) vibration of the crystal as a whole.   Power losses are too complicated to make a complete analysis possible.

The problem has been attacked empirically by Mason,[B35,338] who treats not only the dielectric constant but the piezoelectric and elastic constants as well as complex quantities.   He derives an expression for the impedance of a crystal vibrated at any frequency, involving Debye's theory of relaxation times, but does not apply it quantitatively.   The equivalent network of the crystal according to Mason is discussed further in §375.

In §425 we touch upon the question of the reversibility of the piezo-electric process in Rochelle salt.   One might hope that light would be thrown on this problem by the observations of energy losses in vibrating crystals under various conditions.   On the one hand, there is the intimate relationship between the piezoelectric and the dielectric constants.   On the other hand, it is the square of the piezoelectric constant d_{14} that appears in the resonator equations, and this square is really the product of the direct- and converse-effect values of d_{14}.   The analytic and experimental separation of these two contributions would not be easy.

---

* For the magnetic analogy see C. W. Heaps, *Phys. Rev.*, vol. 54, pp. 288–293, 1938.

† He reports relaxation times of the order of 10^{-4}, 10^{-5}, and 10^{-6}, which correspond to the smallest of Vigness's values in §422.

CHAPTER XXII

ROCHELLE SALT: DIELECTRIC OBSERVATIONS

As often happens, the phenomena which are the easiest to observe are the most difficult to interpret.
—E. C. Stoner.

429. This chapter has to do chiefly with fields in the X-direction. The dielectric constants in the Y- and Z-directions, which have no anomalies, were treated in §408.

The dielectric properties of Rochelle salt for fields parallel to the X-axis are very complex. The dielectric constant varies enormously with temperature, field strength, and mechanical strain. The literature is so extensive that it is impossible to do more than select and correlate some of those data which are most significant and trustworthy. Beyond the material in this chapter, further observations are recorded in §474 and Chap. XVIII.

Whenever the subscript x is omitted, it is to be understood that fields and polarizations are in the X-direction.

Owing to the large value of d_{14} and its reaction upon the permittivity, dependable values of k_x are difficult to obtain, since it is not easy to mount the crystals with their adherent electrodes in a manner sufficiently free from external stress. It is partly for the latter reason that most observers have failed to record the extremely large k_x that is to be expected at the Curie points. Much of the experimental work, especially that prior to about 1934, is of only qualitative value, and there has been a considerable amount of premature theorizing. Especially conspicuous is the lack of trustworthy quantitative data with static fields; perhaps this is because experience soon taught that more reproducible results could be obtained with alternating currents, though even here the observations of different workers are often far from harmonious. One reason for discrepancy doubtless lies in differences between unrecorded "room temperatures," an unfortunate circumstance, since such temperatures are so little removed from the upper Curie point. Other reasons, which will be made clear in the following discussion, are differences in thickness and degree of unipolarity of different specimens, previous history of the specimens used, differences in electrodes and in the cement between electrodes and crystal, and surface impurities on the crystals. Some of these sources of discrepancy are not present in alternating fields. The only results under static fields that can fairly be compared with those obtained with l-f alternating current are at smallest and largest fields.

The *permittivity* has usually been deduced from observations of polarization P, at various field strengths E, temperatures, and degrees of mechanical constraint. Observations may be classified as follows: (1) Under static fields, polarization curves obtained by a point-by-point method, usually with ballistic galvanometer; it is chiefly by this means that the phenomena of lag, fatigue, and unipolarity have been studied. (2) Observations at low frequencies, up to 1,000 or in a few cases up to 10,000∿. The three effects just mentioned, which vary from crystal to crystal, are mostly eliminated. The most nearly reproducible results are obtained by this method, using an a-c bridge or oscillograph. (3) At high frequency, with the crystal in or coupled to a tube generator circuit. The principal disturbing effects in Cases (2) and (3) are resonance with various vibrational modes and heating of the crystal.

As long as the frequency is sufficiently far from resonance with any vibrational mode, methods (2) and (3) may be assumed to give approximately the dielectric constant corresponding to the tips of the hysteresis loop. Depending on the circuit employed, the bridge method gives either the equivalent parallel capacitance C_p of the resonator or the equivalent series value C_s, as defined in §§271 and 273. These two quantities differ very widely in the resonance range but approach equality in either direction away from this range. Sufficiently far from resonance one may therefore write $k = 4\pi e C_p/A = 4\pi e C_s/A$, where e and A are thickness and area of plate and C_p and C_s are in esu. That the departure from resonance may have to be very great before the value of k thus derived is even approximately free from the effect of resonance is clear from Fig. 55, p. 326.

430. Definitions and Symbols. We shall have occasion to use several different expressions for permittivity and susceptibility, illustrated in Fig. 116 (*cf.* Fig. 168 for the magnetic analogy). In the first place there is the "normal," or "over-all," permittivity k_x at a point such as A (the subscript x will often be omitted, since only X-polarizations are here considered), defined as $k = 1 + 4\pi\eta$, where $\eta = P/E$. In some cases, especially in the discussion of hysteresis loops, the *differential permittivity* $k_d = 1 + 4\pi\eta_d$ will be used, where $\eta_d = \partial P/\partial E$ (the slope of the curve at any point) is the *differential susceptibility;* the point in this case may be on the virgin curve or on the hysteresis loop. The *initial permittivity* k'_0 (susceptibility η'_0) is the differential permittivity for $E = 0$. The *saturation permittivity* k_{ds} is the differential value k_d with large fields, on the linear portion of the polarization or hysteresis curves, while the value of k_d at the steepest portion of the curve is denoted by k_{dm}. The *reversible permittivity* k_r is the limiting value of the quantity

$1 + 4\pi \, \delta P/\delta E$ observed when a *small alternating* field is applied at any point on the $P:E$ diagram. The vanishingly small variations in P are then linear and show no hysteresis; the slope of the short $P:E$ lines, from which the reversible permittivity is calculated, is that of the hysteresis curve which has its tip at the point in question. Unfortunately, in the literature it has not always been made clear which of the foregoing definitions of permittivity was meant. All that has been said concerning the different permittivities applies equally to the susceptibilities.

All the types of permittivity are derivable from data obtained with ballistic galvanometer or oscillograph. Alternating-current bridge

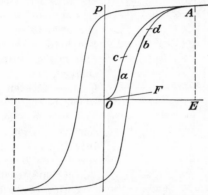

Fig. 116.—Types of permittivity. The "normal" value is $1 + 4\pi P/E$ at A. The differential permittivity is indicated at a and b, reversible permittivity at c and d. Differential and reversible values unite at large fields to become the saturation permittivity, and at small fields to become the initial permittivity at the origin.

observations give the "normal" value, which obviously varies widely with the field strength employed, becoming the initial value when the field is small. Unless otherwise specified, k will be understood to denote the normal value for the mechanically free crystal.

With Rochelle salt, in many cases it is sufficiently accurate to write $k \approx 4\pi\eta = 4\pi P/E$ (or $4\pi \, \partial P/\partial E$).

Most of the observations recorded here lie in the region of spontaneous polarization. Outside this region, except close to the Curie points, the anomalies disappear. The best data outside the Curie points have been obtained with alternating current and are considered later in this chapter.

431. Observations with Static Fields. In the earlier publications, for example by Valasek[541] and Kurchatov,[B32] one finds polarization curves, but they are of little quantitative value owing to the incompleteness in the data. We shall discuss here only enough of the very meager material to illustrate the salient facts.

The general form of the polarization curve as well as the effect of lag (§427) is illustrated in Fig. 117, curves *a* and *b* from Schwartz.[454] The resemblance to a magnetization curve with its three stages is evident. The highest values of polarization, around 500 esu, are of the same order as the saturation values obtained by other methods. From about 500 volts/cm on, the polarization is independent of the charging time. In order to show how variable the results by ballistic methods are,

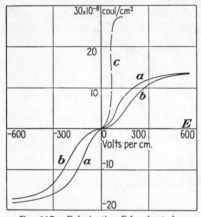

curve *c*, based on Kurchatov's observations,* is included in Fig. 117. This curve is at 0°C, charging time 0.07 sec, thickness of crystal plate 7.2 cm; the thickness of Schwartz's crystal is not stated. Kurchatov, like Schwartz, finds the polarization to increase with charging time.

A second example is Fig. 118 in which the charging time is 10 sec. The difference lies chiefly in the somewhat stronger polarization. In this figure is shown also the permittivity $k_x \approx 4\pi P/E$ as function of field strength (*cf.* Fig. 127).

FIG. 117.—Polarization *P* for short charging times (field parallel to *X*). Curve *a* is for charging time 0.148 sec, curve *b* for 0.007 sec, temperature 19°C, from Schwartz. Curve *c* is from Kurchatov, charging time 0.07 sec, temperature 0°C.

Owing to the danger of error caused by lag and the conductivity of the crystal, most observers have measured the static polarization in terms of discharge rather than of charge. It has been found that as long as the charging time does not exceed a few minutes, the entire discharge is so nearly instantaneous that a ballistic galvanometer can be used.

When the charging time is allowed to run into hours instead of minutes, the *fatigue effect* is encountered. In such cases the discharge is not sensibly instantaneous, but a considerable portion of the charge is returned slowly, at a rate depending on the time of charge, and lasting sometimes for days. The effect is also dependent on the strength of the charging field.

Since the entire charge is returned sooner or later,[397] (*i.e.*, there is no *permanent* remanence as result of a polarizing field), it may be concluded that the area of a hysteresis loop, at sufficiently low frequency, should be zero. That is, there should be no hysteresis if the observations with increasing and decreasing fields were made by a step-by-step

* Ref. B32, Fig. 24; see also §432.

method, sufficient time for complete adjustment to take place being allowed to elapse at each stage. This is by no means the case at the speed with which such observations are commonly made (*cf.* §422). For example, Valasek's observations* with a ballistic galvanometer (time intervals between observations not stated) yielded typical hysteresis loops in good agreement with those obtained by alternating current.

The field necessary to reverse the domains, when measured slowly by the d-c method, is several times smaller than by a-c (§436). The

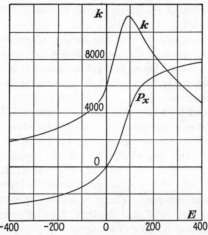

Fig. 118.—Polarization P and permittivity k for Rochelle salt at 20.3°C, as functions of field strength E (in volts/cm) in the X-direction. The polarization is in arbitrary units; at 400 volts/cm the estimated value is about $18(10^{-8})$ coul/cm². From Oplatka, ref. 397.

smallest recorded value, less than 15 volts/cm (presumably at room temperature), seems to be that of B. and I. Kurchatov.[293] This observation means that with static fields the initial permittivity k_0 extends over a range of less than 15 volts/cm.

432. Both fatigue and lag are illustrated in the following table from Valasek,[544] from observations at 20°C, charging field 900 volts/cm. The first two data may be compared with Fig. 117; from them it is evident

Charging Time, Sec	Discharge, Galvanometer Divisions
0.03	2.15
0.50	2.46
180	2.47
1,200	2.33
5,800	1.94

* Ref. 541.

that the charging process is over in about a second.   The last two show the effect of fatigue, not all the charge being instantaneously discharged through the galvanometer.*

Valasek also records some interesting observations on the removal of fatigue by an opposing field.   Thus, the effect of a field of 100 volts/cm applied for 24 hr in one direction can be eliminated by subsequent application for 20 min of an equal field in the opposite direction.   He also finds that the discharge through a ballistic galvanometer after application of a field in a given direction is greater after the crystal has been strongly fatigued in the opposite direction.   Further effects of fatigue are discussed by David.[119]

Kurchatov's explanation[295] of the fatigue effect is that it is due to the migration of ions into the surface layers of the crystal: when the crystal is short-circuited through a galvanometer, the ions migrate very slowly back again.   He found that fatigue was absent when solution electrodes were used (see §427).

Mention should be made of certain differences in behavior between thick and thin plates, even though their significance lies mainly in directing attention to the importance of avoiding even minute surface layers or gaps between crystal and electrodes.   Such layers form a region of relatively low permittivity, as was pointed out in §111.   They therefore make the actual field strength in the crystal less than that computed from the potential difference V and thickness e; moreover, they give rise to a depolarizing field that hastens the discharge.   The situation is further complicated if the surface layer is a partial conductor.   Thin plates should show these effects more than thick ones.   This dependence on thickness was indeed found to be the case by Kurchatov[295] and by Kurchatov and Shakirov,[296] who also offered the explanation given above. A few of their representative results will now be summarized, illustrating the fundamental dielectric properties of Rochelle salt as well as the effect of surface layers.   They found, for example, that while for plates of all thicknesses the final state of charge corresponding to the applied field was in general attained in a few hundredths of a second—except that with increasing thickness longer charging times were required when the field strength was relatively weak—there was a marked difference in the case of discharge.   Provided that the crystals were not left charged long enough for fatigue to set in, it was found that for thin crystals the times of charge and of discharge were about equal, but that the discharge was much slower in the case of thick crystals; for a crystal 7.2 cm thick it amounted to 30 sec.   The same crystal, on application of 130 volts/cm, became fully charged in 0.02 sec, while with 45 volts/cm the charge had not attained one-tenth of its final value in 0.07 sec.

* Somewhat similar observations are recorded by Oplatka.[397]

Using a series of plates from 0.23 to 7.2 cm in thickness, the time of charge being 1 to 2 min, Kurchatov found that the approach to saturation required very much higher applied potentials with thin than with thick plates, in accordance with the explanation offered above. He also found the initial permittivity, with $E = 0.1$ volt/cm, to be 1,340, whereas with alternating current at 50 $\sim$ or 500 $\sim$ it was only 150.

The following conclusions seem justified: (1) that the characteristic properties of Rochelle salt can be studied better with thick than with thin plates, unless the effects of surface layers are completely eliminated; (2) that, insofar as it is desirable to avoid the effects of lag and fatigue, polarization measurements with alternating currents should be more reliable and reproducible than those made with static fields, and the effect of differences in thickness should be less pronounced. In the following sections we shall see that this expectation is realized.

No investigator seems to have measured k_x by a ballistic method over the entire range of spontaneous polarization, with a crystal so well prepared and mounted and with a field strength of such a value that the highest attainable values were recorded. At 15°C, B. and I. Kurchatov[293] observed a differential value of 190,000, with a very pure crystal that showed saturation at only 15 volts/cm. With a strong field (value not specified) Schwartz[454] found k_x to reach maxima of about 4,000 and 3,500 at the upper and lower Curie temperatures, respectively, with almost equally high values between; obviously, his observations corresponded to points too far along on the polarization curve to show the highest values of k_x. From the theory one would expect that at either Curie point an extremely small field would cause a relatively great polarization, yielding a very large value of k_x. Between the Curie points the coercive force, though small, is greater than at the critical temperatures, with a corresponding decrease in k_x. Yet even here very large differential values of k_x are to be expected—as witness that of 190,000 at 15°.

433. *Static Observations on Unipolarity.* This characteristic of Rochelle salt was discovered by Anderson (§404). The reader may already have noted a peculiarity in Figs. 117 and 118: the polarizability of Rochelle salt along the X-axis is not symmetrical upon reversal of field, although the symmetry of rhombic crystals is such that both directions along the X-axis are equivalent.

This effect is a consequence of the spontaneous polarization of the crystal, by virtue of which there exists, between the Curie points, a "natural moment" for each domain in the direction of the X-axis. As is explained in Chap. XXV, in this region the crystal is properly to be considered *monoclinic*. In any given specimen, unless the opposing domains happen exactly to neutralize one another, there is a resultant moment. Under ordinary circumstances the polarization charges may be assumed to be neutralized by equal and opposite compensating surface charges.

If now a unipolar crystal consisting of a single domain is provided with electrodes to which an external potential is applied and if the field thus impressed is opposed to the spontaneous polarization, the latter undergoes a more or less sudden *reversal* when the field reaches a certain value. Enough charge must flow to remove the compensating charges mentioned above in addition to polarizing the crystal to an extent depending on its susceptibility. On the other hand, if the impressed field is in the same direction as the spontaneous polarization, these compensating charges remain and the charge flowing to the electrodes is much less. For the same applied voltage the apparent susceptibility is greater in the former case than in the latter. · This effect is further discussed in connection with Fig. 139. If, as is practically always the case, several domains with opposing polarities are present, some trace of the effect will be found unless the domains are exactly balanced.

The degree of unipolarity may be expected to be greater with small specimens than with large. Large plates should show unipolarity in opposite senses over different portions of the surface, corresponding to the pyroelectric patterns described in §521. Such regions were identified by Kurchatov[B32] on a large crystal that showed as a whole no unipolarity: by moving a small electrode across the surface he found regions of very unsymmetrical polarizability.

Evidences of unipolarity were also recorded by Valasek[541] and by Frayne.[149]

The Dielectric Constant of Rochelle Salt at Low Frequencies. The range of frequencies considered here extends from 50 or less to 10,000 cycles/sec. Since the effects of lag and unipolarity are inappreciable, the results are more consistent and reproducible than those obtained under static conditions. As a rule, for frequencies in this range no effects from resonant vibrations need be feared. As the frequency increases from 50 to 10,000 the results differ mainly in increasing width of the hysteresis loops, as will be seen in §436. See also §416a.

434. Observations of the Initial Dielectric Constant k_0' of Free Crystals at Small Field Strength. When the field is sufficiently weak, the relation between P and E is linear, without appreciable hysteresis. The range of linearity depends on the temperature. The critical field strength at which the $P:E$ curve begins to turn upward is zero at the Curie points, increasing rapidly to an indefinitely large value outside these points. In the ferroelectric region the available data indicate that the value is of the order of 50 volts/cm except close to the Curie points, for frequencies at least from 50 to 10,000 cycles/sec. Under static conditions (point-by-point method with ballistic galvanometer) the field range is smaller.

In the parelectric regions the values of k_0' obtained by different observers are in very close agreement. The agreement is not so good in the ferroelectric region, especially in the middle of the region where the values are smallest. Among those who have published values of k_0' (in most cases by a bridge method) may be mentioned Frayne,[149] Errera,[134] Schwartz,[454] Kurchatov and Eremeev,[292] B. and I. Kurchatov,[293] David,[119] Bradford (§474), Mueller,[376] Bancroft,[20] Hablützel,[198] and Mason.[335] Further reference to some of these measurements will be

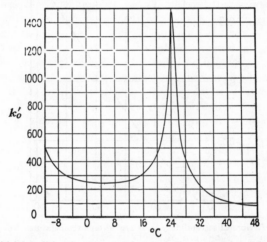

FIG. 119.—Initial free dielectric constant k_0' of Rochelle salt, field parallel to the X-axis, from Mason, ref. 335. The field strength was not over 5 volts/cm.

made in the paragraphs immediately following. Bradford's values are shown in Figs. 145 and 147, Bancroft's in Fig. 132, and Hablützel's in Figs. 134 and 135.

A typical curve showing the dependence of k_0' on temperature is given in Fig. 119, obtained with a 1,000-cycle bridge.

The most careful and complete measurements of the initial dielectric susceptibility η' at low fields (less than 10 volts/cm), chiefly outside the Curie points, are those of Mueller,[376] who used a 1,000-cycle bridge method, and of Hablützel (§444). Mueller's observations, extending from $-140°$ to $-18°$, and from $+21°$ to $+50°$C, verify the Curie-Weiss laws discussed in §465. The results at the higher temperatures are shown in Fig. 120. From 25 to 32° the following relation holds (all temperatures centigrade):

$$\chi' = \frac{1}{\eta'} = \frac{t - t_c}{C} \tag{490}$$

where $t_c = 23.0 \pm 0.5°$ and $C = 178 \pm 5$. t_c is the "Curie temperature" and C the "Curie constant."

Above 34° the crystal is well outside the influence of the ferro-electric range, in a region which, by analogy with paramagnetism, may

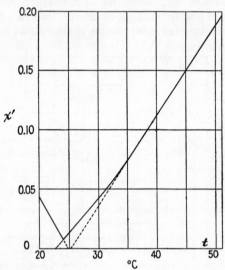

FIG. 120.—Reciprocal susceptibility $\chi' = 1/\eta'$ at high temperatures, from Mueller.

be called the *parelectric* range. Here the relation is very strictly linear; from 34 to 50° Mueller finds $t_c = 25.3 \pm 0.05°\mathrm{C}$ and $C = 136 \pm 0.5$.

The corresponding relation for the range below the lower Curie point, from −18° to −28°, is

$$\chi' = \frac{1}{\eta'} = \frac{t'_c - t}{C'} \tag{490a}$$

where $t'_c = -17.9°$ and $C' = 93.8$.

Data for the entire low-temperature range down to −140°C are shown in Fig. 121. It will be observed that χ' rises almost linearly until the temperature −160° is reached, after which it assumes the constant value 2.1, corresponding to a dielectric constant of 7.

The slight bend in the curve for χ' at about 33° in Fig. 120 was found also by Mueller in his observations of the Kerr effect. Such bends are also encountered in the experimental curves for magnetic suscep-tibility.

Mueller's values of the two Curie points are the temperatures at which the lowest values of χ' were recorded. These values are adopted in this book, *viz.*,

$$\theta_l = -18°C \qquad \theta_u = +23.7°C$$

Mueller derived the same value of θ_u from the Curie-Weiss law in the Kerr effect.

Attention is called especially to the linear relation shown in Fig. 120 just below the Curie point: in accordance with theory (§465), the downward slope is just twice as steep as the upward slope above the Curie point. The Curie point is to be taken as the temperature at which the two lines meet. In an ideal crystal, with sufficiently small field strength,

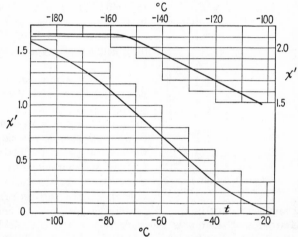

Fig. 121.—Reciprocal susceptibility $\chi' = 1/\eta'$ at low temperatures, from Mueller.

the two lines would be expected to converge on the axis of abscissas, indicating an infinite susceptibility at the Curie temperature. In the actual crystal, t_c and t'_c are not quite the same as the Curie temperatures.

These observations of Mueller are in excellent agreement with those of Hablützel, illustrated in Fig. 135.

An experimental and theoretical study of initial susceptibility has been made by Shulvas-Sorokina[468] with fields up to 12 volts/cm and frequencies from 3 to 3,000 $\sim$.

Further data on the susceptibility between the Curie points are discussed in connection with Fig. 145.

435. Observations in Stronger Fields: Oscillograms and Hysteresis Loops. *The Oscillograph Circuit.* In most of the oscillographic work referred to below, the horizontal deflection of the electron beam in a cathode-ray oscillograph is sinusoidal in time and proportional to the supply potential, while the vertical deflection is proportional to the charge on a condenser in series with the crystal and hence approximately proportional to the polarization in the crystal. The result is not a correct hysteresis loop, since the impedance of the crystal is variable; the potential drop across the crystal is not sinusoidal and hence not proportional to the abscissas. The ideal circuit, discussed by David,

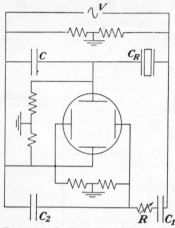

would have the crystal connected directly to one pair of deflection plates, so that the corresponding deflection would be proportional to the field in the crystal. This has not been found feasible, and all the experimenters used circuits that are in principle of the type shown in Fig. 122.*

FIG. 122.—Oscillograph circuit for Rochelle-salt hysteresis curves, from Mueller.

The resistance R corrects for the power loss in the crystal C_R. Since the resistance across C is very high, the instantaneous charges on C and C_R are approximately equal, so that the vertical sweep (ordinates of the curves) is approximately proportional to the polarization P in the crystal. If the vertical scale value (oscillograph sensitivity) is $s_y = V_c/y$ volts/cm, where $V_c =$ instantaneous volts across C and y is the deflection of the electron beam in centimeters, the polarization is given by

$$P = \frac{CV_c}{A} = \frac{Cs_yy}{A}$$

A being the area of the crystal plate in square centimeters. The horizontal sweep is proportional to the potential drop across C_2, and this in turn is proportional to V, provided that R is sufficiently small. Calling V and V_c the instantaneous voltages across the entire circuit and C, respectively, we have, approximately, for the drop across C_R,

$$V_R = V - V_c = \frac{C_1 + C_2}{C_1} s_x x - s_y y$$

where s_x and x are the horizontal scale value and deflection. If, as was the case with Sawyer and Tower, resistances R_1 and R_2 were used in

---

* The circuit shown in Fig. 122 is Mueller's modification[376] of that introduced by Sawyer and Tower.[449]

place of the condensers C_1 and C_2, the ratio $(C_1 + C_2)/C_1$ would be replaced by $(R_1 + R_2)/R_2$. Setting r for this ratio, we have in either case

$$V_R = r s_x x - s_y y$$

This equation can be used to compute the potential drop across the crystal corresponding to any measured point x, y on the actual curve.

436. *Some Typical Hysteresis Loops.* The most complete series of hysteresis loops, for temperatures from $-19.5°$ to $+27°$C and frequencies from 100 to 100,000 cycles/sec, are those of Hablützel.[198] In §444 we discuss the similar loops obtained by him with heavy-water Rochelle salt. His photographs show that, up to 10^4 cycles/sec, variations in

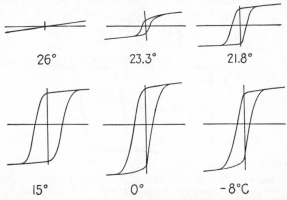

FIG. 123.—Rochelle-salt hysteresis curves, 60 cycles a-c, from Sawyer and Tower. X-cut plate 85 × 85 mm, 5 mm thick. Abscissas in volts/cm, max 387; ordinates are proportional to polarization.

frequency have but little effect on the form of the loops. From that point on, the width of the loop begins to increase, the polarization at saturation is less, and the loop becomes distorted. The distortion sometimes appears in the form of ripples, which may be due to natural vibrational frequencies or to shock excitation induced by the rapid variations in polarization.

The oscillographic records shown in the following figures are in general agreement with those made by Hablützel under similar conditions, except that in most cases the steep portions are less nearly vertical and the saturation regions less flat. It will be observed that the hysteresis loops are widest from 0 to 15°C, becoming narrower and smaller as the Curie points are approached. At temperatures outside these points the hysteresis vanishes.

Figure 123 shows oscillograms at 60 cycles by Sawyer and Tower;

those of David, obtained by a closely similar method at 50 cycles, are illustrated in Fig. 124.

Owing to the very large permittivity it is usually sufficient, even with thick plates, to compute this quantity from the simple formula for capacitance, $C = kA/4\pi e$. Only under extreme conditions of temperature or mechanical stress should there be any appreciable gain in precision by the use of a guard ring[119] or by applying Kirchhoff's correction for the edge effect.[87] Nevertheless, David claimed a slight improvement in the form of the hysteresis loop when a guard ring was used.

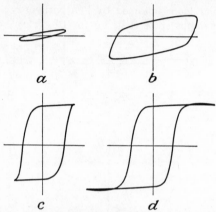

Fig. 124.—Rochelle-salt hysteresis curves, slightly retouched, 50 cycles a-c, from David. X-cut plate 20 × 20 mm, 9 mm thick, edges at 45° with the Y- and Z-axes, at room temperature. For a, b, c, d the maximum field strengths are, respectively, 30.7, 61.4, 123, and 384 volts/cm; remanence at zero field 0.76, 0.75, 23.8, and 23.1 × 10⁻⁸ coul/cm².

Figure 123 shows the effect of varying the temperature. In Fig. 124 the effect of varying the maximum voltage (presumably at room temperature) is seen.

Examination of all available data indicates that the coercive force E_c with alternating fields rises gradually from zero at the Curie points to a maximum somewhere between 5 and 15°C, of the order of 200 volts/cm, as shown in Fig. 147 (for the theory, see §482). Mueller finds that it is greater with thick plates, as shown in Fig. 125, while according to David it varies with maximum field strength. Hablützel[198] finds no dependence of E_c upon thickness.

The forms of the curves in the foregoing figures are in full agreement with theory. Especially noticeable are the disappearance of hysteresis, the small polarization, and the linear relation between polarization and field at 26° in Fig. 123, *i.e.*, at a temperature slightly above the upper Curie point. Figures 124 and 127 indicate that even in the range of spontaneous polarization the observed polarization is almost linear and reversible for maximum field strengths up to about 50 volts/cm. We see here the first stage in the process of polarization described in §431. At 61.4 volts/cm in Fig. 124b the hysteresis is already large. This observation is at variance with that of Kobeko and Kurchatov,[263] who found no hysteresis with their crystal even up to 70 effective volts/cm.

The second stage in the polarization process is that in which the polarization increases rapidly with increasing field. The differential permittivity k_d has here its greatest value, owing to the contribution made by the piezoelectric deformation. This stage lasts until the knee

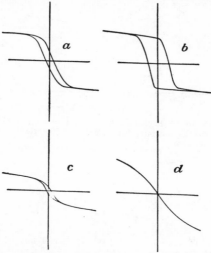

FIG. 125.—Rochelle-salt hysteresis curves, 500 cycles a–c, from Mueller. Curve a, X-cut plate 3 mm thick at 0°C; b, thickness 12 mm, 0°C; c, at 22°; d, below the lower Curie point.

of the curve is reached, at about 150 volts/cm. From this point on we have the third stage, characterized by an approach to saturation, with a value of the differential permittivity k_{ds} of the same order as that in the first stage, as is shown in Fig. 124, curves a and d.

From any of the curves the over-all permittivity $k = 4\pi P/E$, the initial permittivity k_0, or the differential permittivity $k_d = 1 + 4\pi \partial P/\partial E$, may be calculated. For example, from the slope in Fig. 123 at 26° we find k of the order of 650, in fair agreement with 740 as calculated from Eq. (490). Values of k corresponding to the tips of the curves in Fig. 123 have been calculated, to show how the over-all dielectric constant varies with temperature, the field strength having a maximum value of 387 volts/cm in each case.

Temperature, deg C	26	23.3	21.8	15	0	−8
k	650	1,430	2,250	3,900	4,710	4,250

At room temperature and 387 volts/cm Fig. 127 indicates a value of k twice as great as do the data above. Possibly David's crystal was less constrained than Sawyer and Tower's.

From the slope of the "saturation" portion of the curve for 15° in Fig. 123 the saturation permittivity k_{ds} is estimated as about 330; the corresponding value from Fig. 124 at room temperature is about 200.*

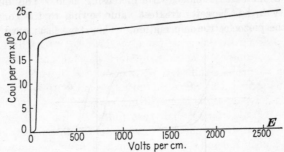

FIG. 126.—Polarization of Rochelle salt at room temperature, from David. The abscissa for each point is the maximum field strength at 50 cycles/sec, and the ordinate is the corresponding polarization.

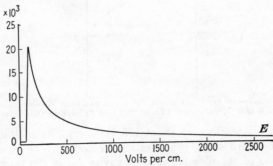

FIG. 127.—Dielectric constant of Rochelle salt as a function of field, 50 cycles/sec. from David. The curve is derived from Fig. 126.

In these curves, as in all polarization curves with Rochelle salt, complete saturation is never observed. Only under enormously large fields could the susceptibility be made to approach zero.

As in the analogous case with magnetic hysteresis loops, the highest permittivities are found along the steep portions of the curves. For example, the highest value of the differential permittivity derived from Fig. 123 is at least 200,000; the highest value from Fig. 124, about

* One would expect the value at room temperature to be *greater* than at 15°. The discrepancy must be due to causes other than the properties of Rochelle salt.

100,000; and the highest value observed by Kurchatov was 190,000 by a ballistic method.

The dependence of polarization on field strength is represented in another manner by David in the paper cited.   Figure 126, obtained by plotting the extreme tips of hysteresis curves at different maximum fields, shows clearly the three stages in the growth of polarization, again recalling the magnetic analogy.   From Fig. 126 David has derived Fig. 127, showing the dependence of k_x upon field strength.   The data for these curves were presumably obtained at room temperature.   The fact that as long as the peak value of the field strength is below 50 volts/cm the value of k_x as thus obtained is small and independent of the field is of special significance, as was pointed out in §§403 and 434. David finds that in this range the initial permittivity k_0 is from 400 to 500 and that hysteresis is almost if not entirely absent ($cf.$ Fig. 124a). This value of k_0 is larger than that found by other observers.   For example, B. and I. Kurchatov[293] assign to the initial permittivity at 15°C the value of 150 and state that it holds up to 70 maximum volts/cm. From Fig. 119, the value at 15°C is about 250.

437. *Other Observations with Alternating Fields.*   The contrast between the effects of weak and strong fields is illustrated in Fig. 128.   Curve a, from B. and I. Kurchatov,[293,B32] was obtained with fields not exceeding 15 volts/cm at 50 $\sim$, by a bridge method.   Values of k_0 from 100 to 400 are found except in the regions close to the Curie points.   Sharp maxima were found at $-15°$ and $+22.5°$; the Kurchatovs considered the Curie points to be thus determined.   These temperatures differ somewhat from Mueller's values of $-18°$ and $+23.7°$ (§434), which he obtained from both dielectric and optical observations.   An extremely sharp maximum at the upper Curie point is also recorded by Shulvas-Sorokina,[466] of exactly the same form as in the analogous case for iron. Such maxima are to be expected with weak fields, in view of the theoretical vanishing of the coercive force at the Curie points.   Curve a agrees satisfactorily with Fig. 147.

Curve b is from ballistic observations by Schwartz,[454] with strong fields and long times of charge.   In accordance with theory (§455) the values at the Curie points are lower than in curve a, but between these points they are higher.   Curve c, also from Schwartz, at maximum field strength of 10 volts/cm, frequency 500, represents the initial permittivity k_0.   In the range of spontaneous polarization, k_0 is in the neighborhood of 250, rising to maxima of 500 and 850 at the lower and upper Curie points.   At 20° the value is about 350, in good agreement with that calculated from Mueller's observations (§434).   It is impossible to say whether Schwartz's failure to record high maxima at the Curie points, comparable with those of B. and I. Kurchatov, is due to his slightly weaker field or to greater mechanical constraint. The latter is a plausible explanation, since his plate was clamped between the cells that held the mercury electrodes.

In a stronger field (100 to 1,200 volts/cm), Kobeko and Kurchatov[263] found, on the other hand, in agreement with Valasek and Schwartz,[454] an almost uniformly high value of k_x between the Curie points, falling off sharply outside of this range. The theoretical explanation of this is given in §479. Their paper is among the first to give data on dielectric saturation at large field strengths.

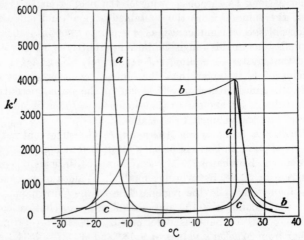

Fig. 128.—Effects of temperature on the dielectric constant of Rochelle salt.   Curve *a* from Kurchatov, *b* and *c* from Schwartz.

A very curious dependence of dielectric constant upon frequency at very low frequencies has been reported by Shulvas-Sorokina and Posnov.[469] They find a sharp maximum in *k* at a frequency between 2 and 30 cycles/sec, the value of the frequency depending on field strength, temperature, and thickness of plate. They offer a theoretical explanation in terms of relaxation times, support for which is found in the slow growth of piezoelectric polarization under small mechanical stresses (§427).

438. *The Spontaneous Polarization* $P°$. The earliest estimates were made from the remanent polarization in hysteresis loops obtained by a step-by-step method, using static fields. From the work of Valasek[541,542] and Frayne,[149] as well as from Figs. 117 and 118, values may be derived ranging from 30 to 180 esu. These values are not unreasonable for temperatures just below the Curie point; they are on the whole probably too small, owing to the leakage of charge between observations. The most reliable data are from oscillograms of hysteresis loops at frequencies from 50 to 1,000 cycles/sec. Mueller's curve for P^0 in terms of temperature, obtained by this method, is shown in Fig. 147. It is in excellent agreement with Hablützel's observations (Fig. 136). Fair approximations to these values may be deduced from the observations of Kobeko and Kurchatov and from the oscillograms of Sawyer and Tower, of David, and of Mueller, which were shown in previous sections.

At temperatures well outside the region of spontaneous polarization the results of all observers show that hysteresis is absent and that the polarization is directly proportional to the field. For temperatures only slightly outside the Curie points there is still some variation with field. The effect at low temperature is shown in Fig. 125d. Under extremely large magnetic fields certain paramagnetic substances show an analogous dependence of permeability upon field strength.

439. *Hysteresis Loops with Mechanical Bias.* If while in an alternating electric field the crystal is also kept under a constant mechanical stress of such a nature as to produce a fixed piezoelectric polarization on which the polarization due to the field is superposed, the hysteresis loops are distorted and unsymmetrical. Such curves, first mentioned by Valasek, have been recorded by Sawyer and Tower,[449] David,[119] Mueller,[376] and others. Ballistic observations of the effects of mechanical or electrical bias have been made by Anderson (§404), Valasek,[542] and Schwartz.[454]

Some of the results are shown in Figs. 129 and 130. The interpretation of the oscillograms is further discussed in §441. Sawyer and Tower cemented their crystal plate between two thick aluminum plates; the others applied mechanical pressures at 45° to the Y- and Z-axes by means of flat blocks of solid material.* We shall use the term "single constraint" for equal and opposite pressures along one of the two 45° directions, and "double constraint" for two pairs of pressures, one pair along each of the 45° directions. Under the single constraint a piezoelectric polarization becomes superposed upon that due to the electric field, thus shifting the position of the origin on the hysteresis loop. Unless the mechanical arrangement is such as to keep the stress actually constant throughout the cycle, the oscillograms are of more qualitative than quantitative value. Under double constraint, if the pairs of pressures are always equal they produce equal and opposite contributions to the polarization. The bias is thus reduced to zero. This restores the symmetry, but the polarization recorded on the oscillograms is diminished, since the crystal is no longer free.

---

* As is shown in §139, a pressure Π at 45° causes a shearing stress $Y_z = \Pi/2$. The resulting polarization is $P = -d_{14}Y_z = d_{14}\Pi/2$, subject to correction for capacitance connected to the crystal. All the investigators named used rectangular (in most if not all cases square) X-cut plates with edges at 45° to the Y- and Z-axes.

The following conclusions may be drawn from Figs. 129 and 130. Any constraint, whether single or double, flattens the hysteresis loop, until under heavy pressure the polarization is so suppressed that the

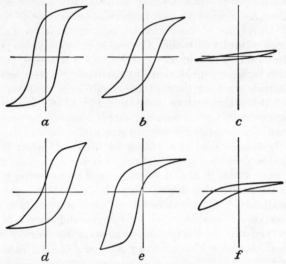

FIG. 129.—Effect of mechanical constraint on the hysteresis curves for Rochelle salt at 500 cycles, 0°C, from Mueller.   Maximum field strength 2,000 volts/cm.   Curve a, free crystal; b, double constraint, pressure 1 kg/cm²; c, double constraint, 7 kg/cm²; d, single constraint, 2 kg/cm²; e, single constraint, 3 kg/cm², applied in a direction 90° from that in d; f, single constraint, 7 kg/cm² in same direction as in e.

loop approaches a straight line having approximately the slope of the "saturation" portion of the unconstrained curve.   The effective permittivity then becomes the same as the differential permittivity at saturation, which in §436 was seen to be of the order of 200.   The fact that 200 is also the order of magnitude of the (monoclinically) clamped

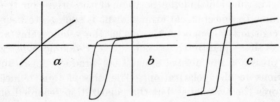

FIG. 130.—Effect of single constraint on Rochelle-salt hysteresis curves at pressure 8.35 kg/cm², from David.   Maximum volts per cm: a, 383; b, 768; c, 1532.   Frequency 50 cycles.

dielectric constant, as may be seen from the curve for χ_s'' in Fig. 145 at 20°C, is evidence that David's constraint was sufficient to cause the crystal to be very effectively clamped.

Sawyer and Tower[449] also obtained oscillograms with a constrained plate, finding a dielectric constant of 430 at 15°. This value agrees fairly well with that which they found for the unconstrained plate at saturation, but it is so much greater than the value for a clamped crystal derived from Fig. 145 as to indicate that the constraint was far from complete.

The characteristic effect of a *single* constraint is the *asymmetry* that it introduces in the hysteresis loop, and is especially conspicuous in Fig. 130b and c. Furthermore, Fig. 130a shows that the range of field strengths over which the initial permittivity is practically constant is greatly extended by a single constraint: the maximum field strength for this curve is 383 volts/cm, whereas in §436 the value for a free crystal was only 50. On the other hand, David finds that the initial permittivity is diminished by a single constraint and that the diminution is made greater by repeated mechanical loading.

If the mechanical bias used in conjunction with a-c experiments is to be constant throughout the cycle, the natural frequency of the mechanical pressure system must be higher than that of the crystal. Or if the pressure is simply due to the gravitational weight of a certain mass, the maximum acceleration of the face of the crystal plate must be less than 980 cm/sec[2].

A little consideration shows that, if the mechanical pressure varies cyclically, the effective bias at one end of the hysteresis loop will be greater than at the other. The loop is thus still further deformed. Furthermore, a variable pressure causes variable piezoelectric charges to be liberated, which produce a disturbing periodic field unless the resistances in the bridge arms are sufficiently low.

Friction between the pressure blocks and the crystal must tend to suppress the slight periodic changes in dimensions and thus to reduce the polarization. This fact may possibly account for the observed reduction in polarization under double constraint.

David also made oscillograms with the plate under a *hydrostatic* pressure (in oil) of 35 kg/cm[2]. The curves were exactly the same as when the crystal was free. This result was to be expected, except insofar as the hydrostatic pressure brought the crystal to a slightly different position relative to the two Curie points (§443).

440. *Experiments on the equivalence of mechanical and electrical bias* have been made by David. He found that when, instead of mechanical pressure, a d-c source was connected across the crystal while it was in the oscillograph circuit the same asymmetrical curves were obtained. The asymmetry of mechanical origin could be completely removed by application of a field E_b opposing the piezoelectric polarization. Some idea of the number of volts per centimeter equivalent to 1 kg/cm[2] can be gained from the asymmetry of the curves in Fig. 129 and 130; it appears to range from about 70 to 300. A value of the same order of magnitude as this is derived from the equation $E_b = -Y_z/b_{14}$ in §462, where b_{14} is the piezoelectric strain coefficient according to the polarization theory. In each case the equivalent bias is derived from the estimated horizontal displacement of the origin from the center of the loop. The *sum* of the piezoelectric and purely electric polarizations never exceeds the usual saturation value.

In this connection may be mentioned an experiment of Mueller's,[376] who made measurements, with a low-voltage a-c 1,000-cycle bridge, of the capacitance of a crystal on which there was superposed at the same time a much greater direct potential difference E of various positive and negative values up to ± 800 volts/cm. This potential was put through a step-by-step cycle of increasing and decreasing values in both directions. The bridge measurements gave values of the reversible permittivity $k_r = 1 + 4\pi \delta P/\delta E$ (§430). When plotted in the form of a curve (Mueller's Fig. 22), they gave evidence of hysteresis in the $P:E$ relation. This result is in agreement with that of Valasek, obtained with a ballistic galvanometer, mentioned in §431.

441. *Explanation of the Biased Hysteresis Loops.* It has been stated that the effect of bias, whether electrical or mechanical, is to shift the origin. This is represented in Fig. 131, in which the normal unbiased loop has the total sweep AB in field strength. If a large biasing polarization of value E_1O_1 is imposed on the crystal, the origin for the new curve is at O_1, this being the point on the virgin curve corresponding to the given bias. The bias then has the abscissa OE_1. The same sweep in field strength as before is now represented by A_1B_1, and the resulting loop extends from M_1 to N_1. If the sweep in field strength were a little less, from A'_1 to B'_1, the loop would extend from M'_1 to N'_1. The point O_2 represents the origin for a small amount of bias, and the loop for a small horizontal sweep is then somewhat as indicated by M_2N_2.

The location of the origin with respect to the hysteresis loops is not the same in Figs. 129 and 130 as in the schematic drawing of Fig. 131. The reason for this lies in the fact that in oscillograph circuits of the type shown in Fig. 122 the bias, whether electrical or mechanical, does not cause a biasing static charge on the condenser C. In Fig. 122 the resistance across C, high though it is, prevents this. Hence, taken around the cycle, $\int V_c \, dt = 0$. This result is independent of the time scale of abscissas, which is usually sinusoidal. If the hysteresis loop were redrawn to a *linear* time scale having abscissas proportional to the time, it would be found that *equal areas* would be described on each side of the horizontal axis. With a sinusoidal time scale this is still approximately true, as can be verified from the curves. In Fig. 131

the distorted loops have the locations where they would be recorded if
the biasing polarization were accompanied by a corresponding fixed
charge on the condenser C of Fig. 122.   Distorted hysteresis loops such
as these have their analogy in magnetism, when a ferromagnetic substance is subjected to the combined action of a fixed and an alternating
magnetic field.

By a suitable choice of bias and of horizontal sweep, all the single-
contraint curves in Figs. 129 and 130 can be qualitatively reproduced
on Fig. 131.   The equivalence of biases produced electrically and

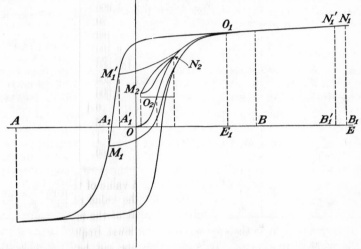

Fig. 131.—Hysteresis loops with various amounts of bias.   Coordinates are field strength E
and polarization P.

mechanically is thus made evident.   The relation between electrically
and mechanically produced polarizations is discussed in Chap. XXIV on
the polarization theory, especially in §§459 and 462.

442. The Dielectric Constant of Rochelle Salt at High Frequencies.
If observations could be made with specimens so small as not to resonate
mechanically at any frequency within the range of investigation, the
dielectric constant measured would be that of the free crystal.   This
procedure is not practicable; in all the h-f observations mentioned below,
resonance conditions were encountered.

We saw in §258 that the measured dielectric constant is always
abnormally high on the l-f side of resonance (just as in optical anomalous
dispersion) and abnormally low on the h-f side.   The expression for the
complex dielectric constant in terms of the mechanical and electrical
characteristics of the crystal is derived in §258.   At the highest fre-

quencies the configuration of the crystal is that described in §450 as "rhombic clamping" outside the Curie points and as "monoclinic clamping" between these points. The concept of rhombic clamping between the Curie points is of only theoretical significance.

Data on values of the dielectric constant k_x are assembled in Table XXXIV. For comparison, some of the l-f values recorded by the same investigators are included, although in most cases they do not appear to be typical of Rochelle salt at low frequency.

TABLE XXXIV

Author	Ref.	Temp., deg C	Maximum field strength, volt cm^{-1}	Frequency, kc sec^{-1}	k_x	Electrodes
Frayne...........	149	Room	3	8	140	Tinfoil
				40,000	100	Tinfoil
Errera...........	134	Room	113	0.68	390	Solution
				1,000	100	Solution
Busch...........	87	0	50	20	225	Mercury
				160	120	Mercury
Bantle and Busch	24	0	?	6,100	100	Tinfoil(?)
				750,000	100	Tinfoil
Evans...........	140	16–17	45	300	114	Mercury
				2,000	114	Mercury
Hablützel........	198	0	8.5	0.1	200	Vaporized
				10	200	gold
Mason...........	338	20	< 5	1	460	"Plated"
				160	140	"Plated"

Most noteworthy is the approach of k_x to a value of the order of 100 at the highest frequencies. It is here that the value of the dielectric constant of the "free" crystal approaches that of the crystal clamped, which we denote by k_x'' (see p. 556). At the lower frequencies the discrepancies in k_x as between different observers can be attributed to differences in frequency, mechanical constraint, and field strength, and also perhaps to the effect of surface layers.

Supplementing the data in Table XXXIV it may be said that Frayne, whose observations had to do only with the *initial* permittivity k_0, found maxima for this quantity at both Curie points at all frequencies; he found also that, below $-80°C$, k_0 was approximately 12 at all frequencies (*cf*. Fig. 121). Errera found a fairly uniform diminution in k_x with increasing frequency, except of course in the various resonance regions. From 1.6 to 20 kc/sec he observed that k_x was increased by about 100 per cent as the field strength increased from 56 to 226 maximum volts/cm. This fact indicates that at these frequencies the steep portion of the polarization curve comes at higher field strengths than it does at lower frequencies.

Busch's observations were made at several different temperatures from 6 to 36°C. His data point to a permittivity in the neighborhood of 100 at the highest frequencies, but at the lower frequencies the values range from about 110 at 36° to 450 at 23°. Bantle and Busch found a maximum in k_x at 23° even at the highest frequencies.

The value from Mason at 1 kc/sec is from Fig. 119. Hablützel's value is from his paper on heavy-water Rochelle salt (which contains much valuable information on ordinary Rochelle salt as well), discussed in §444.

Zeleny and Valasek[600] have also made observations of permittivity at frequencies from 30 to 10^7 cycles/sec at 0°C. They found a general downward drift from 62,000 to 220 as the frequency increased, but otherwise it is difficult to fit their observations into the picture presented above, since their large values of k_x are not reconcilable with the low field strength of only 8.75 volts/cm and, moreover, they report *negative* values of k_x at 10^7 cycles/sec, a frequency far too high for reactions from mechanical resonance. As suggested by Bantle and Busch, this observation may have been due to the self-inductance of the leads to the crystal.

443. Effect of Hydrostatic Pressure on the Susceptibility of Rochelle Salt. The measurements at hand are those of Eremeev, quoted by Kurchatov,[B32] and of Bancroft.[20] Eremeev's results are in the form of polarization curves obtained with 50-cycle alternating current for field strengths extending to 1,800 volts/cm. At 15°C, for any given field strength, the polarization and hence the susceptibility increase with increasing hydrostatic pressures up to 5,000 kg/cm²; at still higher pressures they decrease, and the flattening of the curves at high field strengths gradually disappears, until at 8,000 kg/cm the polarization is proportional to the field. Since a linear polarization curve is characteristic of the region outside the Curie points, it is apparent that high pressure shifts these points so that at 15° the crystal is no longer in the Seignette-electric region. Similar tests at 31°C showed that, while P is proportional to E up to 2,000 kg/cm², it begins to take on saturation characteristics at higher pressures; at 3,000 kg/cm² the curve at 31° is exactly like that at atmospheric pressure and 22.5°. Thus a pressure of 3,000 kg/cm² raises the upper Curie point by about 9°. Kurchatov interprets this result as evidence that the Curie point, on the absolute temperature scale, is proportional to the concentration of the dipoles; for from the elastic constants of Rochelle salt the increase in density for 3,000 kg/cm² amounts to 3 per cent, and this fraction of the absolute temperature is 9°.

By Bancroft's method a precise determination of the shift of both Curie points is made possible. He used 1,000-cycle alternating current with 2 rms volts applied to the crystals (field strength about 8 volts/cm). **Three**

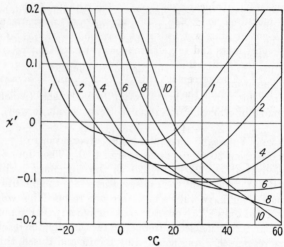

FIG. 132.—Dependence of the reciprocal initial susceptibility of a free crystal of Rochelle salt in the X-direction upon temperature and hydrostatic pressure, from Bancroft's data. Positive values of χ' correspond to the region outside the Curie points, where the susceptibility of the free crystal is $\eta' = 1/\chi'$. Between the Curie points χ' is negative, and the observed susceptibility of the free crystal, by Eq. (499), is $\eta_s' = 1/\chi_s' = -1/(2\chi')$. Curve 1 is for atmospheric pressure. The numbers beside the other curves denote the number of thousands of kilograms per square centimeter.

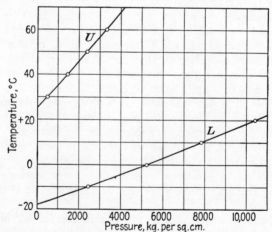

FIG. 133.—Dependence of the upper and lower Curie temperatures on hydrostatic pressure, from Bancroft. U = upper, L = lower Curie point.

crystals were used, of thicknesses 0.424, 0.356, and 0.313 cm.   Temperatures were measured to $\pm 0.1°C$, and pressures were accurate to ± 10
kg/cm^2.   X-cut crystals were suspended in such a way as to eliminate
mechanical constraints and to yield reliable values of the initial susceptibility η' and η'_s the X-direction.   The results are shown in Fig. 132, taken
from Mueller.[381]   The agreement with Mueller's values[376] is better than 5
per cent.   Bancroft found the following approximate relations between the
Curie temperatures and pressure (p in kg/cm^2):

$$\theta_u = 24.5° + 1.073p(10^{-2})$$
$$\theta_l = -19.4° + 3.769p(10^{-3})$$

Under increasing pressure both Curie points are raised and the interval
between them becomes greater, as is seen in Fig. 133.   According to this
diagram there should be found at about 12,000 kg/cm^2 a *lower* Curie
point at the same temperature as that of the upper Curie point at atmospheric pressure.   Under suitable pressure there can be a Curie point
at any temperature above $-18°C$.

Although Bancroft's paper does not record the observed values of
susceptibility at the Curie points, it is evident from his Fig. 2 that they
were finite, though very large, and that the higher the Curie-point
temperature, the greater the measured susceptibility.

Since Kurchatov's data do not indicate with sufficient precision the
susceptibility at small field strengths, direct comparison of his results
with Bancroft's is impossible.   So far as one can judge from Kurchatov's
results at high field strength, the agreement with Bancroft is satisfactory.

For details of Bancroft's theoretical treatment of his results the
original paper must be consulted.   He correlates his results with an
equation of Fowler's[142] for the dependence of susceptibility on temperature and arrives at the conclusion that the increase in the Curie
temperatures under pressure is a volume effect, due to distortion of the
crystal lattice under pressure.   For further discussion of these results
see §470.

444. Heavy-water Rochelle Salt.   The investigation of the effects
of substituting deuterium for hydrogen in Rochelle salt is important
from its bearing on the part played by hydrogen atoms in the dielectric
phenomena.   Hablützel[198] was the first to publish results, followed a
few months later by Holden and Mason[231].   In both cases the crystals
were prepared by dissolving in highly concentrated D$_2$O ordinary
Rochelle salt that had been thoroughly desiccated at a high temperature
(Hablützel, 40°C; Holden and Mason, 100°C).   From this solution the
crystals were grown.   According to Hablützel, not only does the water of
crystallization in these crystals consist of D$_2$O, but the hydrogen atoms
in the OH groups (§405) are replaced by deuterium, so that the formula

becomes $NaKC_4H_2D_2O_6 \cdot 4D_2O$. The density, according to Holden and Mason, is 1.830 ± 0.003. Gold films were evaporated onto the crystals in vacuum in all these experiments, except that at high frequency Hablützel found it necessary to use mercury electrodes, owing to minute sparks between the gold films and the wires with which they made light contact. Hablützel found that the loss of water of crystallization was negligible when the crystals were in vacuum for the short time necessary for the deposition of gold.

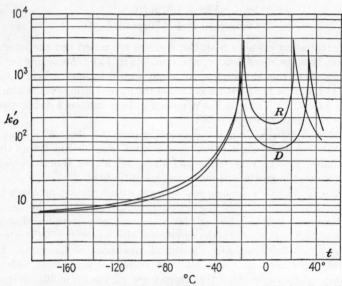

Fig. 134.—Dielectric constant of Rochelle salt (curve R) and deuterium-Rochelle salt (curve D), as functions of temperature, from Hablützel. Below 40°C, $E = 50$ volts/cm, $f = 1,000$ cycles. Above 40°C, $E = 4$ volts/cm, $f = 900$ cycles.

Dielectric Constant. In both papers a bridge method is described, with relatively low frequencies, and with a voltage so low that the measured constant is the initial permittivity k_0. For observations at higher voltages, Hablützel used a cathode-ray oscillograph.

In Fig. 134 are shown Hablützel's values of the initial dielectric constant k_0 for fields parallel to X, for both ordinary and heavy-water Rochelle salt. The values for ordinary Rochelle salt run somewhat lower than those that we have adopted for Fig. 147; those for deuterium–Rochelle salt are in satisfactory agreement with Fig. 5 in Holden and Mason's paper.

Hablützel finds the Curie points for the deuterium salt to lie at $-22°C$ ($251°K$) and $+35°C$ ($308°K$); Holden and Mason find $-23°$ and

+35°. Hablützel's values of k_0 at the Curie points are approximately 4,000 at each point for ordinary Rochelle salt; approximately 2,300 and 1,550 at the upper and lower temperatures, respectively, for the deuterium salt.

From his results Hablützel calculated the reciprocal susceptibility χ', which is shown as a function of temperature outside the Curie points in Fig. 135. The curve for ordinary Rochelle salt agrees completely with Mueller's findings (Figs. 120 and 121). That for the deuterium salt is similar, being nearly linear close to the Curie points, in accordance with the Curie-Weiss law.

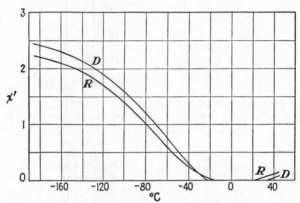

Fig. 135.—Dependence of reciprocal susceptibility upon temperature, illustrating the Curie-Weiss laws outside the Curie points, from Hablützel. R = Rochelle salt, D = deuterium-Rochelle salt.

With fields of 8.5 volts/cm parallel to X, the dielectric constant k_0 of both ordinary and deuterium–Rochelle salt was found by Hablützel at 0°C to be practically the same for frequencies from 100 to 10,000 cycles/sec. The values are approximately 200 for ordinary Rochelle salt (Table XXXIV) and 65 for the deuterium salt.

Hysteresis and Saturation. Hablützel's paper contains two series of very instructive oscillograms. The first series was recorded with 2,000 volts/cm maximum, 50 cycles, at various temperatures from −19.5° to +37.5°C, for both kinds of Rochelle salt. Those for ordinary Rochelle salt are in general agreement with the oscillograms pictured in this chapter; they differ from the latter chiefly in that the steep slopes of the hysteresis loops are more nearly vertical, thus approximating more closely to the ideal loop in Fig. 167. The absence of hysteresis at temperatures outside the Curie points is clearly shown.

For the deuterium salt the loops are both higher and broader than for the ordinary crystal, indicating considerably greater hysteresis loss, greater coercive force, and a higher spontaneous polarization. The remanent polarization, which, as we saw in §438, is a measure of the spontaneous P^0, is shown in Fig. 136, while Fig. 137 indicates the coercive field strength, plotted in terms of temperature. From Fig. 136 we find, for ordinary Rochelle salt, maximum $P_0 \approx 735$ esu/cm² at about

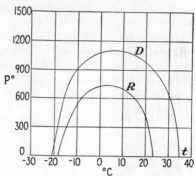

FIG. 136.—Remanent polarization P^0 as a function of temperature, from Hablützel. R = Rochelle salt, D = deuterium-Rochelle salt.   Ordinates are in esu.

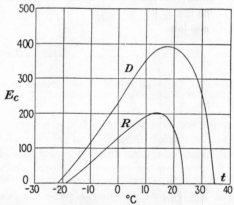

FIG. 137.—Dependence of coercive field strength on temperature, from Hablützel. R = Rochelle salt, D = deuterium-Rochelle salt.   Ordinates are in volts/cm.

3°C, in good agreement with Mueller's value of 740 in Fig. 146. The deuterium salt has $P^0 \approx 1,110$ esu/cm² at about 6°C.

According to Fig. 137, the coercive field strength for ordinary Rochelle salt has a maximum value of 200 at about 15°C (cf. §436). Hablützel finds, contrary to Mueller, that the coercive field strength does not depend on the thickness of the plate. Mueller's coercive field values, shown in Fig. 147, are about twice as large as Hablützel's (see §479).

Hablützel's second series of oscillograms, made at room temperature with 3,000 maximum volts/cm, show the effect of increasing frequency on the form of the hysteresis loops. From 100 to 1,000 cycles/sec there is not much change. From there on, the loops become broader, the maximum slope is less, higher voltages are required for saturation, until at 100,000 cycles/sec the maximum field strength is insufficient for saturation and the curves show pronounced asymmetry. Hysteresis is present at all frequencies.

Fields Parallel to Y and Z. Hablützel's values are given in §408. Holden and Mason assign the value 18.0 to k_y at 30°C, which is so large that its correctness is doubtful. For k_z they find the value 10.4. The piezoelectric constants are given in §143.

CHAPTER XXIII

THEORY OF ROCHELLE SALT, PART I. INTERACTION THEORY AND DIELECTRIC PROPERTIES

All experimental results are compatible with the hypothesis that the clamped crystal has only one transition point at about 5°C, where its dielectric constant has a very high maximum. The two Curie points of the free crystal are due to the interaction between the elastic deformation and the electric polarization. —H. MUELLER.

After a brief account of the historical development there will follow, in this chapter and the next, a formulation of the "interaction theory," based chiefly on the researches of H. Mueller. The formulation is as free as possible from molecular assumptions and general enough to apply to all crystals exhibiting the ferromagnetic analogy; thus it is well suited to serve as a basis for discussion of the more specialized theories of the various ferroelectrics, of which Rochelle salt is the original and so far the most important member.

It is historically interesting to recall that the first attempt at a quantitative theory of ferromagnetism employed a method that had been developed for the study of *electric* dipoles. That theory, grown to maturity, has now returned to the field of dielectrics.

The ferromagnetic analogy in Rochelle salt seems to have been first discussed in a paper by Valasek.[542]

The foundation for the theory of Rochelle salt was laid by I. Kurchatov. From observations of the dielectric constant of this crystal, made by himself and his collaborators, he was led to formulate a theory, based on the earlier work of Langevin, Debye, and Weiss, in which Rochelle salt was treated as possessing dielectric properties analogous to the magnetic properties of ferromagnetic substances. A brief account of his theory, as well as of the somewhat parallel work of Fowler, can most appropriately be given in this chapter, even though their theoretical investigations were of a molecular nature.

445. *Kurchatov's Theory.* In an important paper by Kobeko and Kurchatov in 1930[263] appeared the first formulation of Rochelle-salt theory in mathematical terms similar to those employed in the Langevin-Weiss theory of ferromagnetism. From the dependence of the dielectric constant upon temperature, these authors concluded that Rochelle salt must contain rotatable dipoles, each having a moment that they computed to be of the order of 10^{-18} esu and a molecular field of the order of 10^7 volts/cm.

This molecular theory was elaborated by Kurchatov and his associates in later papers and is now available in Kurchatov's book. Reference to their experimental work is made in other chapters. The theory, as set forth in Chap. XXVI, is based on Debye's theory of electric dipoles, an essential feature of which is Langevin's treatment of the effect of thermal agitation [Eq. (556)], originally derived for paramagnetism and adapted by Debye to the analogous electrical problem. It is assumed, as in the case of paramagnetism, that the dipoles are free to rotate in all directions, like those of a gas. The dipolar property is supposed to reside in the H_2O molecules, a hypothesis that was first suggested by Valasek. Kurchatov shows that the electric interaction between dipoles causes an internal field of sufficient magnitude to account for spontaneous polarization below a critical temperature, without the need of invoking anything corresponding to the exchange forces. as was the case with ferromagnetism.

The Kurchatov theory predicts a critical temperature (the upper Curie point) at which the dielectric susceptibility η_{11} parallel to the X-axis has an infinite value and below which the crystal is in a state of spontaneous polarization. In order to account for the lower Curie point it postulates a "reciprocal action" between dipoles which leads to the formation of mutually neutralizing chains, so that the number of dipoles effective in producing a spontaneous polarization decreases with decreasing temperature. The fact that most dipolar crystals fail to exhibit Seignette properties is explained on the supposition that in them the reciprocal action is so strong as to prevent orientation by an external field.

It is noteworthy that this theory postulates separately polarized domains analogous to those in iron, but erroneously supposed to be, just as in iron, of submicroscopic size. Those peculiarities which have come to be recognized as due to a *large-scale* domain structure were attributed by Kurchatov to imperfections in the crystal. To Rochelle salt and those crystals isomorphic with it that possess similar electric properties, Kurchatov applied the term "Seignette-electrics."

446. *Fowler's Theory.* The route followed by R. H. Fowler[B18,142] in arriving at an expression for the dielectric constant as a function of temperature was that of "cooperative states," a concept similar to the "cooperative phenomena" introduced by Zwicky and which, though without precise formulation, enters into Kurchatov's theory of Rochelle salt. According to Fowler's theory there exist, for each dipole of a Rochelle-salt crystal, certain preferred positions, owing to the effect of neighboring dipoles. The energy of each dipole is a function of the amount of rotation present. The dipoles are subject to a restraining field that becomes more effective as the temperature decreases. This is closely similar to Kurchatov's hypothesis of a decrease in the effective number of dipoles.

The dipoles are assumed to be the molecules of the water of crystallization. Above the upper Curie point there is complete disorder and no spontaneous internal field. Between the Curie points a certain portion of the dipoles form groups or filaments, their polarities oriented in either the positive or the negative direction of the X-axis. This is the cooperative state, giving rise to a field that prevails throughout an entire domain. Whichever orientation prevails determines the spontaneous polarization, the value of which depends on the temperature. Below the lower Curie point the dipoles become "frozen" in small local groups with external fields so weak that spontaneous polarization disappears. Cooperation is here replaced by association.

The internal field constant γ is assumed by Fowler to have different values parallel and perpendicular to the X-axis of the crystal. In the region of spontaneous polarization the energy of interaction between dipoles is found (in agreement with Kurchatov) to be of the right magnitude to account for the large internal field. An expression is derived for the dielectric constant, which, on substitution of suitable trial values for certain parameters that cannot be quantitatively determined from theory, gives a dependence on temperature over a range extending beyond both Curie points that agrees at least qualitatively with experiment. It predicts, in agreement with Kurchatov's theory, infinite permittivity at the two Curie points. Fowler considers the rotation of dipoles in Rochelle salt as a special case of the large group of recently discovered oscillation-rotation transitions in various solids, for example in halogen hydrides and ammonium salts.

The theories of Kurchatov and of Fowler, interpreting the state of spontaneous polarization as one stage in the progressive transition from complete disorder at high temperatures toward complete order as the temperature is diminished, may still play an important part in the theory of the Seignette-electrics. Their greatest defect is the failure to take account of the deformation of the lattice in an electric field; i.e., they ignore the effect of the piezoelectric property on the dielectric constant, which was pointed out by Cady,[100] and later developed very fully by Mueller in a series of papers that will presently be discussed.*

447. Mueller's Theory. The chief observational materials out of which a theory of Rochelle salt is to be built are the following:

1. Normal dielectric and piezoelectric properties for fields perpendicular to the X-axis, at all temperatures.

---

* Critical comparisons of the various theories of Rochelle salt are found in Mueller's papers.[376,378,382]

The following phenomena are confined to fields and polarizations in the X-direction:

2. With fields of certain strengths parallel to the X-axis, the dielective constant k'_x, the piezoelectric constant d_{14}, and the isagric elastic compliance s^E_{44} all rise to very large values over a certain range of temperature. Their behavior is normal outside of this range.

3. Within this temperature range the dielectric polarization, as well as the direct and converse piezoelectric effects, shows saturation and hysteresis.

4. There is a time lag in the response to electric or mechanical stress, together with certain effects dependent on the previous history of the crystal.

5. The existence of a spontaneous polarization P^0 parallel to X, accompanied by a spontaneous strain y^0_z, between two well-defined temperatures, the lower and upper Curie points, θ_l and θ_u. Maxima in P^0 and y^0_z are found at about 5°C.

6. Between the Curie points the strain x_x is proportional to the square of the polarization P_x.

7. Linear relations exist outside the Curie points and over small ranges between these points, between temperature and the dielectric, piezoelectric, and elastic constants (the Curie-Weiss laws).

8. With small fields and stresses, k'_x, d_{14}, and s^E_{44} tend toward infinite values at the Curie points, with minima at about 5°C. The ratio d_{14}/k'_x is nearly constant.

9. The compliance coefficient s^D_{44} of an isolated crystal (§199) is very nearly independent of temperature.

10. Between the Curie points anomalous optical effects are observed.

11. Rochelle salt consists normally of domains some millimeters in extent, characterized by opposite spontaneous polarizations (always along the X-axis) in adjacent domains.

Most of the properties of Rochelle salt—as in the analogous case of iron—are characteristic of the single domain, although some require the assumption of adjacent domains of opposing polarities for their explanation.

Many details of considerable importance have been omitted in the list above. Among other phenomena to be considered in the theoretical treatment are the properties of clamped crystals, the possible change in specific heat at the Curie points, the effect of hydrostatic pressure on the Curie points, and the modification of Rochelle salt by isomorphic mixtures and by heavy water.

The earlier theories of the anomalous electric behavior of Rochelle salt proceeded from the ferromagnetic analogy and attributed the anomalies to the rotation of free dipoles. From this concept grew the first theory of Mueller,[376] which related the dielectric and piezoelectric effects to the strong internal field accompanying the dipoles, although the dipole moments and rotations were not explicitly introduced. In this form the theory was in excellent agreement with observations outside the Curie points but was not adapted to a quantitative description of effects between these points.

As Mueller pointed out in his second paper,[378] there is no conclusive evidence of the existence of freely rotating dipoles in Rochelle salt. As will be seen in Chap. XXXI, the X-ray analysis of Beevers and Hughes suggests the presence of strain-sensitive bonds that may have dipole moments in terms of which the anomalies of Rochelle salt can be explained. We return to a consideration of dipoles in Chap. XXVI.

448. In his later papers Mueller disregarded the internal field, finding that a satisfactory description of essential phenomena over the entire temperature range could be derived from the following hypotheses:

1. Piezoelectric stresses are proportional to the *polarization* rather than to the field.

2. The electric field strength E is not linear in the polarization P. As a first-order approximation to the non-linearity he introduces a term in P^3.

3. For the anomalous behavior of Rochelle salt the dielectric properties of the unstrained (clamped) crystal are held chiefly responsible. In terms of these properties alone, without invoking any abnormalities in the "true" piezoelectric and elastic coefficients, the peculiar dielectric, elastic, and piezoelectric behavior of the free crystal, including the existence of two Curie points and the spontaneous polarization between these points, finds an explanation. The most fundamentally important critical temperature is that in the neighborhood of 5°C, at which temperature maxima or minima occur in the spontaneous polarization, spontaneous deformation, clamped and free susceptibilities, piezoelectric constant d_{14}, and elastic compliance s_{44}^E; the optical properties also undergo a change at this temperature.

This "interaction" theory of Mueller's is more strictly phenomenological than his earlier one. Although he suggests possible theoretical explanations,[380] his equations are empirical, based on his own observations and those of others. The effects of temperature are expressed in terms of experimentally verified linear relations between the various physical constants and temperature, relations that in the last analysis can be traced to the dependence of the clamped dielectric susceptibility upon temperature. This dependence is of the same form as the Curie-Weiss law in magnetism and strongly suggests an analogous origin.

The germs of the interaction theory, already present in Mueller's first paper (1935), were gradually developed in his papers II, III, and IV (1940) and extended so as to include a quantitative treatment of phenomena between the Curie points.

449. We now undertake a unified presentation of the interaction theory, assembling first the fundamental equations.

Mueller's treatment is expressed in terms of the *polarization theory* of piezoelectricity, which has already been developed in Chap. XI. The present treatment involves the further assumption that the observed relation between polarization P and field strength E requires the addition to the energy functions ξ and ζ of a term in P^4, which contains a new saturation coefficient B. There is, moreover, the assumption of a *quadratic piezoelectric effect* between the Curie points, originating in the monoclinic character of Rochelle salt in this region. Since this effect is dependent on the spontaneous strain, it is not conveniently expressed in the energy equations but will be considered in §464.

The Curie points are defined as the temperatures between which there are a spontaneous polarization P^0 and a spontaneous strain y_z^0. This interval is the *ferroelectric* region, in which the free crystal takes on monoclinic properties.

The theoretical development that is to follow will perhaps be better understood if at this point we indicate the manner in which the experimental data are used to test the theory. In all cases the electric fields and polarizations are parallel to the X-axis, and the observations extend over a wide range of temperatures. First, and most essential, are the observations of the initial susceptibility η_0' of the free crystal and the dependence of susceptibility on field strength, from which the saturation constant B is derived. Beyond this are observations of P^0 (from hysteresis loops and also from pyroelectric measurements), of y_z^0, and of the compliances s_{44}^E and s_{44}^P from resonating bars. From these data are derived the piezoelectric constants d_{14}, e_{14}, a_{14}, and b_{14}, as well as a theoretical expression for the saturation coefficient B. In particular, the clamped dielectric stiffness χ_1 is derived from η', a_{14}, and b_{14}; thereby Mueller's assertion that χ_1 sinks to a very low minimum in the neighborhood of 5°C can be tested.

In his theory, Mueller reverses the experimental sequence indicated above, gives a theoretical reason for the extraordinary variation of the clamped dielectric constant with temperature, and shows that the spontaneous polarization and all other anomalies are a necessary consequence of this variation. That is, the clamped dielectric constant, deprived of all piezoelectric characteristics, turns out to be the culprit responsible for the abnormal behavior of ferroelectric crystals.

450. *Definitions.* Before entering upon the theory, it is necessary to supplement by the following special definitions the explanation given in §193 of the symbols in Eqs. (240) to (245), p. 252. We consider first the dielectric stiffness coefficients χ'' and χ'. With normal piezoelectric crystals these are independent of strain and of stress, respectively, and also independent of the field strength E. In Rochelle salt, χ'' is a function of the strain, χ' a function of the stress, and both depend on temperature (their dependence on field is taken care of by the terms in B). The treatment is simplified by defining $\eta'' = 1/\chi''$ as the susceptibility of a clamped crystal at *zero strain* instead of merely at constant strain; we shall use the special symbols $\eta_1 = 1/\chi_1$ for the initial susceptibility at zero rhombic strain (see the discussion of rhombic clamping below). For a free crystal (zero stress) outside the Curie points, $\eta' = 1/\chi'$ is the initial susceptibility; in the ferroelectric region, as indicated below, we write $\eta'_s = 1/\chi'_s$. In the energy equations (243) and (243a) the dielectric terms therefore represent the electrical energy at zero strain and zero stress, respectively. The effects of strain and stress on the energy are to be regarded as contained in the piezoelectric terms.

As to the strains, unless it is otherwise stated, we shall let y_z signify the strain as for a rhombic crystal, at all temperatures. The reason for mentioning only y_z is that the theory is concerned only with fields E_x parallel to X, and for this direction the only piezoelectric constant for Rochelle salt outside the Curie points is d_{14}, so that y_z is the only strain associated with E_x. It is true that in the monoclinic phase there are three more piezoelectric constants associated with E_x; but they are relatively small, and their possible effect on the behavior of the crystal is postponed to §464. Between the Curie points, where the crystal is properly regarded as monoclinic, y_z would normally be the strain with respect to the monoclinic configuration, which is not the same as the rhombic configuration, owing to the presence of the spontaneous strain y_z^0. When the crystal is so clamped that the rhombic strain is zero, *i.e.*, so that the crystallographic b- and c-faces are at right angles, we shall use the term *rhombic clamping*. At temperatures outside the Curie points this means that the crystal is clamped while in its unstressed state. Between the Curie points, where the b- and c-faces in the absence of stress are at an angle differing from 90° by y_z^0, rhombic clamping implies a stress system such that, starting with the crystal free at the given temperature, these faces are constrained to be at 90°.

On the other hand, it is sometimes desirable to conceive of the crystal as clamped, at a given temperature between the Curie points, while in the monoclinic state, with the spontaneous strain present and not neutralized by the clamping stress. This type of clamping will be called *monoclinic clamping;* the corresponding susceptibility will be denoted by $\eta_s'' = 1/\chi_s''$ (§456).

In general the clamping, whether rhombic or monoclinic, is to be regarded as *complete*, in the sense that the infinitely rigid clamping device is so attached to the crystal as to prohibit all components of strain when an electric field is applied.*

In conformity with the foregoing statements we shall follow Mueller and write the basic equations as if Rochelle salt were rhombic at all temperatures. *Between the Curie points* this assumption involves letting P, in some of the terms, include the spontaneous polarization P^0; y_z then signifies the strain measured from the state of rhombic clamping, *i.e.*, with the b- and c-faces mutually perpendicular; for χ'' we use χ_1 as defined above, and χ', as will be seen, assumes the special value χ_s', where the *subscript means the value between the Curie points* (the ferroelectric region).† This procedure is the more permissible because the monoclinic piezoelectric coefficients that are not present in the rhombic state of the crystal are very small. We shall refer to this method of describing the phenomena in Rochelle salt as the *rhombic method*. As will be seen, it offers the advantage of presenting a unified treatment, valid at all temperatures. Its chief usefulness will be in the development of Mueller's theory in the present chapter. When it is applied to the treatment of practical problems at temperatures between the Curie points, there is a certain awkwardness in having to regard the strain as zero only when the crystal is under stress, and *vice versa*. As long as the field is small, so that all relations are linear, such problems are better dealt with by the *normal method*, which is described in §458.

The concept of rhombic clamping employed in the present chapter defines a sort of dielectric ground state for the crystal, which, though not experimentally realizable, is, according to the theory, the state in which the crystal possesses its fundamental susceptibility, free from piezoelectric influence.

451. Energy equations like (240) and (241), specialized for Rochelle salt, for fields in the X-direction, are given below. The subscript x

---

* In his earlier papers, Mueller regards the clamped state as that in which only y_s is suppressed; this might be called *partial rhombic clamping*. In his fourth paper,[381] he recognizes the distinction between this type of clamping and the complete rhombic clamping defined above. Outside the Curie points the distinction vanishes; in the monoclinic phase, the distinction is small enough to be ignored in formulating the basic equations.

† This subscript s must not be confused with the subscript ds defined in §430 to indicate the differential permittivity at saturation.

will be omitted in the case of symbols denoting electrical quantities. In accordance with the statement in §449, each equation is now to include a term in P^4. This term suffices to account qualitatively for the non-linear relations observed in Rochelle salt and yields expressions which, except for the complications introduced by the multi-domain structure in the ferroelectric region, agree fairly well with experiment up to moderately large fields of perhaps 200 volts/cm. In order to describe the observed flatness of the saturation portion of the polarization curve in larger fields a different theoretical function would be necessary. One might, for example, write $f_1(P)$ in place of BP^4 in Eqs. (491) and (491a), and $f(P) = \partial f_1(P)/\partial P$ in place of BP^3 in (492a), (492c), and succeeding equations. The form of $f(P)$ would have to be determined experimentally.

The equations assume different forms according to whether the rhombic method or the normal method is followed. Outside the ferroelectric range the two methods are identical. Under each method y_s represents the strain, with the understanding that in the rhombic method it is measured from the configuration of rhombic clamping, while in the normal method it is measured from the configuration of the unstressed crystal in zero field at the temperature in question.

From all that has been said it should be clear that the *rhombic method*, to which most attention will be given, treats Rochelle salt as if it were a rhombic crystal at all temperatures, while the *normal method* recognizes the configuration of the free crystal between the Curie points as being monoclinic. Each method pays due regard to spontaneous polarization and spontaneous strain, but in a different way. Methods analogous to these may prove to be useful in the case of other ferroelectric crystals.

With Rochelle salt between the Curie points one ought strictly to include in the term for piezoelectric energy the piezoelectric constants mentioned above that are theoretically present in monoclinic hemimorphic crystals, but not in crystals of the rhombic sphenoidal class to which Rochelle salt belongs in the parelectric regions. In a first-order discussion such terms may be disregarded as of small magnitude; a special treatment of them will be found in §464.

Throughout this chapter the theory will be concerned mainly with the ideal single-domain crystal. Outside the Curie points there are no domains, and theory accords well with observation. The interactions between domains are so little understood that it is not feasible to introduce them in the basic theory. One must therefore be prepared to use the theory, insofar as it is applied to the ferroelectric region, rather as a qualitative than a quantitative description of phenomena. Nevertheless, as will be seen, certain quantitative deductions can be made, and the theory serves as a basis for the later discussion of actual multi-domain crystals.

452. Basic Equations for Rochelle Salt, Rhombic Method. Equations (240) to (245), §191, with additional terms in P^4, will now be specialized for Rochelle salt. Since only the direction parallel to the X-axis is considered, subscripts are omitted from electrical quantities. ξ and ζ are in terms of strains and stresses respectively, confined to shears in the YZ-plane. y_z is the strain measured from the rhombically clamped state. Y_z is the externally applied stress. When $Y_z = 0$, there is a spontaneous strain y_z^0. c_{44}^P and s_{44}^P are the elastic stiffness and compliance at constant polarization. B is a factor to be determined experimentally.

The total polarization P is in general the sum of three terms: P^0, the spontaneous polarization; P^E, the part due to the field E; and P^y or P^Y, the part due respectively to the strain y_z or the stress Y_z. In some cases one or more of these three components is suppressed. In such cases, to avoid confusion, we will indicate the surviving components explicitly. For example, if the external stress Y_z is zero (crystal free), the polarization is $P^E + P^0 = P^{E0}$.

The energy equations are as follows:

$$\xi = -\tfrac{1}{2}c_{44}^P y_z^2 - \tfrac{1}{2}\chi_1(P^{yE0})^2 - \tfrac{1}{4}B(P^{yE0})^4 + a_{14}P^{yE0}y_z \tag{491}$$

$$\zeta = \tfrac{1}{2}s_{44}^P Y_z^2 - \tfrac{1}{2}\chi'(P^{YE0})^2 - \tfrac{1}{4}B(P^{YE0})^4 + b_{14}P^{YE0} Y_z \tag{492}$$

By taking derivatives of these equations, as in §191, we obtain the four equations of state:

$$-\frac{\partial \xi}{\partial y_z} = Y_z = c_{44}^P y_z - a_{14}P^{yE0} \tag{493a}$$

$$-\frac{\partial \xi}{\partial P} = E = -a_{14}y_z + \chi_1 P^{yE0} + B(P^{yE0})^3 \tag{493b}$$

$$-\frac{\partial \zeta}{\partial Y_z} = y_z = s_{44}^P Y_z + b_{14}P^{YE0} \tag{493c}$$

$$-\frac{\partial \zeta}{\partial P} = E = -b_{14}Y_z + \chi' P^{YE0} + B(P^{YE0})^3 \tag{493d}$$

These four equations are similar to Eqs. (242) to (245), §191, specialized for Rochelle salt.

Attention is called first to Eq. (493c), which expresses the strain due to the combined effects of a mechanical stress and an electric polarization. If $E = 0$ and $Y_z = 0$, $P = P^0$, and we find

$$y_z = b_{14}P^0 = y_z^0 \tag{494}$$

y_z^0 is the spontaneous strain, measured from the configuration of rhombic clamping. This part of the total strain is still present when Y_z and E are impressed, so that y_z is then the total strain measured from the rhombically clamped state, as in Eqs. (493).

By use of Voigt's equations it is easy to prove that when $E = 0$, P^{yE0} in Eq. (493a) becomes identical with P^{YE0} in Eq. (493c).

In Eq. (493a) when $y_z = 0$ and $E = 0$, $Y_z = -a_{14}P^0$ is the clamping stress needed to bring the crystal to the state of rhombic clamping. When $Y_z = 0$, the crystal is free, and $c_{44}^P y_z = a_{14}(P^0 + P^E)$; if there is no external field, $c_{44}^P y_z = a_{14}P^0$.

From Eq. (204) on page 204, Eq. (238) on page 248, and (ix) to (xii) in Table XX, page 249, we find for Rochelle salt:

$$b_{14} = a_{14}s_{44}^P \tag{495}$$

$$d_{14} = e_{14}s_{44}^E \tag{495a}$$

$$d_{14} = b_{14}\eta' = a_{14}s_{44}^P\eta' \tag{495b}$$

$$e_{14} = a_{14}\eta'' = b_{14}c_{44}^P\eta'' \tag{495c}$$

$$a_{14} = e_{14}\chi'' = \frac{d_{14}}{\eta''s_{44}^E} = \frac{d_{14}}{\eta's_{44}^P} \tag{495d}$$

$$b_{14} = d_{14}\chi' = \frac{d_{14}}{\eta'} \tag{495e}$$

In these equations the symbols d_{14}, e_{14}, $\eta' = 1/\chi'$ and $\eta'' = 1/\chi''$ are written in the form that we have adopted for piezoelectric crystals in general. They represent here *initial* values, valid only with small stresses and weak fields. Where it is necessary in order to avoid ambiguity the subscript 0 will be attached to these symbols.

Between the Curie points, owing to the spontaneous polarization and non-linearity, some of the quantities in the foregoing equations assume a form different from that in the parelectric regions. In such cases the subscript or superscript s will be used when necessary to designate the ferroelectric region. Where there is no ambiguity, this s may be omitted.

Equations (495) to (495e) are applicable equally to the rhombic or to the normal method.

453. Application of the Interaction Theory. In the remainder of this chapter the equations will be written according to the rhombic method, in which the strain is measured from the condition of rhombic clamping. The basic equations are (493a) to (495e).

The first application to be made of the basic equations is in expressing χ' in terms of χ_1 outside the Curie points.

This relation is derived by setting $E = 0$ in Eqs. (493b) and (493d) and equating the two. We make use of the expressions

$$Y_z = c_{44}^P y_z - a_{14}P^y - a_{14}P^0$$

from Eq. (493a), also $a_{14} = b_{14}c_{44}^P$ from Table XX, page 249, and $P^y = P^Y$ from §452. The result is

$$\chi' = \chi_1 - a_{14}b_{14} \qquad (496)$$

The equivalence of the last equation to Eq. (264) in §204 will be made clear in §461. It is important to note that, since a_{14} and b_{14} are nearly independent of temperature, χ' and χ_1 differ by a nearly constant amount, as is shown in Fig. 145.

In Fig. 138,* curve d represents Eq. (493d) for a free crystal with $Y_z = 0$, and curve e is from Eq. (493b) for a clamped crystal with $y_z = 0$, both at 31.5°C. It will be noticed that the values of E for these curves differ by the amount $a_{14}b_{14}P$. For example, at $P = 400$, the distance KH represents $a_{14}b_{14}P$.

We are now prepared to begin the consideration of the variation of the properties of Rochelle salt with temperature. The interrelationships expressed in Eqs. (493a) to (495e) are such that, when the temperature dependence of any one of the four parameters χ_1, χ', s_{44}^E, or d_{14} is established, the dependence of the rest follows. This subject is treated further in §§468 and 472. For the present we shall abide by Mueller's hypothesis that the seat of the anomalies lies in the rhombically clamped dielectric susceptibility $\eta_1 = 1/\chi_1$. The observed dielectric constant of the *free* crystal varies with temperature in the manner shown in Fig. 147 or Fig. 143; k' and χ' are related by $k' = 1 + 4\pi/\chi'$. By means of Eq. (496) χ_1 can be found at any temperature when χ' is known.

The hypothesis concerning χ_1 involves the assumption that the structure of Rochelle salt is such that χ_1 depends on temperature according to the upper curve in Fig. 143, and in particular that it diminishes as the Seignette-electric region is approached from either direction, with a finite value at each Curie point. From Eq. (496) it is seen that $\chi' = 0$, and hence $k' = \infty$, when $\chi_1 = a_{14}b_{14}$. In the Seignette-electric region $\chi_1 < a_{14}b_{14}$.

In Fig. 138 we have plotted, approximately to scale, curves showing the relation between polarization P and applied field E for free and clamped crystals,† at two different temperatures. In curve e, above the upper Curie point, the initial slope OE at the origin gives $\eta_1 = 1/\chi_1$.

* Figures 138 and 139 are for a *single-domain* crystal. Multi-domain crystals are treated in §479.

† The curves in Fig. 138 are drawn to scale from Mason's observations as summarized in Table 2 of Mueller's second paper[378] and illustrated in Figs. 145 and 146. For curve d the temperature 31.5°C was chosen because at that temperature the initial χ' of the free crystal happens to have the same value, 0.05, as the initial χ'_s (§450) at 15°, as shown in curve a. The lines $O'A$ and OD are therefore parallel. All curves were plotted on the assumption that B has the value $6.5(10^{-8})$; the true

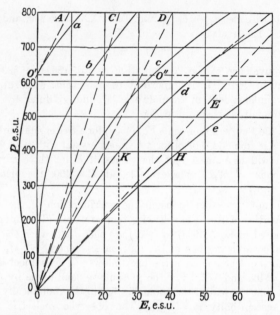

Fig. 138.—Theoretical polarization curves for Rochelle salt. Curve a, at 15°, crystal free; curve b, at the upper Curie point, crystal free; curve c, at 15°, crystal clamped; curve d, at 31.5°, crystal free; curve e, at 31.5°, crystal clamped.

At higher temperatures the slope decreases; in general, outside the Curie points the effect of the B-term in Eqs. (493b) and (493d) is very small at all attainable field strengths. As the temperature decreases, with a corresponding decrease in χ_1, the slope increases, until at 15°C it is represented by the line OC. At 5°C the slope would reach its maximum value (§469). The polarization curve for the clamped crystal at 15°, representing Eq. (493b) with $y_z = 0$, is curve c.

This change with temperature of the curve for the clamped crystal is accompanied by a similar change in the curve for the free crystal. Thus at the Curie point, where $\chi_1 = a_{14}b_{14}$, we see that $\chi' = 0$, and from Eq. (493d) it is seen that the curve for the free crystal coincides with curve b, which represents BP^3. This curve has an infinite slope at the origin, indicating that $\partial P/\partial E \to \infty$ as $E \to 0$. The infinite dielectric constant of the free crystal at the Curie point θ_u is thus accounted for (similar reasoning leads to a like conclusion at θ_l); at the same time it

value at temperatures above θ_u is probably greater than this. The equation for curves a, b, and d is Eq. (493d) with $Y_z = 0$. For curves c and e we use Eq. (493b) with $y_z = 0$. Values of χ', a_{14} and b_{14} are from Figs. 145 and 146, pp. 626, 627, and Eq. (496). See also p. 615.

becomes clear that very large observed values at the Curie points are to be expected only when E is very small.

454. A curious state of affairs is encountered when χ_1 in Eq. (496) becomes less than $a_{14}b_{14}$, *i.e.*, when χ' is negative and the temperature passes below θ_u. The curve for the free crystal, which is already tangent to the axis of ordinates at θ_u, becomes, so to speak, pushed still farther to the left, with a bulge in the negative direction starting at the origin. Close to the Curie point this negative segment is small, with a large negative initial slope. With decreasing temperature the negative slope $(1/\chi')$ diminishes and the height of the negative segment increases, until at 15°C curve a is reached. The maximum height would be found at a temperature around 5°C.

Obviously, χ' cannot be the reciprocal susceptibility of a free crystal between the Curie points, for it implies a positive polarization produced by a negative field. The theory is saved from disaster by the fact that at O' the curve returns to the positive side of the ordinate axis. At O' there is present in the crystal a polarization, although the impressed field is zero. We are thus led by the fundamental equations to the concept of a *spontaneous polarization* in Rochelle salt between the Curie points. We may conclude further that any crystal having a clamped reciprocal susceptibility χ_1 that becomes equal to $a_{14}b_{14}$ (or its equivalent for the class to which the crystal belongs) at a definite temperature must have a Curie point with infinite susceptibility for the free crystal at this temperature, together with a spontaneous polarization when χ_1 is less than $a_{14}b_{14}$. The quantity χ_1 itself can be of quite normal magnitude. It is the condition $\chi_1 < a_{14}b_{14}$ that accounts for all the abnormalities.

In terms of χ_1 the spontaneous polarization P^0 is found by setting $E = 0$ and $Y_z = 0$, in Eq. (493d), whence

$$BP^{0^2} = -\chi' = a_{14}b_{14} - \chi_1 \tag{497}$$

Outside the Curie points, P^0 in this equation becomes imaginary and there is no spontaneous polarization. The curve for P^0 as a function of temperature is shown in Fig. 147. It rises rapidly from the Curie points to a flat maximum at about 5°C; the value shown at the maximum is Mueller's "observed" value of 740 esu, from his third paper.[380] Using this value in Eq. (497), together with B, a_{14}, and $b_{14} = a_{14}s_{44}^P$ from the same paper, one finds, at 5°, $\chi_1 = 0.037$. This quantity is appreciably greater than the hypothetical value at 5° in Fig. 143, but the margin of uncertainty in both theory and observation is considerable.

In Fig. 138, only positive values of polarization are shown. The complete graph for Eq. (493d), in which we set $Y_z = 0$, is shown in

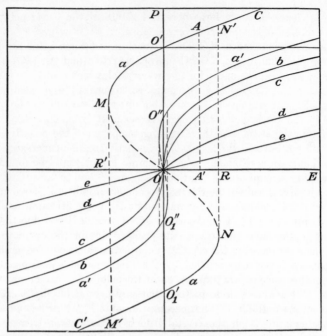

Fig. 139.—Qualitative curves illustrating the theoretical dependence of P on E for a free single-domain Rochelle-salt crystal at different temperatures. Curve a is for 5°, a' for 22°, b for the Curie point θ_u, c for 26°, d for 31.5°, and e for 40°C.

Fig. 139, in which curve a is for 5°C, together with $P^0 = OO'$. Curves a', b, and c correspond to temperatures around 22°, θ_u (approximately 24°), and 26°; curves d and e are for 31.5° and 40°. Considering first curve a, we see that if the crystal consists of a single domain with P^0 positive the total polarization when $E = 0$ is P^0. As E increases in the positive direction, the portion $O'C$ of the curve is traversed, and the observed polarization P^E is the ordinate measured from an axis of abscissas through O'. The equation relating P^E to E is obtained by substituting in Eq. (493d) $P = P^E + P^0$ and $Y_z = 0$. Then, with origin at O, we have

$$E = \chi'(P^E + P^0) + B(P^E + P^0)^3 \qquad (498)$$

When $P^0 = 0$, (498) is the polarization: field equation for temperatures in the parelectric regions, and χ' is the actual reciprocal initial susceptibility. In the ferroelectric region, where χ' is negative, the observable initial susceptibility (§450) $\eta'_s = 1/\chi'_s$ (slope of curve a, Fig. 138, at O') is found by taking the derivative of E with respect to P^E and then setting $P^E = 0$; use is made also of Eq. (497).

$$\chi'_s = \chi' + 3BP^{0^2} = \chi_1 - a_{14}b_{14} + 3BP^{0^2}$$
$$= 2(a_{14}b_{14} - \chi_1) = -2\chi' = -\frac{2D_{14}}{c^P_{44}} = 2BP^{0^2} \qquad (499)$$

The last expression is Eq. (11c) or (17) in Mueller's paper III; D_{14} is defined in Eq. (522a).

On substituting $-\chi'_s/2$ for χ' in Eq. (498), we find, for the ferroelectric region,

$$E = -\tfrac{1}{2}\chi'_s(P^E + P^0) + B(P^E + P^0)^3$$
$$= \chi'_s P^E + 3BP^{E^2}P^0 + BP^{E^3}$$
$$= B(2P^{0^2}P^E + 3P^0P^{E^2} + P^{E^3}) \qquad (500)$$

This equation gives the relation between P^E and E according to the *normal method* described in §458.

P^0 is the spontaneous polarization at the given temperature; it may have either of the two values $\pm(\chi'_s/2B)^{\frac{1}{2}}$ given by Eq. (499).

Equation (500) gives the theoretically observable P^E for any E, with origin at O' in Fig. 138 or 139, for a single-domain crystal polarized in the positive direction OO'.

In the last part of (500), the substitution of $2BP^{0^2}$ for χ'_s follows from Eq. (499). The same substitution may also be made in the equations that are to follow. In this manner the quantity on the left-hand side of the equation is represented in terms of P^0 as the only parameter that varies materially with temperature. The variation of P^0 with temperature is fairly well known, as shown by Fig. 147 and Eq. (526). It must still be remembered, however, that the equations in the present sections apply to the idealized single-domain crystal, with hysteresis loops of the form represented by $M'NN'M$ in Fig. 139, in which the coercive field is far in excess of the E_c found in practice.

If the spontaneous polarization P^0 is negative, then for curve a, Fig. 139, the origin is to be taken at O'_1 instead of at O', and in Eq. (500) the negative sign is to be attached to P^0. The form of the hysteresis loop is the same whether P^0 is $+$ or $-$; the only difference is in the position of the origin of coordinates. This statement remains substantially true also when, as is practically always the case, the crystal has a multi-domain structure (see §479).

The *over-all susceptibility* $(\eta'_s)_n$ of the free crystal (§430), which is the ratio P^E/E for any given value of E, is found from Eq. (500):

$$\frac{1}{(\eta'_s)_n} = (\chi'_s)_n = \chi'_s + BP^{E^2} + 3BP^0P^0 \qquad (501)$$

This susceptibility is the one derived directly from observations with a ballistic galvanometer.

The slope at any point on the $P : E$ curve is the *differential susceptibility* $(\eta'_s)_d$; from Eq. (498) it is given by

$$\frac{1}{(\eta'_s)_d} = (\chi'_s)_d = \frac{\partial E}{\partial P^E} = \chi' + 3B(P^E + P^0)^2 \qquad (501a)$$

The observed *differential permittivity* discussed in §436 would, according to the present theory, be equal to $1 + 4\pi(\eta'_s)_d$.

455. If the field strength E applied to a *single-domain* crystal is increased from zero in the *negative* direction from O' in Fig. 139, a point of instability is reached at M. The spontaneous polarization P^0 is here abruptly reversed by the field, the observed polarization jumps from M to M', continuing along $M'C'$ as E becomes more negative. On the return trip the path $C'M'NN'C$ is followed. This process should be compared with the magnetic analogy described in §555. Along the paths MM' and NN', χ'_d becomes theoretically infinite.

We thus find a theoretical explanation of the dielectric hysteresis in Rochelle salt. According to the theory outlined here, the coercive field E_c ($= OR'$ or OR, for points M and N in Fig. 139) is found from the value of the polarization at M or N, for which $\partial E/\partial P = 0$. Thus from Eqs. (493d) and (497) it follows that at M, $P_M = P^0/\sqrt{3} = 0.577P^0$. Then on substituting this value for P in Eq. (493d) one finds

$$E_c = -\frac{2}{3\sqrt{3}} BP^{03} = -0.385BP^{03} \qquad (502)$$

This theoretical value of the coercive field is many times greater than that which is actually observed. The explanation, which lies in the ease of reversal of domains, is treated in §479, where the theoretical and experimental hysteresis loops will be compared in greater detail. For the present it suffices to point out the following features of Figs. 138 and 139: (1) Since the data for Fig. 138 at 15°C were based on observations of susceptibility of a free crystal at weak fields (§453 and Fig. 145), the slope $O'A$ of curve a at O' may be taken as representative of the values to be expected with weak direct or l-f alternating fields up to about 10 volts/cm. (2) Even with fields as high as 10 esu = 3,000 volts/cm, the polarization does not rise much beyond P^0. (3) Insofar as Eq. (496) is applicable to very strong fields, it indicates that complete saturation, if it exists at all, cannot be expected until the polarization has reached a value several times greater than P^0.

Figure 139 illustrates the gradual diminution in P^0 and E_c from maximum values at 5° to zero at the Curie point θ_u (see also Fig. 147). Above the temperature θ_u, polarizations are measured from a horizontal axis through the origin at O. In the ferroelectric region the origin is displaced vertically by an amount equal to P^0; for example, if P^0

happens to be negative, the origin is at O_1' for 5° and at O_1'' for 22°C. At θ_v, $\chi' = 0$, so that the equation for curve b is simply $E = BP^3$.

Above θ_u there is no hysteresis. With increasing temperature χ' increases (*cf.* Fig. 145), the term BP^3 becomes less and less important, and the curves become approximately straight lines, as is shown by the line e in Fig. 139. In practice, the relation between P and E is found to be linear, for all attainable values of E, from about 32° on.

Figure 139 explains qualitatively a peculiarity noted in Fig. 128 and elsewhere, that while with weak fields the susceptibility

$$\eta' = \frac{1}{\chi'} = \left(\frac{\partial P}{\partial E}\right)_0$$

approaches infinity at θ_u, with relatively *low* values on either side of θ_u, still when E is large the over-all value P/E (for constant E) rises continuously from low values in the parelectric regions to high values between the Curie points.

For a discussion of hysteresis in multi-domain crystals see §479.

456. *The Clamped Crystal between the Curie Points.* Rhombic clamping is always to be understood in this chapter unless monoclinic clamping is specifically mentioned. In Fig. 138 we have already seen $P:E$ curves for the clamped crystal at 31.5 and 15°C. Since according to the polarization theory, as expressed in Eqs. (493b) and (493d), the expressions for the polarization curves for a clamped crystal ($y_z = 0$) differ from those for a free crystal ($Y_z = 0$) only in the initial slope (χ_1 and χ', respectively), it is clear that the curves in Fig. 139 may also be used to illustrate qualitatively the $P:E$ relation for clamped crystals. The straight line e then gives this relation in the neighborhood of +35° and −30°C; curve d is representative for +30° and −25°C; curve c for +28° and −20°C. There is no peculiarity at either Curie point (see the curve for χ_1 in Fig. 143), but between +28° and −20° the curves lie between c and b, coming closest to b at about 5°C, where χ_1 is a minimum. Below −30° and above +35° the curves are linear, lying between e and the E-axis. Curves a and a' in Fig. 139 are for a free crystal and have no place in the present discussion.

Since with rhombic clamping the spontaneous polarization P^0 is suppressed (§459), the quantity P in Eq. (493b) is the polarization due to the field E alone. On setting $y_z = 0$ in (493b) we have, therefore, for the rhombically clamped crystal at any temperature,

$$E = \chi_1 P^E + B(P^E)^3 \tag{503}$$

Between the Curie points the concept of *monoclinic* clamping has both theoretical and practical significance. The configuration of the crystal under monoclinic clamping at any temperature is given by the spontaneous strain y_z^0, measured from the configuration at rhombic clamping as zero: $y_z^0 = b_{14}P^0$. A second relation between y_z^0 and P^0 is found by setting $E = 0$ in Eq. (493b) and writing P^0 for P^E:

$$a_{14}y_z^0 = \chi_1 P^0 + BP^{03} \tag{504}$$

This equation is illustrated graphically in Fig. 138, in which curve *c* may be taken as typical for a clamped crystal between the Curie points. The ordinate is now P^0, the abscissa is $a_{14}y_z^0$, and the point is O''.

Just as O is the origin for the $P:E$ curve for rhombic clamping, so under monoclinic clamping the origin is at O''. The relation between the applied E and the observed polarization P^E, which is the contribution made by E to the total polarization, is found as follows: From Eq. (493b) it is seen that $E + a_{14}y_z^0 = \chi_1 P + BP^3$, where now $P = P^0 + P^E$. On substituting the value of $a_{14}y_z^0$ given above and expanding, we arrive at the relation

$$\begin{aligned} E &= (\chi_1 + 3BP^{02})P^E + 3BP^0P^{E2} + BP^{E3} \\ &= \chi_s''P^E + 3BP^0P^{E2} + BP^{E3} \end{aligned} \tag{504a}$$

This equation is illustrated by a curve such as curve *c* in Fig. 138, with O'' as origin. The coefficient of P^E in the first term determines the slope at O''; it is the reciprocal initial susceptibility for monoclinic clamping, which may be written

$$\chi_s'' = \chi_1 + 3BP^{02} \tag{505}$$

Equation (504a) expresses the relation between P^E and E according to the *normal method* described in §458.

With the aid of Eqs. (496), (497), (499), and (505), χ_s'' can also be expressed as follows:

$$\chi_s'' = \frac{1}{\eta_s''} = \chi_s' + a_{14}b_{14} = \chi_1 + \tfrac{3}{2}\chi_s' = 3a_{14}b_{14} - 2\chi_1 = \chi_1 - \frac{3D_{14}}{c_{44}^P} \tag{505a}$$

The significance of D_{14} is explained* on page 612. This relation between χ_s'' and χ_s' for the region of spontaneous polarization should be compared with Eq. (496).

We shall find use also for the expression for the *over-all susceptibility* $(\eta_s'')_n$ or its reciprocal, for monoclinic clamping between the Curie points. From Eq. (504a),

$$\frac{1}{(\eta_s'')_n} = (\chi_s'')_n = \frac{E}{P^E} = \chi_s'' + 3BP^0P^E + BP^{E2} \tag{505b}$$

457. *Further Remarks on the Clamped Dielectric Constant.* When the statement is made, as in §442, that the value of the dielectric constant observed at very high frequencies approximates the value of the clamped

* The last expression in Eq. (505a) is the same as (9c) in Mueller's paper III.

crystal, it should be obvious, in the light of the foregoing theory, that the word "clamped" implies rhombic clamping in the parelectric regions and monoclinic clamping in the ferroelectric. Practically all available experimental values were obtained with small fields. An idea of the dependence of the initial clamped dielectric constant on temperature can be obtained from the curves in Fig. 145 for χ_1 and χ_s''.

According to Eqs. (503) and (504a), the clamped dielectric constant may be expected to decrease with increasing field, except at temperatures well removed from the Curie points. Thus far the only experimental evidence has been indirect, from the fact that the susceptibility η_x' for the free crystal does show saturation; and since, by Eq. (267),

$$\eta_x' = \eta_x'' + e_{14}d_{14}$$

η_x'' must have the same characteristic.

Although reliable data on virgin curves, either static or by alternating current, are lacking, still one can draw certain conclusions concerning the clamped dielectric constant from the hysteresis loops shown in Chap. XXII. From the linearity of the saturation portions of these loops it is evident that the differential permittivity k_{ds} approaches a constant and relatively small value at large E. It is not unreasonable to inquire whether this k_{ds} may not be identical with the clamped dielectric constant. This will be the case if, when E is large, d_{14} becomes so small that the product $e_{14}d_{14}$ no longer makes an appreciable contribution to the susceptibility. That the polarization is subject to very great saturation under large mechanical and electric stresses is evident from Figs. 108 to 115. Nevertheless, the data do not suffice to prove convincingly that at the strongest fields appearing on the hysteresis loops the product $e_{14}d_{14}$ is in fact negligible.

On the experimental side two values of k_{ds} have been given in §436: at 15°C, $k_{ds} = 330$; at 20° (estimated), $k_{ds} = 200$. Values of the clamped constant k_s'' can be derived from the curve for χ_s'' in Fig. 145: at 15°C, $k_s'' \approx 120$; at 20°, $k_{ds}'' \approx 195$. These values are for small fields; at large E they would be smaller. This evidence, though slight, indicates that k_{ds} is somewhat greater than the clamped dielectric constant (§416a).

Mueller's theory does not throw light on this question, because, as stated in §451, the cubic equations that describe the non-linear effects are not valid up to large values of E and do not predict the constancy in k_{ds} at saturation.

From the theory in Chap. XXV and especially from §479, it is evident that the polarization of the free crystal in a given static field and its variation with the field must depend very greatly on the domain structure of the specimen. This fact doubtless accounts in large measure for the wide variety of polarization curves and values of k'_z recorded by different observers. On the other hand, the clamped dielectric constant, although not directly measurable, still must be regarded as independent of domains.

458. Equations for Rochelle Salt according to the Normal Method. This is the method referred to in §450 as being preferable to the rhombic method when the field is weak and relations are linear. It is simply the method that would be applied to any normal piezoelectric crystal devoid of anomalies. Strains are measured from the normal configuration of the crystal at any given temperature, whether the configuration is rhombic or monoclinic. The reason why this method is not as well suited as the rhombic method to the treatment of large fields and large stresses can be illustrated by considering the relation between polarization and field for a free crystal between the Curie points. In Fig. 139, the origin is at O for curves representing Eq. (493d) by the rhombic method. Such curves, for example curve a, are centrosymmetrical with respect to the point O. When $E = 0$, there is a spontaneous polarization in the domain equal to $+P^0$ or $-P^0$, represented by OO' or OO'_1. As E increases from zero, if P^0 is positive the observed polarization is the ordinate, say P^E, measured from a horizontal axis through O'. As was stated in §454, the slope of the curve at O' gives the observed initial susceptibility at the temperature in question. The curve is not symmetrical about any axis through O'. This lack of symmetry is indicated by the term in P^{E^2} in Eq. (500). Corresponding to this lack of symmetry is the fact that the energy equation for the normal method would not be as simple as Eqs. (491) and (492) for the rhombic method, except at temperatures outside the Curie points. Nevertheless, as long as the field is so weak that only the first power of P^E need be retained in the derivatives of the energy equations, all equations are equally simple by either method. Outside the Curie points, even when higher powers of P are included, the two methods are identical.

Similar considerations apply to the clamped crystal. In this case, if we regard curve c in Fig. 138 as typical of a clamped crystal between the Curie points, the origin is at O by the rhombic method, with initial susceptibility $\eta_1 = 1/\chi_1$. By the normal method the origin is at O'', and the initial (actually observed) susceptibility is $\eta''_s = 1/\chi''_s$. Equation (504a), for a clamped crystal, corresponds to a curve with origin at O'', and it shows the asymmetry characteristic of the normal method in the region of spontaneous polarization.

Since the normal method deals with actually observed initial susceptibilities, it is well suited to the treatment of practical problems in which only small stresses and weak fields occur.

The equations according to the normal method, applicable at all temperatures (except that between the Curie points they are valid only for weak fields and small stresses), do not include explicitly the spontaneous polarization P^0. Spontaneous polarization may or may not be present. For example, tourmaline, although not ferroelectric, has a spontaneous polarization (§519), which does not play a part in the piezoelectric equations.

The equations of state are specialized from Eqs. (255):

$$y_z = s_{44}^P Y_z + b_{14} P^{YE} \tag{506a}$$

$$E = - b_{14} Y_z + \chi' P^{YE} \tag{506b}$$

$$Y_z = c_{44}^P y_z - a_{14} P^{yE} \tag{506c}$$

$$E = - a_{14} y_z + \chi'' P^{yE} \tag{506d}$$

Subject to the conditions prescribed above, the Voigt formulation, as given in Eqs. (254), §197, can be used equally well.

458a. It may be helpful to indicate how the equations of state (493a) to (493d) as used in this chapter can be derived from Voigt's theory. As an example we now derive Eq. (493a) from Eqs. (183) and (183a), §124, or from Eqs. (252) and (253), §197. When these equations are specialized for the present problem, we have

$$Y_z = c_{44}^E y_z - e_{14} E$$
$$P = e_{14} y_z + \eta'' E$$

P includes the spontaneous polarization P^0, and y_z includes the spontaneous strain when present. Upon eliminating E between the two equations we find

$$c_{44}^E y_z - Y_z = \frac{e_{14}}{\eta''} (P - e_{14} y_z).$$

Therefore

$$Y_z = c_{44}^E y_z - \frac{e_{14} P}{\eta''} + \frac{e_{14}^2 y_z}{\eta''}.$$

Now from Eq. (279), §208, $c_{44}^E + e_{14}^2/\eta'' = c_{44}^P$, and by definition, from Table XX, §188, $e_{14} = a_{14}\eta''$. Upon making these substitutions we see that

$$Y_z = c_{44}^P y_z - a_{14} P$$

as in Eq. (493*a*).

By similar procedures the other three equations (493) can be derived.

CHAPTER XXIV

THEORY OF ROCHELLE SALT, PART II. PIEZOELECTRIC AND ELASTIC PROPERTIES, CURIE-WEISS LAWS, AND CONCLUSIONS

The history of physics shows that the search for analogies between two categories of distinct phenomena has perhaps been, of all methods employed for the construction of physical theories, the method which is most certain and most fruitful.
—P. DUHEM.

The discussion of the interaction theory is brought to a conclusion in this chapter, with consideration of the distinguishing characteristics of ferroelectric crystals and with a presentation of the experimental evidence for the findings of the interaction theory.

Piezoelectric Properties of Rochelle Salt for Fields Parallel to the X-axis. It was stated in §191 that the main experimental justification for the polarization theory lies in the approximate temperature-independence of a_{14} and b_{14}. We consider now the effect of electric and mechanical stress on these constants and also on the Voigt constants e_{14} and d_{14}. In Eqs. (493b) and (493d) for the direct effect, the non-linearity is expressed, at least to a first approximation, by the term in B, so that a_{14} and b_{14} are not required to show a dependence on stress. In Eqs. (493a) and (493c) for the converse effect, B does not appear explicitly, yet the non-linearity of the relation between Y_z (or y_z) and E is deducible from the fact that P is non-linear in E, as is shown by the equations for the direct effect. We may therefore confidently expect, as is, indeed, indicated by Mason's observations,[338] that a_{14} and b_{14} will be found approximately constant under all circumstances. This being the case, it follows that d_{14} and e_{14} must be very variable with temperature, field, and mechanical stress.

459. Direct Effect. The assumption that the application of Y_z is equivalent to the application of a biasing field $-b_{14}Y_z$ makes it easy to find the relation between Y_z and the polarization that it causes when $E = 0$ in a single-domain crystal; that is, we find thus the equation for the *direct effect* in terms of stress, a relation that in Rochelle salt is non-linear. When $E = 0$ in Eq. (493d), $b_{14}Y_z = \chi'P^{Y0} + B(P^{Y0})^3$. The abscissa in Fig. 139, §454, and for curves a and d in Fig. 138, §453, is now $b_{14}Y_z$, with origin at O. The equation for the curve in all cases, between or outside the Curie points, is*

$$Y_z = \frac{\chi' P^{Y0}}{b_{14}} + \frac{B(P^{Y0})^3}{b_{14}} \tag{507}$$

where P^{Y0} is the polarization due to Y_z when $E = 0$, plus the spontaneous P^0. Outside the Curie points $P^0 = 0$.

In the ferroelectric region the relation between Y_z and the polarization P that it causes is expressed more directly by shifting the origin to O' (Fig. 139; see also Fig. 140). This is done by writing P^Y in place of P^{Y0}, and making use of Eq. (499):

$$b_{14}Y_z = \chi'_s P^Y - 3BP^0(P^Y)^2 + B(P^Y)^3 \tag{508}$$

The similarity of Eq. (508) to (500), (504a), (510), and (511) should be noted. In §460 we shall find analogous expressions for d_{14} and e_{14}. All these expressions apply only to single-domain crystals. For multidomain crystals see §479.

The effective *differential piezoelectric constant* is given, from Eqs. (184a) and (495e), by

$$\frac{1}{(d_{14})_d} = \frac{\partial Y_z}{\partial P^Y} = \frac{1}{b_{14}}[\chi'_s - 6BP^0P^Y + 3B(P^Y)^2] \equiv \frac{1}{(d_{14})_0^s} + \frac{6BP^0P^Y + 3B(P^Y)^2}{b_{14}} \tag{509}$$

Outside the Curie points this becomes $[\chi' + 3B(P^Y)^2]/b_{14}$. The initial value at small Y_z between the Curie points is

$$(d_{14})_0^s = \frac{b_{14}}{\chi'_s} = b_{14}\eta'_s \tag{509a}$$

which is the form assumed by Eq. (495b) in the ferroelectric region. In the parelectric regions we have, in agreement with Eq. (495b),

$$(d_{14})_0 = \frac{b_{14}}{\chi'} = b_{14}\eta' \tag{509b}$$

From the last two equations it is evident that at the Curie points, where η'_s and η' become infinite, the initial value of the piezoelectric constant must also approach infinity, since b_{14} does not vanish. The over-all value of d_{14} is given by Eq. (512b) below.

The equation for the *direct effect in terms of strain* is a relation between y_z impressed on an unclamped crystal and the polarization that it pro-

---

* This is equivalent to Mueller's Eq. (3c) in his third paper,[380] with a correction in sign.

duces while $E = 0$. *Outside the Curie points* we simply set $E = 0$ in Eq. (493b), and find that $a_{14}y_z = \chi'P^y + B(P^y)^3$. Except close to the Curie points the second term on the right is small and the relation is nearly linear. *Between the Curie points* $P^{y0} = P^y + P^0$, and y_z, which we now call $\bar{y}_z$, is measured from the normal, or monoclinic, configuration. Since in the foregoing equations y_z is measured from the configuration of rhombic clamping, it follows that $\bar{y}_z = y_z - y_z^0$. Now, from Eq. (493b), when $E = 0$, $a_{14}y_z^0 = \chi_1 P^0 + BP^{03}$. Then from (493b) and (505) we find

$$a_{14}\bar{y}_z = \chi_s''P^y + 3BP^0(P^y)^2 + B(P^y)^3 \quad (510)$$

This relation is represented graphically by curves of the form of curve c in Fig. 138. P and $\bar{y}_z$ are measured from an origin at O'', and P is an increment added to or subtracted from P^0.

Attention is next called to the contrast between Eqs. (510) and (508): in (510) the strain is prescribed and the coefficient of P^y is χ_s'', while in (508), with the stress prescribed, P^Y has the coefficient χ_s'. If y_z is due to Y_z, $P^Y = P^y$.

In Fig. 140 curve a represents Eq. (508) and curve b Eq. (510).

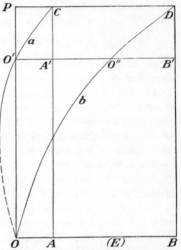

FIG. 140.—Rochelle salt between the Curie points. Curve a, polarization in terms of mechanical stress; curve b, polarization in terms of strain. The abscissa (E) represents $-b_{14}Y_z$ for curve a, $a_{14}y_z$ for curve b.

For any polarization on a, $OA = b_{14}Y_z$, $A'C = P^Y$. For curve b, $OB = a_{14}\bar{y}_z$, $B'D = P^y$. The origin for the relation between $b_{14}Y_z$ and P^Y is at O'; for the relation between $a_{14}\bar{y}_z$ and P^y, the origin is at O''. In both cases OO' represents P^0. The reciprocal slopes at O' and O'' are χ_s' and χ_s''.

Any piezoelectric polarization, measured from the axis $O'B'$, is thus given by Eq. (510) in terms of strain and by (508) in terms of stress, according to the normal method. In both cases $E = 0$; therefore the quotient y_z/Y_z gives the isagric compliance s_{44}^E at zero field [see Eq. (517)].

The distinction between curves a and b in Fig. 140 becomes important when an electric field is applied to a crystal already under mechanical stress. The abscissas for both curves are thereby increased by an amount E, but the polarizations are no longer the same. This is because curve a represents a *free* crystal, which, as long as the stress Y_z is constant, is free to be deformed by the field, while in curve b the crystal is clamped if y_z remains constant.

Equation (510) can be used to prove that when the strain is reduced by clamping from y_z^0 to $y_z = 0$ (rhombic clamping), the spontaneous polarization is also suppressed. Remembering that $\bar{y}_z$ in (510) is measured from y_z^0, we seek the value of y_z required to make $P = -P^0$ and thus reduce the total polarization to zero. Calling this strain y_z' and setting $P^y = -P^0$ in (510), we find by the use of Eqs. (504) and (505) that

$$a_{14}y_z' = -\chi_s''P^0 + 2BP^{03} = -P^0(\chi_1 + BP^{02}) = -a_{14}y_z^0 \quad (510a)$$

Hence $y_z' = -y_z^0$, and the strain is reduced to the condition of rhombic clamping.

In §439 the effects of mechanical constraint on the form of the hysteresis loops have been considered. The nature of these effects becomes clear from a consideration of Figs. 138 and 139. A constraint may consist in clamping the crystal at some arbitrary strain or in impressing a fixed stress on a crystal that is otherwise free to deform itself in the electric field, or it may be of a more complicated sort. If we regard the impressing of a fixed strain or stress as equivalent to impressing a fixed biasing field on the crystal, certain conclusions can be drawn at once. It will be recalled that in Fig. 138 curve c is for a crystal at 15° clamped with $y_z = 0$ and that for monoclinic clamping the origin of the theoretically observed polarization curve is at O'', with initial susceptibility χ_s''. If the crystal is clamped with any arbitrary $+y_z$, the origin becomes displaced to a point farther up on curve c, having an abscissa displaced to the right of O'' by the amount $a_{14}y_z$. Wherever the origin falls, the portion of the curve traversed when any not too large alternating voltage is applied is not far from a straight line; hence for a clamped crystal between the Curie points there is no hysteresis, but only a practically linear polarization curve.

The result is quite different when the mechanical bias is a *constant stress*, as was approximately the case with Figs. 129 and 130. Equation (493d) is to be used with a constant value assigned to Y_z. The polarization curves are then the same as in Fig. 139, with the origin displaced by the amount $b_{14}Y_z$ to the right or left from O according to the sign of Y_z. If the origin is at A', the polarization, including that due to Y_z, will be at A (curve a at 5° being taken as an example). A is then the origin for the observed polarization curve. As E is varied to the right and left from A, a distorted curve results, like those in the oscillograms.

From what has been said, it follows that a small mechanical bias, whether constant strain or constant stress, may be expected to cause an increase or decrease in the observed susceptibility, according to the sign of the bias. On the other hand, a *large* bias of either sign, exceeding the limits of the hysteresis loop, should cause always a decrease in susceptibility.

460. Converse Effect. Just as Eq. (507), relating a stress to the polarization that it causes, expresses the direct effect, so from Eq. (500) one can express the converse effect, with the strain produced by E as a function of E. All that is necessary is to substitute for P^E its equivalent in terms of the associated strain, which by setting $Y_z = 0$ in Eq. (493c) is found to be y_z/b_{14}. The converse effect is then expressed as[*]

$$E = \frac{\chi'_s}{b_{14}} y_z + \frac{3BP^0}{b_{14}^2} y_z^2 + \frac{B}{b_{14}^3} y_z^3 = \frac{y_z}{(d_{14})_n^s} \qquad (511)$$

This non-linearity between y_z and E has been verified by several observers, as has been shown in Chap. XXI.

For small E and Y_z, at any temperature outside the Curie points, the initial $(d_{14})_0$ is found from Eqs. (495), (497), (509b), and (522a):[†]

$$(d_{14})_0 = b_{14}\eta' = \frac{a_{14}}{D_{14}} \qquad (512)$$

Between the Curie points, from Eqs. (495), (499), (509a), and (522a),

$$(d_{14})_0^s = b_{14}\eta'_s = -\frac{a_{14}}{2D_{14}} \qquad (512a)$$

For any E and Y_z the differential $(d_{14})_d$ is given by Eq. (509). The *over-all value* of d_{14} between the Curie points, which would be obtained experimentally from observations of P by the *direct effect* with a ballistic galvanometer on applying a stress Y_z, is found from Eqs. (495e) and (508):

$$\left(\frac{1}{d_{14}}\right)_n^s = \frac{Y_z}{P^Y} = \frac{1}{b_{14}}(\chi'_s + BP^{Y2} - 3BP^0P^Y)$$

$$= \frac{1}{(d_{14})_0^s} + \frac{1}{b_{14}}(BP^{Y2} - 3BP^0P^Y) \qquad (512b)$$

For the treatment in the case of multi-domain crystals see §479. Outside the Curie points Eq. (512b) holds, with $P^0 = 0$ and χ' in place of χ'_s. From Eqs. (493b) and (500) it is easily proved that (512b) holds also for the *converse effect*,[‡] in which case P is the polarization due to E in the free crystal [see also Eq. (511)].

---

[*] By means of Eq. (493b), this expression is easily seen to be an extension of Eq. (3b) in Mueller[380] (in the latter equation the sign of E_x should be changed).

[†] Equation (522a) may be anticipated here, since its derivation is independent of the present discussion.

[‡] For experimental data on the converse effect, including observations of hysteresis, see Chap. XXI.

Expressions symmetrical with the foregoing are easily derived for e_{14}. First there are the initial values [cf. p. 591, Eq. (495c)]

$$(e_{14})_0 = a_{14}\eta_1 \qquad \text{and} \qquad (e_{14})_s^s = a_{14}\eta_s'' \tag{513}$$

outside and between the Curie points, respectively; the relation between $\eta_1 = 1/\chi_1$ and $\eta_s'' = 1/\chi_s''$ is given in Eq. (505a). The differential value $(e_{14})_d = a_{14}\eta_d''$ is found from Eq. (510):

$$\left(\frac{1}{e_{14}}\right)_d^s = \frac{\partial Y_z}{\partial P^y} = \frac{1}{a_{14}}(\chi_s'' + 3BP^{y2} + 6BP^0P^y)$$

$$= \frac{1}{(e_{14})_0^s} + \frac{1}{a_{14}}(3BP^{y2} + 6BP^0P^y) \tag{513a}$$

Outside the Curie points we write χ_1 in place of χ_s'' and set $P^0 = 0$.

From Eq. (510) the *over-all value* $(e_{14})_n^s = P^y/y_z$ can be found, where $P^y = (e_{14})_n^s y_z$ is the polarization due to the impressing of a strain y_z of any magnitude:

$$a_{14} = \chi_s''(e_{14})_n^s + 3BP^0 y_z(e_{14})_n^{s2} + By_z^2(e_{14})_n^{s3} \tag{513b}$$

The solution of this cubic equation would give $(e_{14})_n^s$ for any y_z in terms of the practically constant a_{14}. The dependence of e_{14} on strain is here made evident, while the dependence on temperature is introduced through χ_s'' and P^0. The over-all value can also be expressed in terms of P:

$$\frac{1}{(e_{14})_n^s} = \frac{y_z}{P^y} = \frac{1}{a_{14}}(\chi_s'' + BP^{y2} + 3BP^0P^y) = \frac{1}{(e_{14})_0^s} + \frac{1}{a_{14}}(BP^{y2} + 3BP^0P^y)$$

$$\tag{513c}$$

461. *A Correlation between the Voigt and Polarization Theories.* The general relation between the free and clamped susceptibilities according to Voigt's theory, as applied to Rochelle salt for fields in the x-direction, is found from Eq. (264) to be $\eta' = \eta'' + e_{14}d_{14}$. With Rochelle salt, as we have seen, a distinction must be made between the initial, over-all, and differential susceptibilities. We now write the expressions for the relations between the initial and over-all susceptibilities, both between and outside the Curie points.

From Eqs. (496), (501), (505a), and (505b), the difference between the free and clamped over-all dielectric stiffnesses between the Curie points is the same as that between the initial values χ_s' and χ_s'':

$$(\chi_s')_n - (\chi_s'')_n = \chi_s' - \chi_s'' = \chi' - \chi_1 = -a_{14}b_{14} \tag{514}$$

In terms of e_{14} and d_{14}, $a_{14}b_{14}$ can be expressed by means of Eqs. (509a), (509b), and (513):

Between the Curie points, $\quad a_{14}b_{14} = (e_{14})_0^s(d_{14})_0^s\chi_s'\chi_s''$ $\qquad$ (515)

Outside the Curie points, $\quad a_{14}b_{14} = (e_{14})_0(d_{14})_0\chi'\chi_1$ $\qquad$ (515a)

The corresponding equation in terms of over-all values can be found from Eqs. (512b) and (513c), but it is less simple. The Voigt theory does not lend itself easily to expressing the relation between the susceptibilities except for the initial values.

From Eqs. (514), (515), and (515a) one arrives at an independent proof of Eq. (264), particularized for the regions between and outside of the Curie points:

Between the Curie points, $\quad \eta_s' - \eta_s'' = (e_{14})_0^s(d_{14})_0^s$ $\qquad$ (516)

Outside the Curie points, $\quad \eta' - \eta_1 = (e_{14})_0(d_{14})_0$ $\qquad$ (516a)

The symmetry between Eqs. (514) on the polarization theory and Eqs. (516) and (516a) on Voigt's theory is obvious. The choice of expression for the difference between the susceptibilities is a matter of convenience.

462. The Elastic Constants s_{44} and c_{44}. Experimental evidence indicates that the constant-polarization value $s_{44}^P = 1/c_{44}^P$ is nearly independent of stress and temperature (§375). On the other hand, the isagric $s_{44}^E = 1/c_{44}^E$ varies greatly with both temperature and stress. The relation between s_{44}^E and s_{44}^P for large stresses is most simply expressed in terms of the Voigt coefficient $(d_{14})_n^s$, in which n signifies the over-all value given in Eq. (512b), applicable to large as well as to small stresses; outside the ferroelectric region the superscript s disappears. The desired relation is obtained by assuming P_t to be held equal to zero while Y_z is applied, so that $y_z = -s_{44}^P Y_z$. The field strength needed to make $P_t = 0$ during this process is $E = b_{14}Y_z$ by Eq. (493d). This E causes an additional strain, which we call $y_z^E = (d_{14})_n^s E = b_{14}(d_{14})_n^s Y_z$. With $E = 0$, y_z^E is absent, and the total strain is

$$y_z - y_z^E = [s_{44}^P + b_{14}(d_{14})_n^s]Y_z \equiv s_{44}^E Y_z$$

or from Eq. (512b)

$$s_{44}^E = s_{44}^P + b_{14}(d_{14})_n^s = s_{44}^P + \frac{P^Y b_{14}}{Y_z} \qquad (517)$$

where P^Y is the polarization due to Y_z when $E = 0$.* When Y_z is small, (517) becomes identical with (522c), since in the latter equation d_{14} is the initial value.

The isagric relation between y_z and Y_z, for zero field, can be expressed as follows, from Eqs. (517) and (495):

$$y_z = s_{44}^E Y_z = \frac{b_{14}}{a_{14}}Y_z + b_{14}P^Y = s_{44}^P Y_z + b_{14}P^Y \qquad (518)$$

where P^Y is given by Eq. (508).

---

* Equation (517) is a special case of Eq. (283).

Theoretical curves of the form suggested by this equation are shown in Fig. 142.

By making use of Eq. (517), together with the relations $y_z = s_{44}^E Y_z$, $s_{44}^E = 1/c_{44}^E$, and $s_{44}^P = 1/c_{44}^P$, one arrives at the following expression for s_{44}^E in terms of strain, in which the relation between P and y_z is given by Eq. (510):

$$\frac{1}{s_{44}^E} = c_{44}^E = c_{44}^P \left(1 - \frac{b_{14}P^y}{y_z}\right) \tag{519}$$

If a Rochelle-salt crystal could hold out under a sufficiently great stress, the isagric stiffness would approach the value for constant polarization. This fact can be seen from Eq. (517) or (519), for owing to the non-linear relation between stress and polarization the second term on the right approaches zero with increasing stress.

Equation (517), valid at all temperatures, states that the strain when $E = 0$ is that which would be produced by Y_z at constant polarization plus a term proportional to the polarization caused by Y_z. Since according to Eq. (517) saturation effects are present, it follows that a curve relating y_z with Y_z would show saturation, as is indeed the case in Fig. 142 and as was found experimentally by Iseley.[243] Thus not only are there mechanical and electrical saturation effects under an impressed electric field, as expressed in Eqs. (500) and (511), but also under an impressed mechanical stress.

As will be seen later in Eq. (528), a relation can be written between y_z and Y_z, valid above θ_u, in which the temperature enters explicitly.

If the assumption that Y_z produces the same polarization as a field $E = Y_z/b_{14}$ is justified, then at a critical value of Y_z there should be a sudden reversal of P^0. If Y_z were put through a cycle of positive and negative values, one would therefore expect to find the relation between P and Y_z or between y_z and Y_z in the form of a hysteresis loop. The coercive stress would be $(Y_z)_c = E_c/b_{14}$, of the order of 0.2 kg/cm².

The slope $-dy_z/dY_z$ of the $y_z : Y_z$ curve (with constant E) at any point may be called the *differential compliance* $(s_{44}^E)_d$, by way of analogy with the differential susceptibility. The over-all compliance is of course $s_{44}^E = y_z/Y_z$. By the same reasoning as in the discussion of mechanical bias in §459, so here it may be shown that the observed value of s_{44}^E should be less when a large constant biasing field E is impressed on the crystal. Such was indeed found to be the case by Mueller[380] in experiments on vibrating Rochelle-salt crystals: the resonant frequencies, which involve s_{44}^E, were found to be greater the larger the biasing constant field was made (see also §466).

No observations on this strain:stress hysteresis seem to have been made. The only pertinent data are those of Iseley, discussed in §418;

while they have the same form as the $P:E$ curves, they throw no light on the question of hysteresis. In any case, the analogy between Y_z and E must not be pushed too far: when Y_z is impressed, the lattice moves the dipole (or its equivalent), while the converse takes place when E is impressed. A very simple expression relating s_{44}^E to s_{44}^P is found when Y_z is so small that powers of P higher than the first can be omitted. From Eqs. (510) and (508) one finds with the aid of Eq. (495b), for small Y_z,

$$s_{44}^E \approx \frac{b_{14}}{a_{14}} \frac{\chi_s''}{\chi_s'} = s_{44}^P \frac{\chi_s''}{\chi_s'} = s_{44}^P \frac{\eta_s'}{\eta_s''} \tag{520}$$

The same relation follows directly from Eq. (495d). Since s_{44}^P is a finite constant nearly independent of temperature and $\eta_s' = \infty$ at the Curie points, it follows that for small stresses s_{44}^E should approach infinity at these points. This deduction from the theory is confirmed by the observations described in connection with Fig. 141.

Since for Rochelle salt $s_{44}^E = 1/c_{44}^E$ and $s_{44}^P = 1/c_{44}^P$, it follows from Eqs. (520) and (505a) that the isagric and isopolarization stiffness coefficients for small stresses are related thus:

$$\frac{c_{44}^P}{c_{44}^E} = \frac{s_{44}^E}{s_{44}^P} = \frac{\chi_s''}{\chi_s'} = \frac{\eta_s'}{\eta_s''} = 1 + \eta_s' a_{14} b_{14} \tag{521}$$

Similar reasoning for the region *outside* the Curie points leads to the analogous relations

$$\frac{c_{44}^P}{c_{44}^E} = \frac{s_{44}^E}{s_{44}^P} = \frac{\chi_1}{\chi'} = \frac{\eta'}{\eta_1} = 1 + \eta' a_{14} b_{14} \tag{521a}$$

463. In interpreting the results of experiments with *isolated* plates (electrodes far removed from crystal), account must be taken of the fact mentioned in §§190 and 199, that deformations then take place at constant electric displacement* D. The relation between s_{44}^E and s_{44}^D, the value at constant displacement, is readily found by specializing Eq. (281) for fields parallel to X in Rochelle salt:

$$\frac{s_{44}^E}{s_{44}^D} = \frac{k'}{k''} \tag{521b}$$

This equation gives the ratio of the compliance at zero gap (adherent electrodes) to that at infinite gap, for small stresses. In adopting as the value of s_{44}^P that derived from observations with a wide gap we disregard the fact that the ratio η_s'/η_s'' in Eq. (521) or η'/η_1 in Eq. (521a) is not quite the same as k'/k'' in Eq. (521b). However, in the least favorable

---

* The present chapter has to do only with X-cut plates of Rochelle salt, in which the polarization and displacement are parallel to the field. Under these conditions s_{44}^D is identical with the quantity s_{44}^* derived from Eq. (273a).

case, when k' has its smallest value, of the order of 75, the difference amounts to only about one-half of 1 per cent, which is not greater than the uncertainty in the observed value (see also §211).

From Eqs. (499), (505a), (520), and (521), s_{44}^E between the Curie points for small stresses may be expressed in the following ways:

$$s_{44}^E = \frac{\chi_s''}{c_{44}^P\chi_s'' - a_{14}^2} = -\frac{\chi_s''}{2D_{14}} = -\frac{\chi_1}{2D_{14}} + \frac{3}{2c_{44}^P} = (\eta_s'\chi_1 + \tfrac{3}{2})s_{44}^P \quad (522)$$

where

$$D_{14} \equiv \chi_1 c_{44}^P - a_{14}^2 = \frac{1}{s_{44}^E\eta' - d_{14}^2} = -c_{44}^P BP^{02} \quad (522a)$$

The parameter D_{14}, a function of the fundamental dielectric, elastic, and piezoelectric constants, plays a prominent part in Mueller's expression of his theory. The third of the expressions in (522) is identical with Eq. (11a) in his third paper.[380]

Outside the Curie points the equations are analogous but somewhat simpler:

$$s_{44}^E = \frac{\chi_1}{D_{14}} = \eta'\chi_1 s_{44}^P \quad (522b)$$

The last expression is equivalent to Eq. (521a) and also to Eqs. (4a) and (4c) in Mueller's paper II.

The general equations (275) and (276) as applied to s_{44} and c_{44} in Rochelle salt can also be derived from Eqs. (521) and (495b). Between the Curie points, for small stresses,

$$s_{44}^E = s_{44}^P + a_{14}b_{14}s_{44}^P\eta_s' = s_{44}^P + b_{14}^2\eta_s' = s_{44}^P + d_{14}^2\chi_s' \quad (522c)$$

$$c_{44}^E = c_{44}^P - a_{14}^2\eta_s'' = c_{44}^P - e_{14}^2\chi_s'' = c_{44}^P - \frac{e_{14}^2}{\eta_s''} \quad (522d)$$

Outside the Curie points the same equations hold, with η', χ', η_1, and χ_1 substituted for η_s', χ_s', η_s'', and χ_s''.

464. The Quadratic Piezoelectric Effect in Rochelle Salt. In a monoclinic crystal with constant angle β (corresponding to y_z in Rochelle salt), there is a linear converse piezoelectric effect expressed* by

$$x_x = b_{11}P_x \qquad y_y = b_{12}P_x \qquad z_z = b_{13}P_x$$

Since we are concerned here only with fields parallel to X, the monoclinic coefficients b_{26} and b_{35} (or d_{26} and d_{35}) play no part. In Rochelle salt the monoclinic angle is not constant but is represented by the spontaneous strain $y_z^0 = b_{14}P^0$ mentioned in §456; moreover, under electric or mechanical stress the strain can be altered by amounts even greater than y_z^0. According to Mueller's theory,[381] the extent to which Rochelle salt becomes monoclinic is measured by the departure of the configuration

---

* For the monoclinic terminology employed here, see §450.

of the crystal from the unstressed rhombic form. Thus even outside the Curie points the crystal takes on monoclinic characteristics when subjected to a shear y_z, and the magnitude of the monoclinic coefficients b_{11}, b_{12}, and b_{13} is assumed to be directly proportional to y_z, as expressed by the equations $b_{11} = \varphi_1 P_x$, $b_{12} = \varphi_2 P_x$, $b_{13} = \varphi_3 P_x$, where φ_1, φ_2, and φ_3 are constants. We are thus led to the following quadratic piezo-electric equations, in which the subscript x is omitted from P, with the understanding that only polarizations in the X-direction need be considered.

$$x_x = \varphi_1 P^2 \qquad y_y = \varphi_2 P^2 \qquad z_z = \varphi_3 P^2 \tag{523}$$

Beyond these there are also $y_z = b_{14}P$, $z_x = x_y = 0$.

When a field E is applied at a temperature between the Curie points, $P = P^0 + P^E$, where P^E is the polarization caused by E. It is sufficient to consider x_x alone, for which, if $E = 0$, we have $(x_x)_0 = \varphi_1 P^{0^2}$. If E is present, $x_x = (x_x)_0 + (x_x)_E = \varphi_1(P^0 + P^E)^2$, whence

$$(x_x)_E = \varphi_1 P^E(2P^0 + P^E) \tag{523a}$$

Several deductions can be made from this equation. (1) Outside the Curie points, where $P^0 = 0$, $(x_x)_E = \varphi_1 P^{E^2}$; this irreversible converse quadratic effect was observed by Mueller[381] at 25.5°C. (2) As long as E is less than the coercive E_c, there should be, between the Curie points, a reversible linear converse effect $(x_x)_E = 2\varphi_1 P^0 P^E$ of large magnitude. This effect does not seem to have been observed. (3) If $E > E_c$, the polarization P^0 has the same sign as E, and both the linear and the quadratic terms in Eq. (523a) are irreversible.

From his observations Mueller estimates φ_1 of the order $-1.2(10^{-9})$ cm³/erg. The crystal contracts in the X-direction for a sufficiently large field of either sign; this contraction at 3,000 volts is of the same order as that caused by a pressure of 100 atm (§82).

Mueller finds in this quadratic effect an explanation of the anomalous thermal expansion of Rochelle salt in the range of spontaneous polarization, to which reference has been made in §407. He also discusses an analogous quadratic optical effect.[381]

The production of the strains x_x, y_y, and z_z makes a contribution to the specific heat, and it also suggests slight changes in a_{14}, c_{44}^P, and B at the Curie points.[380,381]

To such effects as those treated in this section, in which new physical constants come into being in a crystal as the result of a deformation, Mueller gives the name "morphic effects."* Pushed to its logical

---

* The magnitude of d_{11}, calculated from Mueller's values of x_x and E_x by the equation $d_{11} = x_x/E_x$, is quite astonishingly large, except at fields of only a few volts per centimeter. Thus we find, from Mueller's data, $d_{11} = 500(10^{-8})$ when $E_x = 1$ esu.

conclusion, this concept is equivalent to asserting that a crystal belongs to its assigned class only as long as it is free from stress of any sort. When under strain it possesses a different, usually a lower, set of elements of symmetry. Attention is called to this fact in §531 in connection with the piezo-optic effect (see also §482). With most phenomena in the great majority of crystals, morphic effects are doubtless of a high order, thus escaping detection.

Mueller also points out that the quadratic effects of the type described differ in principle from electrostriction, since they occur only when the strain y_z is not suppressed. Moreover, their magnitude in Rochelle salt is thousands of times greater than any known electrostrictive effect.*

465. The Curie-Weiss Laws. For ferromagnetic substances above the Curie point, as is seen from Eq. (561), the Curie-Weiss law is

$$k_m = C/(T - \theta)$$

where k_m is the magnetic mass susceptibility, C a constant, and T any absolute temperature above the Curie temperature θ. By proper choice of C, the volume susceptibility may be written in place of k_m. Over a narrow range just below the Curie point the susceptibility is $k_m/2$, as shown in §552.

In §552 it is proved that the linear relations between $1/k_m$ and temperature, both above and below the Curie point, are independent of the coefficients p and q in the generalized Langevin function [Eq. (562)]. In the first form of his theory of Rochelle salt, as will be seen in §485, Mueller postulated a cubic equation relating the polarization P with the molecular electric field F, together with an expression similar to Weiss's Eq. (557). The molecular-field theory led to the Curie-Weiss law for the dielectric susceptibility in exactly the same manner as in the magnetic case.

The interaction theory that has been discussed in the foregoing sections does not of itself predict the Curie-Weiss law or any other depend-

---

rising to $1,600(10^{-8})$ when $E_x = 10$ esu. These values are of the order of d_{14} itself. It must be noted, however, that this is not a true longitudinal effect in the ordinary sense, for the following reasons: (1) Since the effect is *quadratic* in E_x, the strain x_x maintains the same sign (a contraction) on reversal of E_x when $E_x > E_c$. (2) Being "morphic," it is a converse effect only. There can be no morphic direct effect involving d_{11}, since neither in the rhombic nor in the monoclinic system is there an elastic coefficient s_{14}. For this reason there should be no piezoelectric contribution from the morphic d_{11} to the dielectric constant at any temperature, although Mueller holds that there should be an effect on the dielectric constant of the *clamped* crystal. It is also conceivable that Rochelle salt, being monoclinic between the Curie points, may in this region also possess small but measurable coefficients d_{11}, d_{12}, d_{13}, d_{26}, and d_{35} that are not morphic (see §483).

* See also Matthias.[353]

ence of electric or piezoelectric properties upon temperature. Such prediction is impossible without some form of molecular theory. Hence on the basis of the interaction theory the Curie-Weiss law has to be accepted as an experimental fact. From it, as will now be shown, can be deduced certain other linear relations that have an important bearing on the general theory.

The discovery of the Curie-Weiss law for Rochelle salt may be credited to Kurchatov and Eremeev.[292] As explained in §§434 and 444, it has been most exactly established by the experiments of Mueller and Hablützel. According to Eq. (490), the initial reciprocal susceptibility above θ_u is given by

$$\chi' = \frac{t - t_c}{C} \qquad (524)$$

When this value is substituted in Eq. (498), the following equation results, giving the relation between P and E for any temperature for the first few degrees above θ_u:*

$$E = \frac{t - t_c}{C} P + BP^3 \qquad (524a)$$

In his paper I, Fig. 10, Mueller shows a set of experimental $P:E$ curves for temperatures from 24.3 to 31.2°, which are in full agreement with Eq. (524a) for $t_c = 23°$, $C = 170$, $B = 10(10^{-8})$. The values of these three constants are not far from those given in connection with Eq. (490), which are based on other data. The curves have forms varying between that of curve c, Fig. 139, at the lowest temperature, and that of curve e at the highest.

Below θ_u the Curie-Weiss law, expressed by Eq. (490a), is illustrated in Fig. 120. The slope of the $\chi':t$ curve is here twice as great as that above θ_u; this agrees with theory, since according to Eq. (499) $\chi'_s = -2\chi'$, where χ'_s is the initial value in the ferroelectric range.

Since from Eqs. (496) and (505a) $\chi_1 = \chi' + a_{14}b_{14}$ (rhombic clamping) and $\chi''_s = \chi'_s + a_{14}b_{14}$ (monoclinic clamping), it follows that the Curie-Weiss relation holds for the clamped as well as for the free crystal. for a few degrees on each side of θ_u. Above and below θ_u we find, from Eqs. (499) and (524),

$$\chi_1 = \frac{t - t_c}{C} + a_{14}b_{14} = \frac{t - (t_c - a_{14}b_{14}C)}{C} \approx \frac{t - 18°}{C} \qquad (525)$$

$$\chi''_s = \frac{2(t_c - t)}{C} + a_{14}b_{14} = \frac{t_c - (t - a_{14}b_{14}C/2)}{C/2} \qquad (525a)$$

The slopes of the lines representing these equations, as indicated in Figs. 143 and 145, are $1/C$ and $-2/C$, respectively. The constant C

* Ref. 376, Eq. (38).

is the same for the clamped as for the free crystal. The significance of the temperature 18° in Eq. (525) is pointed out in §468.

The linear relations between χ' (or χ_1) and temperature lead to other linear relations, or Curie-Weiss laws, for all physical quantities dependent on the susceptibility. They will now be summarized.

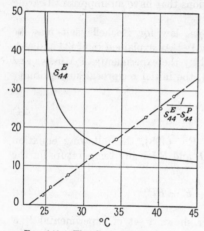

FIG. 141.—The Curie-Weiss law for the elastic compliance s^E_{44} of Rochelle salt, from Mueller. For the curve the ordinates should be multiplied by 10^{-12}; for the straight line, by 10^{10}. The circles are from Mason's experimental data.

466. For the *spontaneous polarization* P^0 we find from Eqs. (497) and (524)

$$P^{02} = \frac{t_c - t}{BC} \equiv h(t_c - t) \quad (526)$$

where h is a constant. This equation expresses the parabolic form of the curve for P^0 in Fig. 147. It is necessary, however, to assign different values to h for the right and left portions of the "parabola." According to Mueller[376] the values are approximately $1.5(10^4)$ and $2.65(10^4)$ for the higher and lower temperatures, respectively.

From Eqs. (502) and (526) an analogous expression is derived for the *coercive field* E_c.

For the *elastic compliance* s^E_{44} the following expressions for the value with small stress follow from Eqs. (495b), (499), (522c), and (524): Outside the Curie points,

$$s^E_{44} - s^P_{44} = \frac{Cb^2_{14}}{t - t_c} \equiv \frac{\sigma}{t - t_c} \quad (527)$$

where C is the "electric Curie constant" and $\sigma = Cb^2_{14}$ is the "elastic Curie constant" (Mueller). Between the Curie points,

$$s^E_{44} - s^P_{44} = \frac{Cb^2_{14}}{2(t_c - t)} \quad (527a)$$

For $t_c = 23°$ and $Cb^2_{14} = 66.7(10^{-12})$, Mueller[378] finds Eq. (527a) very exactly in accord with experiment at temperatures above θ_u, as is evident from Fig. 141. The curve for s^E_{44} is derived from Mason's observations,* which are illustrated also in Fig. 146. From this curve, together with the constant $s^P_{44} = 1/c^P_{44}$, values of $1/(s^E_{44} - s^P_{44})$ are plotted. They are

* See §§375 and 474.

a linear function of temperature, thus confirming Eq. (527a). Of special interest in Fig. 141 is the pointing of s_{44}^E toward an infinite value at the Curie point, according to the prediction in §462. The physical meaning of this fact is that at the Curie point Rochelle salt is in an unstable condition, which makes it elastically "soft" with respect to small stresses, just as it is dielectrically soft, with a dielectric constant approaching infinity, on the application of a small field. It was pointed out in §455, in explanation of Fig. 128, that close to the Curie points the dielectric constant is smaller in large than in small fields; similarly, as the mechanical stress Y_z is increased from a very small value at a temperature close to either Curie point, the crystal becomes stiffer (see §§459 and 462). That is, the phenomenon of saturation is most striking close to a Curie point. No static elastic observations are at hand indicating abnormally large values of s_{44}^E under small stresses. In agreement with Mason, Busch[87] observed a decrease of 30 per cent in the resonant frequency of a vibrating Rochelle-salt plate as the temperature passed through the upper Curie point. The magnitude of the observed effect depends on how small the field is, as well as on the elastic constants other than the temperature-sensitive s_{44}^E that enter into the expression for the frequency.

From Eq. (527) and the general equations of the polarization theory given above, Mueller[380] has derived the following expression for the relation between Y_z and the strain y_z that it causes *at zero field*, valid for the first 10° above θ_u. In the present notation the equation is

$$Y_z = (Y_z + c_{44}^P y_z)\frac{\Delta t}{\sigma c_{44}^P} + (Y_z + c_{44}^P y_z)^3 \left(\frac{\Delta t}{\sigma c_{44}^P} + 1\right)\frac{B}{\chi_1 a_{14}^2} \quad (528)$$

where $\Delta t = t - \theta_u$ and $\sigma = Cb_{14}^2$ as in Eq. (527). A plot of this theoretical curve is shown in Fig. 142 for several temperatures.

There are no experimental data with which a quantitative comparison can be made, except at small stresses. The observations of Iseley[243] on a 45° X-cut bar yield curves relating y_y' to Y_y' that have the form of those in Fig. (142); hence they may be regarded as a qualitative verification of the saturation effect expressed in Eq. (528), since by Eqs. (43) the compliance $s_{22}' = y_y'/Y_y'$ contains $s_{44} = 1/c_{44}$.

The values of s_{44}^E calculated from the initial slopes of the curves in Fig. 142 agree closely with the values in Fig. 141 for the same temperatures.

467. For the *piezoelectric coefficient* $(d_{14})_0$ under small stresses, a Curie-Weiss law is to be expected, owing to the close relationship between d_{14} and η'. Above θ_u we have, from Eq. (495b), $d_{14} = b_{14}\eta'$, whence from Eq. (524) it follows that

$$(d_{14})_0 = \frac{b_{14}C}{t - t_c} \quad (529)$$

Below θ_u, where $\eta'_s = -\eta'/2$, the corresponding expression is

$$(d_{14})_0^s = \frac{b_{14}C}{2(t_c - t)} \tag{529a}$$

These two equations show clearly the relation between the Voigt piezo-electric coefficient d_{14}, which is highly variable with temperature, and the piezoelectric constant b_{14} according to the polarization theory, which is found experimentally to be almost independent of temperature. The product of b_{14} by the electric Curie constant C may be called the *piezo-electric Curie constant*.

Satisfactory confirmation of Eqs. (529) and (529a) is found in the experiments of Norgorden, described in §424.

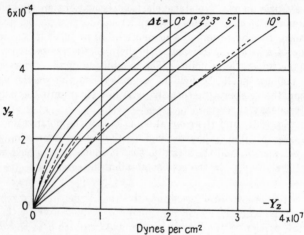

Fig. 142.—Theoretical isagric stress-strain relation for shear in the YZ-plane of Rochelle salt, above the Curie point, from Mueller.

Mueller[378,381] also finds linear relations corresponding to the Curie-Weiss law for the Kerr effect and for the monoclinic strain x_x described in §464.

In the foregoing paragraphs little has been said concerning the Curie-Weiss laws *below the lower Curie point*. Inasmuch as the law holds with respect to the dielectric susceptibility below θ_l, it can hardly be doubted that linear relations like those given above hold for all the physical quantities involved.

The dependence of the dielectric, elastic, and piezoelectric coefficients on temperature over the entire range between the Curie points is treated in §474.

468. Theory of Rochelle Salt between the Curie Points. From Eqs. (495b), (497), and (522c) it is clear that between the Curie points the spontaneous polarization P^0, the compliance s_{44}^E, and the piezoelectric coefficient $(d_{14})_s$ can all be expressed by equations in which the only quantity that varies with temperature is the initial susceptibility η_s'. Hence any theory that accounts for the dependence on temperature of η_s', or indeed of any one of these four quantities, will at the same time explain the temperature dependence of the other three. In §§445 and 446 we have referred to the early attempts of Kurchatov and of Fowler to find a relation between susceptibility and temperature. More recent attacks on this problem have been made by Mueller[376,378,380,381] and by Busch.[88] Like Busch (§485), Mueller in his first paper used a method closely analogous to that of Weiss in ferromagnetism, in which the concept of the molecular field F was involved. Mueller's explanation of the Curie points and of the variability of susceptibility with temperature, which he accomplished by postulating a slight effect of temperature on the molecular polarizability, will be discussed in Chap. XXVI.

For the present we are concerned with Mueller's later theory, according to which Rochelle salt possesses a single anomaly, inherent in the clamped crystal. The type of constraint is that which in §450 we have called "rhombic clamping," by which all strains are prohibited, including in particular, between the Curie points, the spontaneous strain y_z^0. As may be seen from Eq. (510a), this clamping completely neutralizes the spontaneous polarization P^0. The fundamental dielectric properties of Rochelle salt are regarded as inhering in the rhombically clamped crystal, in which the prohibition of strains ensures the absence of all piezoelectric deformations.

The particular property on which the theory depends is expressed by the Curie-Weiss law for χ_1 in Eq. (525) and is illustrated by the high-temperature portion of the χ_1 line in Fig. 143. Starting at the highest temperature, χ_1 slopes downward linearly, threatening to vanish at about 18°C; and if the crystal were not piezoelectric, χ_1 *would* vanish at this temperature, rising again at temperatures below 18°C, somewhat as indicated by the dotted lines.*

By Eq. (497) the χ' line for the free crystal is at a nearly constant distance $a_{14}b_{14}$ below the χ_1 line, with the consequence that $\chi' = 0$ at about 24°C and also at some temperature below 18°C. The presence of the two Curie points is thus accounted for.

* The infinite susceptibility of the completely clamped crystal, implied in the vanishing of χ_1, seems at first sight paradoxical, since large susceptibilities are usually associated only with *free* crystals. The physical explanation probably lies in the unstable state of the clamped crystal. The spontaneous polarization P^0, which the crystal would possess at 18° if free, is suppressed. Just as the introduction of an extremely small strain y_z would cause a relatively large polarization to develop, so a weak field may so deform the crystal lattice as to produce the same result. The same explanation may be offered for the low value of χ_1 at 5°C.

469. It is pertinent at this point to quote from Mueller's paper IV, on the possible nature of the hypothetical transition in the neighborhood of 18°C and on the reason why the course of the χ_1 line between the Curie points, as calculated from observations on the free crystal, has the particular form shown in Fig. 143.

"If the crystal of Rochelle salt were not piezoelectric it would show only a single transition point. The two Curie points and the large number of dielectric, piezoelectric, optical, caloric and thermal anomalies of the free crystal can all be explained

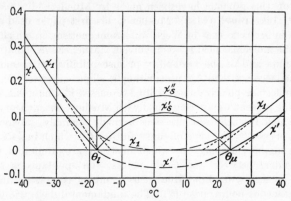

FIG. 143.—Schematic diagram of the dependence of the reciprocal susceptibilities on temperature, for small fields, from Mueller. It is based on measurements of χ' outside the Curie points, from Figs. 120 and 121, and of χ'_s between these points. From these values, χ' between the Curie points was calculated from Eq. (499) and χ_1 from Eq. (496), $\chi'_1 \ (\equiv 1/\eta'')$ is the dielectric stiffness for rhombic clamping; χ''_s is for monoclinic clamping. calculated from Eq. (505a). The ordinate differences $\chi'_1 - \chi$ and $\chi''_s - \chi'_s$ are approximately constant and equal to $a_{14}b_{14}$.

on the basis of laws which are logical extensions of the laws of classical crystal physics. There remains, therefore, only the problem of understanding the nature of the transition of the clamped crystal. This transition is characterized by a high maximum of the [rhombically clamped] dielectric constant, but the available evidence does not indicate any changes of the internal energy or of the structure. The temperature gradient of the birefringence is altered but there is no sudden change of the optical constants. These peculiarities indicate that the transition can involve only a change of the position or of the dynamics of the protons of either the OH groups or the water of crystallization. The transition may be similar to those in HBr, HI, H_2S, PH_3.* It differs, however, from the modifications of these crystals by the fact that the transition of Rochelle salt produces no change of the specific heat. To account for this we propose the hypothesis that the transition is suppressed, i.e., with decreasing temperature the crystal approaches a transition point without actually reaching it, because in the initial stages of the transition secondary effects are created which suppress the modification and the crystal remains in its original state because at lower temperature the protons have not sufficient energy to change their positions."

* For a review of these transitions see A. Eucken, *Z. Elektrochem.*, vol. 45, p. 126, 1939. See also J. A. Hedvall and R. W. Pauly, *Z. physik. Chem.*, vol. 29, *Abt.* B, pp. 225–230, 1935.

In explaining the nature of this suppression of the transition point, Mueller advances the hypothesis that it is related to the piezoelectric morphic effects discussed in §464. One may carry this suggestion somewhat beyond the point where Mueller leaves it, by considering that in the clamped crystal between the Curie points these morphic effects (the development of strains x_x, y_y, and z_z when a field E_x is applied) try to assert themselves just as y_z does. Although suppressed by the clamping stresses so far as the *external* configuration is concerned, they may be accompanied by changes in the *internal* structure of such a nature that the polarization, when a field E_x is applied, is less than it would be if only the strain y_z were concerned. The whole question concerning the tendency toward a transition point in the clamped crystal at 18°C and of its suppression cannot be satisfactorily answered until more is known about the lattice structure of Rochelle salt.

Whatever the mechanism may be, the result is a rounding off of the χ_1 line to a minimum at about 5°C. It is therefore at this temperature, according to Mueller's theory, that the maxima in χ'_s and P^0 occur, together with hysteresis curves of greatest width and greatest energy loss.

If the χ_1 line actually touched the horizontal axis in Fig. 143, the rhombically clamped Rochelle-salt crystal would have a single Curie point like that in ferromagnetic materials, with infinite clamped dielectric constant at this point. On the other hand, the two Curie points of the unconstrained *heavy-water* Rochelle-salt crystal are so far apart that the χ_1 line would certainly intersect the horizontal axis twice.* The clamped crystal would therefore still have two Curie points with a spontaneous polarization between them.

470. One conclusion that can be drawn from Fig. 143 is that a *partial mechanical constraint* would be expected to draw the Curie points of Rochelle salt closer together. In §204 we have shown that a partial constraint diminishes the effective piezoelectric contribution to the susceptibility, yielding a value intermediate between those of a free and a fully clamped crystal. The effect in the case of Fig. 143 would be a decrease in the vertical separation of the χ_1 and χ' lines: if the χ_1 line remained constant, the χ' line would move vertically upward so that its intersections with the horizontal axis, at θ_l and θ_u, would be separated by a smaller interval. No systematic investigation of this effect seems to have been made, although it was mentioned by Mueller[376] as a possible explanation of the lack of agreement on the part of different observers as to the values of θ_l and θ_u. From the hysteresis loops in Fig. 129,

---

* That this is so can be seen from the fact that the elastic and piezoelectric properties of ordinary and heavy-water Rochelle salt are so nearly the same, as shown in §§87 and 143, that the vertical separation of the χ' and χ_1 lines for the heavy-water variety is nearly the same as in Fig. 143.

however, it is evident that mechanical constraint at least makes the $P:E$ curve approximate that of a fully clamped crystal. The only experimental data on the Curie point of a partially constrained crystal are those of Mason,[338] who finds the maximum susceptibility of a "longitudinally clamped" vibrating crystal to come at a temperature that, from his diagrams, appears to be substantially the same as for a free crystal, about 24°C. Mason used an X-cut 45° bar with full-length plated electrodes, to which a voltage of twice the fundamental lengthwise-vibration frequency was applied. The piezoelectric contribution to the polarization, so far as lengthwise movements are concerned, was thus neutralized (§61), while lateral movements were allowed to develop. The dielectric constant was indeed found to lie between the values for a free and a clamped crystal; it is difficult to see why this degree of constraint should not have been accompanied by an easily detectable decrease in the temperature for maximum dielectric constant, unless it be that the constraint imposed by inertia in the dynamic case differs, in its effect upon the temperature dependence of the dielectric susceptibility, from the constraint due to static externally applied clamping stresses. In this connection it may be recalled that under the constraining effect of *hydrostatic* pressure both Curie points are *raised* (§443), whereas a consideration of Fig. 143 led us to expect that *externally* applied mechanical constraint would increase θ_l but decrease θ_u. The discrepancy becomes resolved if we assume, with Bancroft, that the observed raising of the Curie points under hydrostatic pressure is due, not to mechanical constraints in the ordinary sense, but rather to distortion of the crystal lattice under pressure.

471. *What is a Ferroelectric?* We conclude this consideration of the theory of Rochelle salt with a brief retrospect to the essential ferroelectric phenomena, as described in the foregoing chapters. In spite of the knowledge acquired through the observations with mixed tartrates (§491) and the phosphates and arsenates (§493), conclusions must still be drawn chiefly from Rochelle salt. The investigations on the mixed tartrates have contributed to the dipole theory (§490) without throwing new light on Mueller's interaction theory. For lack of piezoelectric and elastic data on the phosphates and arsenates, it is not yet possible to say how completely all the details of the interaction theory apply to them. It can at least be said that no observations hitherto recorded on crystals other than pure Rochelle salt contradict any of the following statements:

So far as macroscopic observations are concerned, a ferroelectric crystal may be defined as having a critical temperature, on one side of which the dielectric properties exhibit non-linearity and hysteresis (the *ferroelectric* region), while on the other side there is no hysteresis and the relation between polarization and field is nearly or quite linear (the parelectric region).   The possession of such a critical temperature, or Curie point, is the basic criterion.   Rochelle salt has two such points; some of the isomorphic mixtures as well as the phosphates and arsenates may have only an upper Curie point.   Possibly a crystal with only a lower Curie point will one day be discovered, or one that is stable only in the ferroelectric temperature range, so that no Curie point is observable.

Among the directly observed concomitant effects, at least in Rochelle salt, may be mentioned the following:

1. A Curie-Weiss law for dielectric, elastic, and piezoelectric effects on both sides of the Curie point.

2. The crystal is piezoelectric on both sides of the Curie point.

3. A reversible spontaneous polarization on one side of the Curie point, falling to zero at that point.

4. The crystal is pyroelectric in the region of spontaneous polarization (but see §521).

5. In the region of spontaneous polarization, abnormally large values of the dielectric constant of the free crystal, the piezoelectric constant, and the isagric elastic constant, as well as large dielectric losses (§375), are observed under certain field strengths and stresses.   As the Curie point is approached, these three quantities tend toward infinite values under small field strengths and stresses.

6. At all temperatures the dielectric and piezoelectric constants become diminished by mechanical constraints.

7. Except with occasional very small specimens, the crystal has, in the region of spontaneous polarization, a multi-domain structure with opposing polarizations in adjacent domains.

The interaction theory leads to the following conclusion, which is at least partly corroborated by experiment:

8. The *clamped* crystal obeys a dielectric Curie-Weiss law.   Beyond this, the anomalous behavior of the clamped crystal with varying field and temperature is such as to furnish, through the equations of the interaction theory, a description of all the other anomalies.

It is too early to say whether all the effects 1 to 8 are essential properties of all ferroelectric crystals.   It is hardly conceivable that the ferromagnetic analogy can exist without 3 and 6.   It appears possible, however, that the essential features of the analogy might be present in a single-domain crystal, so that 7 cannot be regarded as a necessary characteristic.

According to the interaction theory, a ferroelectric crystal is one which, from §453, has $\eta_1 > a_{14}b_{14}$ in a certain range of temperature. The corresponding condition according to the dipole theory, from §485, is $\alpha_M > 1/\gamma$. This correspondence is discussed in §486. The two expressions are equivalent inasmuch as each postulates the attainment at a certain temperature of a critical polarizability in excess of a certain value. It is only when this condition is fulfilled that there can be a spontaneous polarization and a spontaneous strain, which can be reversed by an applied field, giving rise to the appearance of abnormally large values of the dielectric, piezoelectric, and elastic constants.

One may ask why ferroelectric properties are not observed in more cases among crystals. The answer is partly that very few crystals have been investigated over wide ranges of temperature and partly that these properties are due to a fortuitous combination of circumstances. In the first place, the polarizability must be great enough to satisfy the condition mentioned above. This is a necessary condition, but it is not sufficient; for although it implies an instability and a structural modification at a certain temperature, still of itself it does not give assurance that the crystal, on one side or the other of the critical temperature, will have a symmetry low enough for spontaneous polarization to be possible. Furthermore, on both sides of the critical temperature, the substance must be a solid dielectric with crystalline structure.

472. Owing to the impossibility of experimenting with a completely clamped crystal, Mueller's theory of Rochelle salt, based, as we have seen, on the assumption of a suppressed transition in the neighborhood of 18°C, must remain a matter of hypothesis. If, as was pointed out at the beginning of this section, a theoretical explanation could be established for the dependence of any one of the quantities P^0, s_{44}^E, $(d_{14})_s$, or η_s' upon temperature, it would serve as well as χ_1 for the basic parameter.

For example, a molecular theory of the spontaneous polarization P^0 that predicted the correct dependence of P^0 on temperature could be used as the starting point, and with the aid of the foregoing equations the various elastic, piezoelectric, and dielectric properties could be expressed in terms of this theory. To illustrate this fact, we tabulate below the principal dielectric equations: at the left, the various quantities are expressed in terms of χ_1; at the right, in terms of P^0. It is assumed that a_{14}, b_{14}, B, and C are determined experimentally and that Eq. (526) is established on a molecular-theoretical basis, giving the spontaneous polarization in agreement with experiment.

FUNDAMENTAL EQUATIONS

$\chi' = \chi_1 - a_{14}b_{14}$	(497)		$\chi' = -BP^{02}$		(497)
$BP^{02} = a_{14}b_{14} - \chi_1$	(497)		$\chi_1 = a_{14}b_{14} - BP^{02}$		(497)
$\chi_s' = 2(a_{14}b_{14} - \chi_1)$	(499)		$\chi_s' = 2BP^{02}$		(499)

DEPENDENCE ON TEMPERATURE

$$\chi' = \frac{t - t_c}{C} \qquad (524) \qquad P^{0^2} = \frac{t_c - t}{BC} = -\frac{\chi'}{B} = \frac{\chi'_s}{2B} \quad \begin{cases} (526) \\ (497) \\ (499) \end{cases}$$

$$\therefore \; \chi' = \frac{t - t_c}{C} = -BP^{0^2} \quad \begin{cases} (526) \\ (497) \\ (499) \end{cases}$$

$$\chi'_s = \frac{2(t_c - t)}{C} \qquad (499) \qquad \chi'_s = \frac{2(t_c - t)}{C} = 2BP^{0^2} \quad \begin{cases} (526) \\ (497) \\ (499) \end{cases}$$

$$\chi_1 = \frac{t - t_c}{C} + a_{14}b_{14} \qquad (525) \qquad \chi_1 = a_{14}b_{14} - BP^{0^2} \qquad (497)$$

$$\chi''_s = \frac{2(t_c - t)}{C} + a_{14}b_{14} \quad (525a) \qquad \chi''_s = a_{14}b_{14} + 2BP^{0^2} \quad (499), (505a)$$

473. The existence of a spontaneous polarization on one side of the Curie point but not on the other suggests a change from a pyroelectric to a non-pyroelectric class at this temperature. In terms of crystal energy, one may regard the crystal as having a state of minimum energy U for one of these two configurations, represented by curve A in Fig. 144 and by curve B for the other configuration. If B were lower than A at all temperatures, the state corresponding to A would not exist at all. If $B > A$ above some temperature θ_u, be-

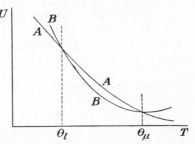

FIG. 144.—Two overlapping states of minimal energy.

coming less than A below this temperature, a change will take place in lattice configuration and crystal classification; and if B corresponds to a configuration in which there is a spontaneous polarization, there will be an upper Curie point at θ_u. If the two curves happen to have a second intersection at a lower temperature θ_l, there will be a lower Curie point here.

Similarly, if there were theoretical grounds for treating the temperature dependence of either s^E_{44}, $(d_{14})_s$, or η'_s as the cornerstone of the theory of Rochelle salt, a table of relationships analogous to the foregoing could be drawn up, in terms of which all the parameters could be expressed. With η'_s, P^0, and the experimental values of a_{14}, b_{14}, and B given, it can be seen from Eq. (499) that the minimal value and absence of Curie points for χ_1 follow necessarily. The behavior of the clamped crystal would then appear, not as the cause of the anomalies, but as an incidental circumstance.

474. Experimental Confirmation of the Theoretical Curves in Fig. 143. The only complete data available at present are those derived by Mueller[378,380] from observations by Mason. Following Mueller, we use here for the dielectric constant of the free crystal and for the spontaneous polarization the values obtained by Bradford,* which are in substantial

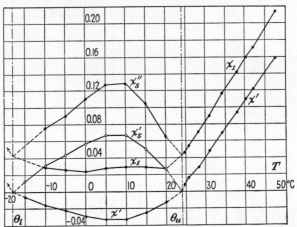

Fig. 145.—Reciprocal susceptibilities of Rochelle salt for free and clamped crystals as functions of temperature. Bradford's observations, as reported by Mueller.

agreement with the results of other observers. All values are "initial," obtained with small fields.

From Mason's resonance observations with an X-cut plated 45° bar, values of d_{14} and s_{44}^E are derived at each temperature. From these data, with the aid of Eqs. (497), (499), (505a), and (522b) and with

$$c_{44}^P = 11.6(10^{10})$$

dynes/cm², Figs. 145 and 146 have been drawn. The saturation coefficient B is obtained from χ_s' and P^0 by means of Eq. (499).

In Fig. 145 the observed quantities are χ' and χ_s', for the free crystal above and below θ_u. χ_1 for rhombic clamping,† χ_s'' for monoclinic clamping, and χ' between the Curie points are all derived by means of the equations mentioned above. The general similarity with Fig. 143, in which the curves between the Curie points are based on Mueller's theory, should be especially noted. The only obvious discrepancy lies in the value of χ_1, which in Fig. 145 fails to have a minimum close to zero. Now χ_1 is calculated from the equation

$$\chi_1 = \chi' + a_{14}b_{14} = -\frac{\chi_s'}{2} + a_{14}b_{14}$$

* E. B. BRADFORD, B.S. thesis, Massachusetts Institute of Technology, 1934.
† Outside the Curie points χ_1 is identical with $1/\eta_x''$.

It may be that $a_{14}b_{14}$, which we have taken from Mueller's calculations, is too large. At present one can only say that experimental verification of Mueller's hypothesis concerning the extremely low minimum in χ_1 is still lacking. At θ_u, however, χ_1 in Fig. 145 is in good agreement with Mason's[378] Fig. 7; and χ_s'' agrees well with Mason's curve for a (mono-clinically?) clamped crystal.

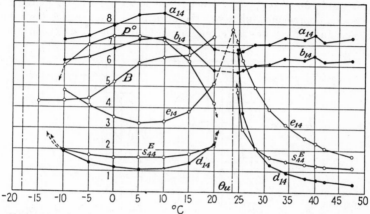

FIG. 146.—Piezoelectric and elastic constants of Rochelle salt in terms of temperature, from Mueller, calculated from Mason's observations. Ordinates are to be multiplied by the following factors:

Quantity	a_{14}	b_{14}	P^0	B	e_{14}	$s_{44}{}^E$	d_{14}
Factor	10^4	10^{-7}	100	10^{-8}	$2(10^5)$	10^{-11}	10^{-5}

In both Figs. 145 and 146 the dotted lines indicate gaps in the observational data that were used in the construction of these curves. The arrows show the trend to be expected beyond the observed limits. Of the values in Fig. 146, P^0 and s_{44}^E may be accepted with a fair degree of confidence as being representative of average well-prepared Rochelle salt crystals to within a few per cent. From Fig. 142 it is evident that with larger fields, and hence with larger stresses, considerably smaller values of s_{44}^E would be observed. The relatively low values of s_{44}^E obtained by Mandell and by Hinz (Table IV) were probably due to the use of large stresses.

In calculating d_{14} Mueller employed the gap method described in §310 [Eq. (452)], the essential data being the frequencies f_0 and f_∞ at series resonance, for gaps $w = 0$ and $w = \infty$, together with the density ρ, length l, and the dielectric constant. e_{14} is calculated from $e_{14} = d_{14}/s_{44}^E$; a_{14} and b_{14} are found from Eq. (495b), and s_{44}^E from f_0.

As is shown in §142, Mason, by a different method, found a_{14} to be practically independent of temperature. If his finding is accepted, one must conclude that the gap method employed in Mueller's calculation is incapable of yielding correct results with Rochelle salt. On the other hand, there may be unsuspected temperature dependencies among the various quantities appearing in Eq. (495d), which, if introduced, would confer on a_{14} a variation with temperature. All that can confidently be said at present is that the variability of a_{14} and b_{14} with temperature is at least an order of magnitude lower than that of e_{14} and d_{14}.

It will be observed that e_{14} depends less on temperature than does d_{14}. Instead of approaching infinity at the Curie points, e_{14} has at θ_u the value a_{14}/χ_1. In §546 reasons are given for considering the piezoelectric stress

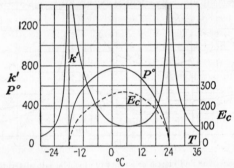

Fig. 147.—Dielectric constant k' at small fields, spontaneous polarization P^0, and coercive field E_c (in volts per centimeter), for Rochelle salt, from Bradford. Frequency 1,000 cycles per second.

coefficient e_{hk} in general of more fundamental significance than the strain coefficient d_{hk}.

The observations of Bradford[*] on which Fig. 145 is based are presented in another form in Fig. 147, taken from Mueller.[382] The curve for $k' = 1 + 4\pi\eta'$ corresponds to $\chi' = 1/\eta'$ and $\chi'_s = 1/\eta'_s$ in Fig. 145. P^0 is the same as in Fig. 146. The values of E_c may be compared with the data recorded in §436.

The dynamic value of d_{14} has also been measured by Mikhailov[368] from 0 to 40°C, by the use of $X45°$-bars with a small gap and a field of 1 to 2 volts/cm. His curve relating d_{14} to temperature is like that in Fig. 146, but the values over most of the range are only about one-third as large, owing possibly to the presence of the gap.

It has already been pointed out in §426 that relatively small values of d_{14} are to be expected when weak fields are used at frequencies as high as those in resonators. Comparison of Fig. 146 with the experimental results obtained with static and l-f alternating fields, as recorded in Chap. XXII, shows that in the h-f dynamic case this expectation is

* See footnote, p. 626.

fulfilled. According to §480, the discrepancies between the curve for d_{14} in Fig. 146 and Figs. 106, 109, and 115 are explained simply by the fact that in the resonator experiments the field and stress were so small that d_{14} never exceeded its initial value. As the Curie points were approached, this initial value became very large; midway between these points it was very small indeed in comparison with the values that it attains under larger stresses, and especially in static fields, as illustrated in Fig. 106.

475. Conclusions Respecting the Polarization Theory. In the foregoing pages we have given, with certain elaborations, an account of Mueller's interaction theory of Rochelle salt, in terms of the polarization theory, which was developed independently by Mueller and the author from premises first suggested by Mason. While the interaction theory might have been written in terms of Voigt's field theory, still the concepts of the polarization theory provide a description of the properties of Rochelle salt (and, without much doubt, of all other Seignette-electrics as well) that presents a clearer picture of the physical nature of the phenomena. The chief experimental justification lies in the fact that the coefficients a_{14} and b_{14} are found to have values nearly, if not quite, independent of temperature, and probably also independent of stress. a_{14} and b_{14} are therefore to be regarded as the true piezoelectric constants. As has been seen, the "constants" d_{14} and e_{14} vary enormously with both stress and temperature.

On the other hand, if the "true" dielectric constant is defined as that which would be observed with a clamped crystal, this constant so defined is not linear in E or independent of temperature, although the dependence on temperature is small in comparison with that of the free crystal.

Mueller has pointed out[382] that effects that are not directly related to the electric properties may be expected to vary linearly with temperature if at all, except for very slight changes at the Curie points and small effects caused by an electric field. An example of such a property is the elastic compliance s_{44}^D at constant electric displacement. s_{44}^D is the quantity derived from measurements of the elastic stiffness of a completely isolated crystal (§463), and it is found to have a very slight dependence on temperature, with a minute anomaly at the upper Curie point (§375). The compliance s_{44}^P at constant polarization, which plays an important part in the polarization theory, is numerically practically identical with s_{44}^D (§211).

In the basic equations (493a) to (493d) of the polarization theory no provision is made for variation of s_{44}^P with stress. A linear relation is assumed between stress and strain at constant polarization. The justification for this assumption lies in the approximate agreement of theory with observation as far as present experimental data go.

476. *Comparison of the Polarization Theory with Voigt's Field Theory.* As has been stated, both "theories" are only different ways of describing the same phenomena. If it were not for the great dependence of the elastic and piezoelectric constants of Rochelle salt on temperature, the polarization theory would probably never have arisen. The superiority of the polarization theory lies entirely in the fact that the elastic coefficients at constant polarization, and the piezoelectric coefficients when defined in terms of polarization rather than of field, are practically independent of temperature. The polarization theory does not reveal these facts; it only takes advantage of them. In particular, it gives clearer expression than does the field theory to this very important fact: To a high degree of approximation the piezoelectric strain, at all temperatures and up to the attainable limits of saturation, is *proportional to the polarization.* Mathematically, this statement is equivalent to saying that a_{14} and b_{14} are approximately constant, whereas e_{14} and d_{14}, which relate stress and strain with the *field*, vary greatly with temperature.

In the theoretical treatment of practical applications, whenever the polarization rather than the field can conveniently be used as the electrical parameter, the polarization theory is to be preferred. Voigt's formulation, using e_{14} and d_{14}, is to be used when the phenomena can more conveniently be described in terms of the applied field. For example, the latter is the case in dealing with the piezoelectric resonator. The question of the applicability of the polarization theory to piezoelectric crystals other than Rochelle salt is dealt with in §196.

CHAPTER XXV

THE DOMAIN STRUCTURE OF ROCHELLE SALT

La donna è mobile
Qual piuma il vento, . . .

—"RIGOLETTO."

477. Frequent reference has been made in the preceding chapters to the hypothesis that between the Curie points Rochelle salt, like iron, normally consists of an aggregate of distinct domains. The experimental evidence will now be examined, and the bearing of domain structure on dielectric and piezoelectric observations will be discussed. An account is included of Jaffe's theory of polymorphism in Rochelle salt, leading to the conclusion that Rochelle salt is properly to be regarded as monoclinic in the ferroelectric region.

The remark has been made by Debye* that a sample of unmagnetized iron is analogous to a mixture of microcrystalline tourmaline crystals with random orientations. The analogy is still closer if Rochelle salt is substituted for tourmaline.

The first suggestion that the spontaneous polarization in Rochelle salt might be due to *groups* of atoms having different orientations of the same probability in the lattice seems to have been made by Debye in the discussion of a paper by Dorfman.† This idea, adopted by Kurchatov and verified by Mueller and others, made the ferromagnetic analogy even more complete.

The experimental evidence is of several sorts. First, there is the electrical Barkhausen effect indicating discontinuous jumps in the process of polarization as the field is gradually increased; it constitutes an additional item in the long list of magnetic analogies (§555). This effect in Rochelle salt was described by Kluge and Schönfeld[261] and also by Mueller.[376] It is observed only between the Curie points.

Second may be mentioned the pyroelectric tests with Bürker's powder (§517), which reveal discrete regions of opposite polarity. The pyroelectric effect would be zero if the domains were very small and their polarities were equally divided in opposite directions. One evidence of the minute size of the domains in iron lies in the fact that iron is not pyromagnetic.

* "Handbuch der Radiologie," vol. 6, p. 750, 1925.

† J. DORFMAN, in "Magnetisme," *Rapports 6ème Conseil phys. (Inst. Solvay),* 1930 (pub. 1932), pp. 381–387.

From the size of the regions observed in his pyroelectric tests (§521), Mueller concludes that the domains in Rochelle salt are of the order of 1 cm in extent, enormously greater than in the case of ferromagnetism. His small crystals appeared to consist of single domains. That the domains are much less numerous than in iron is indicated by the relatively small number of Barkhausen "clicks," though it must be admitted that they are still sufficiently numerous to make one suspect that, if each domain is of the order of 1 cm^3, its polarity does not become reversed all in one jump. The effects of domain structure are manifest only between the Curie points.

To account for the large size of the domains, Mueller offers a hypothesis that may be stated thus: In the process of growth the crystal is constantly surrounded by a conducting liquid, which makes the surface equipotential and prevents the development of an opposing field. On the contrary, the domains in iron, while still very small, find themselves in the presence of opposing magnetic fields, which prevent further growth.

A necessary consequence of the presence of fairly large domains is *unipolarity*, which has sometimes been found, especially with small crystals or, as recorded by Kurchatov,[B32,294] in portions of a large crystal. In §433 unipolarity is further considered.

The domains in Rochelle salt preserve their individuality to a remarkable degree. Kurchatov states that after the large crystal, to which reference has just been made, had been kept for several hours at 40°C and then allowed to cool, the diminution in unipolarity was very slight. It would appear that the state of thermal disorder at high temperatures is unable to destroy either the configuration of the domains or the characteristic direction of the polarity in each domain, even though above the Curie point the spontaneous polarization is gone, only to reappear as the temperature passes downward through the critical temperature. This view is confirmed by Mueller's remark that no permanent reversal of the spontaneous field has ever been observed by him, even when a crystal was cooled while in a reversing field of 1,000 volts/cm. It is an interesting question whether the magnetic domains in iron also retain their individuality after being heated above the Curie point.

The persistence in polarity of individual domains can perhaps be explained in terms of the large mechanical stresses at the boundaries of adjacent domains when the crystal is in an electric field. Such stresses would tend to restore the original configuration and the original polarities on removal of the field. But a *single-domain* specimen might be expected to have its polarity permanently reversed by a strong reversing field.

Another consequence to be expected from the stresses between domains is that such stresses will prevent the isagric compliance s_{44}^E for very small stresses from being as great with a multi-domain crystal as in a single domain (§462 and Fig. 141).

478. *Can Large Single-domain Crystals Be Produced?* When a Rochelle-salt crystal is grown by the method of cooling from a hot solution, the gradual lowering of temperature must give rise to internal stresses. Since the solution is usually considerably above the upper Curie point at the start, the stresses may be expected to be especially large as the temperature passes through this point. It is conceivable that such stresses are an important factor in the breaking up of the crystal into domains. If this is the case, then it seems possible that, by growing crystals at a *constant temperature* between the Curie points, single domains, or at least multi-domain crystals with larger domains, might result. As has been stated in §412, a few experimenters have used crystals grown by evaporation at constant temperature. Although it must be admitted that the properties of such crystals do not appear to be recognizably different from those in the case of growth by cooling, still there is not found in the literature a satisfactory answer to the question whether the domain structure is dependent on the method of growth.

A little light was thrown on this problem by W. S. Stilwell, who compared the pyroelectric patterns formed on crystals grown by evaporation at a constant temperature between the Curie points with those on crystals grown by cooling.* Seeds were placed in a 1,500-cm³ flask containing a saturated solution at $1.8 \pm 0.02°C$. This flask, together with a large coil of copper tubing through which ice water was circulated, was immersed in a large container of water surrounded with good thermal insulation. In this container were also a heating coil, thermostat, and stirrer. An exhaust pump in constant operation kept the pressure of the air above the solution at a few millimeters of mercury. The water evaporated from the crystallizing flask was condensed in a second flask, which was cooled by a mixture of dry ice and alcohol.

The best crystal was grown to a size of 18.5 by 18 by 12 mm in 16 days. It is impossible to say what sort of domain structure this specimen might have been found to possess if it could have been tested at the temperature at which it was grown. It may be that in warming up to room temperature after removal from the solution and then in having its temperature changed by a few degrees during the pyroelectric test it took on a multiple-domain structure. At any rate, when it was sprinkled with a mixture of red lead and sulphur, it showed the presence of many domains. These appeared to be predominantly in the form of flat slabs of the order of 1 mm thick, with their planes normal to the Y-axis. Instead of being relatively large, the domains were found to be actually smaller than those observed by the same method on crystals grown by

* W. S. Stilwell, thesis for distinction, Wesleyan University, 1939.

cooling [crystals grown by R. W. Moore (§412), and from the Brush Development Company].

While these tests are not fully conclusive, they do not offer a hopeful prospect for the growth and permanence of single-domain Rochelle-salt crystals.

479. Effect of Domain Structure on the Hysteresis Loops. In Fig. 139 we have shown idealized curves for a single-domain crystal. It will be recalled that if the spontaneous polarization P^0 is represented by OO', then when the field E is impressed the observed polarization is given

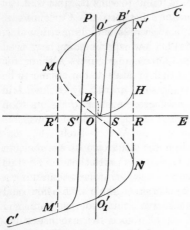

by Eq. (500) and illustrated by curve a, with origin at O'. Since the domain is already polarized at the start, there is no "virgin curve."

If a crystal contains a number of domains whose positive and negative spontaneous polarizations just balance, it shows no unipolarity as a whole. Such a case is represented theoretically in Fig. 148, in which OO' and OO'_1 are the average positive and negative values of P^0. In the ideal case, such as has hitherto been treated, the $+$ and $-$ domains make separate contributions to the observed polarization. As E increases from

Fig. 148.—Theoretical hysteresis loop for a multidomain Rochelle-salt crystal.

zero in the positive direction, the contribution of the positive domains is represented by $O'N'C$, with O' as origin; that of the negative domains is $O'_1NN'C$, with O'_1 as origin, the portion NN' representing the sudden reversal of the negative domains. The total observed polarization, which can now be depicted with origin at O, is half the sum of the two contributions, or $OHN'C$. The form of the virgin curve thus finds a theoretical explanation. If now E is put through a cycle from $+$ to $-$ and back, the hysteresis loop $CO'MM'C'O'_1NN'C$ results, exactly as in Fig. 139, where only domains of a single sign were considered. If the average $+$ and $-$ spontaneous polarizations do not exactly cancel, the foregoing discussion need be modified only to the extent of moving the origin to a position somewhat above or below O in Fig. 148.

Even with a single-domain crystal it is probable that local inhomogeneities would facilitate the reversal of polarity, so that the virgin curve would begin to turn upward at some such point as B, and the coercive force E_c would be $OS = -OS'$ instead of $OR = -OR'$. The corners of the loop would become rounded, leading to the form indicated in Fig. 148. The diminution of E_c must be still greater in a multi-domain crystal, in which the spontaneous deformation of each domain is hindered by adjacent domains. A field applied in either direction finds it easier to reverse those domains which oppose it, especially if, as in the case of iron (§555), some domains can grow at the expense of others.*

As to the actually observed field values, it will be recalled from §432 that under static excitation saturation has been recorded with a field strength as low as 15 volts/cm, while in a-c measurements from 50 to 1,000 cycles/sec the coercive field E_c is found to vary from zero at θ_u to about 200 volts in the neighborhood at 15°C, according to Hablützel. Mueller, as shown in Fig. 147, finds E_c to have a maximum of about 270 volts/cm at 5°C. Such discrepancies are not surprising in view of the variability in the domain structure. The foregoing values are only of the order of one-tenth as great as that calculated with the aid of Eq. (502). This fact does not invalidate the data in Fig. 147, which are based on actual measurement. It only goes to show that Eq. (502), which does not involve the domain structure, is incapable of furnishing the correct value of the coercive field.

In Fig. 128 it is seen that between the Curie points the dielectric constant is very much higher with moderately strong than with weak fields, just as is the case with the permeability of iron. As in the case of iron, the explanation lies in the shape of the polarization curve $OBB'C$ in Fig. 148. It is obvious that from point B on, the ratio $P:E$, and hence the dielectric constant of the free crystal, increases with increasing E up to the knee of the curve and remains relatively large up to very great values of E.

The foregoing account of dielectric hysteresis in Rochelle salt assumes that the energy loss per cycle, represented by the area of the loop, is involved in the work done in reversing the domains. This description is necessarily only qualitative; moreover, it does not take account of those viscous losses which may be independent of the reversal of domains. Nevertheless, the view that domain reversal plays an essential part in the phenomenon of hysteresis is not incompatible with the theory of hysteresis in Rochelle salt advanced by W. P. Mason, which is discussed in §375.

In Fig. 148 it will be observed that the initial slope, for $E = 0$, is the same at points O, O', and O'_1. Hence, so far as *small* fields are concerned, the observed dielectric properties of Rochelle salt are the same whether the specimen consists of a single domain or not, and all that has

---

* A painstaking, if not fully convincing, theory of domain structure has been attempted by David.[119]

been said from §452 on, concerning effects at weak fields and small stresses, becomes applicable to all specimens.

In a single-domain crystal or in a multi-domain crystal having a preponderance of spontaneous polarization of one sign, it is theoretically impossible, owing to the reversal of domains, to find any field strength whatever that will reduce the net polarization to zero.

480. A word is needed concerning the bearing of domain structure on the piezoelectric coefficient d_{14}. Outside the Curie points Rochelle salt is always rhombic dextrogyrate, and the sign of d_{14} is positive. In the ferroelectric region, where the crystal is monoclinic enantiomorphous, d_{14} is still positive, retaining the same sign whether the domain has a positive or negative spontaneous polarization. The sign of d_{14} would be negative only in a left-crystal. Owing to the close relationship between the susceptibility of a free crystal and d_{14}, it follows that the interaction between domains will have an effect on d_{14} similar to that on the susceptibility.

When the dielectric constant of Rochelle salt is measured with a low-voltage a-c bridge while a relatively large static field is impressed on the crystal, the value is diminished to an extent depending on the static field. An inspection of Fig. 148 shows this. The phenomenon is analogous to the effect of a mechanical bias discussed in §459. This effect has been recorded by Errera[134] and also by Mueller.[376]

In §§453 and 459 it was shown that the quantities $a_{14}y_z$ and $-b_{14}Y_z$ are equivalent to E in the production of polarization. It follows that when, as can be the case in Rochelle-salt resonators, there are periodic changes in strain or stress of sufficient magnitude for non-linear effects to be appreciable, the polarization:strain or polarization:stress curves must have the form indicated in Fig. 148. Some evidence of this is afforded by Figs. 112, 114, and 115. Unfortunately, no data are available for comparing, with the *same crystal*, the dependence of P_x on the mechanical stress Y_z, the dependence of the strain y_z on the electric stress E_x, and that of P_x on E_x, over wide ranges of these stresses.

We are now in a position to consider the dependence of the over-all piezoelectric coefficient $(d_{14})_n^s$ upon stress, in a multi-domain crystal. According to Eq. (512b), in a single-domain crystal this coefficient has its largest value at small stresses, when P is small, up to the point where the stress is great enough to cause a reversal of P^0. In the usual case of a multi-domain crystal, when static stresses of varying magnitude are applied, the $P:Y_z$ relation should be similar to the $P:E$ virgin curve in Fig. 148, with $(d_{14})_n^s = -P/Y_z$. Obviously, $(d_{14})_n^s$ is small up to the point B and has an approximately constant value identical with $(d_{14})_0^s$ in Eq. (509a). With increasing Y_z it increases rapidly toward a saturation value. This effect is to be expected over the temperature range in which hysteresis is present. Such experimental evidence as can be found is mentioned in §418. In particular, it follows from the dependence of P^0, and hence of the size of the hysteresis loop, upon temperature that under large stresses $(d_{14})_n^s$ is greatest midway between the Curie points, sloping gradually downward through the Curie points; at these points $(d_{14})_n^s$ fails to show maxima when the stress is large, as is illustrated in Fig. 106, p. 533.

Similar results are indicated by theory for the converse effect, in which case the hysteresis loops are plotted with y_z- and E-coordinates, and $(d_{14})_n^s = y_z/E$, as in Fig. 114.

Evidence for the existence of domains in Seignette-electric crystals other than Rochelle salt will be found in §498.

481. Polymorphism in Rochelle Salt. It has been pointed out by Jaffe[246] that whenever a transition takes place from a non-pyroelectric to a pyroelectric crystal class at a definite temperature an infinite value of the electric susceptibility is to be expected at this temperature, provided that the transition does not involve latent heat. In an earlier paper[245] Jaffe also discusses the question whether the Weiss region in iron should not be considered as tetragonal paramorphic rather than cubic, even though a single crystal, with its random orientations of domains, is externally cubic. It may be added that in 1916 Perrier[412] attempted to correlate the high-low inversion in quartz with the ferromagnetic Curie point and looked for a sharp maximum in the permittivity. That the result was negative can now be understood from the fact that neither high nor low quartz possesses primary pyroelectricity.

The rhombic system has three mutually perpendicular axes of unequal lengths. Hitherto Rochelle salt has always been assigned to the rhombic hemihedral (or bisphenoidal) class, No. 6, from goniometric measurements made presumably at room temperature and hence in the Seignette-electric range. In this class each of the three crystallographic axes is a twofold symmetry axis, which precludes the possibility of a polar axis. This means, physically, that it is impossible for any scalar agent, as temperature or hydrostatic pressure, to give rise to a vectorial phenomenon such as magnetic or electric polarization or for a linear electro-optic effect to exist in this class. Hence, in accordance with Neumann's principle as elaborated by Voigt, any pyroelectricity exhibited by this class must be of the "false" type.

Outside the region of spontaneous polarization the physical properties of Rochelle salt are entirely in accord with its rhombic hemihedral symmetry. Within this region, on the other hand, as was emphasized by Jaffe,[245] there are several one-way effects indicating that the X-axis is physically a polar axis and therefore should be so regarded crystallographically: spontaneous internal field, pyroelectricity (§521), unipolar conductivity (§410), asymmetry in polarizability (§433) and in the converse piezoelectric effect §(422), and a linear electro-optic effect.[376]

These effects are all characteristic of the domain, just as the large internal field in iron is a domain property. If in Rochelle salt as in iron the domains were very small, with their polarities distributed at random in space or equally divided along the $+$ and $-$ X-directions, none of the effects associated with a polar axis would be externally observable, and there would be no doubt about assigning Rochelle salt to the rhombic hemihedral class. For example, consider the pyroelectric effect, which Mueller found to be very strong in the range of spontaneous polarization. In view of what has been said, we must conclude either that this effect is only "apparent" as a result of the spontaneous polarization, or that between the Curie points Rochelle salt belongs properly to a class of lower symmetry. The latter view seems clearly the logical one, at least in the case of a crystal consisting of a single domain. The spontaneous polarization makes the X-axis a polar axis of symmetry in the physical sense; we shall now show that this is also true in the crystallographic sense.

In assigning Rochelle salt in the region between the Curie points to the appropriate class we confine the discussion to the single domain. The only rhombic class other than hemihedral that is piezoelectric is the hemimorphic, and this is excluded because of the absence of d_{14}. The proposals of Valasek[543] and of Taschek and Osterberg[504] in this regard are therefore of no avail. Now, if the X-axis is recognized as a polar axis, the Y- and Z-axes can no longer be axes of symmetry. With only one twofold axis of symmetry left the crystal must be monoclinic hemimorphic. It will be recalled that, while in both the rhombic and monoclinic systems the three axes are unequal, the rhombic system has its axes mutually perpendicular. On the other hand, in the monoclinic system one axis is perpendicular to each of the other two, the latter forming an angle different from 90°. Thus the transition from rhombic to monoclinic involves crystallographically only a change in the angle between two axes, in this case the Y- and Z-axes. These are the considerations that lead to the assignment of Rochelle salt to the monoclinic hemimorphic class.

According to Voigt's convention as stated in §5, the monoclinic polar axis b would be called the Z-axis. To avoid confusion we adopt Jaffe's suggestion that it now be called the X-axis, the rhombic Y-axis remaining unchanged, being now the same as the monoclinic Y-axis with sign reversed. The a-axis of the monoclinic crystal then makes a small angle β with the negative direction of the rhombic Y-axis. The rhombic Z-axis coincides with the monoclinic X- (or c-) axis.

This convention requires a revision of the subscripts of the piezoelectric constants with respect to Voigt's usage. It is brought about by exchanging the index 1 with 3, and 4 with 6.   The tabulation of constants then becomes, instead of that given in §131,

$$\begin{array}{cccccc} d_{11} & d_{12} & d_{13} & d_{14} & 0 & 0 \\ 0 & 0 & 0 & 0 & d_{25} & d_{26} \\ 0 & 0 & 0 & 0 & d_{35} & d_{36} \end{array}$$

The tabulation includes five new constants in addition to d_{14}, d_{25}, and d_{36}. No search for them seems to have been made beyond the experiments described in §§464 and 483. The chief difficulty in their detection and measurement lies in eliminating stray effects due to the large d_{14}. In the new matrix, d^{14} means the same as in §131.

The angle β between the c-axis and the orthogonal Z-axis is simply the angle of shear y_z imposed upon the domain by its own spontaneous field in the absence of an external field. This angle varies with temperature between the Curie points, having a maximum of the order of 3' at about 5°C. Reversal of the polarity of the domain by application of an external field reverses the direction of the polar axis and changes the sign of β.

It is not surprising that so small a departure from the orthogonal relation has escaped notice, especially since goniometric measurements have presumably been made with crystals in which there were complexes of opposing domains. The point to emphasize is that the structure of Rochelle salt is essentially that of the domain, for which β has a value different from zero. In Jaffe's paper are mentioned other instances of recognized transitions from one crystal classification to another in which the changes in parameters are very small.

From these considerations it follows that between the Curie points an ordinary Rochelle-salt crystal with its complex of positively and negatively oriented domains is to be regarded as twinned, the twinning being of the Dauphiné (orientational) type, like that in low quartz produced by cooling from uniform high quartz (electrical twinning).

The Curie points are inversion points from monoclinic to rhombic hemihedral symmetry. For this inversion the piezoelectric effect is responsible. An isolated unit cell would be rhombic at all temperatures, but between the Curie points the interaction between the dipoles (or their equivalent) in neighboring cells is such as to produce an internal field with attendant deformation, making the domain as a whole monoclinic.

482. In §436 it was pointed out that the coercive field E_c has a value of about 200 volts/cm at 0°C, approaching zero at the two Curie points, We can now go a step further in the explanation, recognizing E_c as a measure of the energy required to reverse the polar axis of the crystal. That E_c is so small at all temperatures is because the transition temperatures are so close together. When the field E reaches the critical value

E_c, the dipoles that are responsible for the spontaneous polarization become reversed from their stable state in one direction to that in the opposite direction. As they do so, the angle β changes sign. Midway between the two stable states, then, is the configuration of higher (rhombic) symmetry, for which $\beta = 0$. As either Curie point is approached the stable states come nearer and nearer to the higher symmetry; this explains why the energy necessary to effect the reversal approaches zero. Now a finite change in strain and polarization caused by an electric field of vanishing magnitude means that at the Curie points both d_{14} and η_x approach infinity. Experimental evidence (§474) tends to confirm this conclusion.

The angle β referred to above is the *spontaneous strain* y_z^0 that was discussed in §§403 and 452. To Vigness[566] belongs the credit for the first experimental work from which its magnitude could be calculated, while Jaffe first recognized it as a characteristic feature of Rochelle salt and treated its theoretical significance in the manner outlined above. From Vigness's data Jaffe calculated $y_z^0 = 8(10^{-4})$ at temperatures from 0 to 10°C, whence $\beta = 2.7'$. Vigness's crystal showed distinct unipolarity; yet it is unlikely that he happened to have a strictly single-domain specimen. Hence the foregoing value is probably too small rather than too large.

From the observations of Hinz shown in Fig. 114 an estimate can be made of y_z^0 on the assumption that by analogy with the spontaneous polarization P^0, y_z^0 can be calculated from the remanent strain when $E = 0$. In this manner one finds, at 18.5°C, $y_z^0 = 0.95(10^{-4})$, a value smaller than would be expected from Vigness's results, even after making allowance for the greater nearness to the Curie point; but the reason may lie in the multi-domain structure.

Mueller[380] made a direct measurement of the variation with temperature of the angle between the Y- and Z-faces of a Rochelle-salt block. He found no temperature effect above the upper Curie point but observed an angular change beginning at θ_u which amounted to about

$$3' \quad (y_z^0 = 8.7 \times 10^{-4})$$

at 11°C and to $3'45''$ ($y_z^0 = 10.9 \times 10^{-4}$) at 0°C.

Finally, from Eq. (494), $y_z^0 = b_{14}P^0$, the spontaneous strain can be computed by taking b_{14} and P^0 from Fig. 146. At 0°C, $b_{14} = 6.8(10^{-7})$, $P^0 = 740$, whence $y_z^0 = 5.03(10^{-4})$. This value agrees as well as can be expected with the results of Vigness and of Mueller, considering the differences in domain structure of the specimens employed.

Although observations of spontaneous strain in the neighborhood of the lower Curie point θ_l are still to be made, there is little reason to doubt that the relation between spontaneous strain and temperature can be represented by a curve similar to that for P^0 in Fig. 147, with a maximum for y_z^0 of the order of 10^{-3}.

From the thermal point of view, the spontaneous strain would be described as due to an anomaly in the coefficients of thermal deformation (§407). A discussion of thermal expansion in monoclinic crystals will be found in Voigt* and in Wooster.[B56]

Induced Monoclinic Properties. In an important sense Rochelle salt has monoclinic properties even outside the Curie points, namely in an electric field. The class to which any crystal is normally assigned depends on goniometric measurements on specimens that are unstressed, either mechanically or electrically. The change in crystallographic symmetry in a crystal under stress is mentioned in §531, and more especially in §464. As an example of an effect theoretically observable with monoclinic but not with rhombic crystals and that nevertheless has been found above the upper Curie point in Rochelle salt, we may cite the linear electro-optic effect discussed in §535.

483. *A Search for Monoclinic Coefficients by Hydrostatic Pressure.* If, as is indicated in the footnote on page 613, there is a detectable monoclinic piezoelectric effect in monoclinic Rochelle salt between the Curie points, independent of morphic effects, its presence should be revealed by means of hydrostatic pressure. According to the axial system adopted in §481, the piezoelectric constants that would play a part in such an effect are d_{11}, d_{12}, and d_{13}. A uniform hydrostatic pressure Π would then produce, through the direct effect, a polarization given by Eq. (193), p. 194:

$$-P_x = (d_{11} + d_{12} + d_{13})\Pi$$

An X-cut plate immersed in insulating oil, with electrodes connected to a measuring device, should respond to a change in pressure of the oil. An advantage in this method is that it entirely eliminates disturbing effects from d_{14}, since no shear is caused by hydrostatic pressure.

A preliminary investigation of this sort has been made by A. C. Grosvenor.† An X-cut Rochelle-salt plate 4.2 mm thick, area 8.3 cm², was connected to a d-c amplifier. Substantially the same results were obtained with a second crystal. There was no difficulty in obtaining a deflection of the milliammeter when a pressure of a few kgs/cm² was applied to the paraffin oil surrounding the crystal in a metal container. The difficulty lay in interpreting the results. In the temperature range under investigation Rochelle salt is pyroelectric. The adiabatic heating of the oil and of the crystal itself when pressure is applied causes a pyroelectric contribution to the deflection. Now the pyroelectric effect is greatest at the Curie points, having opposite signs at these points and

* Pp. 289–294.

† A. C. Grosvenor, master's thesis, Wesleyan University, 1940.

passing through zero in the neighborhood of 0°C. It should therefore be possible to eliminate the pyroelectric disturbance by applying the pressure at a temperature sufficiently below 0°C so that the net pyroelectric polarization, due to the rise in temperature on application of pressure, would be zero.

At present only preliminary results have been obtained by this method, indicating a value of $(d_{11} + d_{12} + d_{13})$ of the order of $3(10^{-11})$.

It was also observed that at 11.3°C the deflection was zero. On the assumption that the pyroelectric and piezoelectric effects at this temperature were equal and opposite, a crude calculation of $(d_{11} + d_{12} + d_{13})$ was made by estimating for the pyroelectric coefficient p the value of about 20 by the method indicated in §521 and calculating the rise in temperature due to compression. Owing particularly to the fact that the crystal plate used had presumably a multi-domain structure, for which the assumed value of p may have been many times too large, the calculation would be expected to yield too high a value of

$$(d_{11} + d_{12} + d_{13})$$

The value by this method was, in fact, of the order of a thousand times greater than that obtained by the first method.

It is possible that a repetition of these experiments with greater refinement, coupled with a thorough pyroelectric investigation of the specimen, would prove of value in the attack on the problem of Rochelle salt. And let the observer not forget to use several different specimens!

CHAPTER XXVI

INTERNAL-FIELD THEORY
OF FERROELECTRIC CRYSTALS

Doch im Innern scheint ein Geist gewaltig zu ringen . . .

—GOETHE.

484. Although doubt has been thrown on the importance of the orientation of free dipoles in explaining the nature of the ferroelectrics, still the dipole theory, which involves the concept of the internal field, has figured so prominently in the literature—and may still continue to do so in a modified form—that it is advisable to survey the subject briefly, with special reference to the work of Kurchatov,[B32,263] Mueller,[376] and Busch.[88] At the end of the chapter an account is given of the attempts to calculate the dipole moment of Rochelle salt.

The outstanding differences between the internal-field and the interaction theories are these: (1) The polarization P is expressed as a cubic function of the internal field F by the former theory and as a cubic function of the ordinary field $E = V/e$ by the latter. (2) The two Curie points and the properties of the crystal in the region between them are attributed in the former theory to small changes in the molecular polarizability and in the latter to small changes in the susceptibility of the clamped crystal. Further comparisons between the two theories will be found in the following paragraphs.

From Eqs. (171) and (174) it is seen that the polarization may be expressed as

$$P = N\alpha_{ea}F + P_0 L(a) \qquad (530)$$

where $L(a)$ is the Langevin function, P_0 is the polarization in infinite field, α_{ea} is the polarizability by distortion (electronic plus atomic), and $a = \mu F/KT$. If $L(a)$ is written in the generalized approximate form of Eq. (562), one finds*

$$P = \left(N\alpha_{ea} + \frac{P_0 p\mu}{KT}\right)F - \frac{P_0 q\mu^3}{(KT)^3}F^3 \qquad (530a)$$

---

* In §552 it is stated that the value of the coefficient p depends on the restrictions imposed on the degrees of orientational freedom of the dipoles, *i.e.*, on the quantum number n. For unrestricted orientation $n = \infty$ and the equation becomes the original Langevin function, Eq. (556) or (556a), with $p = \frac{1}{3}$. If the orientation is restricted to parallel and antiparallel positions with respect to a single direction, $n = \frac{1}{2}$ and

It was shown in Eq. (168), p. 170, that

$$F = E + \gamma P \tag{531}$$

By means of this equation, (530a) could be converted into a theoretical expression for polarization in terms of applied field E, which would include both the non-linearity and the dependence on temperature. Although a step in this direction was taken by Busch, still the various parameters and the dependence of N and P_0 on temperature are so little known that such an expression could not be put to experimental test.

485. Mueller's Internal-field Theory. This theory, an elaboration of that of Debye and Kurchatov, assumes the existence of a field F, related to P by an empirical equation of the same form as (530a),

$$P = \alpha_M F - \beta F^3 \tag{532}$$

where α_M is the *polarizability per unit volume* in small fields (to avoid confusion with the *molecular* polarizability, we write α_M in place of Mueller's α). α_M includes the effects of dipoles, as well as that due to piezoelectric deformation; the theory is phenomenological to the extent that the constituents of α_M do not appear in the equations.

Both α_M and β are dependent on temperature.[*] The kernel of Mueller's theory is the assumption that α_M may be expressed by

$$\alpha_M = \frac{\theta(T)}{\gamma T} \tag{533}$$

where γ is the internal field constant of Eq. (531), T the absolute temperature, and $\theta(T)$ is a function which Mueller calls the "Curie temperature." Although $\theta(T)$ is of the nature of a temperature, equal to θ_u or θ_l at the Curie points, still it might more properly be called the *Mueller function*, in order to avoid confusion with the Curie *point*, which is often referred to as the Curie temperature. At present there is no convincing theoretical expression for $\theta(T)$ that can be put to quantitative test.[†]

$p = 1$. Since the dielectric anomalies in Rochelle salt have to do with the X-direction alone, one might be led to set $p = 1$ in Eq. (530a). The objection to this form of the function is that it requires absolute quantization with respect to one direction, an assumption for which there is no theoretical justification in solid dielectrics. Yet it may well be that $p = 1$ comes closer to the truth than $p = \frac{1}{3}$. Too little is known of the numerical values of N, μ, F, and γ to decide this question. For the present we must remain content with the assumption that for not too large values of the field the relation between $\bar{\mu}$ and a, and correspondingly the relation between polarization and field, can be represented by a cubic equation like (530a) in which the constants have to be determined empirically.

[*] Mueller shows that the saturation coefficient B of his later papers is identical with $\beta\gamma^4$.

[†] Busch[88] derived a theoretical relation between $\theta(T)$ and T, but it contains parameters whose numerical values are still unknown.

Since in Rochelle salt the anomalies are present only with fields in the X-direction, we are concerned with the value of γ in this direction only. Rochelle salt may be expected to be anisotropic with respect to γ, which presumably has different values parallel to the three axes.

Unlike Mueller, Busch, whose work is based largely on Mueller's internal-field theory, makes explicit use of the Langevin function. It will perhaps aid both in interpreting the theory and in emphasizing the ferromagnetic analogy if we follow here the method outlined in §550 for ferromagnetism. If P and F in Eq. (532) are plotted as ordinate and abscissa, respectively, a curve similar to that in Fig. 165 results. That which corresponds to the "Weiss lines" is obtained by writing Eq. (531) in the form

$$P = \frac{F}{\gamma} - \frac{E}{\gamma} \qquad (534)$$

At higher temperatures, down to a few degrees above the upper Curie point, we have the purely parelectric region. In this region, as has been suggested by Scherrer,[451] the dipole system behaves like a dipolar gas embedded in a polarizable matrix.

The upper Curie point θ_u is the temperature at which, with small fields, the slope of the Weiss line is the same as that of the curve:

$$\frac{\partial P}{\partial F} = \alpha_M = \frac{1}{\gamma} = \frac{\theta(T)}{\gamma \theta_u}$$

Since $\theta(T) = \theta_u$ at the Curie point, it follows that at this critical temperature $\alpha_M = 1/\gamma$. As the temperature falls below θ_u, the slope of the Weiss line diminishes, thus accounting for the spontaneous polarization, as illustrated, for the magnetic case, by the point P' in Fig. 165.

In order to account for the lower Curie point θ_l, Busch elaborates upon Kurchatov's theory of the variability of the number of free dipoles with temperature and deduces a different Langevin curve for each temperature. θ_l is then the temperature at which the Weiss line again becomes tangential to the curve at the origin. Mueller, who does not make explicit use of the number of free dipoles, simply assumes $\gamma \alpha_M = 1$ at each Curie point.*

The significance of the quantity $\gamma \alpha_M$ is shown by writing, from Eqs. (531) and (532),

$$E = (1 - \gamma \alpha_M)F + \gamma \beta F^3 \qquad (535)$$

* Debye (ref. B15, p. 89) predicts large values of the dielectric constant of polar liquids when the quantity $(4\pi/3)N(\alpha_{ea} + \alpha_d)$ approaches unity. Since $4\pi/3$ corresponds to γ and $N(\alpha_{ea} + \alpha_d)$ to α_M, it is evident that Mueller's assumption that $\gamma \alpha_M = 1$ at the Curie points is the analogue for Rochelle salt to Debye's condition for liquids. Mueller's piezoelectric constituent of α_M supplies the amount needed to make $\gamma \alpha_M = 1$, thus yielding an infinite dielectric constant at certain temperatures.

Outside the Curie points, $\gamma\alpha_M < 1$, F vanishes when $E = 0$, and Rochelle salt behaves like an ordinary dielectric. In the region where $\gamma\alpha_M > 1$, the inner field has two real values, differing from zero, thus accounting for the spontaneous polarization. The ferroelectric region is that in which α_M is slightly greater than $1/\gamma$. According to this theory, a small and gradual change in α_M with temperature is responsible for the anomalies, just as in the later interaction theory (§468) the anomalies are attributed to a small and gradual change in the clamped susceptibility

The cubic equation (535) corresponds to Eq. (493d) with $Y_z = 0$. For $P \approx \alpha_M F$ from Eq. (532), $\eta' = 1/\chi' = \alpha_M/(1 - \gamma\alpha_M)$ from Eq. (536) below, while, as has been stated, $B = \beta\gamma^4$.

Obviously, the numerical value of α_M depends on that of γ (Mueller's f). As we have seen in §113, in all crystals one would expect γ to be of the same order of magnitude as the theoretical Lorentz factor $4\pi/3$ At present, a theoretical calculation of γ for Rochelle salt is impossible; moreover, as Busch points out, γ may be expected to have different values for the lattice and the dipoles. Without making this distinction, Mueller derives γ empirically from Eq. (536), as will be seen. The point to emphasize here is that it is not necessary, as in ferromagnetism (§549), to postulate a very great value of γ in order to account for the large internal field in the ferroelectrics. Moreover, since the X-ray observations of Warren and Krutter[579] indicate no change in the lattice structure of Rochelle salt over the entire temperature range, it can safely be assumed that γ is not appreciably affected by temperature.

486. The Curie-Weiss law for Rochelle salt outside the Curie points is derived from Eqs. (531) to (533). We thus find, for the free crystal in small fields, where the second term in Eq. (532) can be omitted,

$$\eta' = \frac{P}{E} = \frac{\alpha_M}{1 - \gamma\alpha_M} = \frac{\theta(T)}{\gamma[T - \theta(T)]} \tag{536}$$

This equation is a special form of the general relation between dielectric susceptibility and polarizability given in Eq. (173).* $\theta(T)$ signifies the "Curie temperature," which in §434 is denoted by t_c. The quantity $\theta(T)/\gamma$ is the theoretical equivalent of the experimental C in Eqs. (490) and (524). For a few degrees above the upper Curie point θ_u, $\theta(T) = \theta_u$. Equation (536) then becomes (written in reciprocal form for comparison with the earlier equations)

$$\chi' = \frac{1}{\eta'} = \frac{\gamma(T - \theta_u)}{\theta_u} \tag{537}$$

* When Eq. (536) is written $-1/\eta' = -\chi' = \gamma - 1/\alpha_M$, it is analogous to Eq. (497): $-\chi' = a_{14}b_{14} - \chi_1$. Mueller[380] calls $a_{14}b_{14}$ (in his notation f_{14}^2/c_{44}) the "apparent Lorentz factor." χ_1 is analogous to $1/\alpha_M$. Numerical equality is not to be expected, since γ is the factor for the *internal* field.

At higher temperatures $\theta(T)$ assumes values differing somewhat from θ_u, as is indicated in the discussion of Eq. (490).

By analogy with ferromagnetic theory one may say that the experimental confirmation of the Curie-Weiss law expressed by Eq. (537) by Mueller and by Hablützel (§465) indicates that, if the effect is due to dipoles, the latter must be nearly all free at temperatures outside the Curie points.

Since Mueller found experimentally that for all temperatures above 34°C the relation between $1/\eta'$ and T was very exactly linear, he was able to derive from Eq. (536) a value for the internal field constant γ, namely $\gamma = 2.19$.

It should be observed that the internal-field theory, together with the basic assumption expressed in Eq. (533), provides a theoretical basis for the Curie-Weiss law in Eq. (536). In this respect the internal-field theory is more potent than the interaction theory, which provides no theoretical relation between susceptibility and temperature, simply accepting the Curie-Weiss law as an experimental fact (see §465).

In the ferroelectric region also, the internal-field theory predicts a Curie-Weiss law that agrees with observation. For small fields and for temperatures distant by not over a few degrees from the Curie points, one finds by the same process that is used in §552 for deriving Eq. (566) that the initial susceptibility is given by

$$\chi'_s = \frac{1}{\eta'_s} = \frac{2\gamma(\theta_u - T)}{3T - 2\theta_u} \tag{538}$$

From this expression it follows that the susceptibility between the Curie points is given theoretically by

$$\eta'_s = \frac{T}{2\gamma(\theta_u - T)} - \frac{1}{\gamma} \tag{538a}$$

an equation that is in approximate agreement with experiment.

Comparison of Eq. (538a) with (537) shows that the initial susceptibility varies about twice as rapidly with temperature below the upper Curie point as above it, as has already been pointed out in §465; for the ferromagnetic case see Fig. 166. In Eqs. (529) and (529a) we have seen that the same relation holds for the piezoelectric constant.

The infinite value of the susceptibility of the free crystal at the Curie points follows from Eq. (536) or (538) on setting $\gamma\alpha_M = 1$.

487. Theoretical expressions for the spontaneous internal field F^0 and the spontaneous polarization P^0 are found by setting $E = 0$ in Eqs. (535) and (531):

$$F^{02} = \frac{\gamma \alpha_M - 1}{\gamma \beta} = \frac{\theta(T) - T}{\gamma \beta T} \tag{539}$$

$$P^{02} = \frac{F^{02}}{\gamma^2} = \frac{\gamma \alpha_M - 1}{\beta \gamma^3} = \frac{\theta(T) - T}{\beta \gamma^3 T} \tag{539a}$$

Mueller's original paper[376] must be consulted for the ingenious manner in which he combined the results of both dielectric and electro-optic measurements at different temperatures and different field strengths, in order to derive the values of the various unknown quantities. It must suffice here to say that, in addition to the data already mentioned, an estimate was made of the value of β (2.5×10^{-9}), whence, from Eqs. (539) and (539a), F^0 and P^0 could be calculated for any temperature. For example, at $0°C$, $F^0 \sim 2,600$ esu = 770,000 volts/cm, and $P^0 \sim 1,200$ esu. This latter value agrees as well as can be expected with the values of P^0 from pyroelectric and oscillographic data.

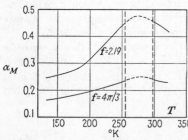

FIG. 149.—Polarizability α_M per unit volume as function of temperature, from Mueller's data.

From Mueller's observations we have plotted values of α_M as a function of T, both for $\gamma = 2.19$ and $\gamma = 4\pi/3$; the result is shown in Fig. 149.

In general, it may be said that Mueller's internal-field theory is in good quantitative agreement with experiment in the parelectric regions and in qualitative agreement in the Seignette-electric region. It was only by making explicit use of the piezoelectric effects in his interaction theory that Mueller was able to obtain quantitative agreement between theory and observation over the entire temperature range. A unification of the two theories remains as a problem for the future.

488. While the internal-field theory as outlined above deals explicitly only with dielectric properties, still it can be used to describe the elastic and piezoelectric properties also. For this purpose one may employ the method indicated in §188 for treating the problem in terms of the internal field F, with equations analogous to those in Table XX. Corresponding to a_{14} and b_{14} of the polarization theory, or e_{14} and d_{14} of Voigt's formulation, are the internal-field piezoelectric constants, which may be called a_{14}^F and b_{14}^F. The latter are easily shown to be very nearly proportional to a_{14} and b_{14}. b_{14}^F is related to d_{14} by the equation $d_{14} = (1 + \gamma\gamma')b_{14}^F$, where γ is the internal field constant.

The only application that we find of the internal-field theory to piezoelectric observations is that of Norgorden,[393] whose experiments have been described in §424 and whose work appeared before the advent of the interaction theory. Norgorden finds b_{14}^F (his d_{14}) practically independent of temperature from 14 to 33°C, with a very slight increase as the field strength increases. Now from the relation given above between d_{14} and b_{14}^F, together with $d_{14} = \eta' b_{14}$ from Eq. (495b), it follows that $b_{14} = (1/\eta' + \gamma)b_{14}^F$. Since η' is large, it is evident that the approximate independence of b_{14}^F on temperature and field lends support to the conclusion already reached that b_{14} is essentially constant. Norgorden's experimental data could, of course, be discussed entirely in terms of the polarization theory, without reference to the internal field, but this seems hardly necessary.

489. Correlation between the Theories of Mueller, Kurchatov, and Fowler. In his application of Debye's theory (§445), Kurchatov assumes that the Clausius-Mosotti relation

$$\frac{k_0 - 1}{k_0 + 2} = \frac{4\pi}{3} N\alpha \tag{540}$$

can be extended to include the case in which the molecular polarizability α contains a dipole term. k_0 is the initial dielectric constant of the free crystal, and N the number of molecules per cubic centimeter. In order to express the dependence of $N\alpha$ on temperature, he writes

$$\frac{k_0 - 1}{k_0 + 2} T = \frac{4\pi}{3} N\alpha T \tag{540a}$$

In comparing this equation with Mueller's corresponding Eq. (533), we recall first that Mueller's α (which we have denoted by α_M) is the polarizability *per unit volume*. Equation (533) may be put in the form

$$\theta(T) = \gamma \alpha_M T \tag{541}$$

If for the field constant γ the value $4\pi/3$ is taken, (541) becomes identical with (540a), and $\alpha_M \equiv N\alpha$.

The excellent agreement between Kurchatov and Mueller in their measurements of k_0 is attested by the close similarity in their diagrams. Kurchatov plots $(k_0 - 1)T/(k_0 + 2)$ as function of T in Fig. 9 of the French edition of his book,[B32] while Mueller calculates α_M from Eq. (536), and then from Eq. (533) plots $\theta(T)$ in terms of T (Fig. 25 of his paper[376]). The latter diagram contains two curves for $\theta(T)$, corresponding to $\gamma = 4\pi/3$ and $\gamma = 2.19$.* It is the one with $\gamma = 4\pi/3$ that should be compared with Kurchatov's curve. Mueller's assumption that $\gamma \alpha_M > 1$ in the ferroelectric region corresponds to writing $4\pi N\alpha/3 > 1$ in

---

* As was pointed out in §485, the numerical value of α_M (and of α) depends on the choice of γ. Values of α_M in terms of temperature are shown in Fig. 149.

Eq. (540a).* Although it is not stated explicitly by Kurchatov, it is implicit in his equations and diagrams that in the ferroelectric region $4\pi N\alpha/3 > 1$.

Kurchatov does not discuss the theoretical significance of the fact that letting $4\pi N\alpha/3$ become greater than unity on the right side of Eq. (540a) leads to *negative* values of k_0. Mueller's interaction theory also introduces the concept of a negative dielectric constant, the relation of which to the actual dielectric constant between the Curie points is explained in §454.

From Kurchatov's data we have calculated the values of $N\alpha$ for several temperatures. When plotted in Fig. 149 they fall very nicely on Mueller's curve.

Although Fowler's treatment gives no observational data, still it is possible to ascertain whether his theory predicts a relation like Mueller's between $\theta(T)$ and T. The expression that corresponds to Mueller's $\theta(T)$ is Fowler's $T_d^0 g$,† which when plotted with T as abscissa yields a curve of the same general characteristics as Mueller's.

The chief limitation in the theories of Kurchatov and of Fowler lies in their neglect of the piezoelectric contribution to the dielectric constant. By taking this effect into account, together with the non-linear effects in large fields, Mueller was able, as we have seen, to trace the dielectric anomalies of Rochelle salt back to their origin in the clamped crystal.

490. Calculation of the Moment of Rochelle-salt Dipoles. Much of the theoretical work on Rochelle salt has centered in the hypothesis of rotatable dipoles, which are most commonly considered to be the molecules of the water of crystallization. It seems desirable, therefore, to show how the dipole moment can be estimated, even though, as will be seen in §542, it is likely that the dielectric peculiarities are due to hydrogen bonds rather than to rotating dipoles.

In estimating the dipole moment, only the formulas for weak fields need be used. We begin with Mueller's Eq. (533), in which α_M is the polarizability *per unit volume*. α_M may be expressed in terms of Eq. (177), with the assumption that N_1 and N_2 are the number of lattice elements and permanent dipoles, respectively, per unit volume:

$$\frac{\theta(T)}{T} = \gamma\alpha_M = N_1\gamma\alpha_{ae} - N_2\gamma\frac{p\mu^2}{KT} \qquad (542)$$

Appropriate values for the molecular field coefficient γ and the coefficient

---

* The identity of Kurchatov's Eq. (540a) with Mueller's formulation is quickly shown by setting $\gamma = 4\pi/3$ and $k_0 = 1 + 4\pi\eta'$ in Eq. (536).

† Ref. B18, p. 818.

p of the generalized Langevin function (§114) will be introduced later. For the present purpose it is not necessary to discriminate between the different values that should, in view of §485, be assigned to γ in the two terms of Eq. (542).

If we agree with Kurchatov and others in regarding the dipole moments as residing in the H_2O molecules, there may be four such separate moments for each Rochelle-salt molecule. But if the Rochelle-salt molecule is a single dipole, the number N_2 will, at least at sufficiently high temperatures, be the same as the number of molecules per cubic centimeter, $3.8(10^{21})$. N_2 will then be either $3.8(10^{21})$ or $15(10^{21})$ according to whether n, the number of dipoles associated with the molecules, is 1 or 4.

At either Curie point Eq. (542) becomes equal to unity. It is necessary in calculating μ to use the *upper* temperature $\theta = 296.7°$ abs, since only then are we justified in assigning to N_2 the values given above.

A further step that must be taken before μ can be found is to determine the magnitude of the first term in Eq. (542). This can be done by means of Kurchatov's data[B32] on the susceptibilities of crystals grown from a mixture of Rochelle salt with its isomorphic relative sodium–ammonium tartrate (§491). This latter is not of itself ferroelectric. In the mixed crystals Kurchatov found that, if the Rochelle-salt component did not amount to more that 41 per cent of the whole, the quantity $(k_0 - 1)/(k_0 + 2)$ in Eq. (540a) was independent of temperature, indicating that only the lattice polarization, represented by the first term in Eq. (542), is then effective. From the experimental data, and on the assumption that the lattice polarizability is the same for all isomorphic mixtures, including pure Rochelle salt itself, it is found that $N_1\gamma\alpha_{ae} \approx 0.6$ at the upper Curie point. This value is deduced directly from the susceptibility [for example by means of Eq. (536)] and does not require any knowledge of N_1, γ, or α_{ae} separately.

Recalling that, by §485, $\gamma\alpha_M = 1$ at the Curie point θ_u, and setting $T = \theta_u$ in Eq. (542), one finds $N_2\gamma p\mu^2/K\theta_u = 1 - 0.6 = 0.4$, whence

$$\mu^2 = \frac{0.4 K \theta_u}{N_2 \gamma p} \qquad (543)$$

In Table XXXV are given values of μ calculated from Eq. (543) for $n = 1$ or 4 dipoles per Rochelle salt molecule, for $\gamma = 4\pi/3$ or 2.19 (Mueller's value), and for $p = \frac{1}{3}$ or 1 (§484). In order to show what the dipole moment would be if the polarizability were due to the dipoles alone, the column designated as $\mu' = \mu/\sqrt{0.4}$ has been added, obtained by omitting the factor 0.4 in Eq. (543).

All the values of μ below are of the order of magnitude commonly accepted for polar molecules. All things considered, for Rochelle salt the value printed in boldface type is perhaps the most acceptable.

TABLE XXXV.—CALCULATED VALUES OF DIPOLE MOMENTS
(In esu)

γ	p	n	μ^2	μ	μ'	$\dfrac{\mu}{\bar{\mu}}$
			$\times 10^{-36}$	$\times 10^{-18}$	$\times 10^{-18}$	
$\dfrac{4\pi}{3}$	$\frac{1}{3}$	1	2.98	1.73	2.74	9
		4	0.75	0.86	1.37	17
	1	1	0.99	1.00	1.58	5
		4	0.25	0.50	0.79	10
2.19	$\frac{1}{3}$	1	5.69	2.38	3.78	12
		4	1.43	1.20	1.89	25
	1	1	1.89	1.38	2.18	7
		4	0.47	**0.69**	1.09	14

Still another estimate of μ can be made by making use of Mueller's value of $\beta = 2.5(10^{-9})$ [see §487 and Eq. (532)]. We assume that (532) can be represented by a Langevin function of the type given in Eq. (176). When the latter equation is solved for P and compared with (532), it is found that at the Curie point $\alpha_M = Np\mu^2/KT$, $\beta = Nq\mu^4/K^3T^3$, whence $\mu^2 = \beta p K^2 \theta_u^2/q\alpha_M$. The value of μ depends on the choice of p and q. If the original Langevin function given by Eq. (175) is accepted, $q/p = \frac{1}{15}$. Or, using Eq. (176), $q/p = \frac{1}{3}$ (see §§552, 484). With $\beta = 2.5(10^{-9})$, $\alpha_M = 0.257$, $K = 1.37(10^{-16})$, there results $\mu = 12(10^{-18})$ or $5.2(10^{-18})$, respectively. These values indicate at least the right order of magnitude, with the odds in favor of the second formula.

From the observed spontaneous polarization an estimate can be made of $\bar{\mu} = P/N_2$, the average component of dipole moment in the direction of the field (§548). This quantity is a function of both field and temperature, but only the value at $0°C$ and $E = 0$ need be considered. P is then the spontaneous polarization P^0 at $0°C$, at which temperature it has its greatest experimental value of 740 esu. Using the values of N_2 given above, one finds $\bar{\mu} = 0.20(10^{-18})$ or $0.049(10^{-18})$ according to whether the number of dipoles per molecule is 1 or 4. Values about twice as large as this are obtained if for P^0 one uses the theoretical value derived from Eq. (539a).

In any case, it appears that the maximum spontaneous polarization is but a small fraction, $P^0/P_{max} = \bar{\mu}/\mu$, of the absolute maximum

$$P_{max} = N_2\mu$$

which would be present if all the dipoles lay in the same direction parallel to the field.   The reciprocal of this fraction is given in the last column of Table XXXV.   It follows that on the Langevin diagram (Fig. 165) the operating point is never far from the origin, so that even with the strongest electric fields that Rochelle salt can withstand the first two terms in the development of the Langevin function should suffice.   This is in marked contrast to the spontaneous polarization in iron, which, as stated in §553, has at room temperature a value not very far below the theoretical maximum at 0° abs.   The reason for this difference between Rochelle salt and iron is that Rochelle salt has a *lower Curie point* that lies near enough to the upper Curie point so that there is no temperature in the region of spontaneous polarization at which we are not fairly close to one or other of these points.

CHAPTER XXVII

OTHER FERROELECTRIC CRYSTALS

Was man an der Natur Geheimnisvolles pries,
Das wagen wir verständig zu probieren,
Und was sie sonst organisieren liess,
Das lassen wir kristallisieren.

—GOETHE.

Except Rochelle salt, the only substances known at present that have dielectric properties analogous to ferromagnetism are certain mixed crystals isomorphic with Rochelle salt, and a few tetragonal phosphates and arsenates. These two groups of crystals will now be considered.

491. Crystals Isomorphic with Rochelle Salt, and Mixed Tartrates. The substances thus far investigated are those in which the K of Rochelle salt is replaced by NH_4, Rb, or Tl. The crystals have molecular radii and axial ratios sufficiently alike so that mixed crystals can be grown in any proportion.

Pure crystals of $NH_4NaC_4H_4O_6 \cdot 4H_2O$, $RbNaC_4H_4O_6 \cdot 4H_2O$, or $TlNaC_4H_4O_6 \cdot 4H_2O$ have quite normal dielectric behavior. From the point of view of the ferromagnetic analogy they are, down to the lowest temperatures investigated, parelectric rather than ferroelectric. If they have Curie points, they must come at extremely low temperatures. For example, the dielectric constant k_x of the ammonium salt is about 10^{B32} and independent of temperature. As we have seen in §144, the piezoelectric constants of this crystal, though large, show no anomalies at least down to $-17°C$, and from the constancy in k_x down to very low temperatures one can feel fairly confident that a like constancy obtains with the piezoelectric coefficients.

Peculiar effects are observed with crystals that have been grown from solutions containing mixtures with the KNa salt of any one of the three isomorphic salts named above. The first papers on the subject were those of B. Kurchatov and M. Eremeev[133,292] in 1932. The present account is based on their work, together with the following: B. and I. Kurchatov,[293] Bloomenthal,[55] Evans,[140] and especially the book by I. Kurchatov.[B32] Investigations have been chiefly with Rochelle salt containing the NH_4Na admixture, as described below. Results with the rubidium and thallium salts, as far as they go, are at least qualitatively similar.

Some of the principal results with crystals containing various proportions of $NH_4NaC_4H_4O_6 \cdot 4H_2O$ are shown in Fig. 150, from ref. B32.

Since the field strength is not given, the values of the dielectric constant must be regarded as of only relative significance. The addition to the pure Rochelle salt of only 1 per cent of the NH_4 salt (molar ratio) reduces the temperature range of the ferroelectric region by about one-half. An addition of 3 per cent (curve marked 97 per cent) completely elim- inates the ferroelectric properties, leaving only a maximum in the curve. Further increase in NH_4 makes this maximum lower and flatter, rising again slightly at 83 per cent of Rochelle salt.

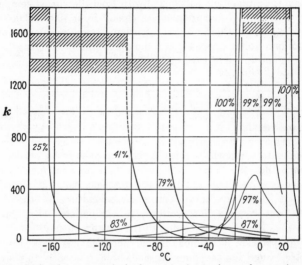

Fig. 150.—Dielectric constant of mixed crystals of potassium and ammonium Rochelle salt, from I. Kurchatov. The percentages indicate the relative numbers of molecules of the potassium salt in the mixture.

Further reduction in the Rochelle-salt content to 79 per cent ushers in a second ferroelectric region at low temperature, which persists down to 25 per cent. Kurchatov's explanation of this curious behavior may be somewhat freely summarized as follows: It is assumed that the rotatable dipoles are chiefly those of the Rochelle salt. Small admixtures of the NH_4Na salt raise the lower Curie point only slightly, but larger admixtures loosen the forces that bind the dipoles in the local groups that characterize the lower Curie point, releasing a number of dipoles sufficient to allow the product $4\pi N\alpha/3$ to become greater than unity. One may also predict that the large values of the dielectric constant in this region are attended by correspondingly large values of d_{14}.*

* Bloomenthal in his theoretical treatment of mixed crystals takes account of the piezoelectric effect on the susceptibility by an equation like (516) and (516a), but his experimental data are insufficient to help in the present case.

In a more general manner it may be suggested that for a certain range of percentages of the NH_4Na salt there are certain temperatures at which the settling of the system into a state of minimum energy (§473) is attended by a change in crystal structure to a configuration of lower symmetry, with a spontaneous polarization, as the temperature falls below a critical value.

Further Measurements of the Dielectric Constant in the X-direction. Evans[140] measured the dielectric constant for various molecular percentages of the ammonium salt mixed with Rochelle salt, at temperatures between 16 and 17°C and frequencies chiefly from 400 to 2,000 kc/sec. At these frequencies there was no disturbance from resonant vibrations. The maximum voltage was 45, but the maximum field strength, crystal dimensions, and range of variation of field strength are not stated. The results were as follows:

Molecular percentage of ammonium salt...................	0	10	20	30	40	50	100
Dielectric constant...............	114	25.0	15.8	13.0	11.8	9.9	8.2

From Evans's remarks concerning the precision of his observations it is apparent that the uncertainty in his data may amount to at least 10 per cent. The value 114 for pure Rochelle salt has already been recorded in Table XXXIV. The small magnitude of the dielectric constant from Evans's observations, in comparison with the values shown in Fig. 150, is of course due to the high frequency.

The temperature at which Evans obtained his data lay in the ferroelectric range for the pure Rochelle salt, but with this exception the ammonium content was such that the material was parelectric. The only correlation that can be made between the work of Evans and that of the Russian investigators is in the value of k_x for the pure ammonium salt: here Evans's value of 8.2 at high frequency agrees well enough with Kurchatov's l-f value of 10 mentioned above.

In the Russian edition of his book,[B32] Kurchatov gives some values of the dielectric constant of mixed KNa and TlNa salts, for various molecular percentages, measured at 500 volts/cm. At 0°C the results were as follows:

Percentage Tl...........................	0	0.25	0.5	1	2.5
Dielectric constant......................	10,000	2,300	1,200	600	120

The results at −10°C and +10°C are not essentially different.

Dielectric hysteresis in the NH_4Na + KNa mixture has been investigated by Eremeev and B. Kurchatov.[133,*] As with Rochelle salt, there

* See also ref. B32.

is no hysteresis, fatigue, or lag above the Curie point, and the $P:E$ relation becomes linear at a temperature not far above this point.

In the low-temperature ferroelectric regions the width of the hysteresis loop and the magnitude of the coercive field E_c increase as the temperature diminishes below the Curie point, and many seconds may be required for the attainment of equilibrium. That there is no evidence of a lower Curie point is shown by the fact that the saturation polarization ("knee" of the polarization curve) increases with decreasing temperature down to the lowest recorded temperature, $-190°$C, while at the same time the field strength necessary for saturation increases also. For example, in a crystal containing 45 molecular per cent of KNa salt, the saturation field was 10,000 volts/cm (for Rochelle salt it is less than 200!), while the saturation polarization was 3,000 esu, several times greater than in pure Rochelle salt.

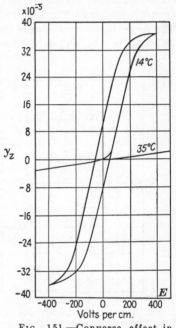

FIG. 151.—Converse effect in Rochelle salt containing 0.37 per cent of TlNa tartrate, at temperatures below and above the Curie point, from Bloomenthal. The strain y_z is calculated from the observed change in length of a 45° X-cut bar.

Kurchatov used the vanishing of E_c to determine the Curie point, obtaining a value in agreement with that from the Curie-Weiss law. At any temperature in this region there is an initial value of k_x such that over a certain range of field strengths there is no hysteresis; this range is greater the lower the temperature and the higher the percentage of the ammonium salt. Hysteresis is observed as soon as the peak value of the field exceeds this critical value (point B in Fig. 148), the critical field being greater as the content of NH$_4$Na is increased.

492. *Piezoelectric Properties.* Not even qualitative tests seem to have been made of the piezoelectric properties of the pure RbNa and TlNa tartrates. Mandell's measurements on the NH$_4$Na tartrate have been mentioned above. As for mixed crystals, Eremeev and Kurchatov[133] obtained a piezoelectric hysteresis loop below the Curie point by the *direct effect*, by applying to a 45° X-cut crystal containing 26.7 molecules of the NH$_4$Na tartrate to 100 molecules of the KNa tartrate a succession of stresses up to 18 kg/cm², decreasing again to zero. Above the Curie point the polarization:stress relation was linear, with no hysteresis, obeying a Curie-Weiss law.

The *converse effect* in mixed crystals has been investigated by Bloomenthal,[55] by the method described in §422, at temperatures from 10 to 35°C. The plates were 45° X-cut, of the order of 30 by 8 by 1 mm, coated with thin tin foil. The hysteresis loop obtained at 14°C with a crystal containing 0.37 per cent of the TlNa tartrate is shown in Fig. 151. The form of the loop is very similar to that for pure Rochelle salt at 18.5° in Fig. 114, and at the same field strengths the strains are nearly

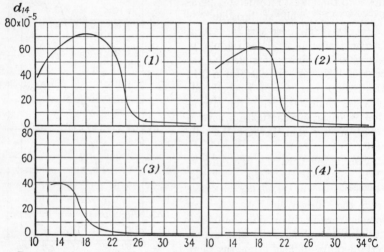

FIG. 152.—d_{14} for Rochelle salt and isomorphic mixtures, by the converse effect, from Bloomenthal. Curve (1) pure Rochelle salt; (2) Rochelle salt with 0.37 per cent $C_4H_4O_6TlNa \cdot 4H_2O$; (3) with 1.0 per cent $C_4H_4O_6NH_4Na \cdot 4H_2O$; (4) with 3.7 per cent $C_4H_4O_6TlNa \cdot 4H_2O$.

as large. The curve for 35°C, in the parelectric region, shows practically a linear relation between y_z and E, with no hysteresis.

Bloomenthal secured similar data at other temperatures, for pure Rochelle salt and for the mixtures shown in Fig. 152. In this figure $d_{14} = dy_z/dE$, which is the same as y_z/E at those temperatures where the relation is linear. In the non-linear ferroelectric region

$$d_{14} = \frac{dy_z}{dE} = \text{slope of the straight portion of the loop}$$

The figure makes evident the decrease in d_{14} of Rochelle salt on adding a small amount of the TlNa salt, as well as the lowering of the upper Curie point with increasing amounts of TlNa salt. The thallium salt does not appear to have as profound an effect as the ammonium salt. For example, 1 per cent of TlNa tartrate reduces the upper Curie point to about 21°C, while from Fig. 150 it is seen that the same percentage of the NH_4Na tartrate reduces it to 10°C.

493. Ferroelectric Properties of Phosphates and Arsenates. Hitherto we have considered the dielectric analogy to ferromagnetism in the case of Rochelle salt and crystals isomorphic with it.

Attention will now be given to another group of crystals that have been found to have similar properties. They are the dihydrogen phosphates and arsenates of potassium and ammonium, isomorphic members of the tetragonal sphenoidal Class 11, symmetry V_d. The piezoelectric constants are the same as for Rochelle salt, namely d_{14}, d_{25}, and d_{36}, but with $d_{14} = d_{25}$. The unique axis, parallel to the field direction for which the ferroelectric anomalies exist, is the crystallographic c- (or Z-) axis: thus the anomalous piezoelectric constant is d_{36}, and the anomalous susceptibility is η_z. Quantitative data on the piezoelectric properties of KH_2PO_4 are given in §146. Qualitatively, piezoelectric properties were detected in $NH_4H_2PO_4$ by Giebe and Scheibe,[164] and in KH_2PO_4, KH_2AsO_4, and $NH_4H_2AsO_4$ by Elings and Terpstra (see footnote, page 232). In all cases measurements over wide ranges of stress and temperature are greatly to be desired.

Quantitative observations have been published on the dielectric constants k_x and k_z and specific heats of all four salts, the spontaneous polarization P_z^0 and the spontaneous Kerr effect in the potassium salts, and some of the elastic properties of KH_2PO_4. Dielectric observations have been made both above and below the Curie points of the potassium salts, but with the ammonium salts only observations above the upper Curie point were possible. In all cases the anomalies occur at liquid-air temperatures.

TABLE XXXVI

Property	KH_2PO_4	KD_2PO_4	KH_2AsO_4	$NH_4H_2PO_4$	$NH_4H_2AsO_4$
Molecular weight......	136.13	138.14	180.02	115.08	158.97
Density..............	2.34	2.34	2.87	1.803	2.311
Melting point, °C......	252.6	—	288	~190*	~300*
Axial ratio c/a.........	0.938	0.973	0.938	1.008	1.004
Curie point, °K........	122.0	213	95.6	147.9	216.1
Max. P°, esu cm^{-2}.....	14,100	14,500	15,000	—	—

* Decomposes with evolution of ammonia and water.

Studies in this field began with a paper on "a new Seignette–electric substance" (KH_2PO_4)* by Busch and Scherrer in 1935.[90] This paper

* It is of historical interest that isomorphism in crystals was first discovered by Mitscherlich in 1819 between the phosphate and arsenate of potassium.

was followed in 1938 by Busch's more complete investigation[88] and in the succeeding years by a series of papers by Busch and his colleagues at Zurich, to which reference will be made below.* Busch's theoretical treatment has been considered in §485. The data summarized in

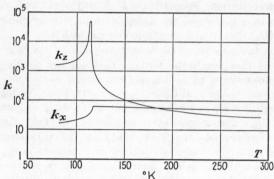

Fig. 153.—Dielectric constants k_z and k_x of KH_2PO_4, from Busch. $E = 200$ volts/cm, frequency 800 cycles.

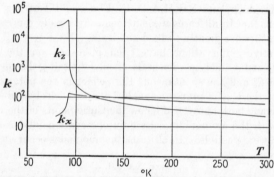

Fig. 154.—Dielectric constants k_z nd k_x of KH_2AsO_4, from Busch. $E = 200$ volts/cm, frequency 800 cycles.

Table XXXVI are assembled from these papers and from the "Handbook of Chemistry and Physics."

The method of growing these crystals is described by Busch[88] and by Bantle.[22]

494. The results of Busch's measurements of the dielectric constants k_x and k_z for the potassium salts are shown in Figs 153 and 154. A capacitance bridge was used. The maxima in k_z at the Curie points are the indications of the presence of ferroelectricity. The maxima in k_x are unexpected: in Rochelle salt, k_y and k_z have normal values with no anomaly in the neighborhood of the Curie point. Busch's explanation

* In Busch's first paper is the erroneous statement that $d_{25} = d_{36}$.

is that the number of free dipoles increases rapidly as the Curie point is approached from the low-temperature side.*

Busch finds that the potassium salts, like Rochelle salt, obey a Curie-Weiss law.

In a later paper[89] Busch and Ganz discuss the theory and measurement of the complex dielectric constants of KH_2PO_4 and KH_2AsO_4 parallel to Z, which they call ϵ_c^*. The measurements, made with a 50-cycle capacitance bridge, differ from the curves in Figs. 153 and 154 in that ϵ_c^*, which is practically the same as k_x outside the Curie points where the losses are negligible, remains at a high level over a wide range of temperature below θ_u. The value for KH_2PO_4 is not far from $3(10^4)$ from the upper Curie point down to about $80°K$, where it begins to fall rapidly to a value around 40 at $50°K$, with still further decrease at lower temperatures. The curve for KH_2AsO_4 has a similar course, the largest value† being $1.95(10^4)$.

As a measure of the spontaneous polarization P_z^0, Busch took the saturation value at the peak of the hysteresis loop, instead of the more commonly adopted remanent value. In the case of KH_2PO_4 the difference is small except close to the Curie point;‡ but with KH_2AsO_4, which has a much narrower loop, the remanent value is a small fraction of the peak value. If the remanent value were used, P_z^0 for KH_2AsO_4 would be considerably smaller than for KH_2PO_4. In any event, the spontaneous polarization in these salts is far greater than in Rochelle salt, the ratio, from Table XXXVI, being of the order of 20:1 in the case of KH_2PO_4.

The dielectric constants of the *ammonium salts* were measured by Busch.[88] Observations could be made only down to $-53°C$ with the arsenate and $-118°C$ with the phosphate. At these temperatures the crystals became converted to an inhomogeneous microcrystalline mass. Busch records the following dependence on temperature:

* From Prof. Hans Mueller the author learns that he finds an explanation of the large value of k_z at the Curie point in the large internal field, without invoking dipoles. The absence of such an effect to a perceptible extent in k_y and k_z for Rochelle salt is attributable to the fact that in Rochelle salt the internal field is very much smaller than in the phosphates. See also P. Bärtschi, *Helv. Ph. Ac.*, vol. 18, pp. 267–295, 1945.

† It will be noted that the largest values of ϵ_c^* for both salts are much lower than the peak values shown in Figs. 153 and 154. The reason is doubtless that Busch and Ganz used a much higher voltage (2,400 volts/cm for KH_2PO_4, 3,300 volts/cm for KH_2AsO_4) than did Busch in his earlier measurements. At high voltages the polarization is brought nearer to the saturation value. Moreover, considerations mentioned in §480 make it evident that the observed persistence of a relatively large dielectric constant over a wide range of temperature below θ_u is what one would expect when the applied voltage is large.

‡ The value of P^0 for KH_2PO_4 in Table XXXVI is taken from a later paper by Arx and Bantle.[10]

(1) $NH_4H_2PO_4$—k_x increases from 55 at room temperature to 90 at $-118°C$; k_z increases from 14.5 at room temperature to 20 at $-118°C$.

(2) $NH_4H_2AsO_4$–k_x increases from 126 at room temperature to 145 at $-53°$; $k_z = 12$ from $+27°$ to $-53°C$.

495. P^0, *Piezoelectric Constants, Coercive Field E_c, and Lower Curie Point θ_l.* It will be recalled that with Rochelle salt P^0 and E_c vanish outside the Curie points, rising to maxima at about 5°C, and that the free dielectric constant rises to a sharp maximum at θ_l just as at θ_u. The Seignette-electric phosphates and arsenates have critical temperatures with the same properties as at the *upper* Curie point in Rochelle salt. Insofar as they can be said to have a lower Curie point at all, this point differs in important particulars from that in Rochelle salt.

The evidence is based mostly on observations on KH_2PO_4. With this crystal, P^0 rises very rapidly from its zero value at θ_u to a value of the order of 14000 esu, without appreciable diminution down to 95°K, the lowest temperature recorded (Arx and Bantle[10]). The dielectric constant decreases continuously as the temperature goes below θ_u, without again having a maximum anywhere. The coercive field increases enormously with decreasing temperature, approaching zero only at θ_u (Bantle, Busch, Lauterburg, and Scherrer[25]). The only thing resembling a lower Curie point is the disappearance of hysteresis, which Busch and Ganz[89] found to take place at about 58°K. With a $50 \sim$ field having a peak value of 3,000 volts/cm they found hysteresis to be present from 58 to 123.5°K, the loops having maximum area at about 62°K.

In Rochelle salt the disappearance of hysteresis at temperatures below θ_l is associated with the *vanishing* of the coercive force at θ_l. On the other hand, in KH_2PO_4 the coercive force was still very large at the temperature at which the hysteresis ceased to be measurable in the experiments mentioned above. As long as the temperature was above this value, Arx and Bantle's peak voltage was sufficient for a hysteresis loop with appreciable area to be traced. From this temperature on downward, the coercive force was so great that their apparatus recorded only a small portion of a complete loop: what was recorded was the reversible permittivity k_r (§430). The hysteresis loop had degenerated to a straight line through the origin. If they had used a higher voltage, they would pretty certainly have observed hysteresis at temperatures below 58°K.

Evidently the disappearance of hysteresis cannot be taken as a criterion for the presence of a lower Curie point. Arx and Bantle very properly refrain from making any such claim in the discussion of their results.

All the evidence supports the view first advanced by Bantle, Busch, Lauterburg, and Scherrer, that the spontaneous polarization does not vanish at any temperature below the "upper Curie point," but that there is nevertheless a temperature below which the elementary domains refuse to be reversed by an applied field. Herein lies the contrast with Rochelle salt. The spontaneous polarization becomes "frozen." The decrease in k_z, the increase in E_c, and the absence of a sudden anomaly either in the specific heat or in the Kerr effect* all support this view. As far as the evidence goes, the same is true also of KH_2AsO_4 and KD_2PO_4 (see below).

In terms of the interaction theory, the persistence of P^0 indicates that the susceptibility η_z'' of the clamped crystal remains greater than the product $a_{36}b_{36}$ at all temperatures below θ_u (see §453). According to the internal-field theory (§485) one would say that the product $\gamma\alpha_M$ remained greater than unity.

The spontaneous polarization P^0 and coercive field E_c are not very different in KD_2PO_4 and KH_2PO_4. The spontaneous Kerr effect has been investigated by Zwicker and Scherrer,[602] whose results agree with those of Bantle, Busch, Lauterburg, and Scherrer on KH_2PO_4 and KH_2AsO_4 in that there is an anomalous change in double refraction at θ_u but not at any lower temperature.

Piezoelectric Constants. The following more recent data supplement the brief statement on p. 209. They are taken from W. P. Mason, reference (51) in Appendix II. For ADP at ordinary temperatures $d_{14} \approx 5(10^{-8})$. An X-cut therefore gives a very weak response. With cuts of this crystal the electric field is usually parallel to the Z-axis. The value of d_{36} varies from 129.5 at 100°C through 148 at 20°C to 270 at −122°C, all multiplied by 10^{-8} esu. For KDP at ordinary temperatures, $d_{14} \approx 4(10^{-8})$. The value of d_{36} varies from 50.4 at 100°C through 69.6 at 20°C to 4400 at −150°C, all multiplied by 10^{-8} esu.

496. *Deuterium Potassium Phosphate*, KD_2PO_4. We saw in §444 that the replacing of H by D in Rochelle salt raises the upper Curie point by about 11°C. An even greater isotopic effect is exhibited by KD_2PO_4.

The present treatment is based on the work of Bantle[22] and of Zwicker and Scherrer.[602] Bantle measured k_z with a 1,000-cycle per sec bridge, the field strength being 40 volts/cm. The upper Curie point is indicated by a sharp maximum in k_z at 213°K (−60°C). From this maximum, k_z diminishes to about 82 at 300°K and 46 at 100°K. The curve has a slight bend at 158°K, which Bantle takes as the lower Curie point, below which the hysteresis vanishes. The dielectric behavior of KD_2PO_4 runs parallel to that of KH_2PO_4. The hysteresis loops have an appreciable area only between 105 and 213°K. The value 213° for θ_u seems well established.

---

* See also Zwicker and Scherrer.[602]

497. *Specific Heats and Internal Field Constants.* In §409 it was shown that in Rochelle salt the anomaly in specific heat is extremely small at both Curie points. From the relatively large values of P^0 for the phosphates discussed above and the marked dependence of P^0 on temperature, one might expect a more pronounced anomaly for them. This expectation has been fulfilled by Bantle[22] for all three phosphates and by Stephenson and Hooley[481] and J. and K. Mendelssohn[364] for KH_2PO_4. Very recently, the specific heats of KH_2PO_4, KH_2AsO_4, $NH_4H_2PO_4$, and $NH_4H_2AsO_4$ were measured over a very wide range of temperatures by Stephenson and his associates.[480-483] They found no anomaly except at the upper Curie point. From their results, which are probably the most precise, we find the following values for the normal specific heat C_n at θ_u (derived from the course of the curve above and below θ_u), the peak value C_θ at θ_u, and the difference $\Delta C = C_\theta - C_n$, all in cal mole^{-1} deg^{-1}, and also the heat of transition ΔH in cal mole^{-1}:

	C_θ	C_n	ΔC	ΔH
KH_2PO_4	118	16	102	87 ± 6
KH_2AsO_4	76	15	61	84 ± 4
$NH_4H_2PO_4$	274	20	254	154 ± 5
$NH_4H_2AsO_4$	279	29	250	220 ± 15
KD_2PO_4*	134	29	105	100.3

* Data for KD_2PO_4 are from Bantle.[22]

As has been shown in §409, the internal field constant γ can be calculated when ΔC and the temperature variation of P^0 are known. Bantle thus finds the following values of γ: for KH_2AsO_4, 0.5; for KH_2PO_4, 0.37 (in contrast with Stephenson and Hooley's value of 0.7); for KD_2PO_4, 0.68.

Although the phosphates here considered have only small internal field constants, the large values of P^0 make it certain that the internal fields themselves must be much greater than in Rochelle salt. For example, the product γP^0 for KD_2PO_4 yields a value of the internal field of about 3,000,000 volts/cm.

498. *Domain Structure.* It was stated in §494 that on cooling below certain definite temperatures, $NH_4H_2PO_4$ (at $-118°C$) and $NH_4H_2AsO_4$ (at $-53°C$) broke down to a microcrystalline mass. When this fact is compared with Busch's remark that the potassium salts tended to become cracked when heated through the upper Curie point, there appears some probability that the temperatures recorded above are close to the Curie points for the ammonium salts. If this assumption is made, the shattering of the crystals can be attributed to the stresses attending the commencement of a domain structure as the Seignette region is approached. The temperatures recorded as "Curie points" of the ammonium salts in Table XXXVI are those for the maximum values of the specific heat, as measured by Stephenson and Adams[480] and by Stephenson and Zettlemoyer.[483] These temperatures are a few degrees lower than those at which Busch's crystal plates broke down. It seems just possible that, if this breakdown could have been avoided, the dielectric constants (values of which are given in §494) might have risen to high values at the Curie points.

Further evidence of domain structure, at least in KH_2PO_4 and KD_2PO_4, is afforded by the experiments of Zwicker and Scherrer,[602] in which the change in double refraction under an electric field, at temperatures below θ_u, takes place in steps, in a manner analogous to the Barkhausen effect in iron. In a discussion of this paper, Quervain and Zwicker[432] reach the conclusion that the domains themselves are microscopic but that they fall into groups some millimeters in extent. They find that sudden cooling through θ_u causes minute cracks perpendicular to the Z-axis, which disappear on warming.

499. Technical Applications. The potassium and ammonium salts mentioned in the preceding paragraphs seem to offer considerable promise of useful applications. The first to receive attention was KH_2PO_4, known as KDP. Somewhat later $NH_4H_2PO_4$, known as ADP, was exploited (§499a). In both its elastic and piezoelectric properties this crystal, like the others in the group, stands between quartz and Rochelle salt. Its piezoelectric effect at room temperature (§146) is about seven times as great as in quartz, while it is much more stable than Rochelle salt and has no water of crystallization. At ordinary temperatures it is so far above its Curie point as to be free from such fantastic behavior as that shown by Rochelle salt in the neighborhood of 24°C. It is practically devoid of hysteresis. Some of its elastic temperature coefficients, however, are considerably greater than those of quartz.

Experiments with KH_2PO_4 resonators are described by Bantle and Lüdy,[27] by Lüdy,[323] and by Bantle.[23] Lüdy measured the values of the elastic constants s_{11} and s_{33}, as recorded in §89. Bantle and Lüdy studied lengthwise vibrations in thin rods, using frequency modulation to sweep rapidly and repeatedly through the resonant frequency. From the curves recorded by means of a cathode-ray oscillograph they found the resonant frequency, effective elastic constant, and damping, at different temperatures down to the Curie point, where certain of the elastic constants had very large temperature coefficients. The only numerical data published thus far are in Bantle's paper. Using Z-cuts he finds, for different modes, temperature coefficients of frequency from

$-205(10^{-6})$ to $-290(10^{-6})$ and considers the possibility of securing cuts with zero temperature coefficient.

Since the matrices of the elastic and piezoelectric constants have the same form as for Rochelle salt, the rules for exciting various vibrational modes are exactly the same as for that crystal.

Matthias and Scherrer[354] have called attention to the advantages of KH_2PO_4 for band-pass filters.

499a. *Notes on Recent Advances.* Two more piezoelectric tartrates have been investigated since this book was first published. They are ethylene diamine tartrate (EDT) and dipotassium tartrate (DKT). Their properties and applications are discussed by W. P. Mason [Appendix II, ref. (51)].

The ADP crystal has had a meteoric career. For most purposes, except for frequency control or in applications where the strongest possible piezoelectric effect is needed, it soon supplanted quartz and Rochelle salt. Its advantage over Rochelle salt is that its Curie point lies far below all ordinary temperatures. Although it operates in its parelectric region, still its piezoelectric response is strong. It can be used at temperatures as high as 100°C. From 100°C to -100°C d_{36} varies from $129.5(10^{-8})$ to $270(10^{-8})$ esu, with value $148(10^{-8})$ at 20°C. As a vibrator it can be used in the form of a Z-cut plate, in a face-shear mode; as a Z-cut 45° bar in a lengthwise extensional mode; or as an X-cut plate rotated 45° about the Y-axis, in which case it vibrates in a thickness shear mode. In the Second World War it was used extensively for underwater transducers, and it is also used for microphones and phonograph pickups, as described in reference (51), Appendix II.

The decline in the use of ADP came with the advent of the ferroelectric ceramics (§570).

CHAPTER XXVIII

MISCELLANEOUS APPLICATIONS OF PIEZOELECTRICITY

Ich werde dies Projekt niemals vollendet sehen, aber die Nachwelt kann es erleben, wenn sie den Plan weiter verfolgt und sich der geeigneten Mittel für die Ausführung bedient.
—FREDERICK THE GREAT.

In dealing with technical applications the discussion will be confined mainly to the types of crystal commonly used, their cuts, electrodes, and general performance. Space forbids detailed descriptions of circuits and of mechanical features.

The application of piezoelectric crystals in electric filters of various types will first be considered. In filter circuits the crystal operates as a resonator; the conversion of electrical into mechanical energy and back, though essential to its performance, is only incidental from the point of view of the filtering action.

The remainder of the chapter will be devoted to the large and important group of applications in which the crystal functions as a transducer, converting mechanical movements into electrical energy or the converse. The first subdivision in this group comprises the *non-resonant* applications, in which the crystal is in a state of forced vibration at a frequency which is usually far below that of any of its normal modes. In the second subdivision the crystal usually vibrates at or near a resonant frequency and is used for emitting or receiving h-f acoustic radiation. The practical applications include submarine signal and echo work, the acoustic interferometer, and intense ultrasonic beams for physical, chemical, biological, and industrial uses.

One of the most interesting effects of ultrasonic waves is their ability to diffract a beam of light. Some of the applications of this effect, especially in the measurement of elastic constants, light relays, and television, will be described.

500. The Crystal Filter. The use of piezoelectric crystals as couplers and sharply tuned circuit elements was first proposed in 1921.* For use as a piezoelectric coupler the crystal is provided with two pairs of electrodes, connecting the output of one circuit with the input of another. The crystal then operates as a filter element, transmitting energy only

*Ref. 91; also W. G. Cady, U.S. patent 1,450.246 (1923) and reissue 17,355 (1929).

at a resonant frequency. The theory of the coupler has been investigated by Watanabe.[581] Its use as a tuned coupling between tubes is described by Rohde and Handrek.[438] Of greater importance is its use in electric filters, to which we now turn. Filters employing crystals were first described by L. Espenschied.[*] The evolution of the filter is described by Buckley in the reference at the end of this chapter.

All electric filters depend for their operation on the change in reactance within a certain band of frequencies. Filters constructed from coils and condensers are limited in usefulness partly by their variability with temperature and partly by the fact that the band width cannot be made sufficiently narrow to meet modern requirements in communication circuits, owing to the unavoidable resistances of the coils. Properly designed crystal filters avoid both these difficulties. In fact, the selectivity of crystals is so great that for many purposes the band width is too narrow, requiring the use of coils associated with the crystals.

In a band-pass filter the width of the band is approximately the frequency interval $(f_p - f_s)$ illustrated in Fig. 62. From Eq. (401) this interval is approximately equal to $f_s C/2C_1$. The ratio C_1/C is therefore a measure of the excellence of the filter. From Eq. (450a), it can be seen that either a capacitance C_2 in series with the resonator $RLCC_1$ or a capacitance C_3 in parallel with it has the effect of reducing the value of $(f_p - f_s)$. Use is made of this fact in the design of filters of very narrow band width.

Most crystal filters in use today in filter circuits are of quartz, with zero gap, the thin metallic electrodes being deposited directly on the quartz. The quartz plates may be supported by the lead wires, which are soldered to the electrodes at nodal points. Some filter circuits require the use of pairs of matched crystal units of identical frequency. In such cases a single crystal plate with two pairs of electrodes can be used. Much ingenuity has been shown in the placing and interconnecting of the electrodes and in the provision of a narrow metallic strip plated to the crystal to serve as a screen between the electrode pairs. Such arrangements are described by Mason and Sykes,[342,343] Mason,[B35] and Rohde.[436,437]

For the higher frequencies, thickness vibrations must be used. From 50 to 500 kc/sec compressional vibrations in the direction of length or breadth of the plate are ordinarily employed. For lower frequencies, use is made of flexural vibrations; the NT-cut described in §359 can be used from 50 down to 4 kc/sec, while Rohde and Handrek[438] describe flexural filter crystals for frequencies as low as 1,000 cycles/sec.

As an example of the band width obtainable without the use of auxiliary condensers may be mentioned the 18.5° cut, for which, from

[*] U.S. patent 1,795,204, filed 1927 and issued in 1931.

Table XXX, $C_1/C = 138$. From this one finds $(f_p - f_s)/f_s = 0.36$ per cent. For this cut, as well as the $-5°$ cut, see §357.

In some lattice filters two crystals of slightly different frequency are used, the resonant value f_s of one coinciding with the antiresonant value f_p of the other. In such cases the band width is twice that of one crystal alone.

Filter elements have also been made from Rochelle salt. For a time, composite resonators consisting of metallic bars with Rochelle-salt crystals attached were tried, but this method has been abandoned. For the lower frequencies 45° bars may be used; to avoid the anomalies that beset the X-cut, the cuts may be made normal to the Y- or Z-axis. Filters of higher frequency employ thickness shear vibrations of oblique plates,* some formulas for which are given in §77.

Whichever type of crystal is chosen, an all-important requirement is the absence, over as wide a range as possible, of all disturbing resonant frequencies.

An attempt by Guerbilsky† to broaden the band by using a wedge-shaped crystal was based on an erroneous concept of the nature of vibrations in solids. The experiments of Zacek and Petrzilka[597] showed, as would be expected, that such a resonator has a large number of closely adjacent frequencies; the subject is also discussed by Wagner.[578]

Crystals can be connected to serve as elements in high-pass, low-pass, or band filters. They are used commercially in pilot channel filters for carrier systems and for separating carrier from side-band frequencies in radio. They have also found application in acoustics, for analyzing the components of complex sounds. Finally may be mentioned their use in radio receiving sets, in which they are commonly placed in a bridge in the i-f amplifier.

A fully equipped section of coaxial cable for carrier communication, with 400 circuits, requires 12,800 crystals for channel filters, in addition to those for channel supply filters.‡

501. Crystals as Mechanical and Acoustic Transducers. For the *measurement of pressures*, plates or blocks of quartz or Rochelle salt are chiefly used, and to a small extent tourmaline. There is a great variety of devices, ranging from quartz or tourmaline plates, used singly or in stacks, for measuring violent explosion pressures, down to delicate apparatus for recording blood pressures. Among the references at the end of the chapter will be found descriptions of piezoelectric methods for

---

* W. P. MASON, U.S. patent 2,303,375. See also Z. Kamayachi, T. Ishikawa, and E. Kamizeki, *Nippon Elec. Comm. Eng.*, January 1941, p. 195, and M. Monji and I. Kuwayama, *Electrotech. Jour. Japan*, vol. 4, p. 235, 1940.

† A. GUERBILSKY, *Jour. phys. rad.*, vol. 8, pp. 165–168, 1937.

‡ A J Gill. in discussion of paper by Booth.[69]

measuring pressures in internal-combustion engines and in various types of firearms and artillery; pressures produced by cutting tools; transient pressures resulting from impact; piezoelectric oscillographs; and applications of piezoelectric manometric devices in biology. Many of the articles cited contain further references to the literature. Applications of optical phenomena produced by vibrating crystals are considered later.

Piezoelectric devices have come into extensive use for the *measurement of vibrations*, especially in machinery, and for analyzing the degree of smoothness of finished surfaces. Owing to its large piezoelectric effect, Rochelle salt is well suited to these purposes. Some references are given at the end of the chapter.

Space forbids an account of the various crystal cuts and mountings that are used for the measurement of stresses and vibrations. It must suffice to say that, in devices employing quartz, X-cuts are commonly used, with either the longitudinal or the transverse effect. Rochelle-salt devices are described in §503. With few exceptions resonance in the crystal or in the assemblage of crystals is avoided. This is usually not difficult, since in most cases the crystal frequency is much higher than any frequency associated with the effect being investigated. Moreover, the mounting can be made in such a way as to tend to damp out any crystal vibrations.

Some of the papers cited at the end of the chapter contain a theoretical treatment of the devices for measurement of pressures and vibrations, for example, those by Gohlke, Kluge and Linckh, Webster, and Zeller.

502. Rochelle-salt Non-resonant Transducers. Rochelle salt is used at the present time more than any other crystal in electroacoustic and electromechanical devices. The operating frequencies are usually well removed from the resonant frequencies of the crystal units, and in any case the construction is such as to tend to damp out all resonances. The outstanding advantage of Rochelle salt, at least in the X-cut commonly employed, is of course the large piezoelectric constant. This advantage carries with it a train of difficulties, due to the great sensitiveness of the piezoelectric property to mechanical constraint, the variability with temperature, the presence of hysteresis, and the large dielectric constant. It is a fortunate circumstance that the constraints imposed on the crystal units by cement, electrodes, clamping, and waterproofing not only suppress resonant frequencies, but at the same time greatly reduce the effects of temperature and hysteresis and lower the dielectric constant to a value approximately that of a completely clamped crystal. The price that has to be paid is a great diminution in the effective values of d_{14} and e_{14}.

Some Rochelle-salt transducers operate as motors, others as generators. The *motor* devices are most sensitive in the neighborhood of the Curie point, 24°C. By suitable mounting it is possible, however, to restrict the response within a few decibels over the allowable temperature range from $-40°$ to $+54°$C ($-40°$ to $+130°$F). It is of the utmost importance never to let the temperature rise above this upper limit, owing to the disintegration of Rochelle salt at 55.6°C. The upper limit of useful operation is 45°C, since above this temperature leakage becomes objectionable.

The dielectric constant of a clamped Rochelle-salt crystal in the X-direction is of the order of 100. The high parallel capacitance thus conferred on a thin plate would be a serious handicap if the purpose were to convert as much mechanical into electrical energy as possible. In most applications, however, in which the crystal acts as a *generator* to produce electrical energy, the crystal is connected to a very high impedance. It is then almost on open circuit; and since stress and temperature affect the dielectric constant in approximately the same manner as they affect the piezoelectric constant, it follows that the potential difference that a given stress on the crystal impresses on the outer circuit is not far from proportional to the stress under all circumstances. Moreover, less trouble is experienced from the capacitance of long lead wires than if the dielectric constant of the crystal were low. The open-circuit output of these generator devices is practically independent of temperature.

The fact that with a high external electrical impedance the crystal is practically on open circuit has a bearing on the theoretical treatment of this form of transducer. When the crystal is on open circuit and well below resonance, its electrical state under mechanical stress is substantially the same as that of a bare crystal with an infinite gap. The polarization remains nearly zero at all strains. Since, as shown in §375, the stiffness at infinite gap is very nearly independent of temperature, it follows that the crystal when connected to a very high external impedance is comparatively free from the effects of the usual anomalies of the X-cut. This is especially true when the crystal is also in a state of partial constraint.

In the theoretical treatment of the Rochelle-salt transducer it is convenient to use the equations of the polarization theory, with the coefficients a_{14} and b_{14}, which vary comparatively little with temperature, in place of e_{14} and d_{14}. This is virtually the method followed by Mason[B35] in his treatment of the problem, although he employs the "charge" theory; as explained in §191, the charge and polarization theories lead to almost identical results.

503. The first published account of acoustic effects with Rochelle salt was that of Nicolson[391] in 1919. He used entire crystals, 2 in. or more in extent, with variously disposed electrodes. Although the crystal structure and the electric field were far from uniform, Nicolson was able to make use of the relative displacements of the faces normal to the Z-axis in such a way as to make the crystals serve as microphones and reproducers. Unpublished experiments in Scott laboratory following Nicolson's work soon showed that equally sensitive units could be made in the form of thin X-cut bars, cut after the manner of Pockels with lengths bisecting the angle between the Y- and Z-axes. These plates were from 1 to 2 cm long, 0.4 to 1 cm wide, and 0.1 to 0.2 cm thick. When the ends were cemented between diaphragms and rigid backings they acted as microphones and reproducers; such plates were also tested successfully as phonograph pickups.*

Much more effective are the Rochelle-salt "bimorphs"† of Sawyer.⁴⁴⁸ These devices generally consist of two X-cut Rochelle-salt plates cemented face to face, usually with a thin metallic electrode interposed.

In the "bender" type, plates are rectangular, square, or trapezoidal, the major axes of the plates making angles of ±45° with the Y- and Z-axes. The X-axes of the two plates are so oriented that as one plate dilates in either direction the other contracts. This type of element is therefore somewhat similar to the "Curie strip" described in §354. There is, however, this important difference, that while in the quartz Curie strip with length parallel to Y the only strain (the small change in thickness of the component plates being ignored) is in the direction of length, with none at all in the direction of breadth, the piezoelectric effect in Rochelle salt is such that both length and breadth are affected (if the element is square either dimension of the major surfaces may be called the "length"). If an applied electric field tends to make one plate longer and narrower, the other plate tends to become shorter and wider. As a result, the element as a whole does not become bent to a cylindrical form but tends to become saddle-shaped; when one surface is convex in the length direction it is concave in the breadth direction.

The foregoing remarks apply to the unconstrained element. If one end of the rectangle is clamped and an alternating field is applied, the other end moves to and fro (*single clamping*). If both ends are clamped, the curvature in the breadth direction is largely suppressed and the central portion vibrates like a diaphragm (*double clamping*). Either of these methods of mounting may be used to make the element act as a transducer for transforming electrical into mechanical energy or the converse.

A second type of bimorph is called the "twister." The two component X-cut plates are square or rectangular, with edges parallel to

---

* See also Schwartz.⁴⁵⁴

† The information concerning bimorphs and their applications was kindly furnished by the Brush Development Company .

Y and Z, or trapezoidal (tapered element), with the two parallel edges AB and CD (Fig. 155) in the direction of Y or Z. When a voltage is applied to the combination, the two plates tend to become sheared in opposite directions, according to the formula $y_z = d_{14}E_x$. If the element is clamped at one end, as at AB, then since the plates are cemented together the small end face CD rotates in its own plane. The end P of a pointer attached to CD moves in a circular arc in the plane of this end face. Twister elements are often mounted and used in this manner. Another common method of mounting the twister element is to clamp it at three corners, the fourth being left free to move.

The principle of the twister is illustrated in Fig. 156, which shows a Rochelle-salt motor that has been found useful for demonstration. By proper design of the ratchet and pawl the device could be made to serve as a synchronous low-speed motor.

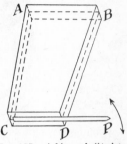

Fig. 155.—A bimorph "twister."

Bender and twister elements are made commercially under the trade name "Bimorph" in sizes from $\frac{7}{32}$ by $\frac{7}{32}$ by 0.015 in. to $2\frac{1}{2}$ by $2\frac{1}{2}$ by $\frac{1}{4}$ in., depending on the uses to which they are put. Among the applications for such elements are pickups and recorders for phonographs, microphones, earphones, vibration meters, oscilloscopes, direct inking oscillographs, light valves, stethoscopes, and pickups to be placed on musical instruments. Rochelle salt has also been used in loud-speakers but is now superseded by the more rugged electrodynamic drive. An instrument known as the "surface analyzer" consists of a combination of crystal pickup, amplifier, and crystal oscillograph that makes a direct record in ink of the surface contour of the test specimen.

Crystal microphones and earphones usually employ either a twister element with three-corner mounting or a long narrow bender element with double end clamping. The free corner of the twister or the center of the bender is coupled to a small acoustic diaphragm.

Another type of microphone is known as the "sound-cell" microphone. The sound cell employs two approximately square bender bimorphs placed close together so as to form a flat airtight cell, with a small gap between them. The elements are supported at the centers of two opposite edges so that they are free to partake of the saddle-shaped curvature. The two elements are so oriented and electrically connected in parallel that their voltages are in phase when sound waves strike the cell, while the device is insensitive to mechanical shock or vibration. Two or more sound cells can be combined in a single microphone; in one type the number is 24. A typical sound cell has elements $\frac{7}{16}$ by

$\frac{7}{16}$ by 0.02 in. with a flat response from 30 to 10,000 cycles/sec. A laboratory type has elements only $\frac{7}{32}$ by $\frac{7}{32}$ by 0.015 in. with a resonant frequency of 45,000 and a flat response to 17,000 cycles/sec.

Vibration meters of the displacement type employ bender or twister elements mounted on a convenient support and arranged for the active portion of the element to be driven by the vibrating object. Both

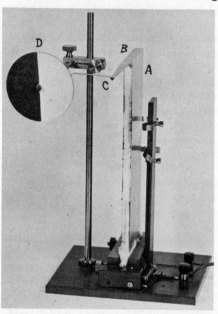

Fig. 156.—Rochelle-salt motor. A is a bimorph "twister" consisting of two X-cut plates, each 4.5 mm thick, cemented together with a tin-foil electrode between, which is connected to one terminal of the 60-cycle 115-volt supply. The length, parallel to Z, is 25 cm, and the breadth, parallel to Y, is 7.5 cm. The two outer tin-foil electrodes are connected together and to the other terminal of the supply, through a high resistance for safety. The lower end of the twister is fixed. When the field is applied, the upper end twists about the vertical axis, rotating the arm B and the light spring C, which acts as a pawl on the knurled circumference of the wheel D. The alternating field causes D to rotate slowly.

bender and twister elements are used also in the acceleration type, the accelerating force being applied to the holder and the deformation of the element taking place through inertia. This type of pickup is especially useful for measuring mechanical vibrations of relatively high frequency. The voltage generated by the crystal element is proportional to the acceleration; for the same amplitude it increases with the square of the frequency. The frequencies investigated must lie well below the resonant frequency of the element in its mounting.

The voltages involved in the operation of bimorph crystal elements vary over a large range depending on the uses to which the elements are put. The voltage developed by a laboratory sound-cell microphone may be far less than 1 mv, while the output of a typical phonograph pickup may be as high as 10 volts. One or two volts is sufficient to produce comfortable volume in crystal earphones, while about 700 volts are required to drive a crystal-actuated direct-inking oscillograph at full amplitude.

504. A Rochelle salt transducer of quite a different type is the L-cut.[108] This is a plate making equal angles with all three crystallographic axes, as described in §140. A field normal to the plate causes a change in *thickness*, while through the direct piezoelectric effect a normal compression produces polarization charges. Plates of this type have been used experimentally as emitters and receivers of sound waves and also as generators of ultrasonic waves. They have recently found application by Groth and Liebermann[190] as microphones in the measurement of the velocity of sound. Unfortunately their usefulness is limited by the prevalence of undesired vibrational modes.

505. Ultrasonics. The study of acoustic waves with frequencies above the range of human audibility began late in the nineteenth century. Koenig's longitudinally vibrating steel rods appeared in 1874, and his ultra-audible tuning forks in 1899. Other early sources of very short acoustic waves were the Galton whistle (1883) and in 1907 Altberg's application of the oscillatory spark discharge, by means of which he recorded acoustic frequencies of over 300,000 vibrations per second. Wavelengths were usually measured by means of the Kundt dust figures.

Although some of these sources were fairly intense, they could emit only decaying wave trains, and they were practically point-sources, radiating in all directions.

Leaving aside certain attempts in the First World War to produce h-f sounds electrostatically from vibrating condenser plates, it may be said that the modern science of ultrasonics began with the introduction of an entirely new source of h-f sound waves by Langevin—a device that also serves for detecting these waves. Langevin conceived the brilliant idea of making use of the piezoelectric property of quartz crystals to cause them to emit a continuous flow of undamped acoustic waves when connected to a h-f electric generator. Moreover, by the use of a mosaic of crystal plates of large area, he was able to produce a system of approximately *plane* waves, resulting in an ultrasonic beam of great intensity, concentrated within a small angle of divergence.

The immediate purpose of Langevin's invention was the detecting and locating of distant objects under water by means of echoes. A principle so novel and so suggestive could not fail to excite the interest of many physicists. Numerous researches were begun, leading to several applications of considerable importance in both pure and applied science.

A second source of continuous ultrasonic waves is the magnetostriction oscillator, introduced by Pierce in 1928,* and developed further by him and by many others. It can generate more intense radiation than the vibrating crystal; but its practicable upper limit of frequency comes at about 60 kc/sec, and it is not so well adapted to the production of some of the effects described below. Descriptions of the magnetostriction oscillator and its uses will be found in the books listed at the end of the chapter.

506. Langevin's Quartz-Steel Oscillator. It has been shown in earlier chapters that an X-cut quartz plate dilates or contracts in the direction of its thickness when an electric field in the X-direction is applied by means of electrodes covering its major surfaces, and that by application of an alternating voltage of suitable frequency it can be set into resonant compressional thickness vibration. Quartz plates of reasonable thickness have resonant frequencies too high to be suitable for submarine signaling and echo production. To surmount this difficulty Langevin cemented a quartz plate a few millimeters thick between two massive slabs of steel. The thickness of these slabs was so chosen that the over-all frequency of the entire "sandwich" was of the desired value. The slabs served also as electrodes. When the unit was vibrating in thickness resonance in air, a system of stationary waves was set up in it, the thickness of the entire unit corresponding to a half wavelength of the compressional wave. When mounted for immersion in water, one steel slab was in direct contact with the water and emitted ultrasonic radiation, while the other slab, in contact with air, reflected the wave energy without appreciable loss.

In his first experiments Langevin used a Poulsen arc generator for his h-f source. This type of generator was soon superseded by the vacuum-tube oscillator.

In order to radiate more energy and at the same time to concentrate the energy in a narrow beam, Langevin increased the lateral dimensions of the steel slabs to 20 cm or more and cemented between them a mosaic of quartz X-cut plates, all carefully ground to the same thickness. In this manner small pieces of crystal could be used for building an ultrasonic emitter of any desired area.

Although the vibrations are heavily damped by radiation into the water, it is none the less important to excite the oscillator at or near its

* G. W. Pierce, *Proc. Am. Acad. Arts Sci.*, vol. 63, pp. 1–47, 1928.

resonating frequency. For example, if 50,000 volts were required to produce a desired amplitude by forced vibrations far from resonance, 2,500 volts would suffice at the frequency of resonance. Moreover, since the oscillator usually serves also as a detector for waves reflected from distant objects, it is of enormous advantage to have it tuned to the emitted frequency.

The best size and frequency for an underwater source of concentrated radiation is determined by the following considerations: Like all other media, water absorbs sound energy to an extent depending on the distance traversed and also on the frequency. The rate of absorption increases with the square of the frequency. Waves in the audible range suffer very little absorption. Langevin points out that at a frequency of 40,000 the amplitude is reduced to one-third of its original value in about 30 km, while at 100,000 cycles/sec the same reduction takes place in about 5 km. If the radiation took place in air instead of water, two-thirds of the energy at this higher frequency would be absorbed in a few meters.

The second consideration has to do with the fact that a plane source of sound comes closer to emitting plane waves, and hence a highly concentrated beam, the greater its lateral dimensions in comparison with the wavelength of the sound. An oscillator designed for 100,000 cycles/sec, with a diameter of 20 cm, producing a wavelength in water of about 1.5 cm, would emit a beam with very sharply directional properties. For the observation of echoes from distant objects such a beam would be inconveniently narrow, and moreover at this frequency the relatively great absorption of energy by the water would be objectionable. For echo detection it is desirable to have most of the energy confined to a cone with total aperture of about 20°. This requirement is met when the diameter of the radiating surface is around six times the wavelength in the medium.

A compromise must be sought between the greater penetrating ability of l-f waves and the requirement of relatively large area to make the beam sufficiently directive. Very fortunately such a compromise is found at frequencies around 40,000. The wavelength is then about 3.5 cm, and a suitable diameter of the radiating surface is about 20 cm. Langevin's calculations showed that for emission of radiation at the rate of 1 watt/cm^2 the amplitude of vibration must be about $5(10^{-5})$ cm. The returning echo may have an amplitude as low as 10^{-10} cm, only $\frac{1}{300}$ of the diameter of a molecule. Even this minute motion is enough for detection when the wave frequency is the same as the resonating frequency of the oscillator. Various devices have been developed for observing or automatically recording both the direction of a submerged object and, from the time interval between the emission and return of a short signal, its distance.   The maximum range in echo work is of course limited by the inverse fourth-power law.

In his experiments Langevin transmitted signals over distances as great as 9 km and received echoes from submerged objects 2,000 meters from the oscillator.   He described the use of a small quartz crystal as a "probe" to explore the sound field in the neighborhood of the oscillator. The radiated power was as high as 10 watts/cm^2.

By turning the submerged oscillator so that it radiated vertically downward, he received echoes from the ocean bottom.   Even in shallow water, at depths as small as 1 m, records could still be made.   This device is of great value in depth sounding, since it enables a survey of the bottom to be made, revealing the location of reefs and sunken wrecks; moreover it can be operated on a vessel in motion.

A more complete account of the quartz-steel oscillator, its theory, and its uses in echo detection and depth sounding is given in the sources listed at the end of the chapter.

507. Piezoelectric Emitters of Ultrasonic Waves.   As in the Langevin oscillator just described, flat crystal plates vibrating in a compressional thickness mode are most commonly used.   For most of the work described below, the desired frequencies are so high that one can employ a fairly thin plate vibrating at its own fundamental resonant frequency or at one of its odd overtones.   For the highest frequencies the plates are excited at very high overtones.   In place of Langevin's massive metallic slabs, various types of electrodes are used, as described below.   Frequencies have been used up to 50,000 kc/sec.   For frequencies below 200 kc/sec, however, single plates or stacks of plates in lengthwise vibration are employed.

If Nature had paid more attention to the production of large and perfect tourmaline crystals, instead of giving birth to so many quartz twins, all who are concerned in the applications of piezoelectricity would be deeply appreciative.   Especially in ultrasonics is this true, for large Z-cut tourmaline plates would make almost ideal emitters.

With the world as it is, tourmaline has been used but little in ultrasonics.   Rochelle salt as a possible emitter has been discussed by Hiltscher[228] and Cady.[108]   For mechanical and thermal reasons Rochelle salt is unsuited to the production of very intense radiation.   For demonstration of the optical diffraction effects described below, as well as for other purposes where low power is sufficient, the author[108] has had good success with the Rochelle salt L-cut described in §§140 and 504. Like quartz, this cut can vibrate in a compressional thickness mode, which recommends it where a large area is desired, whether for emitting or receiving.   Its application in the detection of acoustic waves is mentioned in §504.

Before the introduction of ferroelectric ceramics most of the published work on ultrasonics was done with X-cut quartz, or at the lower frequencies with magnetostriction oscillators. The quartz plates were usually circular, though in a few cases the Straubel contour (§360) has been used, since the radiation is then somewhat more uniformly distributed over the surface and higher voltages can be applied without danger of fracture.[*]

For experiments in non-conducting liquids, such as xylol, transformer oil, or paraffin oil, the simplest arrangement consisted in laying the quartz plate on a sheet or block of lead at the bottom of the vessel, the lead serving as one electrode. A lead support is less likely to cause fracture of the quartz than a harder metal. The other electrode was a thin sheet of metal resting on the quartz, through which the radiation passed with little loss. This is the arrangement used by Wood and Loomis in their experiments.[B55] Wire gauze has been used as an upper electrode by Lindberg. The front surface of the crystal can also be plated, contact being made by a narrow brass ring resting on the crystal at its circumference.

A more efficient use is made of the vibrational energy of the crystal by having one of its sides in contact with a layer of air. The compressional waves in the crystal are practically totally reflected at the boundary between crystal and air, all loss by radiation from the rear of the oscillator being thus eliminated. Several arrangements are possible, some of which are very simple and convenient for demonstration and for approximate measurements of ultrasonic velocities and wavelengths.

508. In Fig. 157a is shown a crystal bar C for lengthwise vibrations at the lower ultrasonic frequencies. The bar has tin-foil or plated electrodes and is cemented to a metal plate a few tenths of a millimeter thick. This plate closes the end of a glass or metal tube T. R is a movable piston for reflecting the radiation and producing stationary waves. The effective impedance of the crystal varies with the position of the piston, passing from one maximum to another as the piston moves through a half wavelength. This periodic change in impedance is observed as a series of changes in the anode current of the tube by which the crystal is driven. This experiment illustrates the principle of the ultrasonic interferometer. It can also be performed in free air without the enclosing tube. An advantage of the tube, however, is that if it contains a fine powder the particles of powder collect at the nodal regions, as in the well-known Kundt experiment, giving visible evidence of the shortness of the wavelengths.

Figure 157b shows a similar device, but with the crystal C in the form of a plate for thickness vibrations, to cover the higher range of frequencies. The rear electrode can be of tin foil or a plated film. At a

[*] Ref. B5, p. 39.

frequency of 10^6 cycles/sec, the wavelength in air is of the order of 0.03 cm, so that for high frequencies a micrometer control is needed for the piston R.

If the medium is a liquid instead of a gas, the tube T may be vertical with the crystal at the bottom. This method is convenient for demonstrating the optical diffraction effects described below. If a piston is to be used, it should be an air cell, in the form of a pillbox with thin metal front, in order to prevent the transmission of radiation.

Experiments with liquids can also be carried out with an open trough or tank in place of the tube. The crystal may be cemented to the inside

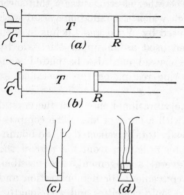

Fig. 157.—Simple arrangements for producing ultrasonic waves. *a* and *b* are for use with air as the medium. The containers shown in *c* and *d* are for immersion in a liquid.

of a small flat-sided can of thin metal, as shown in Fig. 157*c*, which may be moved about at will in the liquid. Since the beam from such an oscillator diverges considerably, reflections from the side walls take place, so that the container is filled with a three-dimensional array of maxima and minima of intensity. This acoustic field can be explored by means of a second crystal in a small open can. Or, better, the exploring crystal, which serves as a microphone, can be a small X-cut 45° block or bar of Rochelle salt, of the order of 0.5 by 1 by 1 cm with tin-foil electrodes, immersed in oil inside of a tube of rubber or thin metal closed at the bottom by a cork, as in Fig. 157*d*. This crystal is connected between grid and filament of the tube in a low-power oscillating circuit of frequency sufficiently removed from that of the ultrasonic emitter to produce an audible beat note in a telephone receiver or loud-speaker.

Even with a low-power oscillator, "dust patterns" can be produced in a tube or trough of liquid. In the course of experiments in 1918 the author had occasion to let a small oscillator radiate continuously for several hours at a frequency around 25,000, at one end of a trough of somewhat turbid water several meters in length. The particles suspended in the water settled in nodal bands crossing the bottom of the trough. A similar effect has been recorded by Ardenne (reference at end of chapter) and by Boyle.[74]

In Fig. 157*b* and *c*, direct radiation from the crystal plate into the liquid can be brought about by having in the metal sheet to which the crystal is cemented an opening nearly as large as the crystal.   The front face of the crystal is then plated and electrically connected to the metal sheet.

One advantage in having the radiating face of the crystal insulated from the surrounding liquid is that the liquid itself need not be an insulator.

Some experimenters have taken pains to support the crystal at points halfway between the two major surfaces, as is sometimes done with quartz resonators (see §344).   Unless the plate radiates to the same extent in both directions—as is rarely the case—this is largely wasted effort, because when the impedances of the media in contact with the two surfaces are different the median plane of the plate is no longer a nodal plane.

The radiation from the surface of the quartz is usually far from uniform in intensity and direction.   The complication that this fact introduces in quantitative work is somewhat reduced by the use of the Straubel contour mentioned above.   A considerable amount of research has been devoted to the study of the acoustic radiation field in the neighborhood of the oscillator.

Theoretically, a piezoelectric plate can be excited to any desired amplitude of vibration at any frequency, however far from resonance, provided that a sufficiently high voltage is applied.   Apart from the danger of puncturing the dielectric when in a strong field, it may be said that the danger of mechanical fracture is no greater with forced vibrations at high voltage than with resonant vibrations at low voltage. Still, even if it were economical to drive the crystal by a strong field at a non-resonant frequency, the crystal would almost certainly be fractured, even when damped by radiation into a liquid, if the frequency by any mischance happened to pass through resonance.   In practice, resonant frequencies are commonly employed.   The experimenter should remember that a resonant voltage that is safe when the crystal is in contact with a liquid can easily shatter the crystal in air.

For concentrating a large amount of ultrasonic energy in a small region, Gruetzmacher's concave quartz oscillator[192,193] may be used (see also the references at the end of the chapter to J. G. Lynn, Zwemer, and Chick, and to Tumanski).   The radiating surface of a large circular X-cut plate is made slightly concave, thus emitting a convergent beam. By this means, with frequencies from 638 to 1,000 kc/sec, Tumanski claims to have produced jets of oil 70 cm high, projected upward from the free surface of the liquid.

For ultrasonic effects in air the crystal may be connected in a Pierce circuit, but in liquids the crystal is too heavily damped to operate in this way.   A suitable and much used source for all purposes is the Hartley oscillator; in some cases two tubes in push-pull connection have been used. To the output of the generator is coupled a coil connected to the crystal. By proper choice of inductance the circuit can be made to operate as a Tesla transformer, supplying a high voltage to the crystal.

An interesting demonstration of interference between the waves from two ultrasonic sources has been described by Müller and Kraefft.[383] Two quartz plates of slightly different dimensions are excited in compressional vibration from independent sources. The plates are a few centimeters apart, with radiating surfaces opposed, and the frequency difference lies in the audible range. Under these conditions a beat note can be heard. When the distance between the plates is varied, the pitch of this note changes by an amount proportional to the relative velocity, thus demonstrating the Doppler effect.

The extreme range of frequencies hitherto attained with ultrasonic waves is from 20 to 500,000 kc/sec. This is a range of about 15 octaves in frequency. The corresponding range of wavelengths in air is from 1.6 cm to $6(10^{-5})$ cm. The maximum power that can be radiated without breaking the crystal depends on mounting, frequency, and medium. Wood and Loomis recorded a value as high as 35 watts/cm². This is an extreme case; usually 10 watts/cm² is considered the upper limit, and even here there is danger of fracture. Ten watts per square centimeter is 10^9 times greater than the output from an average loud-speaker (80 db). At this power, with a frequency of $3(10^5)$ cycles/sec, the amplitude of pressure in the medium is ± 5 atm, maximal acceleration 10^5 times that due to gravity, maximal velocity 40 cm/sec, and radiation pressure 1,300 dynes/cm² = 0.0013 atm.

509. Effects Produced by Intense Ultrasonic Radiation. Although a few of the effects mentioned below had already been observed with oscillators of the Langevin type, it remained for Wood and Loomis to explore the possibilities of the new tool that had been placed at the disposal of science. The spectacular success of their experiments was due to the combination of great intensity with high frequency.

One of the most important consequences of this combination is the generation of large stresses in the irradiated medium, as the following considerations will show: As we saw in the preceding paragraph, extremely high accelerations are produced, with correspondingly large forces on the particles of the medium or on small objects immersed in it. These forces cause compressions and rarefactions in the medium, and since the wavelength is very small it is evident that the stresses are large.

An important result of the large stresses in the liquid is *cavitation*. Its presence in liquids traversed by ultrasonic waves was first investigated by Boyle and his associates. The term "cavitation" is applied both to the liberation from the liquid of bubbles of air or other absorbed gases and to the tearing apart of the liquid itself with the production of hollow spaces filled with vapor. These hollow spaces, in the form of layers a wavelength apart, collapse with great violence, owing to the external pressure, as do also to some extent the bubbles of absorbed gas. Cavitation is accompanied by the generation of intense local electric fields, a process that is thought to account for the accelerating effect of intense ultrasonic fields on certain chemical reactions and also for the luminescence sometimes observed.

At pressure zero, and also under high hydrostatic pressure, there is no cavitation. The optimal pressure for pronounced cavitation effects is about 2 atm. At atmospheric pressure the effect sets in at a power of the order of 0.03 watt/cm^2.

Examples of the applications of intense ultrasonic waves are the production of finely dispersed emulsions; the destruction of bacteria and other biological effects; the acceleration of chemical reactions; the degassing of liquids; metallurgical applications; and the dissipation of fogs. Emulsification is feeble, and in some cases impossible, unless absorbed gas is present in the liquid medium.

510. The Ultrasonic Interferometer. The formation of stationary waves in air between a vibrating quartz plate and a reflecting surface was first observed by G. W. Pierce[424] in 1925, who measured wavelengths in air and CO_2 and made the first observation of the high absorption of CO_2 for ultrasonic waves. Pierce's method has been developed by J. C. Hubbard, W. H. Pielemeier, and others,[B5,B24] into an instrument of high precision for the measurement of the velocity and absorption of sound in gases and liquids.

511. Optical Effects of Ultrasonic Vibrations and Waves. The first optical method to be applied in the study of vibrating crystals was the piezo-optic effect, according to which the amount of light transmitted through an optical system containing a vibrating crystal between a polarizer and an analyzer varies with the strain in the crystal. By this means Tawil[505] in 1926 investigated the strains in a quartz bar, as already stated in §368. In the same paper he also foresaw the applications of optical effects in piezoelectric crystals to light relays and television. The piezo-optic method has been applied by Tawil[516] to the measurement or registration of very short time intervals; by R. A. Houstoun to the measurement of the velocity of light, following a suggestion originated by Grant; and by D. W. R. McKinley to the measurement of small optical activities; see also the paper by C. O. Browne.*

In Tawil's second method of observation[511] he used a vibrating quartz with frequency sufficiently high to produce in the surrounding air a

---

* The papers by the foregoing authors are listed at the end of the chapter.

system of very short waves. It has long been known that sound waves can be observed and photographed by taking advantage of the difference in refractive index between compressed and rarefied regions. This method, originated by Toepler and known as the "schlieren method," was applied to these ultrasonic waves by Tawil. For the lower frequencies he used a quartz-steel composite resonator. The schlieren method has been further developed and refined by Tawil and others, especially for investigating the sound field in the neighborhood of the emitter.

The idea that the closely spaced regions of condensation and rarefaction would make the medium serve as an *optical diffraction grating* occurred independently and almost simultaneously to Debye and Sears[122] and to Lucas and Biquard.[321] The simplest case is that of a transparent liquid in which a system of plane waves, either progressive or stationary, is generated. A collimated beam of light from a slit parallel to the wave fronts is passed through the liquid in a direction normal to the direction of propagation of the waves and becomes diffracted according to a law similar to that for the ordinary plane diffraction grating. When the emergent light is focused on a screen, a system of parallel lines is observed, consisting of a central image and on each side the spectra—or, in the case of monochromatic light, the diffraction lines—of various orders. The effect is easily demonstrated, with xylol as liquid, using thickness vibrations of an X-cut quartz plate or of an L-cut Rochelle-salt plate. A simple mounting for the crystal is that shown in Fig. 157b. From the frequency, the geometry of the system, and the spacing of the lines, the velocity of sound in the liquid and the adiabatic compressibility can be calculated.

512. The diffraction method has been extended and modified in many ways for special purposes and has become an important research tool. For its numerous applications and the literature to which it has given rise the references at the end of the chapter must be consulted. One great advantage of the method as compared with the interferometer is that results almost as accurate are obtained with very small samples of material in a very short time. By the use of high frequencies the wavelengths are so short that even in a specimen of volume no greater than a cubic centimeter the waves behave as if in an infinite medium, so that boundary conditions can be ignored.

Schaefer and Bergmann have applied the diffraction method with great success to the measurement of the elastic constants of transparent solids, both amorphous and crystalline. When the ultrasonic waves pass through a crystal, a diffraction pattern can be photographed that reveals the elastic symmetry of the crystal and also the presence of the three types of elastic waves that the crystal can transmit. From photographs made with the sound beam and the light in suitable orientations, all the elastic constants can be calculated. A cube of the material to be investigated is excited by a quartz plate cemented to one side or simply pressed against it with a layer of oil between. A frequency close to a high harmonic resonant frequency of the quartz is selected with a value to produce stationary waves in the cube. All possible vibrational modes of the material can thus be excited. See Cl. Schaefer and L. Bergmann, *An. Phk.*, vol. 3, pp. 72–81, 1948, also ref. (6), Appendix II.

Even in the case of *opaque* solids the elastic constants can be determined optically, as was proved by experiments by Schaefer and Bergmann after the theory of the method had been given by Ludloff. Advantage is taken of the fact that the surface of a solid subjected to ultrasonic radiation is set into a state of vibration, producing a characteristic diffraction pattern when a beam of light is reflected from it.

513. Piezoelectric Light Relays. The earliest use of a vibrating quartz crystal for controlling the intensity of a beam of light was made by Tawil, by both of the methods described in §511. The second method has been used in the design of a stroboscope for the observation of progressive waves.*

A more effective form of relay, first described independently by Biquard and by Karolus,† makes use of the diffraction effect described in §511. The light beam is passed through a liquid subjected to ultrasonic radiation, as in the Debye-Sears experiment. At zero amplitude all the light energy is in the central image (spectrum of zero order). With increasing amplitude the spectra of the first and higher orders grow in intensity at the expense of the central image. In the light relay the central image is cut out by a narrow opaque diaphragm, so that the amount of light transmitted depends on the total intensity in the portion that is diffracted. Thus the transmitted light is very nearly proportional to the amplitude of vibration of the crystal, and its intensity can be modulated by modulating the current that drives the crystal. For rapid modulation the vibrations of the crystal must be highly damped by the liquid. A liquid that combines good characteristics for this purpose with high transparency is carbon tetrachloride.

Piezoelectric relays have marked advantages over Kerr cells for controlling light beams. They respond well at higher frequencies; they can be used with ultraviolet light; and they require much less power, with lower voltages. Their chief limitation is that if the voltage on the crystal is to remain reasonably low the frequency must remain near resonance.

---

* Ref. B24, p. 210.

† P. Biquard, French patent 752,910 (1932); A. Karolus, U.S. patent 2,084,201 (1932).

Still another type of light relay, making use of the electro-optical effect in quartz, was described by Ardenne in 1939 (reference at end of chapter).

514. *Ultrasonics in Television Reception.* Television images formed on fluorescent screens by means of cathode rays are very limited in both size and brightness. All the light has to be produced by the rapidly moving cathode-ray beam, and the light from any one element of the picture is of very short duration. By using a powerful electric lamp as the light source and modulating the light beam in accordance with the television signals corresponding to the brightness of the various picture elements, the size and brightness of the television images can be vastly increased. One method of such light modulation, which makes use of an ultrasonic light modulator, is known as the Scophony Supersonic Television System and was originated by Jeffree.* A progressive train of waves is propagated along a column of liquid from a quartz plate at one end, as in the Debye-Sears experiment. At the other end of the column the waves are absorbed in order to prevent reflection and the formation of stationary waves. The quartz plate serving as emitter is driven approximately at its resonant frequency by a voltage that is modulated by the received signals. In the liquid there is then an ultrasonic carrier wave similarly modulated. To a given element of the picture there corresponds a short train of waves of a certain amplitude, which progresses with little attenuation along the column.

The light from the lamp, made parallel as it passes across the liquid cell in a direction parallel to the wave fronts, is diffracted. The central image is stopped out by a small barrier, so that only the diffracted light is transmitted; this light is approximately proportional to the amplitude of the quartz and therefore to the brightness of the picture element in question. At any instant different amounts of light are transmitted by different regions in the cell, corresponding to a series of successive picture elements. By means of a lens system an enlarged image of the cell is formed in a certain image plane on a viewing screen. As the wave train for a given element traverses the cell, the image that it produces sweeps across the viewing screen.

In order to fix the position of the individual picture elements on the viewing screen a small drum with a series of mirror faces around its periphery, rotated at high speed, is placed in the path of the light; the mirrors, by their rotation, reflect the light in such a way as to counteract the motion of the image and to hold each picture element at the right location on the line that is being projected onto the screen.

From the foregoing description it is seen that the image corresponding to a single picture element, instead of being projected onto the screen

* J. H. JEFFREE, ref. 20 at end of chapter.

only for the extremely short time during which the element is being received, continues to be projected during the entire time for the train of waves to run the length of the cell (of the order of one-fifth of a micro-second for a picture of 525 lines).   During this time the image is "stored" in the cell and continues to contribute to the brightness of the picture. At any instant a large number of picture elements are thus stored simultaneously, corresponding to as much as an entire line across the screen.

In order to resolve the successive lines into the actual picture, a second mirror drum is used, revolving at relatively low speed.

The ultrasonic cells may have liquid columns from 2.5 to 10 cm in length.   At an ultrasonic frequency of 18 megacycles/sec, the wave-length, when water is used as the liquid, is about 0.08 mm [velocity of sound in water about $1.5(10^5)$ cm/sec].   Several hundred picture elements may be stored simultaneously.   For the high-speed mirror system a 30-sided polygon of stainless steel about 5 cm in diameter is used, rotated at 31,500 rpm for a picture of 525 lines.   The 30 faces of the polygon are polished mirror surfaces, each about 5 by 3 mm.   Glass polygons have also been used.   Pictures up to 18 ft in width have been projected on screens in motion-picture theaters, using a high-intensity motion-picture arc lamp as light source.   For further details and modifications the references at the end of the chapter may be consulted.

Some notes on recent developments will be found in Appendix II.

REFERENCES

The Use of Crystals in Filters

Books

Mason, [B35] Vigoureux.[B50,B51]

Starr, A. T.: "Electric Circuits and Wave Filters," Sir Isaac Pitman & Sons, Ltd., London, 1944, 475 pp.

Vilbig, Fritz: "Lehrbuch der Hochfrequenztechnik," Akademische Verlagsgellschaft m. b. H., Leipzig, 1937, 775 pp.

Periodicals

Bechmann,[37,38] Booth,[69] Booth and Sayers,[71] Mason,[332,334,339] Mason and Sykes,[342] Metschl,[365] Rohde,[436,437] Rohde and Handrek.[438]

Buckley, O. E.: The Evolution of the Crystal Wave Filter, *Jour. Applied Phys.*, vol. 8, pp. 40–47, 1937.

Builder, G.: Resistance-balancing in Wave Filters, *A.W.A Tech. Rev.*, vol. 3, pp. 83–100, 1938.

Burns, G. K.: Manufacture of Quartz Crystal Filters, *Bell System Tech. Jour.*, vol. 19, pp. 516–532, 1940.

Chakravarti, S. P., and N. L. Dutt: On a Wide Band-pass Effect in Crystals Associated with Negative-impedance Elements, and the Development of Wide-band Low-loss Crystal Band-pass filters, *Indian Jour. Phys.*, vol. 14, pp. 295–310, 1940.

D'HEEDENE, A. R.: Effects of Manufacturing Deviations on Crystal Units for Filters, *Bell System Tech. Jour.*, vol. 23, pp. 260–281, 1944.

FLINT, W. A.: New Double-crystal Band-pass Filters, *Electronics and Television and Short-wave World*, vol. 13, pp. 552–554, 1940.

GARDINER, E. L.: Crystal Band-pass Filters, *Wireless World and Radio Rev. (London)*, vol. 43, pp. 382–384, 407–408, 447–448, 463–464, 1938; *T. and R. Bull. (London)*, vol. 15, pp. 75–79, 141–144, 178–179, 213–216, 251–253, 1939.

HUDEC, E.: Calculation and Construction of a Quartz Bridge Filter, and Various Circuits for Quartz Bridge Filters, *Elek. Nachr.-Tech.*, vol. 18, pp. 265–276, 1941; vol. 19, pp. 16–25, 1942.

KAMAYACHI, Z, and T. ISHIKAWA: On Quartz Crystal Vibrators as Elements for Electrical Wave-filters, *Nippon Elec. Comm. Eng.*, no. 18, pp. 103–106, 1939.

KAMAYACHI, Z., and T. ISHIKAWA: Longitudinal Mode of Vibration, *Electrotech. Jour. (Japan)*, vol. 4, pp. 243–246, 1940.

KAUTTER, W.: Wide-band Adjustable Quartz Filters, *Telef. Hausmitt.*, vol. 18, pp. 42–50, 1937.

KNOX, R. E.: The Use of Quartz Crystals in Wave Filters, *Electronics*, vol. 13, pp. 78*f*., November, 1940.

LANE, C. E.: Limitations in Band Filter Design, *Bell Labs. Record*, vol. 16, pp. 56–61, October, 1937.

LANE, C. E.: Crystal Channel Filters for the Cable Carrier System, *Elec. Eng.*, vol. 57, pp. 245–249, 1938.

MASON, W. P.: Quartz Crystal Filters, *Bell Labs. Record*, vol. 13, pp. 305–311, 1935.

MASON, W. P.: Resistance Compensated Band-pass Crystal Filters for Use in Unbalanced Circuits, *Bell System Tech. Jour.*, vol. 16, pp. 423–436, 1937.

PÖHLMANN, W.: Investigations of Crystal Band-pass Filters, *Telegraphen Fernsprech Tech. (Berlin)*, vol. 30, pp. 285–295 and 324–329, 1941.

STANESBY, H.: A Simple Narrow-band Crystal Filter, *Post Office Elec. Eng. Jour.*, vol. 35, pp. 4–7, April, 1942.

STANESBY, H., and E. R. BROAD: A Narrow Band Filter Using Crystal Resonators, *Post Office Elec. Eng. Jour.*, vol. 33, pp. 176–182, 1941.

WALTZ, W. W.: Crystal Filter Design, *Radio Engineering*, vol. 16, pp. 7–10 (January), 14–17 (Febuary), 16–17 (March), 12–14, (April), 1936.

WHITE, G. J.: Crystal I.F. Coupling and Filters, *Proc. I.R.E. Australia*, vol. 1, pp. 50–56, 1938.

WILLIS, E. S.: Channel Crystal Filters for Broad-band Carrier Systems, *Bell Labs. Record*, vol. 17, pp. 62–65, 1938.

WILSON, J. E.: The Crystal Filter Treated as an Impedance Bridge Circuit, *Communications*, vol. 21, pp. 18, 20, April, 1941.

CRYSTAL FILTERS FOR RECEIVING SETS

Books

"Documents du Comité Consultatif International des Radio Communications," 3ème réunion, Lisbon, 1934; Bern, 1935.

"Radio Amateurs' Handbook," American Radio Relay League, West Hartford, Conn.

Periodicals

BACON, D.: Improving Crystal Filter Performance, *QST*, vol. 24, pp. 58*f*., December, 1940.

BATCHER, R. R.: Application of Piezoelectric Crystals to Receivers, *Electronics*, vol. 3, pp. 57–58, August, 1931.

BENSON, J. E.: Crystal Control of the Mixer Oscillator in a Superheterodyne Receiver, *A.W.A. Tech. Rev.*, vol. 4, pp. 127–137, 1939; vol. 5, pp. 29–40, 1940.

BENSON, J. E.: A Note on the History of Piezoelectric Crystal Filters, *A.W.A. Tech. Rev.*, vol. 5, pp. 191–192, 1941.

BUILDER, G., and J. E. BENSON: Simple Quartz-crystal Filters of Variable Bandwidth, *A.W.A. Tech. Rev.*, vol. 5, pp. 93–103, 1941; also in *Wireless Eng. Exptl. Wireless (London)*, vol. 20, pp. 183–189, 1943.

COLEBROOK, F. M.: A Theoretical and Experimental Investigation of High Selectivity Tone-corrected Receiving Circuits, *Radio Res. Board, Nat. Phys. Lab., Spec. Rept.* 12, London, 1932.

CROSBY, M. G.: Communication by Phase Modulation, *Proc. I.R.E.*, vol. 27, pp. 126–136, 1939.

FISCHER, H. B.: A Crystal Control Superheterodyne Receiver, *Bell Labs. Record*, vol. 11, pp. 273–278, 1933.

GRAMMER, G.: A Crystal Filter and Noise-silencer for the "High-performance" Super, *QST*, vol. 20, pp. 28f., October, 1936.

KAUTTER, W.: Quartz Filters with Continuously Variable Band Breadth, *Telefunken Z.*, vol. 18, pp. 22–41, 1937.

KEALL, O. E.: Analysis of Bridge Circuit for Piezoelectric Quartz Resonators, *Marconi Rev.*, no. 59, pp. 19–29, March–April, 1936.

LAMB, J. J.: Short-wave Receiver Selectivity to Match Present Conditions, *QST*, vol. 16, pp. 9–20, 90, August, 1932.

LAMB, J. J.: Developments in Crystal Filters for S-S Superhets, *QST*, vol. 17, pp. 21–24, November, 1933.

LAMB, J. J.: Receiver Selectivity Characteristics, *QST*, vol. 19, pp. 37–41, May, 1935.

LAMB, J. J.: A New I.F. Coupling System for Superhet Receivers, *QST*, vol. 21, pp. 28–30, April, 1937.

LAMB, J. J.: And Now We Have Full-range Superhet Selectivity, *QST*, vol. 21, pp. 16f., June, 1937.

MILLEN, J., and .D. BACON: Modern Design of High-frequency Stages for the Amateur Superhet, *QST*, vol. 19, pp. 13f., January, 1935.

MIZOKAMI, K., and T. FUJITA: Automatic Tuning Control by Means of a Quartz Crystal, *Nippon Elec. Comm. Eng.*, pp. 443–444, November, 1937.

MORRISON, H.: Ten-frequency Receiver, *Bell Labs. Record*, vol. 19, pp. 307–309, 1941.

ORAM, D. K.: Full-range Selectivity with 455-kc. Quartz Crystal Filters, *QST*, vol. 22, pp. 33f., December, 1938.

Radio News Staff: A Modern Receiver for Short Waves and "Ham" Communication, *Radio News*, vol. 16, pp. 603f., 1935.

Radio News Staff: Ultra-selectivity with Crystal Filters, *Radio News*, vol. 15, pp. 477f., 1934; vol. 16, pp. 603f., 1935.

ROBINSON, J.: The Stenode Radiostat, *Radio News*, vol. 12, pp. 590f., 1931. More on this device will be found in *Electronics, Radio News, Wireless Eng. Exptl. Wireless*, and *Wireless World* from 1931 on.

ROESCHEN, E.: Measurements and Investigations on Quartz Crystals for Receiver Control, *Elek. Nachr.-Tech.*, vol. 13, pp. 187–197, 1936.

THIELE, K.: New Developments for the Single-span Superheterodyne Receiver, *Funktech. Monatshefte*, January, 1938, pp. 19–23.

YODA, H., and B. KATO: Filters Employing YT-cut Quartz Plates, *Electrotech. Jour. (Japan)*, vol. 3, pp. 142–143, 1939.

ZIEGLER, A. W.: Channel Crystal Filters for Broad-band Carrier Systems: Physical Features. *Bell Labs. Record*, vol. 17, pp. 66–70, 1938.

ACOUSTIC APPLICATIONS OF CRYSTALS

CADY,[95] NICOLSON.[391]

ALDOUS, D. W.: A New Temperature-controlled Crystal Cutting-head, *Electronic Eng.*, vol. 14, p. 605, 1942.

BALLANTINE, S.: A Piezo-electric Loud Speaker for the Higher Audio Frequencies, *Proc. I.R.E.*, vol. 21, pp. 1399–1408, 1933.

BALLANTINE, S.: High Quality Radio Broadcast Transmission and Reception (Rochelle salt "sound-cell"), *Proc. I.R.E.*, vol. 22, pp. 564–629, 1934.

BEERWALD, P., and H. KELLER: Piezoelectric Crystal Elements for Electro-acoustical Purposes (including bimorph Rochelle-salt systems: equivalent circuits and quantitative results), *Funktech. Monatshefte*. no. 11, pp. 345–348, 1938.

BEERWALD, P., and H. KELLER: Theory and Practice of the Piezo-electric "Sound Cell" Microphone, *Funktech. Monatshefte*, no. 12, pp. 187–190, 1941.

BEGUN, S. J.: Some Problems of Disk Recording, *Proc. I.R.E.*, vol. 28, pp. 389–398, 1940; *Jour. Soc. Motion-Picture Eng.*, vol. 36, pp. 666–674, 1941.

BIRD, J. R.: Recent Improvements in Crystal Pickup Devices, *Proc. I.R.E.*, vol. 25, p. 660, 1937.

CELLERIER, J. F.: On the Scientific Analysis of Musical Sounds, *Compt. rend.*, vol. 190, pp. 45–47, 1930.

COOK, R. K.: Absolute Pressure Calibrations of Microphones (use of tourmaline disk), *Bur. Standards Jour. Research*, vol. 25, pp. 489–505, 1940.

ELLIS, W. G.: New Electrophones for High-fidelity Sound Reproduction, *Radio Eng.*, vol. 13, pp. 18f., Oct. 1933.

FERRARI, A.: Problem of "Touch" in the Pianoforte, *Alta Frequenza*, vol. 4, pp. 582–602, 1935.

GOLDSMITH, F. H.: A Noise and Wear Reducing Phonograph Reproducer with Controlled Response, *Jour. Acous. Soc. Am.*, vol. 13, pp. 281–283, 1942.

KELLER, H.: The Piezoelectric "Flexural Strip" as Electromechanical Converter. *Hochfrequenztech. Elektroakustik*, vol. 60, pp. 5–10, 1942.

LYNCH, T. E., and S. J. BEGUN: General Considerations of the Crystal Cutter, *Communications*, vol. 20, pp. 9f., Dec. 1940.

PIERCE, G. W.: The Songs of Insects, *Jour. Franklin Inst.*, vol. 236, pp. 141–146, 1943 (see also *Radio Rev. Australia*, vol. 5, p. 303, 1937).

SAWDEY, R. S., JR.: "Bimorph" Rochelle Salt Crystals and Their Applications, *Radio*, pp. 23f., September, 1943.

SAWYER, C. B.: The Use of Rochelle Salt Crystals for Electrical Reproducers and Microphones, *Proc. I.R.E.*, vol. 19, pp. 2020–2029, 1931.

SCHAEFER, O.: The Electrical Equivalent Circuit of Piezoelectric Sound-Receivers, *Akust. Z.*, vol. 6, pp. 326–328, 1941.

SENGEWITZ, L.: The Rochelle Salt Crystal and Its Application in the Field of Telephony, *Elektrotech. Z.*, vol. 62, pp. 463–465, 1941.

SIVIAN, L. J.: Absolute Sound Pressure Measurements with Tourmaline (abst), *Jour. Acous. Soc. Am.*, vol. 92, p. 462, 1941.

SUGIMOTO, T.: Rochelle Salt Crystal Microphone and Under-water Acoustic Receiver, *Rep. Radio Research Japan*, vol. 6, absts. pp. 9–10, 1936.

TIBBETTS, R. W.: Rochelle Salt Crystal Devices of Low Impedance (loud-speaker and oscilloscope), *Electronics*, vol. 16, pp. 88f., April, 1943.

VERMEULEN, R.: Perspectives in the Development of the Violin, *Philips Tech. Rev.*, vol. 5, pp. 36–41, February, 1940.

WILLIAMS, A. L.: Piezo-electric Loudspeakers and Microphones, *Electronics*, vol. 4, pp. 166–167, May, 1932; see also *Jour. Soc. Motion-picture Eng.*, vol. 25, pp. 196f., 1934, and *Proc. I.R.E.*, vol. 23, pp. 1420–1421, 1935.

WILLIAMS, A. L., and J. P. ARNDT: Crystal Microphone Design for Single-direction Pickup, *Electronics*, vol. 8, pp. 242–243, August, 1935.

PIEZOELECTRIC TRANSDUCERS FOR THE MEASUREMENT OF PRESSURES, ACCELERATIONS, AND VIBRATIONS

AMBRONN, R.: A New Registering Acceleration Meter with Quartz Plates, *Z. Feinmechanik Präcision*, vol. 39, pp. 199–204, 1931.

ANDREEVSKI, N.: A Piezo-quartz Dynamometer for Measuring Impact Stresses, *Jour. Tech. Phys. (U.S.S.R.)*, vol. 9, pp. 680–686, 1939.

BARTELS, H.: Application of Piezoelectric Methods to the Measurement of Forces in Machines, *Werkstattstechn.*, vol. 31, pp. 187–188, 1937.

BAUMZWEIGER, B.: Application of Piezoelectric Vibration Pick-ups to Measurement of Acceleration, Velocity and Displacement, *Jour. Acous. Soc. Am.*, vol. 11, pp. 303–307, 1940.

BAXTER, H. W.: A Recording Instrument for Transient Pressures, *Electrician*, vol. 113, pp. 121–122, 1934.

BÉKÉSY, G. VON: On the Piezoelectric Measurement of the Absolute Threshold of Audibility in Bone Conduction, *Akust. Z.*, vol. 4, pp. 113–125, 1939.

BERNARD, P.: Reversibility of Piezoelectric Phenomena (quartz manometer), *Compt. rend.*, vol. 199, pp. 1388–1389, 1934; see also vol. 200, pp. 222–223, 1935.

BISANG, L.: On the Development of the Quartz Engine Indicator and Its Application, *Kraftfahrtech. Forschungsarb.*, no. 8, pp. 82–90, 1937 (Stuttgart).

BLOCH, A.: New Methods for Measuring Mechanical Stresses at Higher Frequencies, *Nature*, vol. 136, pp. 223–224, 1935; see also *Electronics*, vol. 8, pp. 212–213, 1935.

DAVY, N., J. H. LITTLEWOOD, and M. MCCRAIG: The Force-Time Law Governing the Impact of a Hammer on a Stretched String, *Phil. Mag.*, vol. 27, pp. 133–143, 1939.

EBIHARA, K.: Researches on the Piston Ring, *Sci. Papers Inst. Phys. Chem. Research (Tokyo)*, vol. 10, pp. 107–185, 1929.

ERVIN, C. T.: A Piezoelectric Gauge for Recording the Instantaneous Pressure in Shotguns, *Jour. Franklin Inst.*, vol. 213, pp. 503–514, 1932.

FAHRENTHOLZ, S., J. KLUGE, and H. E. LINCKH: Quartz Piezoelectric Pressure Gauges, *Physik. Z.*, vol. 38, pp. 73–78, 1937.

FEHR, R. O.: Quartz-crystal Accelerometer, *Gen. Elec. Rev.*, vol. 45, pp. 269–272, 1942.

GOHLKE, W.: Measurement of the Natural Frequency of Piezoelectric Pressure-measuring Devices, *Z. Instrumentenk.*, vol. 61, pp. 197–198, 1941; *Z. Ver. deut. Ing.*, vol. 84, pp. 663–666, 1940.

GOMEZ, M., and A. LANGEVIN: On the Use of Piezoelectric Quartz for the Study of Certain Biological Phenomena and Especially for the Study of Variations of Pressure in Blood Vessels, *Compt. rend.*, vol. 199, pp. 890–893, 1934.

GONDET, H., and P. BEAUDOUIN: Piezoelectric Vibrograph-Accelerograph, *Rev. gén. élec.*, vol. 37, pp. 499–508, 1935; see also *Génie civil*, vol. 109, pp. 552–554, 574–577, 1936.

GRAVLEY, C. K.: An Instrument for Measuring Surface Roughness, *Electronics*, vol. 15, pp. 70–73, 1942.

GUERBILSKY, A.: Piezoelectric Dynamometers of the Resonance Type, *Compt. rend.*, vol. 197, pp. 399–401, 1933.

HAYNES, J. R.: Apparatus for the Direct Measurement of Force/Displacement Characteristics of Mechanical Systems at Audio-frequencies, *Jour. Acous. Soc. Am.*, vol. 13, p. 332, 1942.

HELDT, P. M.: Piezoelectric Indicators, *Automotive Ind.*, vol. 70, pp. 657–658 and 660, 1934.

HELLMANN, R. K.: Piezoelectric Measuring Apparatus, *Archiv tech. Messen.*, vol. 85, J.766-1, 1938.

HERRMANN, A.: Piezoelectric Seismographs, *Beiträge angew. Geophysik*, vol. 4, pp. 296–301, 1934.

HERRMANN, A., and O. MEISSER: A Piezoelectric Acceleration-meter, *Z. Geophysik*, vol. 11, pp. 152–153, 1937.

HERRMANN, P. K.: Piezoelectric Measurement Apparatus (for engines), *A E G Mitt.*, no. 12, pp. 497–502, 1939.

HULL, G. F.: Some Applications of Physics to Ordnance Problems, *Jour. Franklin Inst.*, vol. 192, pp. 327–347, 1921.

IIDA, K.: Determining Young's Modulus and the Solid Viscosity Coefficients of Rocks by the Vibration Method, *Bull. Earthquake Research Inst. Japan*, vol. 17, pp. 79–91, 1939. (In English.)

ILLGEN, H.: Recent Applications of Piezoelectric Methods in Ballistics, *Z. tech. Phys.*, vol. 18, pp. 470–474, 1937.

JUNGNICKEL, H.: Piezoelectric Indicator for High-speed Internal-combustion Motors, *Z. Ver. deut. Ing.*, vol. 80, pp. 80–81, 1936.

KARCHER, J. C.: A Piezoelectric Method for the Instantaneous Measurement of High Pressures, *Jour. Franklin Inst.*, vol. 194, pp. 815–816, 1922.

KATO, Y., and S. NAKAMURA: On the Piezoelectric Accelerometer and Its Use in the Measurement of the Velocity of the Elastic Waves Produced by Artificial Shocks, *Sci. Repts. Tohoku Univ.*, vol. 19, ser. 1, pp. 761–772, 1930; *Proc. Imp. Acad. (Tokyo)*, vol. 6, pp. 272–274, 1930.

KELLER, H.[255]

KENT, R. H.: The Piezoelectric Gauge—Its Use in the Measurement of Gun Pressures, *Army Ordnance (Washington)*, vol. 18, pp. 281f., 1938; see also *Trans. A.S.M.E.*, vol. 61, pp. 197f., 1939.

KEYS, D. A.: Piezoelectric Method of Measuring Explosion Pressures, *Phil. Mag.*, vol. 42, pp. 473–488, 1921.

KLUGE, J., and H. E. LINCKH: The Measurement of Compression- and Acceleration-forces by Piezoelectric Methods, *Z. Ver. deut. Ing.*, vol. 73, pp. 1311–1314, 1929; see also vol. 74, p. 887, 1930; vol. 75, p. 115, 1931; also *Z. tech. Mechanik Thermodynamik*, vol. 2, pp. 153–164, 1931; *Arch. tech. Messen*, vol. 2, Lieferung 15, pp. V132–133, 1932; *Electrotech. Z.*, vol. 54, pp. 158–159, 1933; *Forsch. Gebiete Ingenw.*, vol. 2, pp. 153–164, 1931 (abst. in *Electronics*, vol. 3, p. 115, 1931), and vol. 4, pp. 177–182, 1933.

LANGEVIN, A.: The Use of Piezoelectric Quartz for the Study of Varying Pressures and Vibrations at High Frequencies, *Rev. gén. élec.*, vol. 37, pp. 3–10, 1935.

LANGEVIN, A., H. MURAOUR, and G. AUNIS: Study of Methods of Measuring Explosive Pressures, *Jour. phys. rad.*, vol. 7, pp. 448–452, 1936.

LAWSON, A. W., and P. H. MILLER, JR.: Piezometer for Transient Pressures (crystals of tartaric acid, tourmaline, and sucrose), *Rev. Sci. Instruments*, vol. 13, pp. 297–298, 1942.

LUND, H.: The Measurement of Accelerations of Motors, etc., by a Piezoelectric Equipment, *A E G Mitt.*, vol. 27, pp. 694–697, 1931.

MASON, C. A., and B. B. RAY: Piezoelectric Vibration Meter: Its Use for the Detection of Bearing Vibrations, *Electrician*, vol. 117, pp. 565–567, 1936.

MEURER, S.: Contribution to the Construction of Piezoelectric Indicators, *Forsch. Gebiete Ingenw.*, vol. 8, pp. 249–360, 1937.

MURAOUR, H., A. LANGEVIN, and G. AUNIS: Comparison of Pressure-Time Curves Derived: (a) from Fracture by the "Crusher"; (b) from Registration with a Piezoelectric Quartz, *Journal Physique* , vol. 7, pp. 450–452, 1936.

NIELSEN, H.: The Piezoelectric Indicator, *Arch. tech. Messen.*, vol. 5, pp. T9–10, J. 137-3, 1936.

NOLZEN, H.: Piezoelectric Pressure Measurement, *Deutsche Techniker*, vol. 6, pp. 4–6, 1938.

OKOCHI, M., S. HASHIMOTO, and S. MATSUI: High Speed Internal Combustion Engine and Piezoelectric Pressure Indicator, *Bull. Inst. Phys. Chem. Research (Tokyo)* vol. 4, pp. 85–97, 1925.

OKOCHI, M., and K. EBIHARA: "P.C.R." Piston Ring and the Packing Ring Tester, *Sci. Papers Inst. Phys. Chem. Research (Tokyo)*, vol. 6, pp. 67–80, 1927.

OKOCHI, M., and M. OKOSHI: New Method for Measuring the Cutting Force of Tools and Some Experimental Results, *Sci. Papers Inst. Phys. Chem. Research (Tokyo)*, vol. 5, pp. 261–301, 1927; see also vol. 12, pp. 167–192, 1930.

OKOCHI, M., and M. OKOSHI: Deflection of a Continuous Beam and Force Exerted on the Support by a Moving Load, *Bull. Inst. Phys. Chem. Research (Tokyo)*, vol. 7, pp. 659–667, 1928.

OKOCHI, M., and T. MIYAMOTO: Balancing Machine Utilizing Piezoelectricity, *Bull. Inst. Phys. Chem. Research (Tokyo)*, vol. 7, pp. 383–391, 1928; see also vol. 9, pp. 6–10, 1930.

RASUMIKHIN, V.: The Measurement of Alternating Pressure by the Piezoelectric Method, *Jour. Tech. Phys. (U.S.S.R.)*, vol. 8, pp. 447–452, 1938.

ROTHÉ, E.: Piezoelectric Quartz Seismograph, *Union géodés. géophys. intern., travaux scientifiques*, no. 15, pp. 152–164, 1937.

SAWDEY, R. S., JR.: Piezoelectric Surface Analyzer, *Radio*, March, 1943, pp. 20–23.

SCHILLING, W.: Vibration-width Amplitude and Vibration-Acceleration Measurements with Crystal Transmitter, *A E G Mitt.*, nos. 3–4, pp. 86–87, 1940.

SCOTT, H. H.: A General Purpose Vibration Meter, *Jour. Acous. Soc. Am.*, vol. 13, pp. 46–50, 1941.

SEIDL, F.: Piezoelectric Determination of the Breaking Strength of Thin Metal, Glass and Quartz Fibers, *Z. Physik*, vol. 75, pp. 735–740, 1932.

SEIFERT, E.: Piezoelectric Pressure Indicator, *Automobil tech. Z.*, vol. 40, pp. 144–146, 1937.

SIGRIST, W., and C. MEYER: Ballistic Investigation Employing a Recording Piezo-quartz Pressure Gauge, *Helv. Phys. Acta*, vol. 9, pp. 646–648, 1936.

TEICHMANN, H.: Methods for the Determination of the Velocity of Projectiles, *Electrotech. Z.*, vol. 58, pp. 627–628, 1937.

THOMPSON, L.: Shock Waves in Air and Characteristics of Instruments for Their Measurement (discharge of heavy artillery, use of quartz, Rochelle salt, and tourmaline), *Jour. Acous. Soc. Am.*, vol. 12, pp. 198–204, 1940.

THOMSON, J. J.: Piezoelectricity and Its Applications (quartz and tourmaline for explosion pressures), *Engineering*, vol. 107, pp. 543–544, 1919.

TSCHAPPAT, W. H.: New Instruments for Physical Measurements (pressure gauge for interior ballistics), *Mech. Eng.*, vol. 45, pp. 673–678, 1923; see also vol. 48, pp. 821–825, 1926.

WATANABE, S.: A New Design of Cathode Ray Oscillograph and Its Applications to Piezoelectric Measurements, *Sci. Papers Inst. Phys. Chem. Research (Tokyo)*, vol. 12, pp. 82–98, 1929; see also *Proc. World Eng. Congr., Tokyo*, vol. 5, Paper No. 632.

WATANABE, S.: Study on Impact Test by Means of Piezoelectric and Cathode Ray Oscillograph, *Sci. Papers Inst. Phys. Chem. Research (Tokyo)*, vol. 12, pp. 99–112, 251–267, 1929–1930; see also *Bull. Inst. Phys. Chem. Research (Tokyo)*, vol. 8, pp. 735–745, 1929.

WATSON, H. G. I., and D. A. KEYS: A Piezoelectric Method of Measuring the Pressure Variations in Internal Combustion Engines, *Can. Jour. Research*, vol. 6, pp. 322–331, 1932.

WEBSTER, R. A.: Piezoelectric Gauge and Amplifier (pile of 21 quartz plates, for pressures up to 30,000 lb/in.²), *Jour. Franklin Inst.*, vol. 211, pp. 607–615, 1931.

WEBSTER, R. A.: Piezoelectric versus Mechanical Spring Pressure Gauge, *Jour. Applied Phys.*, vol. 10, pp. 890–891, 1939.

WOOD, H. O.: On a Piezoelectric Accelerograph, *Bull Seismol. Soc. Am.*, vol. 11, pp. 15–57, 1921.

YAMAGUCHI, K.: An Accelerometer Utilizing Piezoelectricity, *Bull. Inst. Phys. Chem. Research (Tokyo)*, vol. 8, pp. 157–163, 1929.

ZELLER, W.: Experimental and Theoretical Investigation of Vibration Meters for Traffic Vibrations, *Z. Bauwesen*, vol. 80, pp. 171–184, 1930.

MISCELLANEOUS APPLICATIONS OF PIEZOELECTRICITY

BAZZONI, C. B.: The Piezo-electric Oscillograph, *Radio News*, vol. 7, pp. 142–143, 233–237, August, 1925.

BECKER, H. E. R., W. HANLE, and O. MAERCKS: Modulation of Light by Means of a Vibrating Quartz, *Physik. Z.*, vol. 37, pp. 414–415, 1936.

CURIE, J., and P. CURIE: Hemihedral Crystals with Oblique Faces as Constant Sources of Electricity (Electrometer), *Compt. rend.*, vol. 93, p. 204, 1881 (also in "Œuvres," p. 22).

GALITZIN, B.: Apparatus for Direct Determination of Accelerations, *Proc. Roy. Soc., (London)*, vol. 95, p. 492, 1919.

GOLAY.[178]

GRUETZMACHER, J.: Piezoelectric Relays (Electrostatic Attraction between Vibrating Crystal and Its Electrode), *Arch. Elektrotech.*, vol. 30, pp. 122–126, 1936.

HARTLEY, J. J., and R. H. RINALDI: Demonstration of the Application of Piezoelectric Properties of a Rochelle Salt Crystal and the Three-electrode Valve to the Determination of Impact Stresses in Granular Material, *Proc. Phys. Soc. (London)*, vol. 38, p. 273, 1926.

HOUSTOUN, R. A.: A New Method of Measuring the Velocity of Light (Fizeau's method, using quartz crystal), *Nature*, vol. 142, p. 833, 1938; see also *Proc. Roy. Soc. Edinburgh*, A, vol. 61, pp. 102–114, 1941, vol. 62, pp. 58–63, 1943–1944, and *Phil. Mag.*, vol. 35, pp. 192–202, 1944.

HUBBARD, J. C.: The Crevasse Phenomenon in Piezoelectric Quartz and Its Application in Physical Measurements (ultramicrometer), *Jour. Acous. Soc. Am.*, vol. 10, pp. 87–88, 1938.

KAZANSKI, V.: A Piezo-quartz Oscillograph, *Jour. Tech. Phys. (U.S.S.R.)*, vol. 9, pp. 673–679, 1939.

MUTH, H., and H. ROOSENSTEIN: A Method of Generating Electric Waves (oscillations from powdered quartz particles), German patent 706,799 (1941); *Hochfrequenztech. Electroakustik*, vol. 59, p. 30, 1942.

MYERS, L. M.: A Piezoelectric Peak Voltmeter, *Marconi Rev.*, November–December, 1934, pp. 4–8.

OFFNER, F.: Recorder for Electrical Potentials. Damping of Piezo-electric Systems, *Jour. Applied Phys.*, vol. 11, pp. 347–352, 1940.

PHILIPPOFF, W. VON: The Piezoelectric Oscillograph, *Arch. tech. Messen*, vol. 2, p. 184, December, 1932; *Electrotech. Z.*, vol. 53, pp. 405–408, 1932.

PLASENCIA, H. T.: Spanish Standard for the Roentgen (piezoelectric device for standard charge), *Radiology*, vol. 34, pp. 82–94, January, 1940.

STEVENS, H. C., and J. M. SNODGRASS: A Piezoelectric Myograph (for measurement of contracting muscle), *Proc. Soc. Exptl. Biol. Med.*, vol. 30, pp. 939–943, 1933.

SYNGE, E. H.: Application of Piezoelectricity to Microscopy, *Phil. Mag.*, vol. 13, pp. 297–300, 1932.

TAKENAKA, S.: On a Piezoelectric Method for the Investigation of the Contraction of Muscles, *Japan. Jour. Phys.*, vol. 12, pp. 81–82, 1938.

TAWIL.[516]

TIBBETTS, R. W.: Rochelle Salt Crystal Devices of Low Impedance (loud-speaker and oscilloscope), *Electronics*, vol. 16, pp. 88f., April, 1943.

WOLOGDIN, V.: Frequency Multiplication by Means of Condenser with Rochelle Salt Dielectric (makes use of non-linear properties), *Z. tech. Physik*, vol. 13, pp. 82–84, 1932.

WOOD, A. B.: The Piezoelectric Oscillograph, *Phil. Mag.*, vol. 50, pp. 631–637, 1925.

WOOD, A. B., G. A. TOMLINSON, and L. ESSEN: The Effect of the Fitzgerald-Lorentz Contraction on the Frequency of Longitudinal Vibration of a Rod (two quartz oscillators, one stationary and one rotating), *Proc. Roy. Soc. (London) A*, vol. 158, pp. 606–633, 1937.

WYNN-WILLIAMS, C. E.: A Piezoelectric Oscillograph, *Phil. Mag.*, vol. 49, pp. 289–313, 1925.

ULTRASONICS

Most of the literature down to 1938 is referred to in the books by Bergmann and by Hiedemann. The following references supplement them and include some of the more recent papers that are of interest from the standpoint of applied piezoelectricity.

Numbers in brackets apply to the special references below.

Books and General Articles. BERGMANN,[B5] HIEDEMANN,[B24] WOOD,[B55] BOYLE,[74] HUBBARD.[237] [15], [30], [34], [41], [42], [46], [51].

The Quartz "Sandwich" for Submarine Use. B51, [11], [23], [24].

Apparatus and Circuits. B5, B24, B35, B55, 145, 146, 192, 228, 445, 474, 511, [1], [5], [6], [7], [10], [25], [28], [31], [38], [40], [48], [49], [51].

Theory of the Ultrasonic Oscillator as a Transducer. B35, 474.

The Acoustic Field Close to the Crystal Oscillator. B5, B24, 145, 192, 422, 445, 511, [9], [22], [28], [36], [49].

Cavitation. [42].

The Ultrasonic Interferometer. 190, 236, 424, [12], [17], [18], [19], [37], [41].

Piezo-optic Effects. 505, 511, 516, [8], [16], [32], [33].

Diffraction Effects. 122, 321, [27], [42], [47].

Measurement of Velocities and Absorption. 145, 190, [1], [4], [13], [14], [25], [42], [45], [48], [50].

Measurement of Elastic Constants. [3], [13], [27].

Light Relays. 505, 511, [2], [21].

Television. B38, [2], [20], [29], [35], [39], [43], [44].

Ultrasonic Sounds in Nature. [26]; see also G. W. Pierce, The Songs of Insects, *J. Franklin Inst.*, vol. 236, pp. 141–146, 1943.

Special References

[1] ARDENNE, M. VON: The Construction of Apparatus for the Generation of Ultrasonic Waves, *Funktech. Mon.*, no. 8, pp. 285–288, 1935.

[2] ARDENNE, M. VON: A New Large-surface Light Relay for Intensity, Color, or Plane-of-polarization Control, *Telegraphen Fernsprech Tech. (Berlin)*, vol. 28, no. 6, pp. 226–231, June, 1939.

[3] BÄR, R.: Supersonic Measurement of Elastic Constants of Isotropic Solids, *Helv. Phys. Acta*, vol. 13, pp. 61–76, 1940.

[4] BENDER, D.: Ultrasonic Velocities in Nitrogen, Nitric Oxide, and Carbon Monoxide between 20° and 200°C, Measured by a New Process (Emission from Both Surfaces of Quartz Plate), *Ann. Physik*, vol. 38, pp. 199–214, 1940.

[5] BOSCH, W. C. and W. G. ALLÉE, JR.: Circuit Details for a Small Supersonic Oscillator of the Piezoelectric Type, *Am. Phys. Teacher*, vol. 6, pp. 272–273, 1938.

[6] BOYLE, R. W., J. F. LEHMANN, and S. C. MORGAN: Some Measurements of Ultrasonic Velocities in Liquids, *Trans. Roy. Soc. Can.*, vol. 22, sec. 3, pp. 371–378, 1928.

[7] BRIGGS, H. B.: A Supersonic Cell Fluorometer, *Jour. Optical Soc. Am.*, vol. 31, pp. 543–549, 1941.

[8] BROWNE, C. O.: Demonstration of High-frequency Fluctuations in the Intensity of a Beam of Light, *Proc. Phys. Soc. (London)*, vol. 40, p. 36, 1927.

[9] CEROVSKA, J.: Ultrasonic Optical Phenomena in the Circular Hole in a Quartz Plate, *Jour. Phys. rad.*, vol. 10, pp. 97–103, 1939.

[10] COCHRAN, D., and R. W. SAMSEL: Ultrasonics—A Method of Determining the Acoustic Properties, Absorption and Velocity, for Materials to be Used as Ultrasonic Windows, Lenses, and Reflectors, *Gen. Elec. Rev.*, vol. 47, pp. 39–41, 1944.

[11] FLORISSON, C.: Ultra-sound and Its Applications, *Bull. Soc. belge électriciens*, vol. 52, pp. 165–170, 263–278, 339–348, 1936.

[12] FOX, F. E.: Ultrasonic Interferometry for Liquid Media, *Phys. Rev.*, vol. 52, pp. 973–981, 1937.

[13] FOX, F. E., and G. D. ROCK: An Ultrasonic Stroboscope for Measuring Sound Wave-length in Liquids, *Rev. Sci. Instruments*, vol. 10, pp. 345–348, 1939.

[14] FOX, F. E., and G. D. ROCK: Ultrasonic Absorption in Water, *Jour. Acous. Soc. Am.*, vol. 12, pp. 505–510, 1941.

[15] FREEHAFER, J. E.: Supersonic Vibrations, *Newark Eng. Notes*, vol. 5, no. 1, pp. 18–19, December, 1941.

[16] GRANT, K.: High-frequency Interruption of Light, Nature, vol. 120, p. 586, 1927.

[17] HERGET, C. M.: A Constant Path Acoustic Interferometer for Gases at Variable Pressure, *Rev. Sci. Instruments*, vol. 11, pp. 37–39, 1940.

[17a] HOUSTOUN, R. A.: The Ultrasonic Diffraction Grating, *Phil. Mag.*, vol. 35, pp. 192–202, March, 1944.

[18] HUBBARD, J. C.: Sound Velocity and Absorption by Ultrasonic Interferometry, *Phys. Rev.*, vol. 59, p. 935, 1941.

[19] HUBBARD, J. C., and I. F. ZARTMAN: A Fixed Path Acoustic Interferometer for the Study of Matter, *Rev. Sci. Instruments*, vol. 10, pp. 382–386, 1939.

[20] JEFFREE, J. H.: The Scophony Light Control, *Television and Short-wave World*, vol. 9, pp. 260f., 1936; see also Brit. patent 439,236 (1934).

[21] KHARIZOMENOV, V. K.: The Modulation of Light by Supersonic Waves, *Jour. Tech. Phys.* (*U.S.S.R.*), vol. 7, no. 8, pp. 844–860, 1937.

[22] LABAW, L. W.: Wave Front Determination in a Supersonic Beam (abst.), *Phys. Rev.*, vol. 66, p. 354, 1944.

[23] LANGEVIN, P.: Sounding by Means of Sound Waves, *Bur. hydrogr. internat.*, *Spec. Pub.* 3, Monaco, 1924.

[24] LANGEVIN, P., and C. CHILOWSKY: Echo Sounding, *Nature*, vol. 115, pp. 689–690, 1925; also *Bur. hydrogr. internat.*, *Spec. Pub.* 14, Monaco, August, 1926.

[25] LINDBERG, A.: Ultrasonic Absorption in Liquids, Measured Optically, *Physik. Z.*, vol. 41, pp. 457–467, 1940.

[26] LITTLE, E. P.: Supersonic Sounds in Nature, *Gen. Radio Experimenter*, vol. 9, pp. 5–8, February, 1935.

[27] LUDLOFF, H. F.: Ultrasonics and Elasticity, *Jour, Acous. Soc. Am.*, vol. 12, pp. 193–197, 1940.

[28] LYNN, J. G., R. L. ZWEMER, and A. J. CHICK: The Biological Application of Focused Ultrasonic Waves, *Science*, vol. 96, pp. 119–120, July, 1942; see also *Sci. American*, vol. 168, p. 115, March, 1943, and *Jour. Gen. Physiol.*, vol. 26, pp. 179–193, 1942.

[29] MAERCKS, O.: Ultrasonic Waves as Optical Shutter, *Z. Physik*, vol. 109, pp. 598–605, 1938.

[30] MAYBERRY, W.: Supersonics, *Electronics*, vol. 10, pp. 7–9, July, 1937.

[31] McGRATH, J. W., and A. R. KURTZ: Isolation of an Ultrasonic Crystal Radiator from Conducting Liquids, *Rev. Sci. Instruments*, vol. 13, p. 128, 1942.

[32] McKINLEY, D. W. R.: Application of Quartz Crystals to the Modulation of Light, *Can. Jour. Research*, sec. A, vol. 16, pp. 77–81, 1938.

[33] McKINLEY, D. W. R.: Measurement of Small Optical Activities with the Quartz Crystal Light Modulator, *Can. Jour. Research*, vol. 17, pp. 202–207, October, 1939.

[34] METSCHL, E. C.: The Nature and Employment of Supersonic Waves (Survey), *Elektrotech. Z.*, vol. 60, no. 2, pp. 33–40, 1939.

[35] OKOLICSANYI, F.: The Wave-slot, an Optical Television System, *Wireless Eng. Exptl. Wireless* (*London*) vol. 14, pp. 527–536, October, 1937.

[36] OSTERHAMMEL, K.: The Optical Examination of the Sound Field of a Quartz Plate Oscillating as a Piston, *Akust. Z.*, March, 1941, pp. 73f.

[37] PIELEMEIER, W. H., H. L. SAXTON, and D. TELFAIR: Supersonic Effects of Water Vapor in CO_2 and Their Relation to Molecular Vibrations, *Jour. Chem. Phys.*, vol. 8, pp. 106–115, 1940.

[38] PITT, A., and W. J. JACKSON: Measurement of the Velocity of Sound in Low Temperature Liquids at Ultrasonic Frequencies, *Can. Jour. Research*, vol. 12, pp. 686–689, 1935.

[39] POGODAEV, K. N.: The Relationship between the Voltages Applied to a Quartz Crystal and the Light Intensity Distribution in the Diffraction Spectra Caused by the Supersonic Waves so Produced, *Jour. Tech. Phys.* (*U.S.S.R.*), vol. 11, pp. 474–478, 1941.

[40] PORTER, B. H.: The Supersonic Oscillator, *Ind. Eng. Chem.*, vol. 12, pp. 748–749, 1940.

[41] RICHARDS, W. T.: Recent Progress in Supersonics, *Jour. Applied Phys.*, vol. 9, pp. 298–306, 1938.

[42] RICHARDS, W. T.: Supersonic Phenomena, *Rev. Modern Phys.*, vol. 11, pp. 36–64, 1939.

[43] ROBINSON, D. M.: The Supersonic Light Control and Its Application to Television with Special Reference to the Scophony Television Receiver, *Proc. I.R.E.*, vol. 27, pp. 483–486, 1939; also papers by J. Sieger (pp. 487–492), G. Wikkenhauser (pp. 492–496), and H. W. Lee (pp. 496–500).

[44] ROSENTHAL, A. H.: Storage in Television Reception, *Electronics*, vol. 14, pp. 46f., October, 1941; also *Electronic Eng.* (British), January, 1942, pp. 578f.

[45] SHAPOSHNIKOV, I. G.: The Propagation of Sound in a Crystal Possessing Piezoelectric Properties, *Jour. Exptl. Theoret. Phys. U.S.S.R.*, vol. 11, pp. 332–339, 1941.

[46] SIEGEL, S.: Review of Supersonic Methods for Measuring Elastic and Dissipative Properties of Solids, *Jour. Acous. Soc. Am.*, vol. 6, pp. 26–30, 1944.

[47] SMITH, A. W., and L. M. EWING: The Diffraction of Light by Supersonic Waves in Liquids; Apparatus for Demonstration and for an Intermediate Laboratory Experiment, *Am. Jour. Phys.*, vol. 8, pp. 57–59, 1940.

[48] TELFAIR, D., and W. H. PIELEMEIER: An Improved Apparatus for Supersonic Velocity and Absorption Measurements, *Rev. Sci. Instruments*, vol. 13, pp. 122–126, 1942.

[49] TUMANSKI, S. S.: The Generation of Supersonic Oscillations by Piezo-quartz Lenses, *Jour. Tech. Phys. (U.S.S.R.)*, vol. 7, pp. 2049–2052, 1937.

[50] WILLARD, G. W.: Ultrasonic Absorption and Velocity Measurements in Numerous Liquids, *Jour. Acous. Soc. Am.*, vol. 12, pp. 438–449, 1941.

[51] ZWIKKER, C.: Oscillating Quartz Crystals and Their Use in Ultra-acoustics, *Nederland Tijdschr. Natuurkunde*, vol. 8, pp. 311–326, 1941; *Tijdschr. Nederland Radiogen.*, vol. 9, pp. 107–122, 1941.

CHAPTER XXIX

PYROELECTRICITY

Un phénomène a au moins la symétrie de ses causes, mais il peut être plus symétrique.
—PERRIER and DE MANDROT.

515. The early history of pyroelectricity has already been sketched in Chap. I. Among later investigators, both experimental and theoretical, may be mentioned Friedel and J. Curie (who in 1883 first recognized the distinction between the effects of uniform and non-uniform heating), Ackermann, Boguslawski, Gaugain, Hankel, Hayashi, Traube, Kundt, Riecke, Röntgen, and Voigt. References to some of these, as well as to other authors mentioned in the text, are at the end of the chapter.

Pyroelectricity can mean any one of several things. First one must distinguish between *vectorial* and *tensorial* pyroelectricity. Vectorial pyroelectricity is the type usually encountered, and it forms the chief subject matter of this chapter. Mathematically, it is a relation between a scalar (temperature) and a vector (polarization). Physically, it is *the change with temperature of positive and negative polarization charges on certain portions of crystals belonging to certain classes.* This phenomenon is the *direct* pyroelectric effect, represented by the arrow $\vartheta \rightarrow P$ in Fig. 10. The *converse,* or electrocaloric, effect, described in §523, is represented by the arrow $E \rightarrow \delta Q$.

The practically negligible tensorial effect is described in §525.

The vectorial effect is complicated by the fact that every pyroelectric crystal is also piezoelectric: a change in temperature of an unconstrained crystal causes a deformation, and this in turn produces a secondary polarization of piezoelectric origin superposed on the primary pyroelectric polarization. The terms *primary* and *secondary* are preferable to the commonly employed "true" and "false." Primary pyroelectricity is that which would be observed in a completely clamped crystal.

The secondary pyroelectric effect must be subdivided according to whether the heating is uniform or not. For non-uniform heating the term "false pyroelectricity of the first kind" has sometimes been used, while the secondary effect of uniform heating has been called "false pyroelectricity of the second kind." We shall restrict the term *secondary* to the effect of the "second kind," and for the case of non-uniform heating we suggest the term *tertiary pyroelectricity,* although it is only a special manifestation of the secondary type.

The distinction is by no means trivial. All the 10 classes listed below that possess *primary* pyroelectricity are of course subject also to secondary and tertiary effects. On the other hand, those crystals, like quartz, which are not included in any of these 10 classes can show only the *tertiary* effect. They become polarized by heating or cooling only in those regions where there is a *temperature gradient*. The reason follows from the fact that such crystals do not, like those in the 10 classes of "true" pyroelectricity, have a single unique polar axis (the direction of the spontaneous polarization). For example, quartz has three equivalent polar axes, but no one of them is unique. Although the application of a scalar agent, like uniform heating, cannot give rise to a polarization in a unique direction, still the *gradient* of temperature is a vector quantity, which can produce a polarization dependent on the direction of the gradient.

In interpreting the extensive literature on pyroelectric observations it is important to keep these distinctions in mind. Only rarely does uniform heating seem to have been employed in qualitative observations. The observed results have therefore in most cases been due largely, if not chiefly, to the tertiary effect, proving merely that the crystals were piezoelectric. Too often has there been reason to suspect that spurious effects of frictional electricity or of a layer of ions deposited from the flame or other heating agent may have been mistaken for pyroelectricity. Even when all spurious effects have been eliminated, one cannot expect more than crude qualitative results unless the specimen is of a definite geometrical form (parallelepiped or sphere), free from defects, cracks, and twinning, and cut in a known orientation with respect to the crystal axes.

It is not even certain that the primary effect is strong enough to be observed in any crystal. Its separation from the secondary effect is extremely difficult, requiring a precise knowledge of the elastic and piezoelectric constants (§§520 and 570).

516. Theory of the Vectorial Pyroelectric Effect. In its broadest sense the vectorial effect includes primary, secondary, and tertiary pyroelectricity and the converse, or electrocaloric, effect. The theory as presented here does not include the tertiary type. The primary and secondary effects may theoretically be present in the following 10 classes, designated by $\underline{P}$ in Table I: Classes 1, 3, 4, 7, 10, 14, 16, 19, 23, and 26, with symmetries C_1, C_2, C_{1h}, C_{2v}, C_4, C_{4v}, C_3, C_{3v}, C_6, and C_{6v}. In these classes the symmetry is such that there is a single polar, or "electric," axis, with the possibility of a permanent (spontaneous) polarization along this axis.*

---

* In Voigt's "Lehrbuch," p. 252, the number of pyroelectric classes is erroneously stated as eleven instead of ten.

In the present treatment we shall follow the method initiated by Lord Kelvin and adopted by Voigt, according to which a pyroelectric crystal behaves as if it had a spontaneous polarization, the variation of which with temperature constituted the primary pyroelectric effect. That this is not the only possible hypothesis will be seen in §545.

We shall treat pyroelectricity, like piezoelectricity in ordinary crystals, as a linear reversible effect. If heating causes a polarization in a particular direction, cooling causes a reversed polarization. Similarly in the electro-caloric effect (§523) a reversal of the electric field causes a reversal in sign of the change in temperature. At some standard temperature T the entire surface of the specimen is assumed to be initially equipotential, with mechanical stress and electric field equal to zero. The internal polarization P^0 is still present, but the polarization charges have been neutralized by leakage. Any charges that appear are then due to a change in the internal polarization caused by a change $\vartheta = \Delta T$ in temperature. The heating is supposed to be uniform. We call the direction of the internal polarization and of its variation with temperature the m-direction, so that only this subscript need be used for electrical quantities. The change in temperature gives rise in general to all six components of strain x_h.

Expressions for both the primary and secondary pyroelectric effects are found by taking the derivative of ξ in Eq. (1), p. 44, with respect to E_m:

$$\frac{\partial \xi}{\partial E_m} = \eta'_m E_m + \sum_h^6 e_{mh} x_h + p_m \vartheta \qquad (544)$$

This expression is an equation of state including a thermal term. P_m is the polarization due to the combined effects of field, strain, and temperature.

We now assume that the only impressed quantity is ϑ. P_m is then identical with ΔP^0, the change in internal polarization. E_m is the counter-field induced by the polarization charges $\pm \sigma_m = \pm P_m$. Each $x_h = a_h \vartheta$, where a_h is an expansion coefficient. The primary pyroelectric constant is p_m.

The counter-field E_m is of such a sign as to decrease the observed polarization. In the experimental determination of the pyroelectric constant the effect of E_m should therefore be eliminated; compensating devices for this purpose are described in the "Lehrbuch," pp. 240 and 255. On the theoretical side, in order to express the primary and secondary effects we can set $E_m = 0$ in Eq. (544), and obtain finally

$$P_m = \vartheta p_m + \vartheta \sum_h^6 e_{mh} a_h \equiv \vartheta(p_m + p'_m) \qquad (545)$$

ϑp_m is the polarization due to the primary effect, while $\vartheta p'_m$ expresses the secondary, or "false" effect. This latter term is illustrated by the path $\vartheta \to x \to P$ in Fig. 10, p. 40. The primary effect is illustrated by the path $\vartheta \to P$.

We call $p = p_m + p'_m$ the *total* pyroelectric constant. It does not include the "tertiary" effect, since uniform heating is assumed. In the most general case the direction m varies with temperature. However, those crystals, including tourmaline and Rochelle salt, for which p has been measured, have, at least for the primary effect, only a single value of m at all temperatures that have been investigated.

The pyroelectric coefficient p_m^* has the dimensions electric moment per unit volume per degree change in temperature. p_m^* is positive when an increase in temperature causes a pyroelectric polarization in that direction which is adopted as positive for the crystal in question. The equation for p_m^* follows from Eq. (545):

$$p_m^* = p_m + p'_m = \frac{P_m}{\vartheta} = \frac{\Delta P^0}{\Delta T} \qquad (546)$$

In experimental work if the counterpolarization due to the field created by the polarization charges [first term in Eq. (544)] is not compensated, the observed p_m^* will be too small. A calculation of the correction for E_m would be difficult, as it depends in a complicated manner on boundary conditions.

517. Tourmaline. Tourmaline has been the object of more study than any other pyroelectric crystal. Considering the variable composition of this crystal (§13) it is surprising that the quantitative results by different investigators and with different specimens show so little variation. It is commonly found that the pyroelectric constant is lower for dark than for light varieties and that the conductivity of black tourmaline is so great that no pyroelectric observations can be made with it. The largest values are observed with pink varieties (Ackermann, Hayashi).

At ordinary temperatures the analogous end (§13) becomes positive on heating. The direction of the spontaneous polarization is from the analogous to the antilogous end, so that heating *decreases* the spontaneous polarization..

The pyroelectric property can be demonstrated in several ways. In all such tests the surface of the crystal should be clean and dry.

1. Kundt's method, by sprinkling over the heated crystal a mixture of powdered sulphur and red lead,* or Bürker's powder.† Positive regions become yellow; negative regions, red. These charged regions are at the ends of the crystal, but they are also detected wherever there are cracks along the sides, owing to local strains.

2. An "electric compass" can be made by suspending an elongated specimen horizontally from a fine thread or fiber, subjecting it to a change in temperature, and holding it near a charged body or between the plates of a condenser connected to an electrostatic machine.

Fig. 158.—Dust patterns from tourmaline crystals. The photograph shows a portion of a white painted shelf in a mineralogical cabinet at Wesleyan University after the tourmalines had been removed. The crystals had lain undisturbed for many years, except that on one occasion they were rearranged, thus accounting for the overlapping effects. A long cyrstal near the border of the picture had been broken into several segments, to the ends of which the dust particles were attracted.

3. When a crystal has been cooled in liquid air, ice filaments from the moisture of the air in the room form at the two ends, like iron filings at the ends of a magnet. Small particles of ice sometimes shoot from one end to the other.‡

Even the small fluctuation in temperature of the air in a room will in time cause dust figures at the ends of tourmaline crystals. An instance of this effect is shown in Fig. 158. Particles of dust tend to move into regions where the electric field is strongest. On touching a crystal, they are repelled, like pith balls from a rubbed rod, and lodge on the adjacent portion of the shelf.

If a tourmaline crystal is laid on a white card in a location in the room where the air is comparatively stagnant but subject to ordinary variations in temperature, a faint smudge on the card begins to be visible at the ends of the crystal in a few months.

Numerical data on tourmaline are considered below.

* For details see the "Lehrbuch," p. 230.

† K. Bürker, Ann. Physik., vol. 1, p. 474, 1900. 1 part carmine and 5 parts sulphur are rubbed together and then mixed with 3 parts lycopodium (by volume). See "Lehrbuch," p. 232.

‡ L. Bleekrode, Ann. Physik., vol. 12, pp. 218–223, 1903; M. E. Maurice, Proc. Cambridge Phil. Soc., vol. 26, pp. 491–495, 1930; C. M. Focken, Nature, vol. 129, p. 168, 1932. Miss Maurice also found that a tourmaline heated to 140°C, discharged by passing it through a flame, and then allowed to cool in a smoke of NH_4Cl showed the formation of similar filaments.

518. Pyroelectric Constants of Various Crystals. Quantitative measurements have been made by a number of observers, notably Ackermann,[1] Hayashi,[210] Riecke,[B20] Röntgen,[439] and Veen.[563] References to their work and that of others, including qualitative results, are given in the "International Critical Tables."[B29,*] Only a few outstanding results need be discussed here.

The most complete investigation is that of Ackermann. Over a range of temperature extending in some instances from $-250°$ to $+375°$C he measured p (primary plus secondary effects; care was taken to have the temperature always uniform) for tourmaline, lithium sulphate, lithium selenate, potassium tartrate, lithium trisodium selenate, potassium lithium sulphate, ammonium tartrate, lithium sodium sulphate, and strontium acid tartrate. In all cases p appeared to approach zero at the absolute zero of temperature. With increasing temperature p increased slowly at first, then more rapidly, and in some cases it approached a saturation value at the highest temperatures. The theory of Ackermann's results has been treated by Boguslawski,[60,61] who discusses the similarity of the $p : T$ curves to the curves relating temperature to specific heat and coefficient of thermal expansion. The work of both Ackermann and Boguslawski was discussed later by Born.†

All numerical values given below are in cgs electrostatic units.

519. *Tourmaline.* The pyroelectric axis is in the Z-direction, so that in §516 the subscript $m = 3$. The following values of p in electric moment per unit volume per degree are from Ackermann:

Temperature, deg C	Color		
	Yellow-green	Rose-red	Blue-green
-250	0.08	0.08	0.04
$+ 20$	1.28	1.31	1.06
$+648$	1.86	1.94	1.52

Hayashi's results, at 18°C, are in good agreement with Ackermann's. He finds for a yellow-green crystal $p = 1.275$; pink, 1.324; blue-green,

---

* The section on Electroelastic and Pyroelectric Phenomena in the "International Critical Tables" was published also in *Proc. I.R.E.*, vol. 18, pp. 1247–1262, 1930. In the references at the end of these publications the following errors occur: ref. (43.5) should be the same as (43), in which the year should be 1882, not 1884. In the "International Critical Tables" are also these further errors, which were corrected in the *Proc. I.R.E.*: ref. (18), the pages should read "444, 471"; Ref. (39) should read "vol. 46, p. 607, 1928." The *Proc. I.R.E.* version has an error in ref. (80), in which the journal reference should be to 188 (*Nachr. Göttingen Math.-physik. Klasse*) instead of 88.

† M. BORN, *Physik. Z.*, vol. 23, pp. 125–128, 1922.

1.057. Both Hayashi and Ackermann, whose work was done under Voigt, used Brazilian tourmalines.

Röntgen observed from -252.5 to $+40.5°C$ with a number of Brazilian crystals. His results, obtained from crystals of various colors, are in general somewhat lower than Ackermann's. At room temperature a light green specimen gave $p = 1.03$.

Riecke[B20] measured p and its temperature coefficient in the neighborhood of room temperature, for several Brazilian crystals. From the average of his results Voigt derived the equation

$$p = 1.13 + 0.0104(t - 18°C).$$

In Voigt's "Lehrbuch"* is the statement, based on the data then available, that p changes sign at the temperature of liquid air. This statement is not confirmed by the careful measurements of Ackermann and of Röntgen, which were made a few years after the appearance of the "Lehrbuch."

The spontaneous polarization of tourmaline. When a tourmaline crystal is broken across the Z-axis, a little time must always elapse before the charges are compensated by conduction effects. The main experimental support of the hypothesis of a permanent spontaneous polarization P^0 is the fact that the charges thus observed are proportional to the area exposed and independent of the length of the segment.

Voigt estimated the value of P^0 at $24°C$ by quickly immersing the two parts, into which a crystal had just been broken, in mercury cups connected to an electrometer. In cgs electrostatic units the value was found to be about 33. According to Voigt's view, this value is only a lower limit, especially since tourmaline does not show distinct cleavage, so that on different portions of a surface of fracture there may be ultimate charges of opposite signs. In contrast with this view is Larmor's theory of pyroelectricity, treated in §545.

520. *Does Tourmaline Possess Measurable Primary Pyroelectricity?* With any crystal that theoretically possesses primary pyroelectricity, the answer to the question concerning the relative magnitudes of the primary p_m and the secondary p'_m requires the evaluation of the piezo-electric term in Eq. (545). It is therefore necessary to know the piezo-electric, elastic, and thermal-expansion constants, as well as the total p, and these should be measured on the same specimen, or at least on specimens from the same mother crystal.

In general, the principal uncertainty may be expected to lie in the observation of the total pyroelectric constant p. If the primary p_m is small, a slightly too low value of p may be sufficient to lead to the conclusion that p_m is altogether negligible.

* P. 245.

Voigt's measurements in 1898[570] with tourmaline indicated that the primary effect contributed about one-fifth of the total pyroelectric constant.* In 1914, Röntgen, on the basis of his observations quoted above, in which p was found to be relatively low, came to the conclusion that all the observable pyroelectricity in tourmaline is secondary. This conclusion was promptly contested by Voigt,[572] who still defended his former observations. The matter was later discussed by Lindman,† whose measurements of the coefficients of expansion, when substituted for those used by Voigt, led to the conclusion that about 12 per cent of the total effect is primary. On the whole, the best evidence at present favors the view that the part played by the primary effect in tourmaline, though small, is not negligible.

521. *Rochelle Salt.* As we have said in Chap. I, the pyroelectric effect in Rochelle salt was discovered by Brewster.‡ Qualitative tests have also been reported by Hankel and Lindenberg, Valasek, and Körner.§ The only quantitative experiments are those of H. Mueller and his pupils. A general account of the subject is given by Mueller,[382] on which most of the following statements are based.

It is only between the Curie points, where Rochelle salt is monoclinic, that there can be primary pyroelectricity, and even here the recorded effects are chiefly due to secondary pyroelectricity, influenced possibly also by the tertiary type.

Pyroelectric tests offer the most convincing proof of the existence of domains of opposite sign in Rochelle salt, as well as a means for estimating their size and distribution and the magnitude of the spontaneous polarization P_x^0.

Qualitative tests have been made by Dr. Jaffe and the author, both on complete crystals a few centimeters in size, of the form shown in Fig. 2, and on X-cut plates. Best results are obtained on heating rather than on cooling, probably owing to the avoidance of the condensation of moisture that takes place on cooling. After the crystal has been kept for 2 hr or more at a cool temperature (15 to 20°C), it is heated approximately to the Curie point and then dusted with the mixture of sulphur and red lead.

In the case of an *entire crystal*, the Z-axis should be vertical. The c-face may or may not show a pattern. That which is characteristic is the alternate stripes of red and yellow along the prismatic faces,

---

* For details see the "Lehrbuch," p. 924.

† K. F. LINDMAN, *Ann. Physik*, vol. 62, pp. 107–112, 1920. See also Geiger and Scheel, ref. B19, vol. 13, p. 315.

‡ D. BREWSTER, *Edinburgh Jour. Science*, 1824.

§ W. G. HANKEL and H. LINDENBERG, *Sächs. Abh.*, vol. 18, pp. 359–406, 1892; J. VALASEK;[543] H. KÖRNER, *Z. Physik*, vol. 103, pp. 170–190, 1936.

parallel to the Z-axis. Corresponding stripes, with colors interchanged, can often be identified at opposite ends of the X-axis. The indication is that the domains tend to be in the form of laminae from 1 to 8 mm thick in the Y-direction and 1 cm or more in extent parallel to X and Z. Different tests on the same specimen give essentially the same pattern.

A small *X-cut plate* 1 cm or so in size may well consist of a single domain. Larger plates may show a checkerboard pattern, each element of which on one side has its counterpart, with opposite sign, on the other side.

The dust patterns offer convincing evidence of a permanent polarization in the X-direction, present only between the Curie points. The sense of the polarization, for each domain, cannot be permanently reversed even after the crystal has been cooled from a high temperature while in a strong opposing electric field or heated almost to the disintegration point between successive tests.

The total pyroelectric constant p and its dependence on temperature have been measured by L. Tarnopol and by H. O. Saunders in Prof. Mueller's laboratory, using a modification of Ackermann's method. Small crystals gave results agreeing within 20 per cent. The constant has upper limits of opposite sign at the Curie points, decreasing to zero and changing sign at about 5°C.

By means of Eq. (546), using the value of p observed for a series of small values of ΔT between the Curie points, one can construct a curve relating P^0 to T. It is here assumed that $P^0 = 0$ at each Curie point. By this process Mueller[376,382] found good agreement with the $P^0:T$ curve in Fig. 147, page 628.

The maximum value of P^0 in Rochelle salt, about 640, is more·than ten times that which Voigt estimated for tourmaline. To produce such a polarization by an external field in an ordinary insulator of low dielectric constant would require a field of the order of 1,000,000 volts/cm.

The primary pyroelectric effect in Rochelle salt. Data are not available for a precise determination of the relative values of p_z and p_z' (Eq. (545)) such as Voigt attempted in the case of tourmaline. Nevertheless, a rough estimate can be made, which is perhaps worth while even if not yet conclusive. When applied to Rochelle salt, Eq. (545) becomes

$$\frac{P_z}{\vartheta} = \frac{\Delta P_z^0}{\Delta T} = p_z + e_{14}a_4$$

where p_z is the constant for the primary effect. For small ΔT, $\Delta P_z^0/\Delta T$ can be found from the slope of the curve for P_z^0 in Fig. 147. e_{14} is taken from Fig. 146. a_4 is the thermal coefficient of the shear y_z. It can be calculated from the rate of change of the spontaneous strain y_z^0 with temperature. We take Mueller's value $y_z^0 = 10.9(10^{-4})$ at 0°C from §482 and assume that the curve relating y_z^0 to temperature is similar to that for P_z^0.

In this manner we find, for small ΔT in the neighborhood of 18°C,

$$p = \Delta P_x^0/\Delta T \approx 50; \; a_4 \approx 4.5(10^{-5}); \; e_{14} \approx 9.1(10^5); \; e_{14}a_4 = p_x' \approx 41;$$

and finally $p_z = p - p_z' \approx 9$.

While this calculation is necessarily crude and the fact that the ratio p_z'/p_z is nearly the same as that which Voigt found for tourmaline is obviously only a coincidence, still it is an indication that the greater part of the pyroelectricity of Rochelle salt is secondary.

522. Other Crystals. *Zinc Sulphide.* This substance is mentioned partly to correct an error in the "International Critical Tables,"* where it is indicated that sphalerite is both piezoelectric and pyroelectric. Zinc sulphide exists in two modifications. Wurtzite, or α-ZnS, crystallizes in the hexagonal hemimorphic Class 26, symmetry C_{6v}. It is stable above 1020°C and metastable below. Sphalerite, or β-ZnS, also called zinc blende, crystallizes in the cubic hemimorphic Class 31, symmetry T_d. It is the more common form, stable at ordinary temperature.† Thus, while both forms are piezoelectric, only wurtzite is pyroelectric. If Veen's value of $p = 0.13$, cited in the "International Critical Tables," was obtained with sphalerite, he must have used non-uniform heating.

Quartz does not belong to a pyroelectric class; hence it possesses only tertiary pyroelectricity, which is observed on non-uniform heating. The direction of the temperature gradient must always be considered in interpreting the pyroelectric patterns on quartz shown in some books. Any results observed on uniform heating must be attributed to causes other than pyroelectricity, as when Röntgen[439] traced his results to expansion of the silver coating on his crystal. The precautions that should be observed in pyroelectric tests of quartz have been described by Van Dyke.[558]

Topaz is usually classified as rhombic holohedral, symmetry V_h, and as such it should posses neither piezo- nor pyroelectricity. Nevertheless, various authors have reported pyroelectric properties, with such qualifications as that the properties are "confused and uncertain" and that different specimens have polar axes in different directions.‡ The last statement suggests that if topaz is pyroelectric at all the effect is tertiary, dependent on the direction of the temperature gradient, and that Neumann's principle may be invoked for placing topaz in Class 6, symmetry V, like Rochelle salt outside the Curie points. One may also raise the

---

* Vol. 6, p. 210.

† On the two types of ZnS see Geiger and Scheel, ref. B19, vol. 24, part 2, p. 269, 1933.

‡ See, for example, N. A. Alston and J. West, *Proc. Roy. Soc. (London) (A)*, vol. 121, pp. 358–367, 1928.

question whether the irregular pyroelectric results, together with the externally holohedral form, may not be the result of twinning.*

It is well recognized that the discordant results with certain crystals, for example *picric acid*, are due to varying degrees of twinning.† The same is true of *axinite*.‡

Among the papers of recent years should be mentioned those by Martin and by Orelkin and Lonsdale,§ which describe the experimental technique as well as the results with various crystals.

A practical application of pyroelectricity in the detection of feeble radiation, especially in the infrared, has been proposed by Yeou Ta.‖ From his experiments with tourmaline and with tartaric acid,¶ which is several times as strongly pyroelectric as tourmaline, Ta finds that he can detect an increase in the temperature of the radiated face of the crystal as small as $(10^{-6})°C$. See also §570.

523. The Electrocaloric Effect. When Lord Kelvin applied the principles of thermodynamics to the pyroelectric effect in 1877, he was led, on the assumption of reversibility, to predict the converse effect. This is the electrocaloric effect, or the change in temperature of a pyroelectric crystal caused by a change in the electric field. Like the magnetocaloric effect (§556) it is very minute.

We now express $\Delta T/E$ in terms of the pyroelectric coefficient $p = \Delta P/\Delta T$. The method is similar to that pursued in §516. When the derivative of Eq. (1), p. 44, is taken with respect to $\vartheta = \Delta T$, with the electric field in the m-direction, we obtain

$$\frac{\partial \xi}{\partial \vartheta} = \frac{C}{T} \vartheta + \sum_{h}^{6} q_h x_h + p_m E_m = \Delta S = 0$$

S is the entropy, and since the process is adiabatic, $\Delta S = 0$. In this equation of state we assume the only impressed quantity to be E. Each component of strain x_h can then be replaced by $d_{mh}E_m$, and we have for the total electrocaloric constant

$$q - \frac{\vartheta}{E} = \frac{\Delta T}{E} = -\frac{T}{C}\left(p_m + \sum_{h}^{6} q_h d_{mh}\right) = q_m + q'_m \tag{547}$$

Here $q_m = -Tp_m/C$ is the constant for the *primary* effect, while

---

* W. A. WOOSTER, ref. B56, p. 230.

† L. BRUGNATELLI, *Z. Krist*, vol. 24, pp. 274–280, 1894–1895; G. GREENWOOD, *Z. Krist*, vol. 96, pp. 81–84, 1937; WOOD and McCALE.[591]

‡ W. A. WOOSTER, ref. B56, p. 230.

§ A. J. P. MARTIN, A New Method for the Detection of Pyroelectricity, *Mineral. Mag.*, vol. 22, pp. 519–523, 1931; B. ORELKIN and K. LONSDALE, The Structure of Symm. (1–3–5) Triphenylbenzene, *Proc. Roy. Soc. (London)*, vol. 144, pp. 630–642, 1934.

‖ YEOU TA, *Compt. rend*, vol. 207, pp. 1042–1044, 1938.

¶ For tartaric acid see "International Critical Tables"[B29] or F. Hayashi.[210]

$q'_m = -T \sum_h^6 q_h d_{mh}/C$ is the constant for the secondary effect, analogous to the "false" piezoelectricity in §516. This secondary effect, which is a change in temperature due to the thermoelastic and piezoelectric properties of the crystal, is discussed briefly by Voigt ("Lehrbuch," p. 260), and dismissed as of negligible magnitude.

Eq. (547) states that, when p is positive, q is negative, so that a positive increment ΔE in field strength leads to a decrease in temperature. This is the case with tourmaline. The density of tourmaline is approximately 3, $C = 0.2$, $p = 1.2$ (§519), whence at 300°K the theoretical value of q is roughly $-1.4(10^{-5})°$ per esu of field strength. This value has been verified within a few per cent by Lange.* The electrocaloric coefficient of Rochelle salt near the Curie points is many times greater than this, as is shown in the next section.

524. *The Electrocaloric Effect in Rochelle Salt.* The earliest observations of a linear effect were those of Kobeko and Kurchatov,[263] who also were the first to predict the effect in Rochelle salt from theoretical grounds. As was stated in §515, this is the converse of the pyroelectric effect, and its presence in Rochelle salt—always assuming reversibility—is a necessary consequence of the dependence of the spontaneous polarization of Rochelle salt upon temperature. Since q in Eq. (547) is proportional to p, it is evident that the electrocaloric coefficient, like the pyroelectric coefficient (§521), has its greatest values, with opposite signs, just within the two Curie points, passing through zero in the neighborhood of 0°C.

With a field strength of various values up to 1,200 volts/cm Kobeko and Kurchatov observed, at the upper Curie point, a proportional increase in temperature (a few hundredths of a degree for the strongest fields, independent of the direction of the field) and a decrease in temperature of the same order of magnitude at the lower Curie point, all in conformity with theory.

There is also theoretically in Rochelle salt, as in all dielectrics, a *quadratic* electrocaloric effect due to electrostriction, which according to Debye and Sack[B16] has been detected experimentally. It is of a lower order of magnitude than the linear effect except in fields at least as large as 30,000 volts/cm.

525. Tensorial Pyroelectricity. This is an excessively minute effect, theoretically observable with all crystal classes except the cubic. It manifests itself in the production of small charges of *like* sign at edges occurring at the ends of certain axes, when the crystal is heated uniformly. In the case of crystals that have vectorial (ordinary) pyroelectricity, the two effects are superposed, making the detection of tensorial pyroelectricity especially difficult.

* F. LANGE, dissertation, Jena, 1905. Further details are given in Voigt's "Lehrbuch," p. 259.

In a crystal with a polar axis, the polarization produced by changes in temperature or mechanical stress is a vector. In general, crystals possess also quadrupole moments, which under the influence of temperature or stress give rise to a polarization that is tensorial rather than vectorial and is characterized by central symmetry. Uniform heating causes changes in the field in the immediate neighborhood of the quadrupoles, with the result that double layers of electricity appear at the surface. The accompanying expansion produces a tensorial *piezoelectric* effect, which by analogy with vectorial pyroelectricity might be called a *secondary tensorial pyroelectric* effect. The total observed tensorial pyroelectricity is therefore the sum of the primary effect due to heating alone and this secondary effect.

Voigt* looked for the effect by experiments with the following crystals, all nonpiezoelectric in order to exclude disturbing effects: calcite, dolomite, beryl, topaz, barite, and celestite. His conclusion was that the real existence of the effect was "very probable."

In the "Lehrbuch,"† Voigt discusses briefly the *tensorial piezoelectric effect*, which, though necessarily minute, is théoretically possible with all crystals and even with isotropic dielectrics. Like tensorial pyroelectricity and elasticity, it involves the relations between two tensors, in this case the tensorial electric field and the elastic stress. Voigt claims to have demonstrated experimentally the probable existence of the effect.‡

526. Actino-electricity. This term was introduced by Hankel,§ to designate an electrification observed by him along the prismatic edges of a quartz crystal exposed to radiant heat. It was soon shown convincingly by Friedel and Curie‖ that the effect could be fully explained as due to piezoelectric deformation (tertiary pyroelectricity, §515).

Recently the term has been revived, in connection with the production of an emf in certain crystals under the influence of light.¶ Such effects have to do probably with internal photoelectricity rather than piezoelectricity.

REFERENCES

General. International Critical Tables,[B29] GEIGER and SCHEEL (vol. 13),[B19] GRAETZ,[B20] POYNTING and THOMSON,[B42] VOIGT,[B52] WIEN and HARMS (vol. 10),[B53] WINKELMANN (vol. 4, part 1),[B54] VOIGT.[569-572,574,575]

Theory. DEBYE and SACK,[B16] "Encyclopadie der mathematischen Wissenschaften" [vol. 5, part 2 (by F. Pockels)],[B17] GEIGER and SCHEEL (vol. 24, part 2, 1933),[B19] GRAETZ [vol. 1 (by E. Riecke)],[B20] BOGUSLAWSKI,[59-61] HECKMANN,[213] LARMOR.[308]

* W. VOIGT,[591] "Lehrbuch," p. 303.

† Page 944.

‡ See also Voigt's later papers.[574,575] The subject is further discussed by Pockels,[B17] Falkenhagen,[B19] and Born[B6] and also in "Problems of Atomic Dynamics," Massachusetts Institute of Technology, Cambridge, Mass, 1926.

§ W. G. HANKEL, *Wiedemann's Ann.*, vol. 10, p. 618, 1880, vol. 19, pp. 818–844, 1883; *Sächs. Ber.*, vol. 33, pp. 52–63, 1881; *Sächs. Abh.*, vol. 12, pp. 457–548, 1883.

‖ C. FRIEDEL and J. CURIE, *Bull. soc. française minéral.*, vol. 5, pp. 282–296, 1882; *Compt. rend.*, vol. 96, pp. 1262, 1389, 1883. *Cf.* also W. C. Röntgen, *Wiedemann's Ann.*, vol. 19, pp. 513–518, 1883.

¶ See, for example, J. J. Brady and W. H. Moore, *Phys. Rev.*, vol. 55, pp. 308–311, 1939.

Measurements.   Geiger and Scheel,[B19] Voigt,[B52] Wooster,[B56] Ackermann,[1] Le Quéré,[315] Mueller,[382] Röntgen,[439] Wood and McCale.[591]

Tourmaline.   Hintze,[B25] Meissner and Bechmann,[362] Riecke,[434] Worobieff.[592]

Quartz.   Kolenko.[286]

The numerous investigations of Hankel in pyro- and piezoelectricity are described in his collected works: Wilhelm Gottlieb Hankel, "Elektrische Untersuchungen," S. Hirzel, Leipzig, 1856–1899, 3 vols.   A partial list of his papers is given in ref. 203. Hankel's investigations were mostly qualitative and are now chiefly of historical value.

A few additional references to various authors are given in footnotes in this chapter.

CHAPTER XXX

PIEZO-OPTIC, ELECTRO-OPTIC, AND OTHER OPTICAL EFFECTS

Lass dir von den Spiegeleien
Unsrer Physiker erzählen,
Die am Phänomen sich freuen,
Mehr sich mit Gedanken quälen.

Spiegel hüben, Spiegel drüben,
Doppelstellung, auserlesen;
Und dazwischen ruht im Trüben
Als Krystall das Erdewesen.

—GOETHE.

527. Introduction. Although it is assumed that the reader is acquainted with the principles of physical optics, still it may be helpful, in order to point the way to the special properties of crystals that are now to be treated, to summarize briefly certain features of the subject. Detailed proofs must be sought elsewhere. We shall have to do chiefly with the laws of double refraction for the various crystal systems, as represented by the optical ellipsoids. A discussion of wave surfaces in crystals is omitted, although it is an important feature in crystal optics, since it is not essential for the present purpose.

We deal first with transparent crystals in the normal state, free from mechanical and electric stresses. It is recalled that the electric field vector E is perpendicular to the *ray* and to the magnetic vector H, while the electric displacement D is perpendicular to the *wave normal* and to H. The *vibration direction* is that of D. It is customary to describe the optical properties of crystals in terms either of the *Fresnel ellipsoid* or of the *index ellipsoid* (Fletcher ellipsoid). The representation of physical properties of crystals by an ellipsoidal surface is a device that we have already encountered in the discussion of dielectric properties (§112) and of elasticity (§28). Indeed, the analogies of these properties with optical phenomena are far-reaching. The equations for the optical ellipsoids are given below.

The Fresnel Ellipsoid. To any given crystal there corresponds, for a given wavelength and temperature, a certain ellipsoidal surface with axes definitely oriented with respect to the crystal lattice, such that the major and minor semiaxes of the ellipse forming the intersection of the surface by any plane through the center are proportional to the velocities

713

of the two polarized rays that can be propagated in the direction normal to the plane. The phenomenon is that of *double refraction*. The electric vectors of the two rays are parallel to the major and minor axes of the ellipse. This ellipsoid is the Fresnel ellipsoid. In the most general case it is triaxial; its principal semiaxes a, b, c are called the *principal velocities** of light in the crystal, the symbols being so chosen that $a > b > c$. It is customary to take as unit vector the velocity of light in vacuum, whence a, b, and c are to be regarded as *relative* velocities and therefore dimensionless.

The equation of the Fresnel ellipsoid is

$$\frac{x^2}{a^2} + \frac{y^2}{b^2} + \frac{z^2}{c^2} = 1 \tag{548}$$

The axes of reference for the ellipsoid are parallel, respectively, to the principal velocities a, b, and c. In an unstrained crystal, except in the

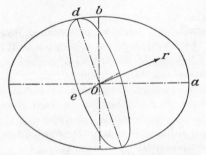

Fɪɢ. 159.—Fresnel ellipsoid. The c-axis is perpendicular to the paper. The ray Or is normal to an elliptical section, the principal axes of which are represented by Od and Oe.

triclinic and monoclinic systems, these axes are identical with the crystallographic a-, b-, c- (or X-, Y-, Z-) axes, but not necessarily in the same order; nor is there any fixed relation between the relative lengths of the principal axes of the ellipsoid and the crystallographic axial ratios.

528. The *principal refractive indices*, denoted by n_1, n_2, n_3 or by α, β, γ are the reciprocals of a, b, and c, respectively. Of these, γ has the maximum value for the crystal and α the minimum. Since for transparent crystals the magnetic permeability $\mu = 1$, the Fresnel ellipsoid is identical with the ellipsoid of the reciprocal square roots of the dielectric constants at optical frequencies (§112).

Figure 159 represents a Fresnel ellipsoid in which Or is a ray in any arbitrary direction. The plane through O normal to Or intersects the ellipsoid in an ellipse. According to the statements made above, the

* In this chapter the symbols a, b, c represent in general the principal velocities, not, as heretofore, the crystallographic axes.

principal axes Od and Oe of this ellipse are proportional to the velocities of the two polarized rays that can be propagated along Or, while the directions of Od and Oe are those of the electric vectors of the two rays.

Figure 159 may be used also to illustrate another property of the Fresnel ellipsoid, *viz.*, that all rays lying in a given plane, such as that perpendicular to the vector Or, fall into two categories: those polarized so as to have the electric vector in the plane, and those having the electric vector perpendicular to the plane, parallel to Or.   For all rays in the latter group, whatever their direction in the plane, there is a common velocity, given by the length of Or.   This property explains why, in tables of principal refractive indices of crystals, the symbols n_a, n_b, n_c stand for the indices for all rays having vibration directions parallel to a, b, or c.   In the general case, for example, rays parallel to c may have either of the two indices n_a or n_b.   If, as is the case with unstrained crystals of Rochelle salt, the a-, b-, c-axes of the ellipsoid coincide with the X-, Y-, Z-axes of the crystal, (though not necessarily in the same order), the principal indices may be denoted by n_x, n_y, and n_z. $(n_a - n_b)/\lambda$ is a measure of the double refraction in the c-direction for wavelength λ.

In unstrained *cubic* crystals the axes of the Fresnel ellipsoid are equal, the ellipsoid becomes a sphere, and all directions are optically, as well as elastically, equivalent, as in isotropic solids.

It is sometimes convenient to express the optical properties of crystals in terms of the *index ellipsoid*, which is the "reciprocal" of the Fresnel ellipsoid, having as principal axes $1/a$, $1/b$, and $1/c$; that is, its axes are the three principal refractive indices.   For *waves* whose normals are in the direction of any radius vector, the two refractive indices are the principal axes of the ellipse in which the ellipsoid is intersected by a plane perpendicular to this radius vector.   The directions of these principal axes are those of the electric displacement, *i.e.*, the vibration directions.

The equation of the index ellipsoid is

$$a^2x^2 + b^2y^2 + c^2z^2 = 1 \tag{549}$$

All symbols have here the same meaning as for the Fresnel ellipsoid.

The number of parameters needed to fix the lengths and orientations of the axes of the Fresnel and index ellipsoids decreases as the crystalline symmetry increases.   These parameters are the polarization constants discussed below.   With triclinic crystals the number is six—three for the axial lengths, and three for the orientation.   Monoclinic crystals require four parameters; rhombic crystals, three.   These three systems comprise the *biaxial* crystals, for which the velocities a, b, and c are all different.

529. Confining ourselves for the moment to the three systems of lowest symmetry, we distinguish between the primary and secondary *optic axes.* The two *primary optic axes* are those directions for which the two wave velocities are equal; there are also two *secondary* optic axes, usually very close to the primary, for which the *ray* velocities are equal. The primary axes are the normals to the two circular sections that can be drawn through the center of the index ellipsoid, while the secondary axes are normal to the two circular sections of the Fresnel ellipsoid. The line bisecting the acute angle (the *axial angle* of the mineralogist) between the primary (or secondary) optic axes is the *acute bisectrix.* It is necessarily parallel to either the α- or the γ-axis of the index ellipsoid. A crystal is called *positive* or *negative* according to whether the acute bisectrix is parallel to γ or to α, respectively.

We pass to the consideration of *uniaxial crystals,* which include quartz. Like biaxial crystals they are doubly refracting except along one direction called the *optic axis;* we are here ignoring circular double refraction, which is treated below. All crystals in the tetragonal, trigonal, and hexagonal systems are uniaxial; two of the axes of the ellipsoid are equal, and the two optic axes merge into one. The Fresnel and index ellipsoids are now ellipsoids of revolution, the rays corresponding to the two equal axes becoming the single ordinary ray, the remaining ray being the extraordinary.

530. The Optical Polarization Constants. In describing the effects of external influences on the optical properties of crystals it is desirable to use an orthogonal axial system. For all classes except triclinic and monoclinic Eq. (549) can be used as it stands; with these two classes a transformation is necessary, leading to an equation for the index ellipsoid in terms of six parameters. For the sake of completeness the expressions for these parameters will be given in full, although they are not all needed in the treatment of those classes with which we are concerned here.

The X-, Y-, Z-orthogonal axes are chosen to coincide with the crystallographic axes of all classes from rhombic symmetry upward. In general form, in the notation of Pockels, Eq. (549) becomes

$$a_{11}^0 x^2 + a_{22}^0 y^2 + a_{33}^0 z^2 + 2a_{23}^0 yz + 2a_{31}^0 zx + 2a_{12}^0 xy = 1$$

The superscript 0 designates the unstrained state of the crystal. $a_{11}^0 \ldots a_{12}^0$ are the six *polarization constants,* defined in terms of a, b, c and the direction cosines $\alpha_1 \ldots \gamma_3$ by Eqs. (550) below. $X'Y'Z'$ are the axes for the index ellipsoid in Eq. (549).

	X	Y	Z
X'	α_1	α_2	α_3
Y'	β_1	β_2	β_3
Z'	γ_1	γ_2	γ_3

The direction cosines are given in the adjoining matrix. In the general case, as has already been pointed out, six parameters are needed for the complete specification of the ellipsoid.

$$
\left.
\begin{aligned}
a_{11}^0 &= a^2\alpha_1^2 + b^2\beta_1^2 + c^2\gamma_1^2 \\
a_{22}^0 &= a^2\alpha_2^2 + b^2\beta_2^2 + c^2\gamma_2^2 \\
a_{33}^0 &= a^2\alpha_3^2 + b^2\beta_3^2 + c^2\gamma_3^2 \\
a_{23}^0 &= a^2\alpha_2\alpha_3 + b^2\beta_2\beta_3 + c^2\gamma_2\gamma_3 \\
a_{31}^0 &= a^2\alpha_3\alpha_1 + b^2\beta_3\beta_1 + c^2\gamma_3\gamma_1 \\
a_{12}^0 &= a^2\alpha_1\alpha_2 + b^2\beta_1\beta_2 + c^2\gamma_1\gamma_2
\end{aligned}
\right\}
\tag{550}
$$

The quantities a_{mn}^0 are the components of a symmetrical tensor, analogous to the elastic strain or stress tensor and to the dielectric susceptibility tensor.

The statement in §527, that in all systems except the triclinic and monoclinic the directions of the principal velocities a, b, c coincide with the three rectangular crystallographic axes, is valid as long as the crystals are unstrained. The last three equations in (550) then vanish, while each of the first three is reduced to a single term, which represents the reciprocal of the square of the principal refractive index in the corresponding direction, since $a_{11}^0 = a^2$, $a_{22}^0 = b^2$, $a_{33}^0 = c^2$. As will be seen, under certain elastic or electric stresses the optical ellipsoid of a crystal may suffer both a deformation and a rotation, which can cause all the polarization coefficients to assume values different from zero. Then a_{23}, a_{31}, and a_{12} do not vanish but become parameters of the new ellipsoid.

Leaving aside the monoclinic and triclinic systems (even these may be included by arbitrarily letting the X, Y, Z axial system coincide in direction with a, b, c), we may write for the surviving terms in Eqs. (550), for an unstrained crystal, $a_{11}^0 \equiv a_0^2$, $a_{22}^0 \equiv b_0^2$, $a_{33}^0 \equiv c_0^2$. a_0, b_0, and c_0 are the principal axes of the Fresnel ellipsoid, parallel (though not necessarily respectively) to the orthogonal crystal axes.

For the *uniaxial systems* (tetragonal, hexagonal, and trigonal), a_0, b_0, c_0 coincide in direction with the X, Y, Z crystal axes, respectively, and $a_0 = b_0$. We then have, calling $o = 1/n_o$ and $e = 1/n_e$ the velocities of the ordinary and extraordinary rays, n_o and n_e being the corresponding refractive indices, $a_{11}^0 = a_{22}^0 = o^2 = 1/n_o^2$ and $a_{33}^0 = e^2 = 1/n_e^2$.

The parameters of the optical ellipsoids are in general functions of wavelength and temperature.

531. The Piezo-optic Effect. This effect consists in a change in the refractive indices of materials under mechanical strain. Singly refracting substances become doubly refracting, while in doubly refracting substances the optical constants are altered by the strain. It was discovered in both crystalline and amorphous substances by Brewster about 1815, and under the name of *photoelasticity* it has come to be of great importance in engineering. The special phenomena in crystals are commonly termed *elasto-optic* or *piezo-optic* effects. They are present in all crystals. Their theory, together with observations on several cubic and uniaxial crystals, was given by Pockels in 1889 and 1890. A summary of this work is in his textbook on crystal optics.[B41] The assumption is made that the optical effects are *linear* functions of the strain.

A full discussion of piezo-optics would be very complicated and quite beyond the scope of this work. We can only summarize and interpret the main points, in order that the nature of the electro-optic effect may be better understood.

In general, a mechanical stress both deforms and rotates the index ellipsoid, with consequent changes in birefringence and in the directions of the optic axes. An electric field, as shown below, has a like effect; but whereas piezo-optic effects are universal, the linear electro-optic effect is possible only in piezoelectric crystals.

The fundamental equations are relations between the components of two tensors, *viz.*, the polarization constants a_{mn} and either the components x_h of elastic strain or those of elastic stress X_h. The piezo-optic strain and stress coefficients are designated by Pockels as p_{mn} and π_{mn}, respectively. Their matrices for the various classes are the same as for the elastic constants, except that it is not in general true that $p_{mn} = p_{nm}$. The latter relation in elasticity is derived from thermodynamic considerations that are not applicable to the piezo-optic phenomena. The maximum number of independent constants (triclinic) is thus raised from 21 to 36, the 15 additional values appearing below the diagonal of the elastic matrix in §26 or 29, with reversed subscripts. For all systems except triclinic, monoclinic, and rhombic, however, Pockels stated that $p_{21} = p_{12}$, hence $\pi_{21} = \pi_{12}$, and in addition, for the cubic system, that $p_{31} = p_{13}$, hence $\pi_{31} = \pi_{13}$. This statement of Pockels rests on the tacit assumption that the symmetry of the crystal is not perceptibly altered by pressure.

From more recent observations on cubic crystals* it has become apparent that this assumption of Pockels is not justified. The explanation, as pointed out by Mueller, is that deformation lowers the symmetry, thus increasing the number of non-vanishing coefficients p_{hk} and π_{hk}; the magnitude of these deformation-induced coefficients is not constant but is *proportional to the stress*. For effects of this nature Mueller suggests the term "morphic" (§464). It follows that the

---

* H. B. MARIS, *Jour. Optical Soc. Am.*, vol. 15, pp. 194–200, 1927, and Y. KIDANI, *Proc. Phys.-Math. Soc. Japan*, vol. 21, pp. 457f., 1939. See also the discussion by H. Mueller.[381]

piezo-optic effect, which according to Eqs. (551) and (551a) should be strictly linear, requires (at least for systems of higher symmetry) correction terms involving the square of the stress. The present treatment omits this second-order effect.

The piezo-optic equations in terms of strain are

$$
\left.\begin{aligned}
a_{11} - a_{11}^0 &= p_{11}x_x + p_{12}y_y + p_{13}z_z + p_{14}y_z + p_{15}z_x + p_{16}x_y \\
a_{22} - a_{22}^0 &= p_{21}x_x + p_{22}y_y + p_{23}z_z + p_{24}y_z + p_{25}z_x + p_{26}x_y \\
a_{33} - a_{33}^0 &= p_{31}x_x + p_{32}y_y + p_{33}z_z + p_{34}y_z + p_{35}z_x + p_{36}x_y \\
a_{23} - a_{23}^0 &= p_{41}x_x + p_{42}y_y + p_{43}z_z + p_{44}y_z + p_{45}z_x + p_{46}x_y \\
a_{31} - a_{31}^0 &= p_{51}x_x + p_{52}y_y + p_{53}z_z + p_{54}y_z + p_{55}z_x + p_{56}x_y \\
a_{12} - a_{12}^0 &= p_{61}x_x + p_{62}y_y + p_{63}z_z + p_{64}y_z + p_{65}z_x + p_{66}x_y
\end{aligned}\right\} \quad (551)
$$

where a_{mn}^0 is the value of a_{mn} for the unstrained crystal, *i.e.*, the value as defined in Eq. (550).

In terms of stress the equations are:

$$
\left.\begin{aligned}
(a_{11} - a_{11}^0) &= \pi_{11}X_x + \pi_{12}Y_y + \pi_{13}Z_z + \pi_{14}Y_z \\
&\qquad\qquad + \pi_{15}Z_x + \pi_{16}X_y \\
&\cdots\cdots\cdots\cdots\cdots\cdots\cdots\cdots\cdots\cdots\cdots\cdots \\
(a_{23} - a_{23}^0) &= \pi_{41}X_x + \pi_{42}Y_y + \pi_{43}Z_z + \pi_{44}Y_z \\
&\qquad\qquad + \pi_{45}Z_x + \pi_{46}X_y \\
&\cdots\cdots\cdots\cdots\cdots\cdots\cdots\cdots\cdots\cdots\cdots\cdots
\end{aligned}\right\} \quad (551a)
$$

The coefficients p_{mn} are dimensionless, while the π_{mn} have the dimensions of an elastic compliance.

The first three equations in (551) and (551a) express a change in the principal velocities, which can be measured by observations on rays parallel to the three axes, respectively, by the usual methods for measuring small changes in the refractive index. For example, if the only applied stress is Y_z and if $\pi_{14} \neq 0$, then the product $\pi_{14}Y_z$ may be interpreted as expressing the change in the refractive index n_1 caused by Y_z, in accordance with the relation $(a_{11} - a_{11}^0) = (1/n_1^2 - 1/n_1^{02}) = \pi_{14}Y_z$, where n_1 and n_1^0 are the values of this particular principal refractive index with and without the application of stress. The last three equations in (551a) represent a rotation of the optical ellipsoid around its axes. This rotation is determined by measuring the change in refractive index under stress with light perpendicular to any one axis and bisecting the angle between the other two. From the change in length of the corresponding radius vector of the ellipsoid the amount of rotation is calculated, from which the coefficients can be determined.*

* Ref. B41, p. 468.

The piezo-optic coefficients are related to the elastic coefficients c and s by the equations

$$p_{hk} = \sum_{i=1}^{6} \pi_{hi} c_{ki} \qquad \pi_{hk} = \sum_{i=1}^{6} p_{hi} s_{ki} \qquad (552)$$

The parameters of the optical ellipsoids are in general functions of wavelength and temperature.

532. *Cubic* crystals become uniaxial for pressures normal to cube or octahedron faces and biaxial for all other types of stress.* Crystals of the *trigonal* system become biaxial under any pressure not parallel to the optic axis. If the pressure is *normal* to the original optic axis, one of the principal axes of the index ellipsoid is parallel to the pressure, while a second remains very near the original optic axis. The two optic axes lie in the plane of these two principal axes if the difference $\pi_{12} - \pi_{11}$ of the piezo-optic constants has the same sign as the velocity difference $o - e$. With a pressure of 1 kg/mm^2 the axial angle was found by Pockels to be 5°54' for *quartz*.

Following are the piezo-optic constants of quartz and Rochelle salt, from Pockels,[B41,428] who used sodium light. Pockels' values in mm^2/gm are here converted into cm^2/dyne:

Quartz (for optical constants see §534).

π_{11}	π_{12}	π_{13}	π_{14}	π_{31}	π_{33}	π_{44}	π_{41}
1.11	2.50	1.97	−0.097	2.77	0.183	−1.015	−0.320, all × 10^{-13}

Rochelle salt (for optical constants see §535). The experimental difficulties were so great that the following results indicate only the order of magnitude. Pockels' values for π_{nn}, converted to square centimeters per dyne, are

$$\pi_{44} = -9 \qquad \pi_{55} = +19 \qquad \pi_{66} = -17 \quad (\text{all} \times 10^{-14})$$

From Hinz's values of the elastic constants in Table IV, we find by the use of Eqs. (552)

$$p_{44} = -0.009 \qquad p_{55} = +0.006 \qquad p_{66} = -0.015$$

Piezo-optic observations on quartz have also been made by Günther.[194] His observations were restricted to the determination of the phase retardation for polarized light in the Y-direction, under a mechanical stress X_x up to 30 kg/cm^2, and yielded a value which in Pockels' notation would be represented by $n_o^3 \pi_{31}/2 - n_o^3 \pi_{11}/2$. The numerical value of this quantity, about $10(10^{-13})$ cm^2/dyne, is in excellent agreement with Günther's theory,† but it is about three times as great as that calculated from Pockels' experimentally determined coefficients.

* The piezo-optic properties of cubic crystals have been treated in a theoretical paper by H. Mueller (reference at end of chapter).

† Günther develops a theory of the piezo-optic and electro-optic effects, based on various properties of quartz, including characteristic frequencies in the infrared and

The piezo-optic effect in quartz can be demonstrated by mounting a polished Z-cut plate in convergent light between a polarizer and analyzer so that the usual concentric circular rings are seen. When the plate is compressed in any direction normal to the optic axis, the circles become ellipses, the orientations of whose axes depend on the direction of the pressure. If in place of compression an electric field normal to the optic axis is applied, a similar result is observed, thus demonstrating the electro-optic effect.

533. Electro-optic Effects. These effects deserve a brief treatment here because of a certain parallelism with piezoelectricity and electrostriction. We first investigate the question as to the manner in which a static electric field may be expected to influence the optic behavior of a transparent crystal. The phenomenon is described in terms of the effect of the electric vector on the symmetrical tensor of the optical polarization constants (§530).

The most general assumption is that the field will change both the magnitudes and the directions of the principal axes of this tensor. A uniaxial crystal becomes biaxial. The difference between the original and the deformed tensors is again a symmetrical tensor. The electro-optic effect is a *symmetrical-tensorial* effect of the electric field. Theory shows that one may expect a *linear* electro-optic effect with exactly the same symmetry conditions as the converse piezoelectric effect, and a *quadratic* electro-optic effect (Kerr effect, §536) corresponding to quadratic electrostriction.

The Linear Electro-optic Effect. This effect is possible with all piezoelectric crystals, and with them only. The relationship between the linear electro-optic effect and piezoelectricity is so close that Kundt and Röntgen, who in 1883 were the first to make a careful study of the former phenomenon, believed that it was only a secondary result of the piezoelectric deformation; the effect of a deformation on the refractive indices is the *piezo-optic* effect discussed above.

The question was decided by Pockels in his classical investigation of 1894, which is still the principal source of our knowledge of the linear electro-optic effect. Pockels found a *direct* influence of the electric field on the optical constants; *i.e.*, the refractive indices of a crystal deformed by an electric field are different from those of a crystal deformed to the same extent by mechanical forces.

Pockels computed the "direct" effect by subtracting from the observed total effect the secondary, or "indirect," effect due to deformation, making use of the known piezoelectric and piezo-optic constants.

ultraviolet. His theory predicts the magnitudes of both effects. Since his observations were made with a single plate, his results cannot yet be regarded as a confirmation of his theory, especially since for the electro-optic effect (§534) his theoretical value of the constant r_{11} is 60 per cent higher than that which he found experimentally.

The relation of this indirect to the direct effect is quite analogous to that between "false" and "true" pyroelectricity discussed in §520.

Pockels' theory relates the change in the optical polarization constants to the electric polarization P by means of 18 coefficients. In accordance with §530 it is assumed that the axes of reference are parallel to the principal axes of the normal ellipsoid. The equations for the change in optical polarization constants caused by the electric field may then be written with a_0^2 in place of a_{11}^0, etc., in accordance with §530. From Pockels' theory these equations are

$$\left.\begin{array}{l}
a_{11} - a_0^2 = r_{11}P_x + r_{12}P_y + r_{13}P_z \\
a_{22} - b_0^2 = r_{21}P_x + r_{22}P_y + r_{23}P_z \\
a_{33} - c_0^2 = r_{31}P_x + r_{32}P_y + r_{33}P_z \\
\quad a_{23} = r_{41}P_x + r_{42}P_y + r_{43}P_z \\
\quad a_{31} = r_{51}P_x + r_{52}P_y + r_{53}P_z \\
\quad a_{12} = r_{61}P_x + r_{62}P_y + r_{63}P_z
\end{array}\right\} \qquad (553)$$

These expressions are analogous to Eq. (190), §128, or to Eq. (*vii*) in Table XX for the converse piezoelectric effect.* The quantities on the left side of the equations can be determined from observations of the refractive indices by standard methods with polarized light. From them and the known electric field strength the coefficients r_{mn} may be calculated.

The matrices for these coefficients are exactly the same as those for the piezoelectric coefficients, in §131. In the most general case there are 18 electro-optic constants.

In the following paragraphs we shall use the symbol r for the observed, or over-all, electro-optic effect. The indirect effect will be designated by r', and the direct effect by $r'' = r - r'$; r'' is the true electro-optic coefficient.

534. Experimental Results in Electro-optics. Data are available only for quartz, tourmaline, sodium chlorate, and Rochelle salt. Until the recent work by Ny Tsi-Ze and Günther on quartz and of Mueller on Rochelle salt, the only observations beyond the earlier work of Röntgen, Kundt, and Czermak were those of Pockels in 1890. In all cases the observations of the dependence of double refraction upon field yield the over-all values of the electro-optic coefficients r_{nm}, including the effect of piezoelectric deformation (indirect effect). The latter contribution,

---

* Following the convention adopted by Mueller,[381] we write r_{mn} in place of Pockels' e_{mn} in order to avoid confusion with the piezoelectric constants. The order of subscripts is the same as with Pockels: the *second* digit in the subscript indicates the direction of the polarization. In his experiments Pockels observed the field $E = P/\eta'$; hence in Eqs. (553) P requires a knowledge of the dielectric susceptibility η' of the free crystal. In all experiments hitherto, P has been parallel to E.

which we shall call r'_{mn}, is calculated from the piezoelectric, elastic, and piezo-optic constants, just as in the case of pyroelectricity. The direct electro-optic coefficients may then be expressed as $r''_{mn} = r_{mn} - r'_{mn}$. It is easily proved from Eqs. (551), (551a), (189), and (190) that

$$\eta'_m r'_{nm} = \sum_{i=1}^{6} p_{ni} d_{mi} = \sum_{i=1}^{6} \pi_{ni} e_{mi} \tag{554}$$

Quartz. The electro-optic constants are $r_{11} = -r_{21} = -r_{62}$ and $r_{41} = -r_{52}$.

Principal refractive indices for the ordinary and extraordinary rays (Na, 18°C): $n_o = 1.54425$; $n_e = 1.55336$. For the optical activity of quartz see §538.

Only the component of field perpendicular to the optic axis is effective. The crystal becomes biaxial, the angle between the two optic axes and the magnitude of the effect being given by r_{11}. The coefficient r_{41} has an influence only on rays oblique to all three axes. In accordance with §5, for the crystal class to which quartz belongs, Eqs. (550) reduce to $a_{11} - o^2 = r_{11}P_x$; $a_{22} - o^2 = -r_{11}P_x$; $a_{33} = e^2 = 0$; $a_{23} = r_{41}P_x$; $a_{31} = -r_{41}P_y$; $a_{12} = -r_{11}P_y$. As in §530 the symbols o and e represent the principal light velocities, ordinary and extraordinary.

The equation for r_{11} becomes

$$r_{11} = \frac{\partial a_{11}}{\partial P_x} = \frac{\partial}{\partial P_x} \frac{1}{n_o} \approx -\frac{1}{n_o^2} \frac{\Delta n_o}{\Delta P_x} \tag{555}$$

where n_o is the refractive index for the ordinary ray and Δn_o is the observed change in n_o for a change ΔP_x in polarization.

For the total effect, using Na light, Pockels found $r_{11}\eta'_x = 1.40(10^{-8})$, $r_{41}\eta'_x = 0.59(10^{-8})$. The effect of quadratic electrostriction upon the results was ruled out, as being small in comparison with the errors of observation. The direct effect was found by subtracting from these values the calculated effect due to deformation alone. The direct coefficients thus obtained are $r''_{11}\eta'_x = 0.73(10^{-8})$ and $r''_{41}\eta'_x = 0.14(10^{-8})$. For the over-all effect the change in n_o per esu of field (300 volts/cm) parallel to the X-axis is only $\Delta n_o / \Delta E_x = 3.3(10^{-8})$; for the direct effect the calculated value is $1.74(10^{-8})$.

The only other observations that have been made on the electro-optic effect in quartz are those of Tsi-Ze and of Günther.* The obser-

* L. M. Myers (*Marconi Rev.*, no. 52, pp. 16–25, February, 1935; no. 53, pp. 9–18, April, 1935) has also described experiments on the optical effects in electrically stressed quartz. Apparently unaware of the work of Pockels, Myers thinks his results to be of purely mechanical origin, *i.e.*, due to piezoelectric deformations. He comes to the practical conclusion that electrically stressed quartz is inferior to an ordinary Kerr cell for controlling light intensity. On this point see §513 concerning the ultrasonic light relay.

vations of Günther, reduced to the foregoing units, yield for the total effect $r_{11}\eta'_x = 1.45(10^{-8})$, in good agreement with Pockels. From Tsi-Ze's paper one finds, by a somewhat roundabout calculation,

$$r_{11}\eta'_x = -1.18(10^{-8})$$

If we ignore the discrepancy in sign, which may be due to a difference in polarity of field or to enantiomorphism, it appears that Tsi-Ze's result is at least of the order of magnitude of the other observers.* Although the calculations of the indirect effect by both Günther and Tsi-Ze are open to question on theoretical grounds, they at least confirm Pockels' conclusion as to the reality of the direct effect.

It may be added that Tsi-Ze also recorded the observation of an electro-optic effect for the *extraordinary* ray in quartz, which is quite contrary to Pockels' theory, since this effect involves the coefficients r_{31}, r_{32}, r_{33}, all of which vanish for quartz.

535. Rochelle Salt. Principal refractive indices† $n_x = \gamma = 1.4954$; $n_y = \beta = 1.4920$; $n_z = \alpha = 1.4900$. Valasek's observations[543] indicate no great change in these values from $-70°$ to $+40°C$, but his observations were not sufficiently precise to record the small anomalies reported by Mueller.[376] The crystal is optically active: rotation of plane of polarization, for Na light, $1.35°/mm$ for each axis.‡ The a-, b-, c-axes of the Fresnel ellipsoid are parallel, respectively, to the Z, Y, X crystal axes. The plane of the optic axes is the XZ-plane (010), the X-axis being the acute bisectrix. The angle between the optic axes is $69°40'$ (Groth, for "yellow" light).

The electro-optic coefficients for crystals of this class (Class 6, symmetry V) are $a_{11} = a_0^2 = 1/\gamma^2$, $a_{22} = b_0^2 = 1/\beta^2$, $a_{33} = c_0^2 = 1/\alpha^2$, $a_{23} = r_{41}P_x$, $a_{31} = r_{52}P_y$, $a_{12} = r_{63}P_z$.

Just as the three piezoelectric coefficients for Rochelle salt have to do with *shears* with respect to the crystal axes, so in the *linear* electro-optic effect a field parallel to any one of the axes rotates the Fresnel ellipsoid slightly around this axis without affecting its shape. Since the principal axes of the ellipsoid coincide with the crystal axes, it follows that the refractive indices, for light parallel to any one of the axes, should remain unchanged.

For electric fields parallel to the Y- and Z-axes, and Na light, Pockels found $r_{52}\eta'_y = -5.1(10^{-8})$ and $r_{63}\eta'_z = +0.95(10^{-8})$. From §408 we may

---

* Günther's selection of data from Tsi-Ze's Table XI to compare with his own (and thereby to show that Tsi-Ze was in error) seems to be based on a misconception. The proper data to use are those in Table VII of Tsi-Ze; the discrepancy between the results of the two investigators is then greatly reduced. Günther also made a slight numerical error in the reduction of Pockels' observations.

† LANDOLT-BÖRNSTEIN, "Tabellen," 5th ed. At 20°, Na light.

‡ H. DUFET, *Jour. phys. rad.*, vol. 3, pp. 757–765, 1904.

call $\eta_y' = 0.70$, $\eta_z' = 0.65$. The two electro-optic constants are then $r_{52} = -7.3(10^{-8})$ and $r_{63} = +1.5(10^{-8})$; they include both the direct and the indirect effects. To calculate the indirect coefficient r_{52}' we must find a_{31} from Eqs. (551) for the piezoelectric strain z_x, remembering that for rhombic crystals $a_{31}^0 = 0$. Calling this value a_{31}', we have $r_{52}'P_y = a_{31}' = p_{55}z_x = p_{55}d_{25}E_y$, whence $r_{52}' = p_{55}d_{25}/\eta_y'$. Similarly,

$$r_{63}' = \frac{p_{66}d_{36}}{\eta_z'}$$

The values of p_{55} and p_{66} are given in §532, while for d_{25} and d_{36} we use the values from Eq. (207); we thus obtain $r_{52}' = -1.4(10^{-8})$,

$$r_{63}' = -0.8(10^{-8})$$

On subtracting these values from those of r_{52} and r_{63} above, there results for the direct effect $r_{52}'' = -5.9(10^{-8})$, $r_{63}'' = +2.3(10^{-8})$.

The fact that the electro-optic constant involves both the dielectric susceptibility and the piezoelectric constant makes the determination of r_{41} for Rochelle salt very inexact. The only recorded measurements are those of Pockels, who found $\eta_x'r_{41} = -6(10^{-8})$, a value of the same order of magnitude as r_{52} and r_{63}. An accurate determination of r_{41} and r_{41}' would demand the same careful attention to temperature control, suitable electrodes, and freedom from mechanical constraint as are needed for dielectric and piezoelectric investigations with this crystal. Without a knowledge of the exact conditions in Pockels' experiments, one can only guess that d_{14} was of the order of $500(10^{-8})$, in which case η' should be around 10. Using these values, one finds $r_{41} \sim -0.56(10^{-8})$ and $r_{41}' \sim -0.42(10^{-8})$. With considerable reservation the coefficient of the true electro-optic effect in Rochelle salt may be taken as

$$r_{41}'' = r_{41} - r_{41}' = -0.14(10^{-8}).$$

The indirect effect, expressed by r_{41}', is apparently very large. This conclusion agrees with Mueller's results, discussed in §536; qualitatively at least it agrees also with Mandell's findings.[326]

536. *The Quadratic Electro-optic Effect.* This is the well-known Kerr effect, which can occur in all substances. Among all crystals hitherto investigated Rochelle salt is the only one in which it amounts to more than a second-order effect. In this crystal the Kerr effect is about a million times greater than the electric double refraction in most liquids. A pronounced effect has recently been found with other Seignette-electrics (see §495).

This effect in Rochelle salt was first detected by Pockels. In his study of the linear effect, with the electric field in the X-direction and the light beam at 45° to the Y- and Z-axes, he found the magnitude of the electro-optic effect to be considerably different for opposite signs of field. In order to separate this apparently non-linear effect from the linear, he prepared an X-cut plate with two pairs of faces normal to the Y- and Z-axes of the crystal. He found that a field in the X-direction had a marked effect on the phase difference for light in the Y- and Z-directions. This effect did not reverse its sign with reversal of the field and was therefore interpreted as a quadratic, or Kerr, effect. The symmetry conditions for the Kerr effect are identical with those for the piezo-optic effect (relation of tensor to tensor) and permit a change in the refractive index along all three axes with the field parallel to one axis.

The Kerr effect in Rochelle salt has been very thoroughly studied by H. Mueller,[376,381] who found a close correlation between the optical and the dielectric properties, including the presence of hysteresis. His observations were made with the field in the X-direction. He observed the differences between refractive indices, $n_a - n_b$, $n_b - n_c$, or $n_c - n_a$, for light parallel to Z, X, or Y, as a function of field and temperature. The outstanding experimental results are as follows: (1) The order of magnitude with a field of 5,000 volts/cm is 0.1λ phase difference per centimeter path. (2) The effect does not change sign with the field. (3) It is quadratic in the field at temperatures well above the upper Curie point; complicated near the Curie points; roughly linear between the Curie points, except when the field is less than the coercive field E_c.

It has been pointed out by Jaffe[245] that this linear effect between the Curie points is to be regarded as a *true linear electro-optic effect* if Rochelle salt is accepted as being *monoclinic* in this range of temperature (§481). From this point of view the failure of the effect to reverse its sign with the field is due to a reversal of the crystallographic a-axis when the field changes sign, owing to the reversal of the domains.

In the earlier of his two papers Mueller's theoretical treatment was in terms of his internal-field theory. In the later paper[381] Mueller replaces his internal-field theory by the polarization theory (change in double refraction dependent on P_x rather than on F_x). He adopts in principle Jaffe's view that Rochelle salt is to be regarded as monoclinic in the Seignette-electric range, and by introducing the second power of the polarization he obtains expressions that satisfactorily describe the peculiarities in the dependence of the electro-optic effect upon temperature and electric field. Even in the absence of an external field he found, between the Curie points, a *spontaneous Kerr effect* due to the internal spontaneous polarization.*

---

* The experimental evidence of this effect is a bend, at each Curie point, in the curve relating birefringence to temperature.

Mueller gives evidence that the Kerr effect in unconstrained crystals of Rochelle salt is due in part, at least, to deformation (the piezo-optic effect).   The only measurements of the photoelastic constants of Rochelle salt are those of Pockels, on the assumption that the crystal is rhombic; they do not suffice for computing the piezo-optic contribution to the Kerr effect when the crystal is in the monoclinic form.

537. Extinction and Optical Activity.   *Determination of Axial Directions by Means of Optical Extinction.*   This method is useful for making a preliminary examination of irregular pieces of doubly refracting crystal and, within limits, for identifying axial directions.   It is applicable to all crystals except those of the cubic system.

In general, when a doubly refracting transparent crystal is viewed between crossed polarizer and analyzer, the field of view is more or less illuminated.   Except under certain special circumstances it is found, however, that when the specimen is rotated about the beam as an axis a minimum of illumination is encountered for every 90° of rotation, with maxima between.   In most practical cases, even with white light, the minima are regions of complete darkness; these are the extinction positions.   As we shall see, when white light is used, the emergent light for the intermediate positions may be colored.

It was shown in §527 that along any direction in the crystal two waves of different velocities may be propagated, the vibration directions being parallel to the major and minor axes of the ellipse in which the plane normal to the wave direction cuts the index ellipsoid at its center, and the two refractive indices being proportional to these axes.   It is when these vibration directions are parallel to those of the polarizer and analyzer that extinction occurs.   If the two indices happen to be equal, as is the case for light parallel to an optic axis in any crystal that is not optically active (§538), the field remains dark for all angular positions of the crystal.

If plane-polarized light of wavelength λ cm and intensity I_0 is incident normally on a plane-parallel plate of any orientation, whose thickness is e cm, the indices of refraction for light in the given direction being n_1 and n_2, then if polarizer and analyzer are crossed the emergent light has the intensity*

$$I = I_0 \sin^2 2\alpha \sin^2 \left[\pi \frac{e}{\lambda} (n_2 - n_1) \right]$$

where α is the angle between the vibration direction of the polarizer and that corresponding to n_1.   An inspection of this equation verifies the general statements made above, and in addition it shows that for

* Ref. B41, p. 213.

any α the illumination varies periodically as e is gradually increased. The variation of I with λ gives rise to the color effects mentioned above when white light is used. Very thin plates—the thickness depending on $(n_2 - n_1)$—fail to show color, because the phase difference between the two waves is too small. If the plate is sufficiently thick, the colors of different orders overlap to such an extent that the emergent light, except in positions of extinction, is sensibly white. With quartz plates parallel to the optic axis, colors are seen only for thicknesses less than a millimeter; with X-cut Rochelle-salt plates, the limiting values of thickness are about 0.2 mm and 3 mm.

Both quartz and Rochelle salt have *parallel extinction:* when the optic axis of quartz or any one of the three crystallographic axes of Rochelle salt is at right angles to the beam, extinction occurs when this axis is *parallel* to the vibration direction of either the polarizer or the (crossed) analyzer.

Extinction can be observed with entire crystals or irregular fragments; it can be used for finding approximately the directions (though not the sense) of the crystal axes. Its application to *quartz* is considered in §333. If a plate of *Rochelle salt* is known to be cut perpendicular to one of the crystal axes, extinction tests quickly give the approximate directions of the other two axes, since the field remains dark when either of the two is parallel or at right angles to the vibration direction of the polarizer. In general, one cannot by this test discriminate between the two axes without the use of auxiliary devices.

In one special case, at least, it is possible to make this discrimination. The author has observed that when a Rochelle-salt X-cut plate whose thickness is such as to show colors in white light between polaroids is rotated about the Y-axis away from the position in which the X-axis is parallel to the beam, the colors persist until the angle of rotation is almost 90°, whereas they disappear after about 20° when the rotation is about the Z-axis.

538. Optical Activity. This phenomenon, known also as "circular double refraction" and "rotatory polarization," is a special property of certain crystals, not derivable from the Fresnel ellipsoid. It is observed by means of an analyzer when plane-polarized light traverses the crystal parallel to the optic axis (or parallel to either of the two optic axes in biaxial crystals). If the velocities of the two oppositely circularly polarized rays into which the incident light can be resolved are appreciably different, the plane of polarization of the emergent light is found to be rotated by an amount depending on the *rotatory power* (angle in degrees per millimeter of path for some specified wavelength) and on the thickness of the specimen. If the incident light is white, the emergent light shows the well-known characteristic tints (rotatory dispersion, *i.e.*, variation of rotatory power with wavelength). The emergent light is not affected by rotation of the crystal about its optic axis.

Crystals belonging to 15 classes may be optically active.* They are all devoid of a center of symmetry; they are also all piezoelectric except one (cubic enantiomorphous hemihedral, symmetry O). Many crystals in these 15 classes, however, have an activity too small to be detected. All enantiomorphous crystals are optically active, the right and left forms rotating the plane of polarization in opposite directions.

From the molecular point of view there are two types of optically active crystals. One consists of individual molecules having no center of symmetry. If such a crystal is melted or dissolved, the liquid also shows circular double refraction; the sense of rotation depends on the solvent. Conversely, a compound whose melt or solution rotates the plane of polarization must crystallize in an enantiomorphous class (Pasteur's law). This first type is exemplified by Rochelle salt. The second type has molecules or ions of high individual symmetry, the low symmetry of the crystal being due to the lattice arrangement. α-quartz and $NaClO_3$ are examples of this type. From a solution of a left-crystal of $NaClO_3$, left- and right-crystals grow with equal probability.

In a right-crystal, the direction of rotation of the plane of polarization appears clockwise to an observer looking into the analyzer [against the beam (§326)]; this is also the direction in which the analyzer would have to be turned to keep the field dark if the thickness of the crystal were increased progressively, assuming the polarizer and analyzer to have been crossed initially.

Observations of the optical activity of quartz are useful for determining the direction of the optic axis in a plate and for detecting Brazilian twinning, as well as for distinguishing between right- and left-crystals. As stated in §15, optical tests can reveal only Brazilian (optical) twinning. Tests are best made in monochromatic light, for which a color screen is sufficient. Tests of quartz crystals by this method, and also in convergent light, are described in §333.

The *true* rotatory power of uniaxial crystals is found to be unaffected by *mechanical strain*. Nevertheless, under certain types of strain the *apparent* rotatory power is changed, but this effect is due to the fact that the crystal becomes biaxial under stress, so that there is double refraction in the direction of the original optic axis, in accordance with the laws of piezo-optics discussed above. The same effects would take place in inactive crystals. Herein lies the explanation of the optical effects recorded by Tawil (§368) for polarized light parallel to the optic axis in vibrating quartz plates. The operation of the author's "optically

* Ref. B41, p. 316.

controlled piezo oscillator" (§398) is also based on the double refraction induced by strain.

REFERENCES

BORN,[B7] GEIGER and SCHEEL,[B19] POCKELS,[B41] ROGERS and KERR,[B44] SOSMAN,[B47] TUTTON,[B48] WOOSTER,[B56] BOND,[64] GÜNTHER,[194] MUELLER,[376,377,381] TSI-ZE.[524]

BHAGAVANTAM, S.: Photo-elastic Effect in Crystals, *Proc. Indian Acad. Sci.*, vol. 16, pp. 359–365, 1942.

CHAPTER XXXI

PIEZOELECTRICITY IN THE LIGHT OF ATOMIC THEORY

Wenn nach der Entdeckung der Gebrüder Curie Deformationen von Kristallen elektrische Erregungen derselben bewirken, und wenn für dieselben, wie ich dargetan habe, je nach der Gruppe, welcher der Kristall angehört, höchst mannigfaltige Gezetze gelten, so ist damit für jede Theorie der Konstitution der Moleküle ein klares und fundamentales Problem aufgestellt. —Voigt.

In spite of the fact that molecular or atomic theories of piezoelectricity began to appear very soon after the Curies' discovery, a satisfactory theoretical treatment of the phenomenon can hardly be said to have passed the initial stage. The resources of modern lattice dynamics are still unequal to the task of predicting anything better than a rough approach to the order of magnitude of the piezoelectric effect, even for the simplest structures. Incomplete though the story is, however, it offers much of interest on both the theoretical and the experimental side.

The piezoelectric effect is, of course, intimately related to the general subject of crystal structure. We shall therefore consider first the atomic structures of some of the more important piezoelectric crystals, as revealed by X-rays, and then summarize such progress as has been made in accounting for the piezoelectric properties. References are given at the end of the chapter.

539. The Binding Forces in Crystals. For the present purpose, the chief types of chemical bond may be listed as follows:

1. *Ionic* bonds, also called *polar* or *heteropolar*. The substance is held together by the electrostatic Coulomb attraction between ions of opposite sign. Each positive ion is surrounded by negatives, and there are no individual molecules. If the substance is a crystalline solid, the entire crystal is to be regarded as a single molecule. An example is NaCl, in which the binding is entirely ionic. Many of the simpler minerals are of this type.

2. *Valence* bonds, also called *covalent* or *electron-pair*. The pair of electrons is shared between two electropositive or two electronegative atoms. With the former case, *viz.*, the metals, we are not concerned. Valence bonding between two electronegative atoms is called *homopolar* (or non-polar) bonding. These bonds have the property of saturation and tend to form discrete and stable molecules. For example, in organic compounds the carbon uses its four available valence electrons to hold four other atoms. Such compounds may take the form of chains, sheets, or three-dimensional structures of indefinitely large extent, as do also various minerals, silicates, and refractory materials.

3. *Van der Waals* bonds. Comparatively weak forces act between molecules, due to the mutual polarization of the molecules. If only forces of this type are present, the result is a gas, a liquid, or a mechanically weak solid of low melting point. Crystals thus bonded are called *molecular crystals*.

4. *Hydrogen bonds.* In recent years it has become recognized that two electronegative atoms may be bound by a single intervening hydrogen nucleus. The bond between the H^+ and each of the negative atoms is often ionic in character and is stronger the more electronegative the atoms are. This type of bond is present in many compounds, and it plays a part in the theory of such physical properties as melting and boiling points and the dielectric constant. Sometimes, as in ice, it is the only bonding agent.

Two or more different types of bond are very commonly present in the same substance. Both ionic and valence types are thought to be present in α-quartz (Wei, Pauling), while β-quartz is a purely ionic crystal. The part played by hydrogen bonds in the Seignette-electric phosphates is discussed below, as well as the problem of Rochelle salt.

Relations between Crystal Structure and Piezoelectric Properties. If the molecule is asymmetric, the crystal is likely to have the asymmetry necessary to make it piezoelectric. For example, if, as in tartaric acid or Rochelle salt, there are asymmetric C atoms in the molecule, the crystal must lack a center of symmetry. The only exception to this rule would be with such crystals as meso- or racemic tartaric acid, where the asymmetric atoms or molecules compensate one another.

Simple ionic salts cannot be expected to be piezoelectric, unless the radii of the constituent atoms are decidedly unlike.

Simple semipolar compounds (containing both ionic and valence bonds) tend to be piezoelectric. Crystals of the zinc blende type fall under this rule. Decidedly homopolar compounds (little or no ionic binding) often have highly symmetrical structures, for example the pyrite type. This subject is further discussed by Wooster.[B56]

We turn next to those features of the structure of quartz and of Rochelle salt that are related to the purpose of this book. For the X-ray methods used in determining the structures the reader may consult the references at the end of this chapter.

540. The Structure of Quartz. In 1914 W. H. Bragg published the first X-ray analysis of quartz and offered the hypothesis of the three interpenetrating lattices mentioned below. The first investigation of the relative positions of the atoms in α- and β-quartz by X-rays was that of Bragg and Gibbs (1925). This work was extended by Gibbs (1926) and especially by Wyckoff (1926), who completely determined the structural parameters of β-quartz. One such parameter is needed for β-quartz and four for α-quartz. References to the later determinations of the parameters are given at the end of the chapter.*

The space-groups for the two enantiomorphous forms of β-quartz are D_6^4 and D_6^5. For α-quartz they are D_3^4 and D_3^6.

---

* An excellent account of the work of Bragg and Gibbs, with diagrams, is given by Sosman.[B47]

The crystallization of SiO_2 in three principal forms, as quartz (including the α- and β-modifications), tridymite, and cristobalite, has been mentioned in §10. All three forms have the same basic structure, *viz.*, a tetrahedral group of four oxygen atoms with a silicon atom in the center. The arrangement of the groups is what distinguishes one form from another. Our interest is in α-quartz and β-quartz. In each of these modifications the structure is based on three interpenetrating hexagonal lattices.

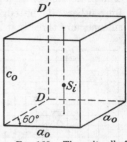

In order to visualize this type of crystal architecture we start with the unit cell of one of the three component lattices, as illustrated in Fig. 160. The unit cell has the form of a right prism of height c_0, having as its base a 60° rhombus. The vertical edges are parallel to the principal (Z-) axis, while the sides of the base are parallel to two X-axes. It contains one Si and two O atoms. We have

Fig. 160.—The unit cell of α- and β-quartz, with one of the three silicon atoms.

arbitrarily placed the Si atom at a distance $c_0/3$ above the center of the base, in order to make it fit into the final scheme. The positions of the oxygens will be considered later.

Suppose cells of this type to be packed regularly in all three dimensions, forming a lattice. A projection on the basal plane, viewed from

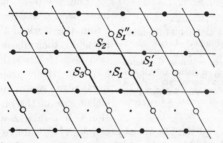

Fig. 161.—Projection, on a plane perpendicular to the optic axis, of the three interpenetrating hexagonal simple lattices, showing the silicon atoms in the configuration for β-quartz.

above, will look like Fig. 161, in which the projection of each unit cell has at its center a silicon atom, indicated by a small dot S_1, corresponding to Si in Fig. 160. The entire array of S_1 dots has hexagonal symmetry, forming a hexagonal lattice. Now imagine two other lattices identical with the first, but rotated about one of the prismatic edges, say DD' in Fig. 160, by 120° and −120°, respectively. In Fig. 161, the axis of rotation may be taken as perpendicular to the paper. In the projection, the Si atoms will appear in the positions shown by the large dots S_1' and the open circles S_1''. Then let these two lattices be displaced vertically, the first downward by $c_0/3$ and the other upward by the same distance (we anticipate by remarking that the result will be right- or left-quartz according to which of the two lattices is displaced upward). The projection of each unit cell now has, in addition to a Si at its center, four others at the edges, located at two different levels. Of the five silicons, any three that are at different levels may be selected as belonging

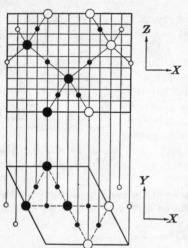

to the unit cell. We choose arbitrarily the three marked S_1, S_2, and S_3 for the cell indicated by heavy lines; the other two silicons then belong to adjacent cells, although bonded to certain oxygens in the indicated cell.

The final structure is the interpenetrating hexagonal lattice system characteristic of β-quartz. The unit cell of the complete structure still has the form and dimensions shown in Fig. 160, but it now contains three Si and six O atoms, as indicated in Fig. 162.

The positions of the O atoms have been a matter of uncertainty. From the work of Wei and of Machatschki their most probable location is as follows: For both α- and β-quartz their projections on the basal plane are at distances $a_0/4$ on either side of the Si, in the a_0-direction. In β-quartz, which has hexagonal symmetry, all the O's are at multiples of $c_0/6$ above the basal plane, as shown in Fig. 162.

FIG. 162.—The unit cell of β-quartz, in elevation and plan. Large black circles are silicons belonging to this cell, the basal outline of which is the outer rhombus. Large open circles are silicons from some of the adjacent cells. Small black circles are oxygens belonging to this cell; small open circles are oxygens from adjacent cells.

Bragg and Gibbs showed that the structural change at the α-β point, to which the crystallographic and physical differences between β- and α-quartz are due, involves only small displacements of the atoms. The movement of the Si atoms is about 0.3 Å. The corresponding modification of Fig. 162 to make it represent the unit cell of α-quartz requires rotating adjacent triangles of Si atoms, as seen in the basal projection in Fig. 162, in opposite directions by about 8° in the plane of the paper. In the upper portion of Fig. 162 the oxygens at the left of the center are raised by $c_0/18$; those at the right of the center are lowered by $c_0/18$. The hexagonal symmetry of β-quartz thus becomes changed to the trigonal symmetry of α-quartz. The dimensions of the unit cell also undergo a slight alteration. For α-quartz there have been two recent determinations. According to Bradley and Jay, $a_0 = 4.90288$ Å, $c_0 = 5.39328$ Å; Miller and Du Mond* found

$$a_0 = 4.91267 \pm 0.00009 \text{ Å}$$

and $c_0 = 5.40459 \pm 0.00011$ Å, at 25°C. For β-quartz, Wyckoff found $a_0 = 5.01$ Å, $c_0 = 5.47$ A.

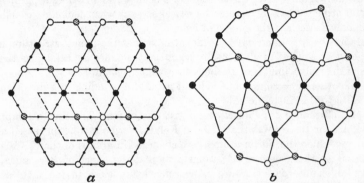

Fig. 163.—Projection, on a plane perpendicular to the optic axis, of the lattices of β-quartz (a) and α-quartz (b), adapted from Bragg and Gibbs.

The complete lattice for β-quartz is shown in projection in Fig. 163a, in which the outline of the unit cell is indicated by dotted lines. Considering three layers of silicon atoms in planes parallel to the paper, we represent the atoms in the first, or lowest, layer (farthest from the observer) by large open circles and those in the third, or uppermost, layer by large black circles. The intermediate layer is indicated by shaded circles. The oxygen atoms are in layers between the silicon atoms. Each oxygen is bonded to the two nearest silicons. Each Si is bonded to four oxygens, two above and two below it. These latter are the four oxygen atoms that form the tetrahedral group referred to above. This interconnecting of all the tetrahedra produces a three-dimensional framework of great rigidity.

In Fig. 163b is the corresponding projection for α-quartz, in which only the Si atoms are represented. The structure is now symmetrical about the X-axis, but no longer about the Y-axis. The X-axis has become a polar axis, and the crystal has acquired the piezoelectric constants d_{11}, d_{12}, and d_{26}.

If the layers of atoms are considered as continued indefinitely in the

* P. H. MILLER, JR., and J. W. M. DU MOND, *Phys. Rev.*, vol. 57, pp. 198–206, 1940.

direction perpendicular to the paper, it becomes evident from Fig. 162 that all the silicons appearing in the projection at the vertices of any one of the small triangles in Fig. 163 form a helix with axis parallel to the principal axis of the crystal. The crystal is of the left or right form according to whether or not the helix advances in the direction of a right-handed screw. The structure shown in Fig. 162 is that for *right*-quartz, since to an observer looking down at the paper the helix appears to wind in a clockwise direction. This statement corresponds to the fact that in a left-quartz the rotation of a beam of polarized light parallel to the principal axis is counterclockwise, as seen when looking through the analyzer toward the source of light.

It has been pointed out by Machatschki that the helical structure is revealed in a more fundamentally significant manner by taking as the axis of the helix a line through the center of a *hexagon* in Fig. 163. About this axis there is a continuous helix of *tetrahedra*, winding in a direction opposite to the silicon helix.

541. *Theory of the Piezoelectric Effect in Quartz.* The first attempt at an atomic theory was that of Lord Kelvin,[256] who in 1893 proposed a model in which the silicon atoms were clustered in groups of three. His guess as to the geometrical arrangement and the effect of mechanical pressure on internal structure came remarkably close to the facts as revealed by X-rays thirty years later. The probable seat of the piezoelectric effect was considered by Bragg and Gibbs (1925) and by Gibbs (1926) on the basis of their X-ray investigations. They express the view that mechanical pressure in the X- or Y-direction distorts the triangles shown in Fig. 163b, resulting in a polarization parallel to X. Gibbs attempted an estimate of the magnitude of the effect, assuming quartz to be an ionic crystal containing effective dipoles. Such an estimate is necessarily defective, since quartz is no longer considered to be purely ionic. Nevertheless, Gibbs arrived at the right order of magnitude. His analysis of the pyroelectric effect in quartz suffers from the failure to discriminate between secondary and tertiary pyroelectricity.

542. The Structure of Rochelle Salt. The complete crystal structure has been determined by Beevers and Hughes, by applying Fourier and Patterson methods to their X-ray observations. The original paper should be consulted for details and for the diagram showing a projection of the structure on the (001) plane. The unit cell contains four molecules. The structure does not change perceptibly on passing through the Curie points, since at these points it is only hydrogen nuclei that change their positions. Of present interest is the conjecture of Beevers and Hughes concerning the origin of the anomalies, which they attribute to repeated zigzag chains containing O (or OH) and H_2O groups, running in the X-direction.

From their discussion one may draw the following conclusions: The peculiar dielectric properties are attributed to the effect of the impressed electric field on the chains; in particular, the normal direction of the bonds can be *reversed* by a field in the proper direction.   The disappearance of the anomalies outside the Curie points is thought to be due to a breaking of some of the contacts in the chains.

These authors do not mention the spontaneous polarization.   Indeed, their diagram pictures adjacent chains in the unit cell as polarized in opposite directions.   One can extend their reasoning by following Jaffe's suggestion[245] that the unit cell is orthorhombic outside the Curie points and, if isolated, would remain orthorhombic between these points.   Between the Curie points each unit cell in a domain tends to become polarized and slightly deformed under the influence of neighboring cells.   In the Seignette-electric region a majority of the chains in a given domain become polarized the same way, just as in the Kurchatov and Fowler theories dipoles were supposed to become rotated into parallelism.   The existence of a spontaneous polarization and its dependence on temperature could thus be accounted for.

If these views are accepted, it is possible still to apply in substance Mueller's internal-field theory given in Chap. XXVI.   A function corresponding to the Langevin function can still be used, with the dipoles quantized in the X-direction.

The space-group of Rochelle salt is V.   The *unit cell* is orthorhombic, containing four molecules.   The unit cell has the following dimensions according to Beevers and Hughes: $a_0 = 11.93$ Å, $b_0 = 14.30$ Å, $c_0 = 6.17$ Å.   These values may be compared with those of Warren and Krutter, who found $a_0 = 11.85$ Å, $b_0 = 14.25$ Å, $c_0 = 6.21$ Å. From these data the axial ratio is $a:b:c = 0.8343:1:0.4315$ according to Beevers and Hughes and $0.8316:1:0.4358$ according to Warren and Krutter.   From Staub's X-ray measurements* we find

$$a:b:c = 0.8317:1:0.4330$$

The mean value of the axial ratio, from the three sources just mentioned, is

$$a:b:c = \mathbf{0.8325:1:0.4334}$$

The value given in Groth[B22] is $0.8317:1:0.4296$.

Further X-ray Investigations on Rochelle Salt.   Kirkpatrick and Ross† conclude that Rochelle-salt crystals have a very uniform structure, since the rocking curve widths are as narrow as those of high-grade calcite. Staub and Német have studied the effects of an electric field on X-ray

---

* H. STAUB, *Helv. Phys. Acta*, vol. 7, pp. 3–45, 1934.

† P. KIRKPATRICK and P. A. ROSS, *Phys. Rev.*, vol. 43, pp. 596–600, 1933.

intensities by the Bragg method, and Staub also measured intensities at different temperatures.* Staub found that, between the Curie points, the reflections from the (111) plane (parallel to any one of the faces marked *o* in Fig. 2) were increased by about 10 per cent when a field of the order of 500 volts/cm was applied. In stronger fields the effect was absent, owing, as Staub thought, to the destruction of the lattice by the field. The change in intensity was not altered when the crystal was vibrated in resonance (see §261).

Német's observations were made with reflections from faces normal to the X-, Y-, and Z-axes. In each case fields up to 700 volts/cm parallel to all three axes were applied. All observations were at room temperature. In all cases the curves relating intensity to field strength showed saturation and, at the strongest fields, a tendency for the intensity to decrease with increasing field, in agreement with Staub. The effect was most pronounced at the (100) faces, where the maximum increase in intensity amounted to as much as 40 per cent. Endwise pressure on an X-cut 45° plate did not affect the intensity of the reflections. The great sensitiveness of Rochelle salt to an electric field stands in sharp contrast to quartz, which Német found to give negative results, and ice, which showed an increase in intensity of 2 or 3 per cent in a field of 1,300 volts/cm.

Staub investigated the change in intensity of reflection from the (111) plane over a wide range of temperatures in the absence of an external field.† Between the Curie points the intensity increased by about 10 per cent. Staub regarded this effect as evidence for the existence of a large internal field, which stabilized the lattice against the effect of thermal agitation. For his theoretical treatment, based on Debye's theory, the original papers should be consulted.

543. A complete discussion of the dielectric and piezoelectric properties of Rochelle salt in terms of the Beevers-Hughes model would require accounting for all three of the piezoelectric constants d_{14}, d_{25}, and d_{36}. In this connection it is of interest to consider a model of the arrangement of dipoles in the unit cell as conceived by Staub,[479] at a time when Rochelle salt was thought to contain free dipoles.‡ This model is shown in Fig. 164; it is applicable to all rhombic crystals of the digonal holoaxial class and has the simplest distribution of charges compatible with this type of symmetry. While it offers a simple qualitative interpretation of the piezoelectric and dielectric effects in Rochelle salt, it is only a model, and as such must be taken *cum*

* H. Staub, *Physik. Z.*, vol. 34, pp. 292–296, 1933, vol. 35, pp. 720–725, 1934; *Helv. Phys. Acta*, vol. 7, pp. 3–45, 480–482, 1934. A. Német, *Helv. Phys. Acta*, vol. 8, pp. 97–116, 117–151, 1935.

† See also S. Miyake, *Proc. Phys.-Math. Soc. Japan*, vol. 23, pp. 378–395, 1941.

‡ For earlier treatment of the "electric axes" of Rochelle salt see Riecke, in Graetz, vol. 1, also W. G. Hankel and H. Lindenberg, *Z. Krist.*, vol. 27, pp. 515–517, 1897.

grano salis (tartari natronati). Four dipoles in the directions of the diagonals are assumed, the positive direction of each being indicated by an arrow. Upon application of mechanical stress or of an electric field the dipoles become rotated.

Outside the Curie points the effects of the dipoles, subject to thermal agitation, neutralize one another so that there is no permanent resultant polarization of the cell. Compression along any one of the axes produces no polarization at any temperature. But a compression applied *diagonally* in a plane perpendicular to any axis causes a polarization parallel to that axis. For example, let the compression be such as to bring the edges EH and BC closer together. This causes a shearing strain, and the deformation is the same as if the face $EFGH$ were slid parallel to itself in the direction EF. The originally rectangular faces $ABFE$ and $OCGH$ become parallelograms, and the dipoles become rotated in such a way as to polarize the cell in the

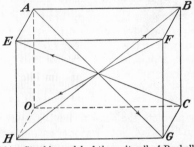

FIG. 164.—Staub's model of the unit cell of Rochelle salt.

direction OA, the face $ABFE$ having a positive polarization charge. This describes the direct piezoelectric effect for which the equation is $P_x = d_{14}Y_z$ (d_{14} is positive, and the stress Y_z is positive when the strain, as assumed above, is positive). According to the *converse* effect, it is evident from the figure that a field applied in the direction from O to A will rotate the dipoles so as to cause a positive shearing strain in the YZ-plane. The freer the dipoles are to rotate, the greater will be the dielectric constant.

In reality, the relation between strain and positions of the dipoles cannot be as simple as this. For example, the symmetry in Fig. 164 is such that the three coefficients d_{14}, d_{25}, and d_{36} all ought to have the same sign. Pockels found that d_{14} and d_{36} are both positive but that d_{25} is *negative*. This can be "explained" only by assuming the configuration of atoms in the cell, and the forces between them, to be such that a positive shearing strain in the ZX-plane is associated with a *negative* polarization along the Y-axis, or else by attributing the effect to interactions between adjacent cells.

In order to reconcile the model with the properties of Rochelle salt between the Curie points one may postulate that the configurations of the cells and their mutual interactions are such that there is a tendency for the dipoles to become aligned more or less closely along the X-axis instead of along the diagonals. Then, when the temperature is sufficiently low, spontaneous polarization sets in, accompanied by a spontaneous strain. This takes the form of a shear y_z and is the ground for the view advanced in §481 that in the region of spontaneous polarization Rochelle salt should properly be classified as monoclinic rather than orthorhombic. The spontaneous strain, however, is so small that the structure as revealed by X-rays appears orthorhombic at all temperatures.

The same model can be used to illustrate the longitudinal effect when the field is oblique to all three axes (§140).   For example, if a compression is applied along *OF*, the strain will rotate the dipoles so as to produce a polarization in the *FO*-direction.

544. The Structure of Primary Potassium Phosphate, KH₂PO₄.

544. The Structure of Primary Potassium Phosphate, KH_2PO_4.   An X-ray analysis of this crystal was made in 1930 by West,[*] who found phosphate groups consisting of a phosphorus atom tetrahedrally surrounded by four oxygens.   Each group is surrounded tetrahedrally by four other groups.   Neighboring PO_4 groups are connected by hydrogen bonds.

Recently, this analysis has been further treated by Slater,[†] by the use of statistical methods.   He considers the possible arrangements of the H atoms, finding that each phosphate group is likely to have two of its neighboring hydrogens close to it, forming $(H_2PO_4)^-$ dipoles.   At low temperatures, in the state of lowest energy the dipoles tend to become oriented one way or the other along the *c*- (*Z*-) axis, thus accounting for the spontaneous polarization.   Above the Curie point (*cf.* §445), the dipoles assume random orientations.   Slater derives an expression for the dielectric susceptibility at small fields, indicating a Curie-Weiss law.

Slater's theory predicts that the transition at the Curie point is a phase change of the first kind, with latent heat and a discontinuous jump from the polarized state at low temperatures to the unpolarized state at higher temperatures.   On the other hand, the experiments recorded in §497 indicate that the transition, while confined to a narrow temperature range, is not abrupt.   Slater considers that the discrepancy between theory and experiment is due to the fact that the theory—like the fundamental theory of Rochelle salt treated in Chaps. XXIII and XXIV—applies only to the individual domain.   As the temperature falls below the Curie point, the crystal breaks up into many domains, with opposing polarizations and opposing spontaneous shearing stresses in adjacent domains.   The result is the appearance of stresses of varying magnitude at the boundaries between domains, which tend to lower the transition point by varying amounts, thus giving a continuous transition process instead of an abrupt change.   In explaining that the transition is trying to be one of the first kind, Slater points to the fact that the analogous transitions in potassium arsenate and in ammonium phosphate are much sharper than in potassium phosphate.

From his observations on the specific heats of KH_2AsO_4, KH_2PO_4, and KD_2PO_4, Bantle[22] finds changes in entropy at the upper Curie points of the order of magnitude predicted by Slater's theory.   Accepting the O—H—O combination as the dipole responsible for the Seignette-

[*] J. WEST, *Z. Krist.*, vol. 74, pp. 306–332, 1930.   See also M. Avrami, *Phys. Rev.*, vol. 54, pp. 300–303, 1938.

[†] J. C. Slater, *J. Chem. Phys.*, vol. 9, p. 16, 1941.

electric properties and assuming two dipoles per molecule, Bantle calculates for the molecular electric moment μ the value $0.74(10^{-18})$.

545. Atomic Theories of Piezoelectricity. The theory of the piezoelectric effect is a part of the theory of the solid state. This subject is much too large for treatment here. We can only point out some of the historical milestones in the journey, which is still far from complete.

Prior to the discovery of piezoelectricity, the molecular theory of pyroelectricity had been the object of much speculation (see references at the end of Chap. XXIX). One contribution was made by *J. and P. Curie* themselves,[*] following Lord Kelvin's suggestion of permanently polarized molecules.

Lord Kelvin's theory of piezoelectricity (1893) has already been referred to in §541. He made a rough quantitative estimate of the piezoelectric effect, based on the assumption that the potential differences between molecules are of the same order as the macroscopic contact potentials between different metals. He thus calculated a value of d_{11} for quartz of the right order of magnitude.

At about the same time Riecke (in 1892) published a somewhat elaborate molecular theory of piezoelectricity for crystals of all symmetries (see Graetz[†]). He assumed the piezoelectric effect to be due to a change in electric Coulomb interaction between molecules, brought about by a mechanical deformation of the crystal lattice. In the light of the later investigations described below, this theory must now be regarded as obsolete. It was an ingenious theory, involving five types of "pole systems" to account for the piezoelectric constants of all classes of crystals. His pole system for crystals of symmetry V led to a model like that of Staub shown in Fig. 164.

An advance more in step with the progress of modern physics was made by *Schrödinger* in 1912. He extended Debye's kinetic theory of dielectrics to anisotropic solids. While his paper has to do mainly with melting points, it discusses piezo- and pyroelectricity as well, with particular reference to quartz and tourmaline, and at some points it has a bearing on the theory of ferroelectrics. His estimate of d_{11} for quartz is of the right order of magnitude. By the use of an approximate Langevin function he reaches the right order of magnitude for the pyroelectric constant of tourmaline. The chief weakness in his theory lies in his assumption of freely rotating dipoles in all crystals.

The theory of piezo- and pyroelectricity was also discussed in 1921 by *Larmor*. The chief importance of this paper for us lies in the emphasis on the correct treatment of the *surface layer* for the piezo- and pyroelectric

---

[*] J. and P. CURIE, *Compt. rend.*, vol. 92, p. 350, 1881; *Jour. phys.* (2), vol. 1, p. 245, 1882.

[†] Ref. B20, vol. 1, 1918.

effects. Born (see below) deals only with the infinite lattice, ignoring the conditions at the surface. Larmor's theory indicates that it is not necessary to postulate a spontaneous polarization in order to account for the pyroelectric effect. He points out that, if the positive and negative ionic charges in the crystal are not uniformly spaced, a change in temperature will alter their relative spacing. Although this alteration is very minute, it is sufficient to account for the observed surface charges. without the existence of a permanent internal polarization. The charge observed on a freshly fractured surface depends on whether more positive or more negative ions are exposed.

Larmor goes so far as to doubt the existence of a spontaneous polarization in any crystal. Without accepting this thesis, one may at least grant that if there are crystals possessing a spontaneous polarization, as seems well established, for example, in the case of Rochelle salt, still the amount of charge observed on a freshly fractured surface may be modified to a considerable extent by the precise position of the fractured surface with respect to the crystal lattice. This possibility has been pointed out in §519 in the case of tourmaline.

The same consideration also suggests an explanation of the author's failure to detect a charge on the freshly fractured surfaces of a bar of Rochelle salt, the length of which was in the X-direction.

546. *The Piezoelectric Effect According to Lattice Dynamics.* Modern atomic dynamics had its beginning at the hands of Madelung in 1909. In 1912 the first work of M. Born appeared, in collaboration with Th. v. Kármán, on vibrations in space-lattices. Born's first treatment of the piezoelectric and pyroelectric effects was in his "Dynamik der Kristall-gitter" in 1915. Eight years later came the "Atomtheorie des festen Zustandes," in which the treatment was extended and simplified. The chapter on the dynamic lattice theory of crystals by Born and Goeppert-Mayer in the second edition of the "Handbuch der Physik"[B19] is practically a new edition of the "Atomtheorie."

Born's theory assumes pure central forces between the atom centers. Considering the advances that have been made in atomic dynamics in more recent years, it is remarkable that his piezoelectric computations could lead even to an approach to the right order of magnitude.

Only for very simple lattices did Born find it possible to make a quantitative estimate of the relation between strain and electric field. He applied his theory to crystals of the cubic system having a diagonal lattice, in which all the particles lie on diagonals of the unit cube. An example of this structure is zinc blende, ZnS, symmetry T_d (see §170). Crystals of this symmetry have only one independent piezoelectric constant, $e_{14} = e_{25} = e_{36}$. For such a structure Born found the following relation between e_{14}, the dielectric constant k at low frequency, k_0 at optical frequencies $(k_0 = n^2)$, and the elastic constants c_{12} and c_{44}:

$$e_{14}^2 = \frac{k - k_0}{4\pi} (c_{12} - c_{44}) \frac{c_{44}}{c_{12}}$$

For ZnS, Born thus calculated $e_{14} \sim -23(10^4)$ esu, about five times greater than the observed value of $-4.2(10^4)$ recorded in §170. At Born's suggestion, Heckmann in 1925 attempted to improve the theory by considering the polarizability of the ions, but the numerical value of e_{14} for ZnS was not improved thereby. Further advances in atomic dynamics must be awaited before agreement can be expected between the theoretical and experimental values of the piezoelectric constant.

In general the piezoelectric stress constant e_{hk} may be considered as of more fundamental significance than the strain constant d_{hk}. Not only is it the constant given by the atomic theory, but it relates mechanical to electric stress in the equation $X_k = -e_{hk}E_h$ and mechanical to electric strain in the equation $P_h = e_{hk}x_k$. Moreover, as has been shown in §474, in Rochelle salt e_{14} remains finite at all temperatures, instead of becoming infinite at the Curie points, as is the case with the piezoelectric strain constant.

REFERENCES

No attempt has been made to compile a complete list of references on matters treated in this chapter. Those references have been selected which were most useful in the preparation of the chapter.

BRAGG,[B8] DAVEY,[B14] GEIGER and SCHEEL,[B19] SOSMAN.[B47]

KELVIN, LORD: "Baltimore Lectures," C. J. Clay & Sons, London, 1904; "Mathematical and Physical Papers," vol. 5, Cambridge University Press, London, 1911; *Phil. Mag.*, vol. 36, pp. 331, 342, 384, 414, 453, 1893.

PAULING, L.: "The Nature of the Chemical Bond," Cornell University Press, Ithaca, N.Y., 1939.

BEEVERS and HUGHES,[48] BRAGG and GIBBS,[75] GIBBS,[157] LARMOR,[308] WARREN and KRUTTER.[579]

BRADLEY, A. J., and A. H. JAY: Quartz as a Standard for Accurate Lattice-spacing Measurements, *Proc. Phys. Soc. (London)*, vol. 45, pp. 507–522, 1933.

BRILL, R., C. HERMANN, and C. PETERS: X-ray Fourier Synthesis of Quartz, *Ann. Physik*, vol. 41, pp. 233–244, 1942.

HECKMANN, G.: On the Lattice Theory of Deformable Ions, *Z. Physik*, vol. 31, pp. 219–223, 1925; *Z. Krist.*, vol. 61, pp. 250–292, 1925.

HYLLERAAS, E. A.: Gleichgewichtslage der Atome, Doppelbrechung und Optisches Drehungsvermögen von β-Quarz, *Z. Physik*, vol. 44, pp. 871–886, 1927.

MACHATSCHKI, F.: Die Kristallstruktur von Tiefquarz SiO_2 und Aluminiumorthoarsenat $AlAsO_4$, *Z. Krist.*, vol. 94, pp. 222–230, 1936.

MAUGUIN, C.: Possible Use of Diffraction Patterns from X-rays for the Complete Determination of the Structure of Quartz, *Compt. rend*, vol. 173, pp. 719–724, 1921.

SCHRÖDINGER, E.: Studien über Kinetik der Dielektrika, den Schmelzpunkt, Pyro- und Piezoelektrizität, *Sitzber. Akad. Wiss. Wien, Math.-naturw. Klasse*, vol. 121, pp. 1937*f.*, 1912.

SLATER, J. C.: Theory of Transition in KH_2PO_4, *Jour. Chem. Phys.*, vol. 9, pp. 16-33, 1941.

UBBELOHDE, A. R., and I. WOODWARD: Isotope Effect in Potassium Dihydrogen Phosphate, *Nature*, vol. 144, p. 632, 1939.

WEI, P'EI-HSIU: Structure of α-Quartz, *Z. Krist.*, vol. 92, pp. 355–362, 1935.

WYCKOFF, R. W. G.: The Crystal Structure of the High Temperature (β-) Modification of Quartz, *Am. Jour. Sci.*, vol. 11, pp. 101–112, 1926; Kriterien für Hexagonale Raumgruppen und die Kristallstruktur von β-Quarz, *Z. Krist.*, vol. 63, pp. 507–537. 1926.

APPENDIX I

FERROMAGNETISM

547. In the discussion of the properties of Rochelle salt and of the other Seignette electrics in Chaps. XX to XXVII, there is frequent reference to the analogies that exist between these dielectric phenomena and the magnetic properties of such substances as iron. As a background for this discussion the pertinent features of the theory of paramagnetism and ferromagnetism are here summarized.* Emphasis will be laid especially on the dependence of magnetic properties upon temperature, with particular reference to the Curie point, and upon the nature of those minute regions of spontaneous magnetization known as *domains*. Some of the effects of mechanical strain upon magnetism will be considered, as well as magnetic hysteresis. For more complete details of ferromagnetic theory the references cited in the footnote may be consulted.

Following the early theory of Weber, and Ewing's successful attempt at a qualitative explanation of residual magnetism and hysteresis by means of his model of small elementary magnets, the basis for the mathematical formulation was laid by H. A. Lorentz's equations for the internal field (§113), which are applicable equally to dielectric and magnetic substances. In the meantime P. Curie had experimentally established the law relating the susceptibility of paramagnetics to temperature (now known as Curie's law) and had made his famous study of the temperature of transition from the ferromagnetic to the paramagnetic state (the Curie point), which for iron is around 770°C.

The Curie law in its original form expressed the relation between mass susceptibility k_m and absolute temperature T by the equation $k_m = C/T$, C being a constant.† With many substances it has been found that the relation is given more precisely by $k_m = C/(T - \theta)$, where for paramagnetic materials the constant θ has a small positive or negative value. A positive θ implies the possibility of a ferromagnetic state; in the ferromagnetic metals θ has relatively large positive values.

548. *Paramagnetism.* The modern theory of paramagnetism is due chiefly to Langevin. By his method the degree of magnetization of a paramagnetic substance is expressed in terms of the ratio $\bar{\mu}/\mu$, where μ is the magnetic moment of the elementary dipole and $\bar{\mu}$ the average component of μ in the direction of the applied field.‡ From classical statistical mechanics Langevin found an expression for $\bar{\mu}/\mu$

---

* For the theory of ferromagnetism see, for example, F. Bitter, "Introduction to Ferromagnetism," New York, 1937; R. M. Bozorth, *Bell System Tech. Jour.*, vol. 15, pp. 63–91, 1936; F. Bloch, in "Handbuch der Radiologie," 2d ed., vol. 6, part 2, Leipzig, 1934; E. C. Stoner, "Magnetism and Matter," London, 1934, or "Magnetism," London, 1936; R. Becker, "Theorie der Elektrizität," vol. 2, Leipzig, 1933.

† Custom sanctions the use of the symbol k for *volume susceptibility*, defined as (magnetic moment per unit volume)/(field strength). The Curie law is usually expressed in terms of *mass susceptibility*, designated as $\chi = k/\rho$. Since in this book the symbol χ is employed for the reciprocal of the dielectric susceptibility, we shall designate the magnetic mass susceptibility by k_m.

‡ The symbol μ must not be confused with magnetic *permeability*, a quantity for which no symbol will be needed in this discussion.

as a function of the quantity $\mu F/KT$. The numerator of this quantity is a measure of the directive effect of the molecular field F acting on the dipole, while the denominator ($K = 1.37 \times 10^{-16}$ erg deg^{-1} = Boltzmann constant; T = absolute temperature) measures the tendency of the dipoles to be kept in a state of disorder by thermal agitation. With paramagnetic substances under all ordinary conditions, F is practically identical with the impressed field H.

Writing a for $\mu F/KT$, we have Langevin's equation for paramagnetism, in which the symbol L is used to denote the Langevin function:

$$\frac{I}{I_0} = \frac{\bar{\mu}}{\mu} = L(a) = \coth a - \frac{1}{a} \tag{556}$$

where $I_0 = N\mu$ is the saturation value of the intensity of magnetization $I = N\bar{\mu}$ (magnetic moment per unit volume); N is the number of dipoles per cubic centimeter. Equation (556) is valid for both para- and ferromagnetic substances and also for dielectrics. It is represented graphically in Fig. 165.

If $a << 1$, as is usually the case with paramagnetic substances, (556) may be written in the approximate form

$$\frac{I}{I_0} = \frac{\bar{\mu}}{\mu} \approx \tfrac{1}{3}a - \tfrac{1}{45}a^3 \tag{556a}$$

The small magnitude of a means that in paramagnetic phenomena, at least at ordinary fields and temperatures, the effect of thermal agitation is large in comparison with the magnetic directive force. Under extremely large fields Eq. (556) and Fig. 165 indicate an approach to saturation. This effect has been detected in gadolinium sulphate.

It is important to point out that the form of the Langevin function in Eqs. (556) and (556a) is based on the assumption that in the absence of an external field all orientations of dipoles are equally probable. When the spatial quantization of dipole directions is considered, this assumption is no longer valid and the function has to be modified. We shall revert to this in §552. So far as the general outline of ferromagnetic theory is concerned, it suffices to consider the Langevin function in its original form.

549. *Ferromagnetism.* Langevin's paramagnetic theory was applied by Debye in his treatment of electric dipoles. We come now to the contributions of Weiss, whose theory of ferromagnetism, combined with Debye's dipole theory, has become the basis of the theory of Rochelle salt.

Langevin's original theory has to do only with feebly magnetizable substances, in which it is assumed that the magnetic dipoles do not interact, but, like the molecules of a gas, are free to rotate in the field H, while subject also to thermal agitation. The theory requires that the magnetic susceptibility increase indefinitely with decreasing temperature—a requirement that is met experimentally, at least until very low temperatures are reached. The chief problems that confronted Weiss were to account for the high magnetizability of ferromagnetic materials and for the existence of the high Curie temperature, at which the material passes from the ferromagnetic to the paramagnetic state. He made the radical assumption that the effective magnetic field strength F acting upon the elementary magnetic particle is given by the equation

$$F = H + \gamma I \tag{557}$$

in which γ, the *Weiss molecular field constant*, instead of being of the order of $4\pi/3$, as in dielectrics (§113) or in diamagnetic substances, has a value of several thousand.

In ferromagnetic theory γ is sometimes considered as having different values in different directions in the crystal. It is shown in §485 that the same is true of Rochelle salt. For the present purpose we may disregard the possible anisotropy of γ.

The value of F under ordinary conditions is determined chiefly by the second term, which is proportional to the intensity of magnetization I already present.* The coefficient γ has the same value in both the para- and ferromagnetic ranges.

The requirement that γ must be large follows from the high polarization produced in ferromagnetic materials by applied fields of ordinary magnitude. It is evident that such fields must be able to align the magnetic dipoles to a very considerable degree. This is possible only if, in the Langevin parameter a, the quantity μF is not too small in comparison with KT. Taking iron as an example, we may assign to μ the order of magnitude 2 (10^{-20}). Since at room temperature $KT = 4$ (10^{-14}) ergs, it follows that F must be of the order of magnitude of 2 (10^6) oersteds. On substituting this value in Eq. (557), together with the representative value 2,000 for I (H being relatively small), we see that γ must be at least of the order of 1,000.

This abnormally large value of γ remained without theoretical justification until in 1928 Heisenberg explained it as due to exchange forces analogous to those which occur in the theory of molecular binding. The ultimate magnetic particle is assumed to be the spinning electron, which has as its magnetic moment one Bohr magneton.† According to quantum mechanics the spins in adjacent atoms must be either parallel or antiparallel. In ferromagnetic materials, the relative distances and grouping of electrons in the atom and the distances between atoms are such that the electron spins and charges can influence one another so as to bring about the parallel orientation. The spinning electrons responsible for electromagnetism are always those in *incomplete* shells.

Heisenberg finds that these exchange forces ("forces of interaction") provide a molecular field F of the right magnitude to overcome thermal agitation and thus to account for the phenomena of ferromagnetism. F may thus be thought of as equivalent to a magnetic field due to parallel spins, the forces that make the spins parallel being more nearly of electrostatic than of magnetic origin. In paramagnetic materials the electrons, of course, also have spins, but the exchange forces are negligible, and the polarization is due entirely to the alignment of magnetic dipoles by the impressed field. The pure magnetic force between dipoles is very feeble; on the other hand, as is shown in Chap. XXVI, in the Seignette analogy the *electric* dipole forces suffice to account completely for the strong internal field.

550. Following the procedure of Weiss, we substitute for I in Eq. (557) its equivalent $\bar{\mu}N$, where N is the number of elementary magnets (dipoles) per unit volume. If then both sides of (557) are divided by $\gamma\mu N$ and F is replaced by KTa/μ, there results the equation

$$\frac{\bar{\mu}}{\mu} = \frac{KT}{\gamma N\mu^2}\, a - \frac{H}{\gamma N\mu} \tag{558}$$

Analytically, by the use of Eq. (557) and the expression $I = \bar{\mu}N$, a may be eliminated between Eqs. (556) and (558), whence $\bar{\mu}/\mu$ or I may be expressed directly in terms of H, μ, T, and γ. A procedure analogous to this in the Seignette-electric case is mentioned in §484. It is simpler and more illuminating to use the customary graphical method of Fig. 165. In this figure the curve represents the Langevin

---

* We shall also refer to I as the *magnetic polarization* or simply the *polarization*.

† A discussion of the Heisenberg theory may be found in the references given in §547 and also in ref. B49.

function, while the straight lines W_p and W_f from Eq. (558) are drawn for temperatures corresponding to the paramagnetic and ferromagnetic cases, respectively. For brevity, we shall call the lines determined by Eq. (558) the *Weiss lines*. Line W_f is drawn through the origin in order to represent the state of affairs when $H = 0$. Equation (556a) shows that at the origin, where $a = \mu F/KT$ vanishes, the slope of the curve is 1/3.

The value of $\bar{\mu}/\mu$, and therefore of the intensity of magnetization I, under any given conditions, is determined by the intersection of the straight line with the curve.

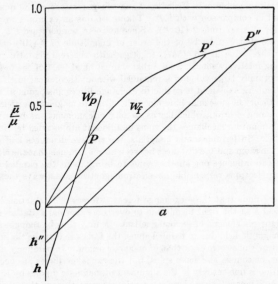

FIG. 165.—The Langevin function. The curve represents Eq. (556). Lines W_p and W_f are from Eq. (558); their slopes depend on T, while the ordinate intercepts are proportional to H.

The higher the temperature, the greater the slope $KT/\gamma N\mu^2$ of the straight line, from Eq. (558).

For slopes greater than 1/3 the substance is *paramagnetic* (line W_p) The intercept $Oh = H/\gamma N\mu$ represents the applied field, and the value of $\bar{\mu}$ is that corresponding to the point P. If H were equal to zero, the line would touch the curve only at the origin, at which $\bar{\mu} = 0$, showing that paramagnetic materials are unpolarized in the absence of an external polarizing field.

As the temperature is decreased from a high value, for which the substance is paramagnetic, the slope of the Weiss lines diminishes until, from a certain critical temperature on, the lines for $H = 0$ begin to intersect the Langevin curve at points beyond the origin. Below this critical temperature the material has *ferromagnetic* properties and is characterized by a *spontaneous magnetization*, $\bar{\mu}$ no longer vanishing when there is no applied field. For example, the spontaneous magnetization for the temperature corresponding to the line W_f is determined by the point P'.

The critical temperature, called the *Curie temperature* and designated by θ, is found by equating the coefficient of a in Eq. (558) to 1/3, the slope of the Langevin curve at the origin. We thus find

$$\theta = \frac{\gamma N \mu^2}{3K} \tag{559}$$

For iron, the value of θ is around 770°C, while $\gamma \approx 3{,}500$.

According to Eq. (559) the high values of the Curie points for ferromagnetic substances are due to the large values of γ. For paramagnetic materials, for which γ is of the order of $4\pi/3$, the Curie point, if it exists at all, must be sought extremely close to the absolute zero of temperature.

That such materials should become ferromagnetic at very low temperatures was predicted by Debye. Recently the transition has been found by Kürti, Lainé, and Simon* in the case of iron alum. This substance shows hysteresis and the characteristic anomaly in the specific heat (§556) at temperatures below 0.034°K, which is regarded as the Curie point.

551. *The Curie-Weiss Law.* We consider next the characteristic equation for the paramagnetic region, which also plays a part in the theory of Rochelle salt. At temperatures sufficiently above the Curie point the second term on the right side of (556a) may, for all ordinarily attainable fields, be ignored, and from (556a), (558), and (559) there results

$$\frac{\bar{\mu}}{\mu} = \frac{\mu H}{3K(T - \theta)} \tag{560}$$

and for the *mass susceptibility* we have the *Curie-Weiss law*

$$k_m = \frac{\bar{\mu}N}{H} = \frac{\mu^2 N}{3K(T - \theta)} = \frac{\theta}{\gamma(T - \theta)} \tag{561}$$

The linear relation expressed in Eq. (561) is illustrated by the straight line in Fig. 166. This law is commonly written in the form mentioned in §547, $k_m = C/(T - \theta)$. The value of θ that satisfies this equation for observed values of k_m with ferromagnetic materials above the Curie point often differs by several degrees from the actual transition point at which ferromagnetism disappears. Equation (560) shows that at these high temperatures the polarization varies linearly with H. On the other hand, at temperatures only slightly above the Curie point the dependence of polarization upon field strength is not linear. The equation corresponding to (561) for temperatures below the Curie point is (566).

Most significant is the fact that Eq. (561) predicts *infinite susceptibility* at the Curie point, where $T = \theta$. Sharp and very high maxima have indeed been observed at this point. Above the Curie point thermal agitation prevails over the exchange forces, and the quantity $a = \mu F/KT$ in Eqs. (556) and (556a) is relatively small. This state of disorder becomes one of comparative order below the Curie point, where the internal field F gains the upper hand. Close to the critical temperature is a narrow region of instability, where a very small applied field strength can effect a large amount of rotation of dipoles. Herein lies the physical explanation of the rapid increase in susceptibility at the Curie point. At this critical temperature the word "susceptibility" in the ordinary sense loses its meaning. There is no *abrupt* change in observed magnetic phenomena at any temperature. Indeed, the Curie "point" is usually determined by extrapolation from observations of susceptibility or of the magnetocaloric effect at temperatures considerably removed from this

---

* N. Kürti, P. Lainé, and F. Simon, *Compt. rend*, vol. 204, pp. 675–677, 754–756, 1937.

critical temperature and is therefore somewhat dependent on the temperature at which observations are made.

In general, it may be said that the outstanding property of ferromagnetic materials is a spontaneous polarization which disappears above a certain critical temperature. From this premise the other features follow in logical sequence. Herein lies also the essence of the analogy with Rochelle salt.

552. *Generalization of the Langevin Function.* The term "Langevin function" has come to be applied generically to any function relating the quantity a in Eq. (556) with $\bar{\mu}/\mu$. A number of variations of the original function have been derived to meet certain conditions of directional quantization. In fact, Eq. (556) is that member of the family for which the quantum number is infinity, the orientation of dipoles being unrestricted.

In its most general form the function may be written

$$L_n(a) = \frac{\bar{\mu}}{\mu} = \frac{I}{I_0} = \frac{\sum_{s=-n}^{n} \frac{s}{n} \epsilon^{(s/n)a}}{\sum_{s=-n}^{n} \epsilon^{(s/n)a}} \qquad (s = -n, \ -n+1, \ -n+2, \ \cdots \ n)$$

where $a = \mu F/KT$ and $I_0 = N\mu$; n, the quantum number, may be any integral multiple of $\frac{1}{2}$. For $n = \infty$ the expression above reduces to Eq. (556), while, for $n = \frac{1}{2}$, it corresponds to parallel or antiparallel orientation in a single direction.

Whatever the form of a polarization function may be, when it is developed in a power series the first two terms can always be written $pa - qa^3$, where p and q are constants. It is easily proved that the coefficient p, which is the initial slope of the curve, is related to n by the equation $p = \frac{1}{3} + 1/3n$. For example, when $n = \frac{1}{2}$ (§484), $p = 1$, and $q = \frac{1}{3}$.

For $a \ll 1$ we may therefore write the following approximate equation, of which Eq. (556a), the original Langevin function, is a special case:

$$\frac{I}{I_0} = \frac{\bar{\mu}}{\mu} = L_n(a) = pa - qa^3 \tag{562}$$

The coefficients p and q become $\frac{1}{3}$ and $\frac{1}{45}$, respectively, in Eq. (556a). We shall consider only the general expression for the Curie-Weiss law with small fields, at temperatures in the neighborhood of the Curie point. The discussion has a bearing on ferroelectric phenomena as well as on magnetism.

a. Above the Curie point, over the range for which Eq. (562) is valid, it is easily proved that

$$\frac{I}{I_0} = \frac{\bar{\mu}}{\mu} = p\,\frac{\mu H}{K(T - \theta)} \tag{563}$$

This equation is the generalized form of Eq. (560). It shows that the association of Weiss's Eq. (557) with any form of the Langevin function [*i.e.,* with any values of p and q in the cubic equation (562) relating the intensity of magnetization I with the molecular field F] leads to a Curie-Weiss law above the Curie point. From Eq. (563) the reciprocal susceptibility is found to be

$$\frac{1}{k_m} = \frac{H}{\bar{\mu}N} = \frac{K(T - \theta)}{p\mu^2 N} = \gamma\,\frac{T - \theta}{\theta} \tag{564}$$

The last part follows from Eq. (565). This relation, as well as Eq. (561), is illustrated by the straight line in Fig. 166.

b. *At the Curie point*, the generalized form of Eq. (559) is

$$\theta = p\gamma \frac{N\mu^2}{K} \tag{565}$$

For any given Langevin function it follows that the value assigned to μ (or to γ) must depend on p.

c. *Below the Curie point* there is a Curie-Weiss law, valid for small values of H (this condition is imposed by the fact that below the Curie point the phenomenon of saturation at large H makes the susceptibility a function of H) and for temperatures not far below the Curie point. We seek an expression for the initial susceptibility k_m^0. This is $\partial I/\partial H$ for $H \to 0$ and is found by taking the derivative of Eq. (562). Then from Eqs. (557), (558), and (565), one finds

$$\frac{1}{k_m^0} = 2\gamma \frac{\theta - T}{3T - 2\theta} \tag{566}$$

In contrast to the relation for $T > \theta$, this equation is not linear in T but is represented by the curve in Fig. 166. Like Eq. (561) it is independent of the special form of the Langevin function. It must be emphasized that Eq. (566) is valid only for temperatures slightly below θ and furthermore that it is characteristic of the single domain and fails to agree accurately with observed values.

Of chief interest from the point of view of the Seignette analogy is the similarity of Fig. 166 to Fig. 120, especially as regards the relative slopes of the lines above and just below the Curie point. From Eq. (566) the initial slope at $T = \theta$ for the curve at the left in Fig. 166 is $-2\gamma/\theta$, numerically just twice

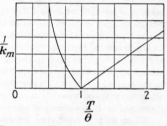

Fig. 166.—Reciprocal initial magnetic susceptibility near the Curie point.

as great as for $T > \theta$, and independent of the special form of the Langevin function.

The manner in which the domain theory explains the high observed magnetic susceptibilities of ferromagnetic materials will be considered below.

553. Domains. Neither the Weiss theory as outlined above nor Heisenberg's theory predicts the existence of discrete "domains." It was to account for the great magnetizability of iron and for the fact that unmagnetized iron shows no external polarity that Weiss made the additional assumption that iron is composed of small regions, each magnetized to a saturation value dependent only upon the temperature, the polarities of the various regions having random orientations in the absence of a magnetizing field. Today there is convincing evidence of their reality. Their origin has been the object of much speculation, especially in relation to the problem of secondary crystal structure and the configuration for minimum energy.

So far as iron is concerned, the evidence at present indicates that each of the minute crystals of which ordinary iron is composed consists of still smaller domains, each having a volume of the order of 10^{-8} cm³ and containing 10^{14} to 10^{15} atoms.[*] The three cubic axes of iron are "directions of easy magnetization," and in each domain the spins associated with the atoms tend to become aligned parallel to one

[*] R. M. Bozorth, *Bell System Tech. Jour.*, vol. 19, pp. 1–39, 1940.

of these directions, in accordance with Heisenberg's theory. The result is the spontaneous polarization. In polycrystalline material the separate crystals themselves have random orientation.

The spontaneous polarization within each domain, which is zero at the Curie temperature, increases at first rapidly with decreasing temperature and gradually approaches a saturation value at 0°K, when all the atoms are similarly oriented.

The Langevin function [Eq. (556)] applies only to the individual domain. For iron at room temperature the polarization of the domain is not far from complete saturation. This state is represented by point P' in Fig. 165. If now a magnetizing field H is applied, represented by Oh'' in Fig. 165, the polarization is increased from P' to P''. This increment is small, owing to the high polarization already present and also to the fact that on the scale to which such diagrams are drawn the distance Oh'', even for large applied fields, is very small. From these considerations it follows that, except near the Curie point, the susceptibility of the individual domain is very low. The observed high permeability of ferromagnetic substances is therefore not a property of the domain but is due, as will be explained in §555, to alterations in the directions of polarization in the domains.

As is seen in §521, the domain structure of Rochelle salt can be superficially explored by dusting powdered sulphur and red lead over a freshly heated crystal. There is a certain degree of analogy between this and the recent technique, employed by Bitter and others, in which a finely divided ferromagnetic powder in the colloidal state is allowed to settle on the surface of a ferromagnetic substance. This method brings to light great complexities in the crystalline structure, the finest details of which have a magnitude in agreement with that which on other grounds is attributed to the magnetic domains. A typical magnetic domain appears to be of the form of either a rod or a flat plate. The fact that a change in temperature (the pyroelectric effect) must be used in the experiments with Rochelle salt, while it is unnecessary in the magnetic case, is of course due to electric conduction in the salt crystal, which, when the temperature is left unchanged, soon causes compensating charges which mask those due to the spontaneous polarization. Nothing like this exists in magnetism.

When we pass from consideration of the single domain to that of aggregates of many domains, as is necessary in order to explain the form of the magnetization and hysteresis curves, we can no longer make use of the Langevin function alone. Its importance in ferromagnetism, as also in the theory of Rochelle salt, lies chiefly in helping to interpret the nature of the Curie point, which is definitely a property of the domain.

554. *Magnetism and Strain.* Just as in piezoelectric crystals, and especially in Rochelle salt, the dielectric properties are affected by the state of strain, so in ferromagnetic materials the magnetism is closely related to strain. The *magnetostrictive effect*, discovered by Joule, is now believed to consist in a deformation of the domain by an applied magnetic field. The converse effect, a change in magnetic properties when the material is stressed, has become of great importance in understanding the nature of magnetization. At first sight these phenomena might appear to be the counterparts of the converse and direct piezoelectric effects, respectively. The effects are somewhat analogous, it is true; but the relations between strain and polarization, both in magnitude and direction, are very much more complicated in the case of magnetism.

The analogue of piezoelectricity is the piezomagnetism discussed in §557. This linear effect is theoretically absent in crystals of the class to which iron belongs.

555. *The Hysteresis Loop.* We now consider briefly the form of the curves of magnetization and hysteresis. It was the observation of strikingly similar curves for the electric polarization of Rochelle salt that first led to the idea of the "ferromagnetic analogy." The simplest possible case would be that of an ideal crystal consisting of a single domain with a single axis of easy magnetization, the susceptibility along the other axes being very small. In conformity with the Weiss theory, such a crystal has a permanent spontaneous intensity of magnetization I_1, the magnitude of which is a function of temperature, but independent of the impressed H, while the direction may be either $+$ or $-$. Starting with I_1 negative, there is a critical H_1 at which the magnetic polarity is abruptly reversed, as indicated in Fig. 167. Under an alternating impressed field, a rectangular hysteresis loop is produced. Loops approximating to this form have been observed with certain pyrrhotite crystals and also with permalloy. Various degrees of magnetic anisotropy have been found in a number of substances.

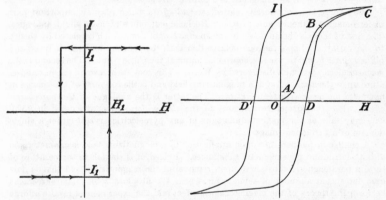

Fig. 167.—The three stages of magnetization in an ideal ferromagnetic crystal.

Fig. 168.—Typical magnetization curve and hysteresis loop.

In most ferromagnetic materials there are many domains, whose polarities neutralize one another when the specimen is in the demagnetized state.

As is well known, a typical virgin curve has three stages, shown in Fig. 168. The form of the portion OA, corresponding to the "initial permeability," is dependent on the magnetostrictive effect between adjacent domains, which, when a small external field is applied, leads to the growth of those domains which happen to be magnetized the right way at the expense of their neighbors. This process is called "translational magnetization." Along the portion AB, the directions of spontaneous magnetization of groups of domains are being changed abruptly from one stable position to another, as is made evident by the Barkhausen effect. At the approach to saturation we have the third stage BC, in which, under the influence of the large H, the direction of polarization of each domain is turned away from the direction of easy magnetization and becomes more and more nearly parallel to the direction of H. By way of analogy it may be added that with Rochelle salt the direction of spontaneous magnetization is actually *reversed* by strong fields, although in the case of Rochelle salt there is evidence that this reversal is only temporary. In contrast with iron, Rochelle salt has only one axis of easy polarization, and its domains are enormously large in comparison with those of ordinary ferromagnetic substances.

The form of the hysteresis loop obtained with an alternating magnetic field, like that of the virgin curve, varies greatly with composition, heat treatment, external and internal stress, and other factors. In the case of single crystals the direction of the field relative to the crystal axes also plays a part. Along the steep portions of the curve the Barkhausen discontinuities find a simple explanation in terms of the domain theory. It is also in agreement with theory that changes in magnetization with temperature proceed smoothly. A useful index to the magnetic properties is the coercive force, represented by OD or OD' in Fig. 168, which is thought to depend on inhomogeneous strains. Permalloy with composition $FeNi_3$, for example, has a coercive force of the order of only 0.05 oersted, while for its permeability, owing to the absence of internal strains, values of over 1,000,000 have been observed. Although the effects of mechanical strain on the magnetic state are very complicated, involving considerations not present in dielectric phenomena, still they offer a striking correspondence between ferromagnetic and ferroelectric substances.

556. There are two closely related *thermal effects* which play an important part in ferromagnetic theory and to which Rochelle salt offers at least slight analogies. The first of these is the anomaly in the *specific heat* of iron, which is related by theory to the variation of spontaneous polarization with temperature and which Weiss and his associates found to rise to a sharp maximum at the Curie point. The second is the *magnetocaloric effect*, also discovered by Weiss. This consists in a small rise in temperature upon the application of a magnetizing field and is the converse of the change in magnetic moment with temperature. The latter is the analogue of the *pyroelectric* effect, while the former corresponds to the *electrocaloric* effect discussed in §523. One may take as the magnetic analogue of any pyroelectric crystal either a single domain or a permanent magnet.

A change in temperature upon application of a magnetizing field is characteristic of both ferro- and paramagnetic substances. Indeed, it is the fall in temperature of certain paramagnetic substances upon removal of the magnetizing field that is now used for the attainment of temperatures near the absolute zero. The agreement between the theory of the magnetocaloric effect and the experimental results affords convincing proof of the essential correctness of Weiss's concept of the internal field. From the experimental results have been derived the most reliable values of the internal field constant γ and of the Curie temperature.

557. Piezomagnetism. For its theoretical interest and its analogy to piezoelectricity we mention this subject briefly. It involves a relation between H, an axial vector, and the symmetrical elastic tensor. By the method of the thermodynamic potential Voigt* derives the fundamental equations for the piezomagnetic "constants" n and "moduli" m. These are analogous to the piezoelectric e and d. The matrices for the various crystal classes, however, are not the same as for piezoelectricity but are related to those for the elastic groups; they comprise all classes except Nos. 29, 31, and 32. Voigt's theory, couched in the language of 1901, assumes that a small magnetic polarization accompanies the change in molecular orientation caused by strain.

Voigt made experimental tests of his theory with quartz and pyrite; the looked-for effect was smaller than the observational errors, so that only an upper limit could be set to the size of the coefficients.

* "Lehrbuch," p. 938.

APPENDIX II

RECENT PROGRESS

Enough of interest in piezoelectricity has happened in the past fifteen years to fill more than one volume. For the present I can only supplement this volume with a short sketch of some of the progress that has been achieved; being a sketch it is not a complete picture. The topics are selected partly for their present importance, partly for their bearing on matters treated in the text.

A list of references, with numbers in parentheses, is to be found at the end of this appendix. In the publications mentioned will be found enough further references to cover the ground more completely.

For general references on piezoelectricity see refs. 19, 23, 27, 31, 39, 51, 54, 59, and 78.

For applications, see refs. 6, 28, 30, 32, 39, 44, 49, 51, 52, 63, and 76.

I.R.E. STANDARDS

558. The Institute of Radio Engineers, through its Committee on Piezoelectric Crystals, has played an important part in establishing definitions and conventions, and in recommending methods of measurement. First organized in 1941, this committee has prepared the following Standards on Piezoelectric Crystals, all of which, except the first, have been published in the Proceedings of the Institute.

1945. Recommended terminology for crystal cuts and rotations, with special conventions for quartz. A left-handed axial system for left-quartz was recommended, as well as Voigt's X and x for components of stress and strain.

This book conforms to the 1945 Standard, except that in the present edition stress and strain both have the same sign.

1949. *Proc. I.R.E.*, vol. 37, pp. 1378–1395, December, 1949. Relations are established between the crystallographic axes and the XYZ orthogonal axes for all systems. A right-handed axial system is adopted for all crystals, including both dextro- and laevo-forms. For right-quartz both X- and Y-axes are reversed with respect to the 1945 convention. For left-quartz the Y-axis is reversed while the X-axis is unchanged. As a consequence, for both right- and left-quartz c_{14} is negative, and s_{14} is positive. For right-quartz d_{11}, d_{14}, and e_{11} are negative, while e_{14} is positive; these signs of piezoelectric constants are reversed for left-quartz. The same convention applies to all hexagonal and trigonal crystals. These changes do not affect the equations for transformed axes in §47.

Voigt's $X_x \ldots$ and $x_x \ldots$ are replaced by $T_1 \ldots$ and $S_1 \ldots$ for stress and strain. Piezoelectric equations of state are given in matrix and tensor notation, not only for Voigt's d and e piezoelectric constants, but also for the new constants g and h. The latter are explained in §197 of this book.

For the monoclinic system, in conformity with modern crystallographic literature, the 1949 Standard selects the unique b-axis as the Y-axis, with Z parallel to the c-axis. This convention requires changing Voigt's XYZ axes (which are used in this book) to ZXY. All subscript digits 1, 2, 3, 4, 5, 6 as used in this book are, according to the new convention, to be changed to 3, 1, 2, 6, 4, 5 respectively, for the elastic and piezoelectric monoclinic constants in §§29 and 131.

1957. *Proc. I.R.E.*, vol. 45, pp. 353–358 (March, 1957). The piezoelectric vibrator, equivalent circuit, methods of measurement, and circle diagram.

1958. *Proc. I.R.E.*, vol. 46, pp. 762–778 (April, 1958). The elasto-piezo-dielectric matrix, electromechanical coupling factor, measurement of elastic and piezoelectric constants.

1961. *Proc. I.R.E.*, vol. 49, pp. 1161–1169 (July, 1961). Measurement of piezo-electric ceramics.

559. *Synthetic Quartz.* In the second world war about 75 million quartz plates were prepared for use by the armed forces of the United States. As the supply of raw material of good quality began to diminish, experiments on artificial growth were renewed. By concentrated effort and modern technology the dimensions of synthetic crystals mentioned on p. 25 have been increased tenfold, so that now an unlimited supply of untwinned specimens large enough to serve all foreseeable needs is assured. The quality is more uniform than that of natural crystals.

Synthetic quartz has been commercially available since 1958. A large crystal may weigh as much as a pound and a half.

References 13, 39, 41, 45, 74.

560. *Crystal Vibrations.* Much theoretical work has been published in this field, mostly on coupled modes, overtones, effect of damping, and the attainment of more exact equations. Among the leading contributors may be mentioned R. D. Mindlin (mostly in *J. Appl. Ph.*, *J. Appl. Mechanics*, and *J.A.S.A.*) and R. F. S. Hearmon (*J. Appl. Mechanics*, vol. 26, Ser. E, No. 4, pp. 537–540, 1959). Jerrard[42] shows theoretically that the thickness vibrations of quartz plates are purer (less coupling) when the surface is slightly convex. Tichy[72] considers various modes, including both even and odd harmonics, from the standpoint of the equivalent electrical network.

On the experimental side mention may be made of a paper by Fukuo,[29] who explored the surface of vibrating quartz crystals by means of a small probe. See also ref. 45.

561. *Recent Determinations of Crystal Constants.* In Table XXXVII are shown a few of the various measurements of elastic and piezoelectric constants of natural quartz that have been made in recent years. The elastic constants are all isagric (at constant field). The data are from Bechmann,[4] Koga, Aruga, and Yoshinaka,[46] and Mason.[51] Algebraic signs conform to the I.R.E. 1945 Standards, which are used in this book. For their relation to the 1949 Standards see §558. All values are reduced to cgs esu.

The average values, given in the last column, are probably more reliable than those in §§90 and 156.

TABLE XXXVII.—ELASTIC AND PIEZOELECTRIC CONSTANTS OF QUARTZ

Constant	This book	Ref. 4	Ref. 46	Ref. 51	Av.
$\times 10^{-12}$ s_{11}	1.27	1.28	1.28	1.279	1.28
s_{33}	0.97	0.96	0.971	0.956	0.97
s_{44}	2.00	2.004	1.997	1.978	2.00
s_{12}	−0.169	−0.179	−0.123	−0.153	−0.152
s_{13}	−0.154	−0.122	——	−0.110	−0.116
s_{14}	−0.431	−0.450	−0.452	−0.446	−0.447
s_{66}	2.88	2.912	2.918	2.865	2.898

TABLE XXXVII.—(*contd.*)—ELASTIC AND PIEZOELECTRIC CONSTANTS OF QUARTZ

Constant		This book	Ref. 4	Ref. 46	Ref. 51	Av.
$\times 10^{10}$	c_{11}	87.5	86.74	86.8	86.05	86.53
	c_{33}	107.7	107.2	105.9	107.1	106.6
	c_{44}	57.3	57.94	58.3	58.65	58.29
	c_{12}	7.62	6.99	——	4.85	5.92
	c_{13}	15.1	11.91	11.9	10.45	11.42
	c_{14}	17.2	17.91	18.1	18.25	18.09
	c_{66}	39.9	39.9	39.9	40.5	40.1
$\times 10^{-8}$	d_{11}	6.9	6.93	7.11	6.76	6.93
	d_{14}	−2.0	−2.181	−2.31	−2.56	−2.35
$\times 10^{4}$	e_{11}	5.2	5.13	5.25	——	5.19
	e_{14}	1.2	1.218	1.22	——	1.20

Values of the elastic and piezoelectric constants of various kinds of crystal may be found in refs. 1, 19, 51, 59, and 70; see also R. F. S. Hearmon, *Brit. J. Appl. Ph.*, vol. 3, pp. 120–124, 1952, and *Phil. Mag. Supplement*, vol. 5, pp. 323–382, 1956.

562. *Notes on Recent Piezoelectric Theory.* A good summary on piezoelectricity and its theory is given by Forsbergh in ref. 27.

Jaffe, Berlincourt, and Shiozawa[40] have made a study of AB compounds crystallizing in the diamond or corresponding hexagonal (wurtzite) structure (see §522). They found that the piezoelectric constants increased with increasing atomic number of the cation and with decreasing atomic number of the anion. Calculated results are given for ZnTe, ZnS, CdSe, and CdS.

563. *New Piezoelectric Crystals.* Over 1,000 piezoelectric crystals have now been identified, for about a tenth of which some, at least, of the constants have been measured. See refs. 23, 39, 47, 59, and 61.

564. *Lithium Sulphate Monohydrate*, $Li_2SO_4 \cdot H_2O$, Class C_2. This monoclinic crystal has received considerable attention owing to its large piezoelectric response to hydrostatic pressure. Other advantages are its low dielectric constant, high electro-mechanical coupling factor, and the fact that the water of crystallization is very tightly bound. The elastic and piezoelectric strain-constants, with their temperature co-efficients, have been measured by Bechmann.[3] For the unit cell he takes $a = 8.18$ A, $b = 4.87$ A, $c = 5.45$ A, $\beta = 107°\ 18'$. His orthogonal axes are Y parallel to b, Z parallel to c; the X-axis is $17°\ 18'$ from a in the ac-plane. This axial system differs from the I.R.E. 1949 Standards in that the a- and c-axes are interchanged.

For the piezoelectric constants of a left crystal, all in 10^{-8} esu, Bechmann finds

$$d_{14} = 11.6 \qquad d_{16} = 9.3$$
$$d_{21} = -0.54 \qquad d_{22} = 49 \qquad d_{23} = -5.15 \qquad d_{25} = -21.4$$
$$d_{34} = -3.1 \qquad d_{36} = 3.3$$

The corresponding values (after a transformation according to §134) for the matrix on p. 190 are found by changing the first digit in each subscript from the sequence

1, 2, 3 to 1, 3, 2; for the second digit the sequence is changed from 1, 2, 3, 4, 5, 6 to 2, 3, 1, 4, 6, 5. Other determinations, by Mason[51] and Spitzer,[70] are discussed by Bechmann.

The large hydrostatic effect is due to the large size of $d_{21} + d_{22} + d_{23} \approx 43(10^{-8})$ esu. The dielectric constant k_{22} is about 10.

565. *The High Q of Quartz.* In §363 it is stated that the highest recorded value of Q was somewhat above 10^6, obtained by Van Dyke in 1938 with a quartz ring. Since then improvements in treatment of surfaces and of mounting, and the use of low temperatures, have led to still higher values. For example, Warner[75] reported $Q = 12(10^6)$ for the eleventh overtone of a quartz plate at room temperature. With an AT plate at 4.2°K, White[77] found $Q = 55(10^6)$. This seems to be the record to date. Smagin[69] obtained $Q = 20(10^6)$.

566. *Quartz Clocks.* The attainment of higher Q and improvements in long-range stability of resonators have led to greater precision in quartz clocks; see refs. 5, 25, 30, 66. For example, the West German standard uses bars of square section, length parallel to Y, with a wide gap between crystal and electrodes and a Q of $7.6(10^6)$.

In the United States the latest quartz standard is a contoured AT-cut vibrating at its fifth overtone at 2.5 Mc. For this standard the stability is 0.2 part per billion per month (T. C. Anderson and F. G. Merrill, *I.R.E. Transactions on Instrumentation*, vol. 1–9, pp. 136–140, Sept., 1960). Quartz standards of frequency have also been constructed with transistors in place of vacuum tubes (W. L. Smith, *I.R.E. Transactions on Instrumentation*, vol. 1–9, pp. 141–148, Sept., 1960).

The primary timekeeper in the United States and Great Britain is now the cesium beam standard. It acts as a resonating monitor, driven by a quartz oscillator which in turn is controlled by a servo circuit.

In so far as a quartz crystal can be regarded as a single molecule it may be said that it is a molecular time standard. The trouble is that the molecule contains too many atoms. Its frequency depends on such statistical quantities as elasticity and density, which are not properties of individual atoms.

567. *Progress in Ultrasonics.* In §508 the value of 500,000 kc/sec is given as the highest recorded ultrasonic frequency at the time of writing. During the past fifteen years the limit has been pushed higher and higher, partly by the use of harmonics of high order in a thin quartz plate, but chiefly by placing the crystal—which is usually quartz with the field in the X-direction—in a micro-wave cavity, where it becomes excited by the high-frequency electric field.

J. S. and E. S. Stewart[71] used harmonics of a quartz plate 0.1 mm thick, and obtained resonance as high as 3,600 Mc.

Baranskii[2] placed a quartz block in a coaxial resonator, and obtained resonance at 2,000 Mc.

Bommel and Dransfield[12] generated both compressional and shear waves in a quartz bar the ends of which extended into two separate re-entrant cavities. One of the latter served for detection. Frequencies up to 4,000 Mc were observed.

Jacobsen[36], who also used a quartz bar and re-entrant cavities, found that at a temperature of 4.2°K he could attain a frequency of 9,370 Mc.

Very recently the piezoelectric effect in a semiconductor depletion layer, for example gallium arsenide, has been used for the generation of ultrasonic waves at above 1,000 Mc (D. L. White, *I.R.E. Convention Record*, Part 6, pp. 304–309, 1961).

These results show that it is now possible to generate ultrasonic waves with frequencies as high as those in the infrared part of the electromagnetic spectrum. When such waves are transmitted from the quartz into other materials, they offer a new and powerful tool for solid state research.

Amplification of ultrasonic waves has been achieved by passing the radiation through a plate of cadmium sulphide crystal that is subjected to a dc bias (A. R. Hutson, J. H. McFee, and D. L. White, *Phys. Rev. Letters*, vol. 7, pp. 237–239, Sept. 15, 1961).

For a general treatment of ultrasonics and its applications, see refs. 6 and 62, also A. E. Crawford, "Ultrasonic Engineering," Butterworth's Scientific Publications, London, 1955; and T. F. Hueter and R. H. Bolt, "Sonics," John Wiley and Sons, Inc., New York, 1955.

568. *The Electromechanical Coupling Factor.* In the application of piezoelectric crystals to mechanical systems it has become customary to use a quantity called the electromechanical coupling factor k, introduced by W. P. Mason[51, 52]; see also I.R.E. 1958 Standards, §558. By analogy with the ac transformer, it is defined basically as the ratio of the mutual elasto-dielectric energy density in the crystal to the square root of the product of the stored elastic and dielectric energy densities. The three energy densities are represented respectively by the third, first, and second terms in Eq. 1, §23. The exact form of this ratio for practical purposes depends on the strain, or vibrational mode, to which the crystal is subjected, as well as on the crystal constants.

The symbol k commonly has two subscripts, analogous to those of the piezoelectric constants. The first designates the axis of the impressed polarization; the second designates the direction of the vibrational strain. Thus k_{33} is used for compressional thickness vibrations of a Z-cut plate, while k_{31} is used for lengthwise vibrations of a Z-cut bar.

For a given crystal the coupling factor can be derived not only from the crystal constants, but also from observation of the frequencies at resonance and antiresonance for the mode considered.

As an example we take the case of a bar in lengthwise vibration at its fundamental mode, with no gap between electrodes and crystal. In the notation of §§228 and 229, the effective piezoelectric stress constant is $\epsilon = d_{in}/s_{nn}^E$, and the effective dielectric constant is k_l. The coupling factor for this case is given by

$$k^2 = \frac{4\pi\epsilon^2 s_{nn}^E}{k_l} = \frac{4\pi d_{in}^2}{k_l s_{nn}^E}$$

In terms of frequencies, we call $\omega_0 - \omega_m = \Delta\omega$ (§278), and find from §279, Eq. (410), and §233, Eq. (324), with $h = 1$:

$$\frac{\omega_0^2 - \omega_m^2}{\omega_m^2} \approx \frac{2\Delta\omega}{\omega_m} = \frac{2\pi f}{f_m} = \frac{C}{C_1} = \frac{32\epsilon^2}{\pi k_l q_0} = \frac{32 d_{in}^2}{\pi k_l s_{nn}^E}$$

From this it follows that for a bar,

$$k^2 = \frac{4\pi d_{in}^2}{k_l s_{nn}^E} \approx \frac{\pi^2}{4}\frac{\Delta f}{f_m} \text{ esu cgs}$$

In rationalized mks units this becomes

$$k^2 = \frac{d_{in}^2}{\epsilon_l s_{nn}^E} = \frac{\pi^2}{4}\frac{\Delta f}{f_m}$$

where ϵ_l is the effective permittivity of the bar.

These expressions show that the coupling factor k is approximately proportional to the square root of the difference between the frequencies at resonance and antiresonance. It is commonly used as a figure of merit for resonators and transducers of this type.

Formulas for other vibrational modes are given in the I.R.E. 1958 Standards on Piezoelectric Crystals, §558.

The numerical value of k, which is necessarily smaller than unity, is as low as 0.1 for quartz and as high as 0.78 for Rochelle salt.

569. *Transducers for Plane Ultrasonic Waves.* Although general transducer theory is outside the scope of this book, a few remarks may be made concerning plane-wave transducers, since they are most directly related to the resonators described in previous chapters.

In a transducer for plane waves the emitted wavelength must be small in comparison with the lateral dimensions of the transducer. The active element may be a piezo-electric plate in thickness vibration, or a mosaic of plates as in the Langevin "sandwich"; or it may consist of an assemblage of short bars in lengthwise vibration. The theory as developed by the author[14] includes the presence of a solid backing, and also of a solid fronting between the crystal and the irradiated medium. The method consists in treating the vibrational state of the transducer as due to the superposition of two systems of progressive waves, in the positive and negative directions. By consideration of boundary conditions, the vibrational amplitude and phase at any point can be calculated.

For comparison with the resonator theory in Chap. V it is enough to consider the special case in which backing and fronting are absent, and the crystal radiates directly into a medium of density ρ_0 and wave velocity c_0. In Eq. (543a) below, ϵ = appropriate piezoelectric stress constant; V_0 = maximal value of applied emf; l = thickness of plate or length of bar; ρ = density of crystal; c = wave velocity in crystal; $m = \rho_0 c_0 / \rho c$; $\beta = \omega l / c$; $N = \epsilon V_0 / \omega l \rho c$. All quantities are in cgs esu.

The amplitude of vibration at the boundary between crystal and medium is found to be

$$\xi = N \frac{(1 - \cos \beta)}{\sqrt{1 - (1 - m^2) \cos^2 \beta}} \qquad (543a)$$

This equation is valid at all frequencies. At resonance, when $\beta = \pi$, it reduces to

$$\xi = \frac{2N}{m} \qquad (543b)$$

In these equations it is assumed that the only damping is that due to radiation, as expressed by the ratio m of the acoustic resistivities. This is the difference between the transducer and the resonator, in the theory of which it was assumed that the damping factor α was due to losses in crystal and mounting. For this reason the two theories are not in exact agreement, although very close agreement is to be expected.

It is obvious that the progressive-wave theory offers an alternative method for solving the problem of the simple resonator. The resonator is treated as a non-radiating crystal without backing or fronting, but having a damping constant α. When this procedure is carried out it leads to Eq. (73), §57.

For frequencies close to resonance one would expect agreement between Eqs. (543a) and (84), page 93. We consider only the fundamental frequency, for which $h = 1$. In this case $\omega = \omega_0 - n$ in Eq. (84), while in Eq. (543a) $\cos \beta \approx -1 + n^2 l^2 / 2c^2$. In the 1953 paper cited above, ref. 14, it is proved that $m \approx al/c$. The denominator in Eq. (543a) reduces to $l^2(\alpha^2 + n^2)/c^2$. On making these substitutions in Eq. (543a) we find

$$\xi = N \frac{c}{l} \frac{2 - n^2 l^2}{\sqrt{\alpha^2 + n^2}}$$

But $Nc/l = \epsilon V/\omega l^2 \rho$, and from §§228 and 254, for both lengthwise and thickness vibrations, the maximum value X_0 of the driving stress is $\epsilon V_0/l$, so that

$$\xi = \frac{X_0}{\rho \omega l} \frac{2 - n^2 l^2}{\sqrt{\alpha^2 + n^2}}$$

This expression is the same as Eq. (84) except for the small term $n^2 l^2$ (the factor ω_0 in Eq. (84) is approximately ω).

Transducers are treated in the following references: 6, 14, 26, 28, 49, 50, 51, 52, 63, 73; also T. F. Hueter and R. H. Bolt, "Sonics," John Wiley & Sons, Inc., New York, 1955.

Until recent years the crystals used in transducers were mainly quartz, Rochelle salt, or ammonium dihydrogen phosphate. At the present time they have all been supplanted, for most practical purposes, by the ferroelectric ceramics (§570), especially lead titanate zirconate.

FERROELECTRICS

570. Two groups of ferroelectric crystals have already been discussed in previous chapters. The first comprises certain tartrates, of which the original example is Rochelle salt. The second group contains alkali metal dihydrogen phosphates. In recent years other groups have been discovered. One is the very important group of the perovskites; another is represented by guanidine aluminum sulphate hexahydrate (GASH).

Rochelle salt, the elder brother in the family of ferroelectrics, still continues to be an object of investigation. Its theory is now a specialized part of general ferroelectric theory, on which the last word has not yet been spoken. Some of the progress on Rochelle salt will be found in refs. 1, 24, 48, 51. For Rochelle salt theory see 22, 41, 51, 56, 57, 67.

It is now generally recognized that the distinguishing properties of a crystal in the ferroelectric state are that it belongs to one of the ten pyroelectric classes; it has a spontaneous polarization (alignment of dipoles by mutual interaction) that can be reversed by a sufficiently intense electric field; it shows dielectric hysteresis; and it has a domain structure.

Above a certain temperature (the Curie point) the ferroelectric properties are absent (unless the crystal is subjected to mechanical or electrical stress). The crystal may still be piezoelectric, but it is no longer in a pyroelectric class.

The perovskites are named after the mineral calcium titanate, which is called "perovskite." For details of structure see refs. 27, 41, 68. Among the perovskites are titanates of barium, calcium, and lead; also lead zirconate and especially lead titanate zirconate.

Of all the perovskites, the one that has received most attention is barium titanate, $BaTiO_3$, especially since single crystals began to be grown in 1947. Much has been published on its structure, twinning, domains, and physical properties.[15, 23, 27, 68] The single domain is piezoelectric, and a good specimen has a spontaneous polarization as high as $28(10^{-6})$ coul cm^{-1}.

Single crystals of usable size have been grown, but most crystals, the largest of which are some centimeters in extent, are highly twinned. Caspari and Merz[15] have made measurements on a specimen consisting of a single domain.

Single crystals have been proposed for use as memory devices.

The Curie temperature of barium titanate is at 120°C. Above this temperature the structure is cubic. From 120°C to a temperature near 5°C the crystal is tetragonal, class C_{4v}; from this point down to −80°C it is orthorhombic; and below −80°C it is trigonal rhombohedral. A spontaneous strain takes place at each transformation (see p. 637 for the spontaneous strain in Rochelle salt).

The tetragonal phase is the one of practical importance. It is in this phase that the crystal has received most experimental and theoretical treatment.

Closely related to the piezoelectric properties of barium titanate are its electro-strictive properties, which are very marked.

For the theory see refs. 18, 21, 27, 31, 41, 43, 51, 55, 68.

The table below contains representative observed values of the constants of some ferroelectric materials. In the literature there is a wide spread of values for what is nominally the same material, owing to differences in composition, treatment, and temperature, as well as to experimental methods and the attendant sources of error. All values are at room temperature and in esu.

TABLE XXXVIII.—CONSTANTS OF FERROELECTRICS

Material	Ref.	d_{15}	d_{31}	d_{33}	k_3'	P^0	C.p.	k_{33}
		$\times 10^{-8}$	$\times 10^{-8}$	$\times 10^{-8}$		coul. cm^{-2}	deg. C	
BaTiO$_3$ sd	15	—	−110	—	203	—	120	—
BaTiO$_3$ sc	68, 8	1180	−103	257	168	24	120	0.56
BaTiO$_3$ pb	64	—	−140	320	—	—	120	—
BaTiO$_3$ pc	38, 8	810	−235	570	1680	7.5	120	0.52
BaTiO$_3$ pc	52	—	−168	440	—	—	120	0.45
BaTiO$_3$ pc	11	550	−150	400	—	—	—	—
PZT-4	38	1410	−350	810	1200	35	340	0.64
PbNb$_2$O$_6$ ceramic	38	—	−33	240	225	—	570	0.42

sd = single domain, strongly polarized

pb = rectangular polycrystalline block

PZT-4 = proprietary variation of lead titanate zirconate made by Clevite Corporation

P^0 = spontaneous polarization of the single crystal, or remanent polarization of the polarized ceramic

k_{33} = electromagnetic coupling factor, for vibrations in the Z-direction (direction of polarization)

sc = single crystal with many domains

pc = polarized ceramic

k' = free dielectric constant in the Z-direction; for the ceramic this is the direction of polarization

C.p. = Curie point

Lead metaniobate has the highest Curie point on record.

Antiferroelectrics. In some ferroelectric crystals phases have been found in which the dipoles are arranged in antiparallel arrays. There is then no observable spontaneous polarization until the impressed electric field has been made strong enough to cause reversals to take place. Among the earlier examples studied were lead zirconate, sodium niobate, and lead hafnate; ammonium dihydrogen phosphate and arsenate (see Chap. XXVII) are also believed to be antiferroelectric. See refs. 20, 27, 37, 43, and 68, also F. Seitz and D. Turnbull, *Solid State Physics*, vol. 4, Academic Press, N.Y., 1957.

There are also solid solutions with sublattices of opposite but unequal electric moments. Such materials, called "ferrielectric" by analogy with ferrimagnetic substances, have been described by Pulvari.[60]

Pyroelectricity. Not only are all ferroelectric crystals pyroelectric, but this effect, at least in barium titanate, is very pronounced. Chynoweth[16] investigated the pyroelectricity in a BaTiO$_3$ single crystal. Perls, Diesel, and Dobrov,[58] from measurements on a $BaTiO_3$ ceramic, separated the primary from the secondary effect (§515), and found for the primary effect γ' (the same as p_m in §516) a value of $-2(10^{-8})$ coul cm^{-2} deg^{-1} = -60 esu. This value may be compared with the estimated value of 9 esu for Rochelle salt in §521, and with the over-all value (primary plus secondary effects) of approximately 1 esu for tourmaline in §519.

Berlincourt[7] measured the over-all effect for a ceramic of $BaTiO_3 + 2\%ZrO_3$, finding at 48°C the very large value of 3,000 esu.

Clingman and Moore[17] and also Hoh[33] discuss the conversion of heat into electrical power by use of the pyroelectric effect.

Ferroelectric Ceramics. Polycrystalline aggregates of perovskite-type ferro-electrics, prepared by ceramic methods, can be made to have piezoelectric properties nearly equal to those of single crystals. Initially the ceramic has no net polarization, but is strongly electrostrictive. When put through a cycle of polarization in a varying electric field it shows hysteresis; and the remanent polarization after removal of a strong static field is the spontaneous polarization P^0 shown in Table XXXVIII. For this purpose the polarizing field is usually of the order of 30 kv per centimeter.

After being thus polarized the ceramic has the same symmetry as Class 26, C_{6v}, with piezoelectric constants d_{15}, $d_{24} = d_{15}$, d_{31}, $d_{32} = d_{31}$, and d_{33} (§§6, 131). The axis of polarization is chosen as the Z-axis, while the mutually perpendicular X- and Y-axes may have any orientation in a plane normal to Z.

One advantage in the use of ceramics is that owing to coupling between individual crystallites the polarization is more stable than with single crystals. Equally important is the fact that the ceramic can be molded in any form—bars, plates, bowl-shaped or hollow cylindrical devices (*cf.* p. 681) for the focusing of ultrasonic beams and other directional effects.

Usually the basic material for ceramics is $BaTiO_3$, or, more recently, lead titanate zirconate, often with certain additions to improve the characteristics for special purposes. The dielectric, elastic, and piezoelectric properties vary greatly with composition.

The advantages in the use of lead titanate zirconate ceramic are that it has a very high Curie point, and that its remanent ferroelectric moment is several times as large as that of barium titanate.

References on ceramics, applications, and methods of measurement: 1, 6, 8, 9, 19, 27, 28, 32, 35, 38, 39, 43, 44, 49, 51, 52, 53, 54, 65, 70.

Applications of Ceramics. The piezoelectric effects most commonly employed are the longitudinal and transverse (§132); these effects involve the constants d_{33} and d_{31}. Despite its relatively great magnitude, the constant d_{15} seems to have been put to few practical applications.

Piezoelectric ceramics have become the chief material for generating and receiving acoustic waves. Other applications include wide-band electric filters where the high Q of quartz is not needed; measurement of forces, strains, and acceleration; delay lines; ignition systems; ultrasonic cleaning; phonograph pickups; non-destructive testing; the ultrasonic drill; and various uses in medicine and dentistry.[76]

The piezoelectric constants of ceramics are such that they respond well to hydro-static pressure (§133). Advantage is taken of this fact in the construction of small probes for investing sonic fields. An extreme example is a minute probe, or stethoscope, that can be inserted directly into the heart.[49]

An interesting application of ferroelectric ceramics is their use as voltage amplifiers. On pp. 303 and 667 there is suggested the use of a crystal with two pairs of electrodes as a coupling device between two circuits. By use of a bar of ceramic as the "crystal" it has been found that the ratio of output to input voltage can be made quite large [A. E. Crawford, *J. Inst. Rad. Eng.* (England), vol. 21, pp. 353–360, April, 1960].

BIBLIOGRAPHY TO APPENDIX II

1. "American Institute of Physics Handbook," McGraw-Hill Book Co., New York, 1957.
2. BARANSKII, K. N.: The Excitation of Vibrations of Hypersonic Frequency in Quartz, *Soviet Physics Doklady*, vol. 114, pp. 517–519, 1957; Engl. transl. in *Sov. Phys. Doklady* 2, No. 3, pp. 237–238, May–June, 1957.
3. BECHMANN, R.: Elastic and Piezoelectric Coefficients of Lithium Sulphate Monohydrate, *Proc. Ph. Soc.*, B, vol. 65, pp. 375–377, 1952.
4. BECHMANN, R.: Elastic and Piezoelectric Constants of Alpha-Quartz, *Phys. Rev.*, vol. 110, pp. 1060–1061, 1958.
5. BECKER, G.: Entwicklung von Quarzuhren hoher Güte für die Quarzuhren der Physikalischen-technischen Bundesanstalt, *Berichtsbuch VI, Int. Congr. Chronom.*, Munich, 1959, Vol. 1.
6. BERGMANN, L.: "Der Ultraschall und seine Anwendung in Wissenschaft und Technik," S. Hirzel Verlag, Stuttgart, 6th ed., 1954.
7. BERLINCOURT, D. A.: Recent Developments in Ferroelectric Transducer Materials, *I.R.E. Trans. on Ultrasonic Eng.*, PGUE-4, pp. 53–65, August, 1956.
8. BERLINCOURT, D. A., and H. JAFFE: Elastic and Piezoelectric Coefficients of Single-Crystal Barium Titanate, *Phys. Rev.*, vol. 111, pp. 143–148, 1958.
9. BERLINCOURT, D. A., C. CMOLIK, and H. JAFFE: Piezoelectric Properties of Polycrystalline Lead Titanate Zirconate Compositions, *Proc. I.R.E.*, vol. 48, pp. 220–229, 1960.
10. BIRKS, J. B. (ed.): "Progress in Dielectrics," vol. 1, John Wiley and Sons, Inc., New York, 1960.
11. BOGDANOV, S. V., B. M. VUL, and R. Y. RAZBACK: The Shear Piezoelectric Modulus of Polarized Barium Titanate, *Kristallografiya*, vol. 2, pp. 115–118, 1957.
12. BÖMMEL, H. E., and K. DRANSFIELD: Excitation and Attenuation of Hypersonic Waves in Quartz, *Phys. Rev.*, vol. 117, pp. 1245–1252, 1960.
13. BROWN, C. S., R. E. KELL, L. A. THOMAS, NORA WOOSTER, and W. A. WOOSTER: Growth and Properties of Large Crystals of Synthetic Quartz, *Mineralogical Mag.* (London), vol. 29, pp. 858–874, 1952.
14. CADY, W. G.: (a) A Theory of the Crystal Transducer for Plane Waves, *J.A.S.A.*, vol. 21, pp. 65–73, 1949; (b) Piezoelectric Equations of State and their Application to Thickness-Vibration Transducers, *J.A.S.A.*, vol. 22, pp. 579–583, 1950; (c) Graphical Aids in Interpreting the Performance of Crystal Transducers, *J.A.S.A.*, vol. 25, pp. 687–696, 1953; (d) Composite Piezoelectric Resonator, *Amer. J. Phys.*, vol. 23, pp. 31–40, 1955.*
15. CASPARI, M. E., and W. J. MERZ: The Electromechanical Behavior of $BaTiO_3$ Single-Domain Crystals, *Phys. Rev.*, vol. 80, pp. 1082–1089, 1950.
16. CHYNOWETH, A. G.: Dynamic Method for Measuring the Pyroelectric Effect with Special Reference to Barium Titanate, *J. Appl. Ph.*, vol. 27, pp. 78–84, 1956.
17. CLINGMAN, W. H., and R. G. MOORE, JR.: Application of Ferroelectricity to Energy Conversion Processes, *J. Appl. Ph.*, vol. 32, pp. 675–681, 1961.
18. COCHRAN, W.: Crystal Stability and the Theory of Ferroelectricity, *Phys. Rev. Letters*, vol. 3, pp. 412–414, 1959; *Advances in Physics* (England), vol. 9, pp. 387–424, 1960.

* In (b), on p. 581, the definition of a_1 should be $a_1 = 2(1 - \cos \beta)(m^2 \sin \beta_d G_1 - m^2 \cos \beta_d G_2) - m_d \sin \beta (m^2 \cos \beta_d G_1 + m_d^2 \sin \beta_d G_2)$.

19. Cook, W. R., Jr., and H. Jaffe: Ferroelectric and Piezoelectric Materials, *Digest of the Literature on Dielectrics*, vol. 24, 1960, Nat. Acad. Sci.—Nat. Res. Council, Washington, D.C.

20. De Bretteville, A. P., Jr.: Antiferroelectric $PbZrO_3$ and Ferroelectric $BaTiO_3$ Phenomena, *Ceramic Age*, vol. 61, pp. 18–22 and 92–93, 1953.

21. Devonshire, A. F.: (a) Theory of Barium Titanate, Part I, *Phil. Mag.*, vol. 40, pp. 1040–1063, 1949; (b) Theory of Barium Titanate, Part II, *Phil. Mag.*, vol. 42, pp. 1065–1079, 1951; (c) Review of Ferroelectricity and Antiferroelectricity in the Perovskites, *Rep. Brit. Elec. Res. Assoc.*, Rep. L/T298, 1953; (d) Theory of Ferroelectrics, *Advances in Physics*, vol. 3, pp. 85–130, 1954.

22. Devonshire, A. F.: Theory of Rochelle Salt, *Phil. Mag.*, vol. 2, pp. 1027–1039, 1957.

23. *Digest of Literature on Dielectrics*, published annually by Nat. Acad. Sci.—Nat. Res. Council, Washington, D.C.

24. Eisner, I. Ia.: On Certain Physical Properties of Rochelle Salt Crystals, *Bull. of Sciences of the U.S.S.R, Phys. Sec.* (English translation), No. 2, vol. 20, pp. 197–200, 1956.

25. Essen, L.: Accurate Measurement of Time, *Phys. Today*, vol. 13, pp. 26–29, 1960.

26. Fischer, F. A.: "Grundzüge der Elektroakustik," Fachverlag Schiele und Sohn, Berlin, 1950.

27. Forsbergh, P. W., Jr.: Piezoelectricity, Electrostriction, and Ferroelectricity, "Handbuch der Physik," vol. 17, S. Flügge, Berlin, 1955.

28. Fotland, R. A.: Ferroelectrics as Solid-State Devices, *Elec. Manufacturing*, March, 1958.

29. Fukuo, H.: Researches in Modes of Vibration of Quartz Crystal Resonators by Means of the "Probe Method," *Bull. Tokyo Inst. Tech.*, Ser. A, No. 1, 1955.

30. Herzog, W.: "Oszillatoren mit Schwingkristallen," Springer-Verlag, Berlin, 1958.

31. Hippel, A. von: Piezoelectricity, Ferroelectricity, and Crystal Structure, *ZS Phys.*, vol. 133, pp. 158–173, 1952.

32. Hippel, A. von: "Molecular Science and Molecular Engineering," Tech. Press of M.I.T., Cambridge, Mass., and Wiley and Sons, Inc., New York, 1959.

33. Hoh, S. R.: Ferroelectric Power Converters, *Program of 7th Region Conference*, *I.R.E.*, Seattle, Washington, May 24–26, 1960.

34. Huibregtse, E. J., W. H. Bessey, and M. E. Drougard: Electromechanical Behavior of Single Crystals of Barium Titanate from 25 to 160°C, *J. Appl. Ph.*, vol. 30, pp. 899–905, 1959.

35. I.R.E. Standards on Piezoelectric Crystals, Measurements of Piezoelectric Ceramics, 1961, *Proc. I.R.E.*, vol. 49, pp. 1161–1169, 1961.

36. Jacobsen, E. H.: Piezoelectric Production of Microwave Phonons, *Phys. Rev. Letters*, vol. 2, pp. 249–250, 1959.

37. Jaffe, B.: (a) Antiferroelectric Ceramics with Field-enforced Transitions, a New Non-linear Circuit Element, *Proc. I.R.E.*, vol. 49, pp. 1264–1267, 1961; (b) Properties of Ferroelectric Ceramics in the Lead-titanate Zirconate System, *Proc. I.E.E.*, vol. 109, Part B, Suppl. No. 22, pp. 351–354, 1962.

38. Jaffe, H.: Piezoelectric Ceramics, *J. Am. Ceramic Soc.*, vol. 41, pp. 494–498, 1958.

39. Jaffe, H.: (a) Piezoelectricity, *Encyclopaedia Britannica*, vol. 17, pp. 9–16, 1961; (b) Piezoelectricity, *McGraw-Hill Yearbook of Science and Technology*, pp. 408–409, 1961; 1962 article in print.

40. Jaffe, H., D. A. Berlincourt, and L. Shiozawa: Systematics of the Piezoelectric Effect in II–VI Crystals, Engineering Memorandum No. 61–7, Clevite Corp., Electronic Res. Div., Cleveland, Ohio, Mar. 20, 1961.

41. JAYNES, E. T.: "Ferroelectricity," Princeton Univ. Press, Princeton, N.J., 1953.
42. JERRARD, R. P.: Vibration of Quartz Crystal Plates, *Quarterly of Appl. Math.*, vol. 18, pp. 173–181, 1961.
43. KÄNZIG, W.: "Ferroelectrics and Antiferroelectrics, Solid State Physics," vol. 4, Acad. Press, New York, 1957.
44. KATZ, H. W. (ed.): "Solid State Magnetic and Dielectric Devices," John Wiley and Sons, Inc., New York, 1959.
45. KING, J. C.: The Anelasticity of Natural and Synthetic Quartz at Low Temperatures, *Bell Syst. T. J.*, vol. 38, pp. 573–602, 1959.
46. KOGA, I., M. ARUGA, and Y. YOSHINAKA: Theory of Plane Elastic Waves in a Piezoelectric Crystalline Material and Determination of Elastic and Piezoelectric Constants of Quartz, *Phys. Rev.*, vol. 109, pp. 1467–1473, 1958.
47. KOPTSIK, V. A., K. A. MINAEVA, A. A. VORONKOV, A. F. SOLOVIEV, A. N. IZRAILENKO, E. G. POPKOVA, and G. I. KOZLOVA: *Vestnik Moskov. Univ.*, Ser. Mat., Mekh., Astron., Fiz., Khim., vol. 13, No. 6, pp. 91–98, 1958. See also A. A. Chumakov and V. A. Koptsik, *Kristallografiya*, vol. 4, pp. 235–238, 1959; Engl. transl. in *Sov. Phys.—Crystallography*, vol. 4, pp. 212–215.
48. KOSMAN, M. S., and A. N. SHEVARDIN: On the Upper Curie Point of Rochelle (Seignette) Salt, *J. Tech. Ph. of the Acad. of Sci. of the U.S.S.R.*, vol. 26, No. 7; Engl. transl. in *Sov. Phys.—Technical Physics*, vol. 1, No. 7, pp. 1407–1412, 1955.
49. LEWIS, D. H.: *Applications of Ferroelectrics*, vol. 195, p. 57, 1956.
50. MASON, W. P.: "Electromechanical Transducers and Wave Filters," D. Van Nostrand Co., Inc., New York, 1948.
51. MASON, W. P.: "Piezoelectric Crystals and their Application to Ultrasonics," D. Van Nostrand Co., Inc., New York, 1950.
52. MASON, W. P.: "Physical Acoustics and the Properties of Solids," D. Van Nostrand Co., Inc., New York, 1958.
53. MASON, W. P., and H. JAFFE: Methods for Measuring Piezoelectric, Elastic, and Dielectric Coefficients of Crystals and Ceramics, *Proc. I.R.E.*, vol. 42, pp. 921–930, 1954.
54. "McGraw-Hill Encyclopedia of Science and Technology," 15 vols., New York, 1960.
55. MEGAW, HELEN D.: "Ferroelectricity in Crystals," Methuen and Co., Ltd., London, 1957.
56. MITSUI, T.: Theory of the Ferroelectric Effect in Rochelle Salt, *Phys. Rev.*, vol. 111, pp. 1259–1267, 1958.
57. MÜSER, H. E.: Measurement of the Dielectric Non-linearity of Rochelle Salt, *ZS. angew. Phys.*, vol. 12, pp. 300–306, 1960.
58. PERLS, T. A., T. J. DIESEL, and W. I. DOBROV: Primary Pyroelectricity in Barium Titanate Ceramics, *J. Appl. Ph.*, vol. 29, pp. 1297–1302, 1958.
59. "Piezoelectricity," P.O. Research Station, London, Her Majesty's Stationery Office, 1957.
60. PULVARI, C. F.: Ferrielectricity, *Phys. Rev.*, vol. 120, pp. 1670–1673, 1960.
61. REZ, I. S., A. S. SONIN, E. E. TSEPELEVICH, and A. A. FILIMONOV: Experimental Investigations on the Development of New Piezoelectric Substances, *Kristallografiya*, vol. 4, pp. 65–68, 1959; Engl. transl. in *Sov. Phys.—Crystallography*, vol. 4, pp. 59–62.
62. RICHARDSON, E. G.: "Ultrasonic Physics," Elsevier Pub. Co., Houston, 1952.
63. RICHARDSON, E. G.: Industrial Applications of Ultrasonics, *Brit. J. Appl. Ph.*, vol. 6, pp. 413–415, 1955.
64. RZHANOV, A. V.: Piezo Effect in Barium Titanate, *J. Exp. Th. Ph. USSR*, vol. 19, pp. 502–506, 1949.

65. SACHSE, H.: Ferroelectrics, "Techn. Ph. in Einzeldarstellungen," vol. 11, Springer, Berlin, 1956. Engl. transl. in Trans. No. AEC TR-2899, Atomic Energy Commission, Washington, D.C.

66. SCHEIBE, A., U. ADELSBERGER, G. BECKER, G. OHL, and R. SÜSS: Ueber die Quarzuhrengruppe der Physikalisch-technischen Bundesanstalt und Vergleichsmessungen gegenüber Atomnormalen, *ZS. angew. Ph.*, vol. 11, pp. 352–357, 1959.

67. SCHMIDT, G.: Piezoelectricity and Electrostriction of Rochelle Salt, *ZS. Ph.*, vol. 161, pp. 579–603, 1961.

68. SHIRANE, G., F. JONA, and R. PEPINSKY: Some Aspects of Ferroelectricity, *Proc. I.R.E.*, vol. 43, pp. 1738–1793, 1955.

69. SMAGIN, A. G.: Methods of Reducing the Energy Dissipated in the Surface Layers of Quartz, *Kristallografiya*, vol. 4, pp. 862–866, 1959; Engl. transl. in *Sov. Phys.— Crystallography*, vol. 4, pp. 812–821.

70. SPITZER, F.: Neuere Synthetische Piezoelektrische Kristalle in der Elektroakustik und Hochfrequenztechnik, *Archiv d. Elek. Uebertragung*, vol. 5, pp. 544–554, 1951.

71. STEWART, J. L., and ELLEN S. STEWART: Hypersonic Resonance of Quartz at 3500 Mc., letter to ed., *J.A.S.A.*, vol. 33, p. 538, 1961.

72. TICHY, J.: Das Elektrische Ersatzschema Schwingender Piezoelektrischer Kr istallstäbchen, *An. Phk.*, Ser. 7, vol. 1, pp. 219–231, 1958.

73. VIGOUREUX, P., and C. F. BOOTH: "Quartz Vibrators and their Applications," London, Her Majesty's Stationery Office, 1950.

74. WALKER, A. C.: Growing Piezoelectric Crystals, *J. Frank. Inst.*, vol. 250, pp. 481–525, 1950.

75. WARNER, A. W.: High Frequency Crystal Units for Primary Frequency Standards, letter to ed., *Proc. I.R.E.*, vol. 42, p. 1452, 1954.

76. WELKOWITZ, W.: Ultrasonics in Medicine and Dentistry, *Proc. I.R.E.*, vol. 45, pp. 1059–1069, 1957.

77. WHITE, D. L.: High-Q Quartz Crystals at Low Temperatures, *J. Appl. Ph.*, vol. 29, pp. 856–857, 1958.

78. WOOSTER, W. A.: "Experimental Crystal Physics," Clarendon Press, Oxford, 1957.

PROBLEMS

1. §19. Make a stereographic projection of KH_2PO_4 showing following faces: (100), ($\bar{1}$00), (010), (0$\bar{1}$0); (101), ($\bar{1}$01), (011), (0$\bar{1}$1), (111). Axial ratio $a:c = 1:0.9391$.

2. §26. Verify Eq. (7), §26, for the special case in which the only stress is Y_z. Use Eqs. (5) and (6).

3. §35. A quartz X-cut bar with length $l = 5$ cm parallel to Z, width $b = 1$ cm parallel to X, thickness 0.3 cm parallel to Y, has one end clamped while a force of 0.8 kg with lever arm $d = 10$ cm is applied at the other end in the XY-plane. Find the torsional strain in degrees per unit length. (*Ans.* 0.00216.)

4. §38. A square 3×3 cm X-cut Rochelle salt plate with edges parallel to Y and Z has one of its faces normal to Z cemented to a base. When an electric field parallel to X is applied, the opposite face is found to move through a distance of 0.0036 cm parallel to Y. Find (1) the strain y_z; (2) the stress Y_z needed to produce the same strain if s_{44} is $9(10^{12})$ cgs; (3) the elongations of the two major diagonals.

5. §56. Derive Eqs. (63) and (64), for wave number and damping constant, by performing the operations indicated.

6. §100. A tourmaline bar with length $l = 2.5$ cm parallel to Z has a cross section 2×2 mm with edges b and e parallel to X and Y. One end is fixed while the other end carries a mass of M grams. How large must M be to make the frequency of flexural vibration equal to (1) 100 cps, (2) 500 cps? Neglect the inertia of the bar. For the frequency use the formula $f = 1/(2\pi\sqrt{k/M})$, where $k = qe^3b/4l^3$. See §§33, 34, 100, for q. In which direction can the end of the bar be made to move piezoelectrically, and where should the electrodes be located? There are two answers to this question.

7. §100. The bar described in Problem 16 is driven with a voltage such as to make the maximal amplitude at each end of the bar $5(10^{-14})$ cm. The driving voltage is now suddenly removed. Find (1) the mechanical energy in the bar; (2) the maximal charge on the electrodes; (3) the maximal potential difference between the electrodes due to the vibration.

8. §107. In what crystal systems do the dielectric cross-susceptibilities (with respect to the XYZ-crystal axes) vanish? Is there any system in which they vanish even with respect to all rotated axes?

9. §124. An X-cut quartz plate of infinite area and with thickness e is placed between infinite parallel electrodes, with a gap w_1 on one side, w_2 on the other. The electrodes are short-circuited. Charges with surface density $\pm\sigma$ are put on the faces of the quartz. Derive expressions for the field in each gap and in the quartz, also for the strain x_x and polarization in the quartz. See §110.

10. §133. A uniform hydrostatic pressure of 10 kg/cm² is applied to a short-circuited tourmaline crystal. Find the six components of strain, also the resultant polarization. See also §§26 and 100.

11. §135. For crystals in Class 6 (D_2), derive equations for d'_{33}, e'_{33}, and e'_{25}, for axes in any orientation. Specialize these expressions for rotation about the Y-axis alone. See also §§38, 127, and 134.

12. §136. Derive general equations for P_x, P_y, and P_z due to a uniform stress Y'_z, also for the component of polarization parallel to the X'-axis. See §§38 and 127.

13. §148. How can bars of Rochelle salt and quartz be so oriented that they become compressed endwise by the converse effect when electrodes are at the ends? See also §139.

14. §152. Prove that when a uniform stress Z'_t is applied in the XY-plane of a quartz crystal, and the direction of this stress about the Z-axis is progressively varied, the resulting polarization P rotates twice as fast as Z'_t and in the opposite direction.

15. §152. A certain textbook contains the statement that if a quartz plate with thickness perpendicular to the Z-axis is compressed in the direction of its thickness, electrodes on its major faces will show equal and opposite charges. Is this true for all directions perpendicular to Z?

16. §228. An X-cut quartz bar with length $l = 3$ cm parallel to Y, width $b = 5$ mm parallel to Z, and $e = 1$ mm parallel to X, with plated electrodes covering the major faces, is driven in lengthwise vibration by an emf of 50 volts rms. The logarithmic decrement of the bar is $\delta = 10^{-5}$. Find the following for $h = 1$ and 3: (1) f_{ho}, f_{ha}, and $f_{h'}$; (2) strain at center of bar; (3) amplitude of vibration at end of bar at resonance; (4) whether the bar is in danger of fracture. See also §§43, 56, 58–60, 90, 328, and 329.

17. §231. Derive Eq. (317) in the manner indicated.

18. §237. Derive Eq. (336b) in the manner indicated.

19. §254. Derive Eqs. (361a) and (362) in the manner indicated.

20. §269. Derive Eq. (383).

21. §361. A force of 100 lbs. compresses a BT-cut quartz plate of 2 cm² area in the direction of its thickness. Find the polarizations P'_x, P'_y, and P'_z. See also §§124 and 151.

22. §362. Find the stiffness q, effective piezoelectric constant ϵ, and meters per millimeter h for an AT-cut quartz plate in thickness vibration. See also §§93, 351, and 361. *(Ans.* $29.7(10^{10})$ dyne cm⁻²; $-2.92(10^4)$ esu; 180.*)*

23. §382. Find the frequency of thickness vibration of a Z-cut tourmaline plate 0.1 mm thick. See also §§76, 100, 165, 166, 244, 247, and 250. *(Ans.* $5.1(10^6)$ cps.*)*

GENERAL BIBLIOGRAPHY

The bibliography is in two sections. First comes the list of books, to most of which reference has been made in the text. The reference numbers of books are prefixed by the letter B.

The second part contains articles from periodicals. It would be several times longer if it contained all references that bear on the subject, including publications in the various technical, popular, and radio periodicals, reports of scientific and engineering congresses, and annual reports of national laboratories.

At the ends of some of the chapters are classified lists of references. These lists consist in part of items in the General Bibliography and in part of books or articles on those special topics with which the particular chapters are concerned.

A fairly complete bibliography on piezoelectricity was published by the author in 1928.[99] Many of the references in that bibliography are here omitted. Those of chief historical interest have been retained, together with certain ones to which reference is made in the text.

The 1928 bibliography contained also a list of patents bearing on the subject. Since then a vast number of patents have been issued in various countries, ranging all the way from inventions of fundamental importance to trifling details. A few of them are mentioned in the text.

A special bibliography for Appendix II begins on page 764.

ABBREVIATIONS OF NAMES OF PERIODICALS

Abh. Gött.	Abhandlungen der Gesellschaft der Wissenschaften zu Göttingen
Abh.Sächs.	Abhandlungen der mathematischen-physikalischen Klasse der Sächsischen Akademie der Wissenschaften zu Leipzig
Alta freq.	Alta frequenza
An. chim. phys.	Annales de chimie et de physique
An. fr. chron.	Annales françaises de chronométrie
An. Phk.	Annalen der Physik (from 1824 to 1899, Annalen der Physik und Chemie)
An. Phq.	Annales de physique
Ann. soc. sci. Brux.	Annales de la société scientifique de Bruxelles
Anz. Wien	Anzeiger der Akademie der Wissenschaften zu Wien, mathematisch-naturwissenschaftliche Klasse
A.P.T.	American Physics Teacher
Arch. sci. phys. nat.	Archives des sciences physiques et naturelles. Geneva
A.W.A. Tech. Rev.	A.W.A. Technical Review. Published by Amalgamated Wireless (Australasia), Ltd., Sydney, Australia
Bell Labs. Rec.	Bell Laboratories Record
Bell Syst. T.J.	Bell System Technical Journal
Ber. Sächs.	Berichte der Königlichen Sächsischen Gesellschaft der Wissenschaften (mathematisch-physikalische Klasse)

Ber. Wien	Sitzungsberichte der Akademie der Wissenschaften zu Wien (mathematisch-naturwissenschaftliche Klasse)
Brit. Rad. Ann.	British Radio Annuals
Bull. soc. min. fr.	Société française de minéralogie, bulletin. Until 1885, société minéralogique de France
Can. J. Res.	Canadian Journal of Research
C.R.	Comptes rendus hebdomadaires des séances de l'académie des sciences
C.R. congrès int. d'élec.	Comptes rendus du congrès international d'électricité, Paris, 1932
C.R. (Russ.)	Comptes rendus (Doklady), Akademia Nauk, S.S.S.R., Leningrad; published in both a Russian edition and a French-English-German edition with French title
Dati e mem.	Dati e memorie sulle radiocomunicazioni, Rome
Denki Hyoron	Denki Hyoron (Kyoto) (in Japanese)
Elec. Comm.	Electrical Communication
Elec. Rev. (Jap.)	Electrical Review (Japan) (Electrotechnical Laboratory Tokyo)
Electrotech. Jour. (Jap.)	Journal of the Electrotechnical Laboratory, Ministry of Communications, Tokyo, Japan
ENT	Elektrische Nachrichten-Technik, Berlin
ENW	Elektrisches Nachrichtenwesen, Berlin
Ergeb. exakt. Naturwiss.	Ergebnisse der exakten Naturwissenschaften, Herausgegeben von der Schriftleitung der "Naturwissenschaften," Verlag von Julius Springer, Berlin
ETZ	Elektrotechnische Zeitschrift
F. M. Mag.	Frequency Modulation Magazine
Funktech. Mon.	Funktechnische Monatshefte
G.E. Rev.	General Electric Review
Helv. Ph. Ac.	Helvetica Physica Acta
Hfr. u. El. ak.	Hochfrequenztechnik und Elektroakustik, Jahrbuch der Drahtlosen Telegraphie und Telephonie (formerly Zeitschrift für Hochfrequenztechnik)
Izv. El. Slab. Toka	Izvestiia Elektromyshlennosti Slabogo Toka, Leningrad and Moscow
J.A.S.A.	Journal of the Acoustical Society of America
J. Am. Chem. Soc.	Journal of the American Chemical Society
J. Appl. Ph.	Journal of Applied Physics
J. Appl. Ph. (Russian)	Journal of Applied Physics, Leningrad and Moscow (in Russian)
J. Exp. Th. Ph. U.S.S.R.	Journal of Experimental and Theoretical Physics, Leningrad
J. Frank. Inst.	Journal of the Franklin Institute
J.I.E.E. (Japan)	Journal of the Institute of Electrical Engineers of Japan
J.I.E.E. (London)	Journal of the Institution of Electrical Engineers (England)
J.I.T.T.E. Jap.	Journal of Institute of Telegraph and Telephone Engineers of Japan (in Japanese)

J.O.S.A.	Journal of the Optical Society of America
J. Ph. U.S.S.R.	Journal of Physics of the U.S.S.R.
J. phq.	Journal de physique et le radium. Until 1919, Journal de physique théorique et appliquée
J. Res. N.B.S.	Journal of Research of the National Bureau of Standards (from 1928 to 1934, Bureau of Standards Journal of Research)
J. Russ. Ph.-Chem. Soc.	Journal of the Russian Physical Chemical Society, Leningrad (in Russian)
J. Sci. Instr.	Journal of Scientific Instruments, London
J. Tech. Phys.	Journal of Technical Physics (in Russian)
Konink. Akad. Amst.	Koninklijke Akademie van Wetenschappen te Amsterdam, Proceedings
L'Elettrot.	L'Elettrotecnica, Milan
L'Onde élec.	L'Onde électrique
Luftfahrt-F.	Luftfahrtforschung
Nachr. Gött.	Gesellschaft der Wissenschaften zu Göttingen, Nachrichten, mathematisch-physikalische Klasse
Naturwiss.	Die Naturwissenschaften, Berlin
Neues Jahrb. Min.	Neues Jahrbuch für Mineralogie, Geologie und Paläontologie
Nippon Elec. Comm. Eng.	Nippon Electrical Communication Engineering, Institute of Electrical Communication Engineers of Japan, Tokyo
Phil. Mag.	Philosophical Magazine
Phys. Rev.	Physical Review
Phys. ZS	Physikalische Zeitschrift
Phys. ZS. d. Sowjetunion	Physikalische Zeitschrift der Sowjetunion
P.O.E.E.J.	Post Office Electrical Engineers' Journal, London
Proc. A.A.A.S.	Proceedings of the American Academy of Arts and Sciences
Proc. A.I.E.E.	Proceedings of the American Institute of Electrical Engineers
Proc. I.R.E.	Proceedings of the Institute of Radio Engineers
Proc. Nat. Acad. Sci.	Proceedings of the National Academy of Sciences of the United States of America
Proc. Ph. Soc.	Proceedings of the Physical Society, London
Proc. Roy. Soc.	Proceedings of the Royal Society of London, *A*, papers of mathematical or physical character
Proc. World Eng. Cong., Tokyo	Proceedings of the World Engineering Congress, Tokyo
QST	QST, published by the American Radio Relay League
QST fr.	QST français
Radio-Centrum	Radio-Centrum, journal of the Nederlandsche vereeniging voor radiotelegraphie, The Hague
Rass. P.T.T	Rassegna delle Poste, dei Telegrafi e dei Telefoni, Rome
Rep. El. Res. Inst. Tokyo	Reports of the Electrical Research Institute of the Tokyo Municipality
Rev. d'opt.	Revue d'optique, théorique et instrumentale, Paris
Rev. gén. de l'élec.	Revue générale de l'électricité
R.R.R.W. Jap.	Reports of Radio Researches and Works in Japan

R.S.I.	Review of Scientific Instruments
Sci.	Science
Sci. Pap. Bur. St.	Scientific Papers of the Bureau of Standards, Washington
Tech. Phys. U.S.S.R.	Technical Physics of the U.S.S.R., Leningrad
Telef. Hausmitt.	Telefunken Hausmitteilungen
Telef.-Z.	Telefunken-Zeitung
T.R. Bull.	T. and R. Bulletin, Official Journal of the Radio Society of Great Britain
Trans. A.I.E.E.	Transactions of the American Institute of Electrical Engineers
Trans. Conn. Acad.	Transactions of the Connecticut Academy of Arts and Sciences
Trans. Roy. Soc. Can.	Transactions of the Royal Society of Canada
U.R.S.I. Gen. Assem.	Proceedings of the General Assembly, International Scientific Radio Union
V.D.I.	Zeitschrift des Vereines Deutscher Ingenieure, Berlin
Wied. An.	Wiedemann's Annalen
W.E.	The Wireless Engineer and Experimental Wireless. Originally, Experimental Wireless, then Experimental Wireless and the Wireless Engineer, London
W. World	Wireless World and Radio Review, London
Zentr. f. Min.	Zentralblatt für Mineralogie, Geologie und Paläontologie, Abt. A
ZS. Elektrochem.	Zeitschrift für Elektrochemie
ZS. Hfr.	Zeitschrift für Hochfrequenztechnik (see Hochfrequenztechnik und Elektroakustik)
ZS. Instr.	Zeitschrift für Instrumentenkunde, Berlin
ZS. Kr.	Zeitschrift für Kristallographie
ZS. Ph.	Zeitschrift für Physik
ZS. ph. Chem.	Zeitschrift für physikalische Chemie
ZS. tech. Ph.	Zeitschrift für technische Physik

BOOKS

B1. AUERBACH, F., and W. HORT: "Handbuch der physikalischen und technischen Mechanik," vol. 3, J. A. Barth, Leipzig, 1927, 468 pp.

B2. BARTON, EDWIN H.: "A Text-Book on Sound," Macmillan & Co., Ltd., London, 1919, 687 pp.

B3. BEDEAU, F.: "Le Quartz piézo-électrique et ses applications dans la technique des ondes hertziennes" (Memorial des sciences physiques, Fasc. VI), Gauthier-Villars & Cie, Paris, 1928, 64 pp.

B4. BERGMANN, L.: "Schwingende Kristalle und ihre Anwendung in der Hochfrequenz-und Ultraschalltechnik," B. G. Teubner, Leipzig, 1937, 47 pp.

B5. BERGMANN, DR. LUDWIG: "Der Ultraschall und seine Anwendung in Wissenschaft und Technik," Berlin, VDI-Verlag G.m.b.H., 1937, 230 pp.; 6th ed., S. Hirzel, Stuttgart, 1954, 1114 pp.; English translation of the 1st edition entitled "Ultrasonics and Their Scientific and Technical Applications," by Dr. H. Stafford Hatfield, George Bell & Sons, Ltd., London, John Wiley & Sons, Inc., New York, 1939, 264 pp.

B6. BORN, MAX: "Atomtheorie des festen Zustandes," 2d ed., B. G. Teubner, Leipzig and Berlin, 1923, 262 pp.

B7. BORN, MAX: "Optik, ein Lehrbuch der elektromagnetischen Lichttheorie," Verlag Julius Springer, Berlin, 1933, 591 pp. (Chapter on Crystal Optics.)

B8. BRAGG, W. L.: "Atomic Structure of Minerals," Cornell University Press, Ithaca, New York, 1937, 292 pp.

B9. CRANDALL, IRVING B.: "Theory of Vibrating Systems and Sound," D. Van Nostrand Company, Inc., New York, 1926, 272 pp.

B10. CURIE, P.: "Œuvres de Pierre Curie," Gauthier-Villars & Cie, Paris, 1908, 621 pp.

Contains reprints of following papers on piezoelectricity (pages in the "Œuvres" are printed in boldface type): (a) *C.R.*, vol. 91, p. 294, 1880 (**6**); (b) *C.R.*, vol. 91, p. 383, 1880 (**10**); (c) *C.R.*, vol. 92, p. 186, 1881 (**15**); (d) *C.R.*, vol. 92, p. 350, 1881; *Jour. d. phys.*, 2d ser., vol. 1, p. 245, 1882 (**18**); (e) *C.R.*, vol. 93, p. 204, 1881; *Jour. d. phys.*, 2d ser., vol. 1, p. 245, 1882 (**22**); (f) *C.R.*, vol. 93, p. 1137, 1881 (**26**); (g) *C.R.*, vol. 95, p. 914, 1882 (**30**); (h) *Bulletin des séances de la société française de physique*, 1887 p. 47, (**33**); (i) *C.R.*, vol. 106, p. 1287, 1888; *Jour. d. phys.*, 2d ser., vol. 8, p. 149, 1889 (**35**); (j) *An. chim. Phys.*, 6th ser., vol. 17, p. 392, 1889 (**554**); (k) *Jour. d. phys.*, 3d ser., vol. 3, p. 393, 1894 (**118**). References (h) and (k) are by P. Curie; (j) by J. Curie; the remainder by P. and J. Curie.

B11. CURIE, MME. P.: "Traité de Radioactivité," vol. 1, Gauthier-Villars & Cie, Paris, 1910; "Die Radioaktivität," (German translation by B. Finkelstein), vol. 1, Akademische Verlagsgesellschaft m.b.H., Leipzig, 1912, 420 pp.

B12. DAKE, H. C., F. L. FLEENER, and B. H. WILSON: "Quartz Family Minerals," Whittlesey House, New York, 1938, 304 pp.

B13. DALE, A. B.: "The Form and Properties of Crystals," University Press, Cambridge, London, 1932, 186 pp.

B14. DAVEY, WHEELER P.: "A Study of Crystal Structure and Its Applications," McGraw-Hill Book Company, Inc., New York, 1934, 695 pp.

B15. DEBYE, P.: "Polar Molecules," Dover Publications, Inc., New York, 1954, 172 pp.

B16. DEBYE, P., and H. SACK: "Theorie der elektrischen Molekulareigenschaften," Handbuch der Radiologie, 2d ed., vol. 6, part 2, pp. 69–204, 1934; also issued as a separate publication by the Akademische Verlagsgesellschaft m.b.H., Leipzig, 1934.

B17. "Encyclopädie der mathematischen Wissenschaften," edited by A. Sommerfeld, vol. 5, B. G. Teubner, Leipzig, 1903–1926.

B18. FOWLER, R. H.: "Statistical Mechanics," 2d ed., Cambridge University Press, London, 1936, 864 pp.

B19. GEIGER, H., and K. SCHEEL: "Handbuch der Physik," Verlag Julius Springer, Berlin. Vol. 6, 1927: F. Pfeiffer, Theory of Vibrations (including crystals), pp. 334–403; J. W. Geckeler, Elasticity of Crystals (with references and numerical data), pp. 404-427. Vol. 8, 1927: H. Lichte, Piezoelectric Transmitters for Sound Waves, pp. 332–335. Vol. 12, 1927: A. Güntherschulze, Electrostriction, pp. 555–559. Vol. 13, 1928: H. Falkenhagen, Pyro- and Piezoelectricity (with some applications), pp. 291–331.

B20. GRAETZ, L.: "Handbuch der Elektricität und des Magnetismus," vol. 1, J. A. Barth, Leipzig, 1918: R. v. Hirsch, Electrostriction, pp. 262–270; E. Riecke. Pyro- and Piezoelectricity, pp. 342–419.

B21. GRAMONT, A. DE: "Recherches sur le quartz piézoélectrique," Éditions de la Revue d'optique théorique et instrumentale, Paris, 1935, 113 pp.

B22. GROTH, P.: "Physikalische Krystallographie," Wilhelm Engelmann, Leipzig, 1905, 820 pp.; also "Elemente der physikalischen u. chemischen Krystallographie," R. Oldenbourg, Munich and Berlin, 1921, 363 pp.

B23. HANDEL, P. VON: "Grundlagen der Kurzwellen-Sendung," in "Hochfrequenztechnik in der Luftfahrt," edited by H. Fassbender, Verlag Julius Springer, Berlin, 1932, pp. 228–248.

B24. HIEDEMANN, EGON: "Grundlagen und Ergebnisse der Ultraschallforschung," Walter de Gruyter & Company, Berlin, 1939, 287 pp.

B25. HINTZE, C.: "Handbuch der Mineralogie," Veit, Leipzig, 1897–1933.

B26. HONESS, A. P.: "The Nature, Origin and Interpretation of the Etch Figures on Crystals," John Wiley & Sons, Inc., New York, 1927, 171 pp.

B27. HUND, AUGUST: "Hochfrequenzmesstechnik," 2d ed., Verlag Julius Springer, Berlin, 1928, 526 pp.

B28. HUND, AUGUST: "High-frequency Measurements," McGraw-Hill Book Company, Inc., New York, 1933, 491 pp.

B29. "International Critical Tables," vol. 6, pp. 207–212, Electroelastic and Pyroelectric Phenomena, McGraw-Hill Book Company, Inc., New York, 1929.

B30. JOFFÉ, A. F.: "The Physics of Crystals," 1st ed., McGraw-Hill Book Company, Inc., New York, 1928, 198 pp.

B31. KOGA, I.: "Elements of Piezoelectric Oscillating Crystal Plate," Institute of Electrical Engineers of Japan, 1933, 76 pp., (in Japanese).

B32. KURCHATOV, I. V.: "Seignette Electricity," Moscow, 1933, 104 pp. (in Russian); French translation, abbreviated, entitled "Le Champ moléculaire dans les diélectriques (le sel de Seignette)," by I. V. Kourtschatov, Hermann & Cie, Paris, 1936, 47 pp..

B33. LAMB, HORACE: "The Dynamical Theory of Sound," Dover Publications, Inc., New York, 1960, 308 pp.

B34. LOVE, A. E. H.: "A Treatise on the Mathematical Theory of Elasticity," 4th ed., Dover Publications, Inc., New York, 1944, 643 pp.

B35. MASON, WARREN P.: "Electromechanical Transducers and Wave Filters," D. Van Nostrand Company, Inc., New York, 1942, 333 pp.

B36. MARX, DR. ERICH: "Handbuch der Radiologie," Leipzig, 2d ed., vol. 6, published by Dr. Erich Marx, Akademische Verlagsgesellschaft m.b.H., Die Theorien der Radiologie, 1934.

B37. MOULLIN, E. B.: "The Theory and Practice of Radio Frequency Measurements," 2d ed., Charles Griffin & Company, Ltd., London, 1931, 487 pp.

B38. MYERS, L. M.: "Television Optics: An Introduction," Pitman Publishing Corporation, New York, 1936, 338 pp.

B39. PETRZILKA, V., and J. B. SLAVIK: "Piezoelektrina—A Jeji Pouziti V Technicke Praxi," Jednoty ceskych matematiku a fysiku, Prague, 1940, 117 pp.

B40. POCKELS, F.: "Uber den Einfluss des elektrostatischen Feldes auf das optische Verhalten piezoelektrischer Krystalle," Dieterisch'sche Verlagsbuchhandlung, Göttingen, 1894, 204 pp.

B41. POCKELS, F.: "Lehrbuch der Kristalloptik," B. G. Teubner, Leipzig and Berlin, 1906, 519 pp.

B42. POYNTING, J. H., and J. J. THOMSON: "A Text-book of Physics," vol. 4, Electricity and Magnetism, part 1, London, 1920; Pyroelectricity and Piezoelectricity, pp. 148–163.

B43. RAYLEIGH, LORD: "The Theory of Sound," Dover Publications, Inc., New York, 1945, vol. 1, 480 pp.; vol. 2, 504 pp.

B44. ROGERS, AUSTIN F., and PAUL F. KERR: "Optical Mineralogy," McGraw-Hill Book Company, Inc., New York, 1942, 390 pp.

B45. SCHEIBE, DR. A.: "Piezoelektrizität des Quarzes," Theodor Steinkopf, Dresden and Leipzig, 1938, 233 pp.

B46. SHUBNIKOV, A. V.: "Quartz and Its Applications," Press of the Academy of Science of the U.S.S.R., Moscow and Leningrad, 1940, 194 pp. (in Russian).

B47. SOSMAN, R. B.: "The Properties of Silica," Chemical Catalog Company, Inc., New York, 1927, 856 pp.

B48. TUTTON, A. E. H.: "Crystallography and Practical Crystal Measurement," 2d ed., Macmillan & Company, Ltd., London, 1922, 2 vols., 746 and 699 pp.

B49. VAN VLECK, J. H.: "The Theory of Electric and Magnetic Susceptibilities," Oxford, Clarendon Press, New York, 1932, 384 pp.

B50. VIGOUREUX, P.: "Quartz Resonators and Oscillators," His Majesty's Stationery Office, London, 1931, 217 pp.

B51. VIGOUREUX, P.: "Quartz Oscillators and Their Applications," His Majesty's Stationery Office, London, 1939, 131 pp.

B52. VOIGT, W.: "Lehrbuch der Kristallphysik," B. G. Teubner, Leipzig, 1st ed., 1910, 964 pp.; 2d ed., 1928, 978 pp., identical with the first except for the addition of an appendix on secondary effects in the flexure and torsion of circular cylinders, based on refs. 573 and 576.

B53. WIEN, W., and F. HARMS: "Handbuch der Experimentalphysik," Akademische Verlagsgesellschaft m.b.H., Leipzig. Vol. 10, 1930: G. Hoffmann, Electrostriction, pp. 262–267; Pyro- and Piezoelectricity (with brief statement of applications), pp. 327–345. Vol. 13, part 2, 1928: H. Rothe, Quartz Resonators, pp. 437–453. Vol. 17, part 1, 1934: H. Schmidt, Vibrations of Solids (including crystals), pp. 285–454; E. Grossmann, Ultrasonics, pp. 469–534.

B54. WINKELMANN, A.: "Handbuch der Physik," Leipzig, vol. 4, part 1, 1905: L. Graetz, Electrostriction, pp. 162–168; F. Pockels, Pyro- and Piezoelectricity, pp. 766–791.

B55. WOOD, R. W.: "Supersonics, the Science of Inaudible Sounds," Charles K. Colver Lectures, 1937, Brown University, Providence, R.I., 1939, 158 pp.

B56. WOOSTER, W. A.: "A Text-book on Crystal Physics," Cambridge University Press, London, 1938, 295 pp.

B57. WYCKOFF, R. W. G.: "The Analytical Expression of the Results of the Theory of Space-groups," Carnegie Institute of Washington, 1922, 180 pp.; 2d edition, 1930, 180 pp.

PERIODICALS

1. ACKERMANN, W.: Dependence of Pyroelectricity on Temperature, *An. Phk.*, vol. 46, pp. 197–220, 1915.

2. AMARI, S.: On the Frequency Variation of Quartz-controlled Short-wave Radio Transmitters, *R.R.R.W. Jap.*, vol. 6, absts, p. 9, 1936.

3. ANDERSON, J. E.: Frequency Characteristics of Piezoelectric Oscillators, *Electronics*, vol. 11, pp. 22–24, August, 1938.

4. ANDREEFF, A., V. FRÉEDERICKSZ, and I. KAZARNOWSKY: The Dependence of the Piezoelectric Constants of Quartz upon Temperature, *ZS. Ph.*, vol. 54, pp. 477–483, 1929.

5. ANGRISANO, G.: Experimental Arrangement for the Determination of the Resonance Curves of Piezoelectric Resonators, *L'Elettrot.*, vol. 17, pp. 678–679, 1930.

6. ANTSELIOVICH, E. S.: On the Stability of Oscillators, *Izv. El. Slab. Toka*, no. 6, pp. 28–39, 1935.

7. ANTSELIOVICH, E. S.: The Frequency Stability of Crystal-controlled Valve Oscillators, *Izv. El. Slab. Toka*, no. 9, pp. 1–9, 1935.

8. ARKHANGEL'SKAYA, A.: Measurement of the Parameters of Quartz Plates, *Izv. El. Slab. Toka*, nos. 8/9, pp. 28–35, 1938.

9. ARNULF, A.: Examination of Raw Quartz Crystals by Immersion, *Rev. d'opt.*, vol. 10, pp. 453–473, 1931.

10. ARX, A. VON, and W. BANTLE: Polarization and Specific Heat of KH_2PO_4, *Helv. Ph. Ac.*, vol. 16, pp. 211–214, 1943.

11. ARX, A. VON, and W. BANTLE: The Converse Piezoelectric Effect in KH_2PO_4, *Helv. Ph. Ac.*, vol. 16, pp. 416–418, 1943.

12. ATANASOFF, J. V., and P. J. HART: Dynamical Determination of the Elastic Constants and Their Temperature Coefficients for Quartz, *Phys. Rev.*, vol. 59, pp. 85–96, 1941.

13. ATANASOFF, J. V., and E. KAMMER: A Determination of the c_{44} Elastic Constant for Beta-quartz, *Phys. Rev.*, vol. 59, pp. 97–99, 1941.

14. AWENDER, H., and E. BUSSMAN: A Heterodyne Adaptor Unit for 1.6 m Wavelength with and without Crystal Control, *Funktech. Mon.*, no. 12, pp. 441–442, 1936.

15. BAHRS, S. and J. ENGL: On the Piezoelectric Effect with Ammonium Chloride Crystals Having a Transition Point at $-30.5°$, *ZS. Ph.*, vol. 105, pp. 470–477, 1937.

16. BALDWIN, C. F.: Quartz Crystals, *G.E. Rev.*, vol. 43, pp. 188–194, 237–243, 1940.

17. BALDWIN, C. F.: Quartz Crystals in Radio, *Communications*, vol. 22, pp. 20f., October, 1942.

18. BALDWIN, F. C., and S. A. BOKOVOY: Practical Operating Advantages of Low Temperature-Frequency Coefficient Crystals, *QST*, vol. 19, pp. 26, 27, 92, January, 1935.

19. BALZER, K.: A Contribution to the Problem of Multiple Waves in Piezoelectric Quartz Plates, *ZS. tech. Ph.*, vol. 18, pp. 169–170, 1937.

20. BANCROFT, D.: The Effect of Hydrostatic Pressure on the Susceptibility of Rochelle Salt, *Phys. Rev.*, vol. 53, pp. 587–590, 1938.

21. BANCROFT, D.: The Velocity of Longitudinal Waves in Cylindrical Bars, *Phys. Rev.*, vol. 59, pp. 588–593, 1941.

22. BANTLE, W.: The Specific Heat of Seignette-electric Substances. Dielectric Measurements on KD_2PO_4 Crystals, *Helv. Ph. Ac.*, vol. 15, pp. 373–404, 1942.

23. BANTLE, W.: Artificial Crystals of KH_2PO_4 as Frequency Stabilizers, *Helv. Ph. Ac.*, vol. 16, pp. 207–209, 1943.

24. BANTLE, W., and G. BUSCH: Dielectric Investigations of Rochelle Salt, *Helv. Ph. Ac.*, vol. 10, pp. 261–264, 1937.

25. BANTLE, W., G. BUSCH, B. LAUTERBURG, and P. SCHERRER: The Spontaneous Kerr Effect in KH_2PO_4 and KH_2AsO_4 Crystals, *Helv. Ph. Ac.*, vol. 15, pp. 324–325, 1942.

26. BANTLE, W., and C. CAFLISCH: The Piezoelectric Effect of the KH_2PO_4 Crystal, Akin to Rochelle Salt, *Helv. Ph. Ac.*, vol. 16, pp. 235–250, 1943.

27. BANTLE, W., and W. LÜDY: The Elastic Properties of Seignette-electric Substances, *Helv. Ph. Ac.*, vol. 15, pp. 325–327, 1942.

28. BANTLE, W., B. MATTHIAS, and P. SCHERRER: The Dependence of Piezoelectric Resonant Frequencies of the Seignette-electrics on Field Strength, *Helv. Ph. Ac.*, vol. 16, pp. 209–211, 1943.

29. BANTLE, W., and P. SCHERRER: Anomaly of the Specific Heat of Potassium Dihydrogen Phosphate at the Upper Curie Point, *Nature*, vol. 143, p. 980, 1939.

30. BAUMGARDT, E.: Velocity of Propagation of Elastic Waves in Piezoelectric Crystals, *C.R.*, vol. 206, pp. 1887–1890, 1938.

31. BECHMANN, R.: Development of Quartz Control for the Telefunken High-power Transmitter, *Telef.-Z.*, vol. 14, pp. 17–29, 1933.

32. BECHMANN, R.: The Temperature Coefficients of the Natural Frequencies of Piezoelectric Quartz Plates and Bars, *Hfr. u. El. ak.*, vol. 44, pp. 145–160, 1934.

33. BECHMANN, R.: The Crystal Control of Transmitters, *W.E.*, vol. 11, pp. 249–253, 1934.

34. BECHMANN, R.: Measurement of the Velocity of Sound in Anisotropic Media, Particularly in Quartz, by Means of Piezoelectric Excitation, *ZS. Ph.*, vol. 91, pp. 670–678, 1934.

35. BECHMANN, R.: Investigations on the Elastic Vibrations of Piezoelectrically Excited Quartz Plates, *ZS. tech. Ph.*, vol. 16, pp. 525–528, 1935.

36. BECHMANN, R.: Quartz Oscillators, *Telef.-Z.*, vol. 17, pp. 36–45, 1936.

37. BECHMANN, R.: Quartz Resonators, *Telef.-Z.*, vol. 18, pp. 5–15, 1937.

38. BECHMANN, R.: On Circuits for Piezoelectric Quartz Oscillators and Resonators for Frequency Stabilization and Filters, *Telef. Hausmitt.*, vol. 19, pp. 60–69, March, 1938.

39. BECHMANN, R.: Thickness Vibrations of Piezoelectrically Excited Crystal Plates, *Hfr. u. El. ak.*, vol. 56, pp. 14–21, 1940.

40. BECHMANN, R.: Elastic Vibrations óf an Anisotropic Body in the Form of a Rectangular Parallelepiped, *ZS. Ph.*, vol. 117, pp. 180–197, 1941.

41. BECHMANN, R.: Lengthwise Vibrations of Square Quartz Plates, *ZS. Ph.*, vol. 118, pp. 515–538, 1942.

42. BECHMANN, R.: Lengthwise Vibrations of Rectangular Quartz Plates, *ZS. Ph.*, vol. 120, pp. 107–120, 1942.

43. BECHMANN, R.: Properties of Quartz Oscillators and Resonators in the Range from 300 to 5000 kc/s, *Hfr. u. El. ak*, vol. 59, pp. 97–105, 1942.

44. BECHMANN, R.: Quartz Oscillators and Resonators in the Region from 50 to 300 kc/s., *Hfr. u. El. ak.*, vol. 61, pp. 1–12, 1943.

45. BECKER, H. E. R.: The Reaction of the Surrounding Liquid on the Vibratiors of a Quartz Plate, *An. Phk.*, vol. 25, pp. 359–372, 1936.

46. BECKER, H. E. R.: On the Vibration Mechanism of a Quartz Plate in Liquids, *An. Phk.*, vol. 26, pp. 645–658, 1936.

47. BECKERATH, H.: The Vibrating Quartz in Communications Technique. Part I —The Mechanical and Electrical Properties of the Vibrating Quartz (Survey), *ENT*, vol. 19, pp. 45–62, 1942.

48. BEEVERS, C. A., and W. HUGHES: The Crystal Structure of Rochelle Salt (Sodium Potassium Tartrate Tetrahydrate $NaKC_4H_4O_6 \cdot 4H_2O$), *Proc. Roy. Soc.*, vol. 177, pp. 251–259, 1941.

49. BENOIT, J.: The Various Modes of Vibration of Piezoelectric Quartz, *L'Onde élec.*, vol 18, pp. 22–36, 1938.

50. BENSON, J. E.: A Piezoelectric Calibrator, *A.W.A. Tech. Rev.*, vol. 5, pp. 47–50, 1940.

51. BENSON, J. E.: Modes of Vibration and Design of *V*-cut Quartz Plates for Medium Broadcast Frequencies, *A.W.A. Tech. Rev.*, vol. 6, pp. 73–89, 1943.

52. BERGMANN, L.: A Simple Method for Detecting the Piezoelectricity of Crystals, *Phys. ZS.*, vol. 36, pp. 31–32, 1935; *Zentralblatt f. Mineralogie* (*A*), pp. 213–222, 1935.

53. BERGMANN, L.: On the Natural Frequencies of Piezoelectric Quartz Plates When Excited in Thickness Vibration, *An. Phk.*, vol. 21, pp. 553–563, 1935.

54. BIOT, A.: Testing Quartz Plates Cut at Right Angles to the Optic Axis, *Ann. soc. sci. Brux.*, vol. 58, pp. 98–100, 1938.

55. BLOOMENTHAL, S.: The Converse Piezoelectric Effect in Mixed Crystals Isomorphous with Rochelle Salt, *Physics*, vol. 4, pp. 172–177, 1933.

56. BOELLA, M.: On the Performance of the Piezo-oscillator in Relation to the Resonance Curve of the Quartz, *L'Elettrot.*, vol. 17, pp. 672–678, 1930.

57. BOELLA, M.: Influence of the Decrement of the Quartz on the Oscillation Frequency of Piezo-oscillators, *L'Elettrot.*, vol. 17, pp. 734–736, 1930; *Proc. I.R.E.*, vol. 19, pp. 1252–1273, 1931.

58. BOELLA, M.: Piezo-oscillators with Neutralization of the Quartz, *Alta freq.*, vol. 8, pp. 512–515, 1939.

59. BOGUSLAWSKI, S.: Theory of Dielectrics; Temperature Coefficient of the Dielectric Constants; Pyroelectricity, *Phys. ZS.*, vol. 15, pp. 283–288, 1914.

60. BOGUSLAWSKI, S.: Pyroelectricity on the Basis of the Quantum Theory, *Phys. ZS.*, vol. 15, pp. 569–572, 1914.

61. BOGUSLAWSKI, S.: On W. Ackermann's Measurements of the Temperature Coefficient of Pyroelectric Excitation, *Phys. ZS.*, vol. 15, pp. 805–810, 1914.

62. BOKOVOY, S. A.: Quartz Crystals—Development and Application, *Elec. Comm.*, vol. 21, pp. 233–246, 1944.

63. BOND, W. L.: Etch Figures of Quartz, *ZS. Kr.*, vol. 99, pp. 488–498, 1938.

64. BOND, W. L.: The Mathematics of the Physical Properties of Crystals, *Bell Syst. T.J.*, vol. 22, pp. 1–72, 1943.

65. BOND, W. L.: A Mineral Survey for Piezoelectric Materials, *Bell Syst. T.J.*, vol. 22, pp. 145–152, 1943.

66. BOND, W. L.: Methods for Specifying Quartz Crystal Orientation and Its Determination by Optical Means, *Bell Syst. T.J.*, vol. 22, pp. 224–262, 1943.

67. BOND, W. L.: Processing Quartz, *Bell Labs. Rec.*, vol. 22, pp. 359–361, 1944.

68. BOND, W. L., and E. J. ARMSTRONG: The Use of X-rays for Determining the Orientation of Quartz Crystals, *Bell Syst. T.J.*, vol. 22, pp. 293–337, 1943.

69. BOOTH, C. F.: The Application and Use of Quartz Crystals in Telecommunications, *J.I.E.E.*, vol. 88, part 3, pp. 97–128, 1941; discussion, pp. 128–144.

70. BOOTH, C. F., and E. J. C. DIXON: Crystal Oscillators for Radio Transmitters: An Account of Experimental Work Carried Out by the Post Office, *W.E.*, vol. 12, pp. 198–200, 1935; *J.I.E.E.*, vol. 77, pp. 197–236, discussion pp. 237–244, 1935; *Proc. Wireless Sec.*, *I.E.E.*, vol. 10, pp. 129–168, discussion, pp. 169–176, 1935.

71. BOOTH, C. F., and C. F. SAYERS: The Production of Quartz Resonators for the London-Birmingham Coaxial Cable System, *P.O.E.E.J.*, vol. 32, pp. 7–15, 88–93, 1939.

72. BORSARELLI, C.: A New Piezo-oscillator, *Alta freq.*, vol. 5, pp. 763–772, 1936.

73. BOSSHARD, W., and G. BUSCH: The Damping of Piezoelectric Vibrations, *Helv. Ph. Ac.*, vol. 10, pp. 329–330, 1937; *ZS. Ph.*, vol. 108, pp. 195–199, 1938.

74. BOYLE, R. W.: Ultrasonics, *Science Progress*, vol. 23, pp. 75–105, 1928.

75. BRAGG, W., and R. E. GIBBS: The Structure of Alpha- and Beta-quartz, *Proc. Roy. Soc.*, vol. 109, pp. 405–427, 1925.

76. BROWN, H. A.: Oscilloscope Patterns of Damped Vibrations of Quartz Plates and Q Measurements with Damped Vibrations, *Proc. I.R.E.*, vol. 29, pp. 195–199, 1941.

77. BROWN, S. L., and S. HARRIS: Measurements of Temperature Coefficient and Pressure Coefficient of Quartz Crystal Oscillators, *R.S.I.*, vol. 2, pp. 180–183, 1931.

78. BROWN, W. F., JR.: Interpretation of Torsional Frequencies of Crystal Specimens, *Phys. Rev.*, vol. 58, pp. 998–1001, 1940.

79. BÜCKS, K., and H. MÜLLER: On Some Observations of Vibrating Piezo-quartz Plates and Their Acoustic Radiation Field, *ZS. Ph.*, vol. 84, pp. 75–86, 1933.

80. BUILDER, G.: Quartz Crystals for the Control and Measurement of Frequency, *A.W.A. Tech. Rev.*, vol. 2, pp. 104–105, 1936.

81. BUILDER, G.: A Note on the Determination of the Equivalent Electrical Constants of a Quartz-crystal Resonator, *A.W.A. Tech. Rev.*, vol. 5, pp. 41–45, 1940.

82. BUILDER, G., and J. E. BENSON: Precision Frequency-control Equipment Using Quartz Crystals, *A.W.A. Tech. Rev.*, vol. 3, pp. 157–214, 1938; *Proc. World Radio Convention*, Sydney, Australia, 1938.

83. BUILDER, G., and J. E. BENSON: Contour-mode Vibrations in *Y*-cut Quartz-crystal Plates, *Proc. I.R.E.*, vol. 29, pp. 182–185, 1941; *A.W.A. Tech. Rev.*, vol. 5, pp. 181–189, 1941.

84. BUILDER, G., and J. E. BENSON: Simple Quartz-crystal Filters of Variable Bandwidth, *A.W.A. Tech. Rev.*, vol. 5, pp. 93–103, 1941.

85. BUISSON, H.: Method of Observing the Optical Purity of Quartz Crystals, *J. phq.*, vol. 8, pp. 25–31, 1919.

86. BUNING, DE C.: Quartz Crystals with Low Temperature Coefficients, *Radio-Centrum*, vol. 1, pp. 25–28, 1935.

87. BUSCH, G.: Anomalous Dispersion of the Dielectric Constants of Rochelle Salt, *Helv. Ph. Ac.*, vol. 6, pp. 315–336, 1933.

88. BUSCH, G.: New Seignette-electrics, *Helv. Ph. Ac.*, vol. 11, pp. 269–298, 1938.

89. BUSCH, G., and E. GANZ: Dielectric Measurements on KH_2PO_4 and KH_2AsO_4 at Low Temperatures, *Helv. Ph. Ac.*, vol. 15, pp. 501–508, 1942.

90. BUSCH, G., and P. SCHERRER: A New Seignette-electric Substance, *Naturwiss.*, vol. 23, p. 737, 1935.

91. CADY, W. G.: The Piezoelectric Resonator (abst.), *Phys. Rev.*, vol. 17, p. 531, 1921.

92. CADY, W. G.: Theory of Longitudinal Vibrations of Viscous Rods, *Phys. Rev.*, vol. 19, pp. 1–6, 1922.

93. CADY, W. G.: The Piezoelectric Resonator, *Proc. I.R.E.*, vol. 10, pp. 83–114, 1922.

94. CADY, W. G.: A Method of Testing Plates from Piezoelectric Crystals, *J.O.S.A.*, vol. 6, pp. 183–185, 1922.

95. CADY, W. G.: Piezoelectrically Driven Tuning-forks and Rods, *Phys. Rev.*, vol. 21, pp. 371–372, 1923.

96. CADY, W. G.: An International Comparison of Radio Wavelength Standards by Means of Piezoelectric Resonators, *Proc. I.R.E.*, vol. 12, pp. 805–816, 1924.

97. CADY, W. G.: Piezoelectric Standards of High Frequency, *J.O.S.A.*, vol. 10, pp. 475–489, 1925.

98. CADY, W. G.: A Shear Mode of Crystal Vibration (abst.), *Phys. Rev.*, vol. 29, p. 617, 1927.

99. CADY, W. G.: Bibliography on Piezoelectricity, *Proc. I.R.E.*, vol. 16, pp. 521–535, 1928.

100. CADY, W. G.: Some Electromechanical Properties of Rochelle Salt Crystals (abst.), *Phys. Rev.*, vol. 33, pp. 278–279, 1929.

101. CADY, W. G.: Electroelastic and Pyro-electric Phenomena, *Proc. I.R.E.*, vol. 18, pp. 1247–1262, 1930.

102. CADY, W. G.: Piezoelectric Terminology, *Proc. I.R.E.*, vol. 18, pp. 2136–2142, 1930.

103. CADY, W. G.: Low Frequency Vibrations in Rochelle Salt and Quartz Plates (abst.), *Phys. Rev.*, vol. 39, p. 862, 1932.

104. CADY, W. G.: Quartz Oscillator with Optical Control, *C.R. congrés int. d'élec.*, vol. 11, sec. 9, pp. 40–48, Paris, 1932.

105. CADY, W. G.: The Application of Methods of Geometrical Inversion to the Solution of Certain Problems in Electrical Resonance, *Proc. A.A.A.S.*, vol. 68, pp. 383–409, 1933.

106. CADY, W. G.: The Potential Distribution between Parallel Plates and Concentric Cylinders Due to any Arbitrary Distribution of Space Charge, *Physics*, vol. 6, pp. 10–13, 1935.

107. CADY, W. G.: The Piezoelectric Resonator and the Effect of Electrode Spacing upon Frequency, *Physics*, vol. 7, pp. 237–259, 1936.

108. CADY, W. G.: The Longitudinal Piezoelectric Effect in Rochelle Salt Crystals, *Proc. Ph. Soc.*, vol. 49, pp. 646–653, 1937.

109. CADY, W. G.: A Survey of Piezoelectricity, *A.P.T.*, vol. 6, pp. 227–242, 1938.

110. CADY, W. G., and K. S. VAN DYKE: Proposed Standard Conventions for Expressing the Elastic and Piezoelectric Properties of Right- and Left-quartz, *Proc. I.R.E.*, vol. 30, pp. 495–499, 1942.

111. CHAIKIN, S.: On a Direct Method for the Measurement of Small Decrements of Piezo-crystal Resonators, *Hfr. u. El. ak.*, vol. 35, pp. 6–9, 1930.

112. CLAY, J., and J. KARPER: Piezoelectric Constant of Quartz, *Physica*, vol. 4, pp. 311–315, 1937.

113. CORTEZ, S. H.: Interferometer Method for Measuring the Amplitude of Vibration of Quartz Bar Crystals, *J.O.S.A.*, vol. 24, pp. 127–129, 1934; erratum, vol. 24, p. 194, 1934.

114. COSTER, D., K. S. KNOL, and J. A. PRINS: Differences in Intensity of X-ray Reflection from the Two 111-Faces of Zinc Blende, *ZS. Ph.*, vol. 63, pp. 345–369, 1930.

115. CROSSLEY, A.: Piezoelectric Crystal-controlled Transmitter, *Proc. I.R.E.*, vol. 15, pp. 9–36, 1927.

116. CROSSLEY, A.: Modes of Vibration in Piezoelectric Crystals, *Proc. I.R.E.*, vol. 16, pp. 416–423, 1928.

117. CURIE, J., and P. CURIE: Development by Pressure of Polar Electricity in Hemihedral Crystals with Inclined Faces, *Bull. soc. min. de France*, vol. 3, pp. 90–93, 1880. This paper, read at the meeting of Apr. 8, 1880, contained the first announcement of the discovery of piezoelectricity.

118. CZERMAK, P.: On the Electric Behavior of Quartz, *Ber. Wien*, vol. 96, pp. 1217–1244, 1887.

119. DAVID, R.: The Dependence of the Dielectric Properties of Rochelle Salt on Mechanical Conditions, *Helv. Ph. Ac.*, vol. 8, pp. 431–484, 1935.

120. DAVIES, R. M.: On the Determination of Some of the Elastic Constants of Rochelle Salt by a Dynamical Method, *Phil. Mag.*, vol. 16, pp. 97–124, 1933.

121. DAWSON, L. H.: Piezoelectricity of Crystal Quartz, *Phys. Rev.*, vol. 29, pp. 532–541, 1927.

122. DEBYE, P., and F. W. SEARS: Scattering of Light by Supersonic Waves, *Proc. Nat. Acad. Sci.*, vol. 18, pp. 409–414, 1932.

123. DIJL, B. VAN: The Application of Ricci-calculus to the Solution of Vibration Equations of Piezoelectric Quartz, *Physica*, vol. 3, pp. 317–326, 1936.

124. DOERFFLER, H.: Flexural and Shear Vibrations in Piezoelectrically Excited Quartz Plates, *ZS. Ph.*, vol. 63, pp. 30–53, 1930.

125. DOHERTY, W. H.: Synchronized FM Transmitter, *F.M. Mag.*, vol. 1, pp. 21–25, December, 1940.

126. DRUESNE, M. A. A.: Quartz Crystals, *Communications*, vol. 23, pp. 46f., September, 1943.

127. DYE, D. W.: Piezoelectric Quartz Resonator and Equivalent Electrical Circuit, *Proc. Ph. Soc.*, vol. 38, pp. 399–457; discussion, pp. 457–458, 1926.

128. DYE, D. W.: The Modes of Vibration of Quartz Piezoelectric Plates as Revealed by an Interferometer, *Proc. Roy. Soc.*, vol. 138, pp. 1–16, 1932.

129. ECCLES, W. H., and W. A. LEYSHON: Some New Methods of Linking Mechanical and Electrical Vibrations, *Proc. Ph. Soc.*, vol. 40, pp. 229–232, 1928.

130. EICHHORN, K.: Photoelastic Investigations of the Piezoelectrically Excited Flexural Oscillations of Quartz Bars, *ZS. tech. Ph.*, vol. 17, pp. 276–279, 1936.

131. EKSTEIN, H.: Free Vibrations of Anisotropic Bodies, *Phys. Rev.*, vol. 66, pp. 108–118, 1944.

132. ENGL, J., and I. P. LEVENTER: On a New Method for Measuring the Piezoelectric Effect in Powdered Crystals, *An. Phk.*, vol. 29, pp. 369–385, 1937; abst. in *Naturwiss.*, vol. 24, pp. 217–218, 1936.

133. EREMEEV, M., and B. KURCHATOV: Electric Properties of the Isomorphic Crystals $NaKC_4H_4O_6 \cdot 4H_2O$ and $NaNH_4C_4H_4O_6 \cdot 4H_2O$, *Phys. ZS. d. Sowjetunion*, vol. 3, pp. 304–320, 1933; *J. Exp. Th. Ph. U.S.S.R.*, vol. 2, pp. 329–338, 1932.

134. ERRERA, J.: Dispersion of Hertz Waves in Solids, *Phys. ZS.*, vol. 32, pp. 369–373, 1931.

135. ESSEN, L.: Description of the Quartz Control of a Transmitter at 1785 Kilocycles per Second, *J.I.E.E.*, vol. 74, pp. 595–597, 1934; *Proc. Wireless Sec., I.E.E.*, vol. 9, pp. 167–169, 1934.

136. ESSEN, L.: Examples of the Electrical Twinning of Quartz, *J. Sci. Instr.*, vol. 12, pp. 256–257, 1935.

137. ESSEN, L.: Oscillations of Hollow Quartz Cylinders, *Nature*, vol. 135, p. 1076, 1935.

138. ESSEN, L.: The Dye Quartz Ring Oscillator as a Standard of Frequency and Time, *Proc. Roy. Soc.*, vol. 155, pp. 498–519, 1936.

139. ESSEN, L.: A New Form of Frequency and Time Standard, *Proc. Ph. Soc.*, vol. 50, pp. 413–423; discussion, pp. 423–426, 1938.

140. EVANS, R. C.: The Dielectric Constant of Mixed Crystals of Sodium Ammonium and Sodium Potassium Tartrates, *Phil. Mag.*, vol. 24, pp. 70–79, 1937.

141. FAIR, I. E.: Using High Crystal Harmonics for Oscillator Control, *Bell Labs. Rec.*, vol. 21, pp. 237–242, 1943.

142. FOWLER, R. H.: A Theory of the Rotations of Molecules in Solids and of the Dielectric Constants of Solids and Liquids, *Proc. Roy. Soc.*, vol. 149, pp. 1–28, 1935.

143. FOX, G. W., and G. A. FINK: The Piezoelectric Properties of Quartz and Tourmaline, *Physics*, vol. 5, pp. 302–306, 1934.

144. FOX, G. W., and W. G. HUTTON: Experimental Study of Parallel-cut Piezoelectric Quartz Plates, *Physics*, vol. 2, pp. 443–447, 1932.

145. FOX, F. E., and G. D. ROCK: The Ultrasonic Radiation Field of a Quartz Disk Radiating into Liquid Media, *Phys. Rev.*, vol. 54, pp. 223–228, 1938.

146. FOX, F. E., and G. D. ROCK: An Ultrasonic Source of Improved Design: Optical Studies of Ultrasonic Waves in Liquids, *R.S.I.*, vol. 9, pp. 341–345, 1938.

147. FOX, F. E., and G. D. ROCK: A Quartz Plate with Coupled Liquid Column as a Variable Resonator, *Proc. I.R.E.*, vol. 30, pp. 29–33, 1942.

148. FOX, G. W., and M. UNDERWOOD: On the Piezoelectric Properties of Tourmaline, *Physics*, vol. 4, pp. 10–13, 1933.

149. FRAYNE, J. G.: Reversible Inductivity of Rochelle Salt Crystals, *Phys. Rev.*, vol. 21, pp. 348–359, 1923.

150. FRÉEDERICKSZ, V., and G. MIKHAILOV: The Dependence of the Piezoelectric Constant of Quartz upon Temperature, *ZS. Ph.*, vol. 76, pp. 328–336, 1932.

151. FRIEDEL, G.: On the Forms of Quartz Crystals, *Bull. soc. min. fr.*, vol. 46, pp. 79–95, 1923.

152. FUJIMOTO, T.: On the Determination of the Piezoelectric Constant of a Quartz Resonator at High Frequency, *Proc. World Eng. Cong., Tokyo, Paper* 369, pp. 399–416, 1929.

153. GALOTTI, F.: Luminous Quartz Resonators, *Alta freq.*, vol. 6, pp. 809–824, 1937.

154. GAUDEFROY, C.: Orientation of Crystals, Especially Quartz, by Means of Etch Figures, *C.R.*, vol. 192, pp. 1113–1116, 1931.

155. GAUGAIN, J. M.: Note on the Electricity of Tourmaline, *An. chim. phys.*, vol. 57, pp. 5–39, 1859.

156. GERTH, F., and H. ROCHOW: The Temperature Dependence of the Frequency of Quartz Resonators, ENT, vol. 5, pp. 549–551, 1928.

157. GIBBS, R. E.: Structure of Alpha Quartz, *Proc. Roy. Soc.*, vol. 110, pp. 443–455, 1926.

158. GIBBS, R. E., and V. N. THATTE: Temperature Variation of the Frequency of Piezoelectric Oscillations of Quartz, *Phil. Mag.*, vol. 14, pp. 682–694, 1932.

159. GIBBS, R. E., and L. C. TSIEN: The Production of Piezoelectricity by Torsion, *Phil. Mag.*, vol. 22, pp. 311–322, 1936.

160. GIEBE, E.: Luminous Piezoelectric Resonators as High-frequency Standards, *ZS. tech. Ph.*, vol. 7, p. 235, 1926.

161. GIEBE, E., and E. BLECHSCHMIDT: Experimental and Theoretical Investigations on Extensional Vibrations of Rods and Tubes, I, *An. Phk.*, vol. 18, pp. 417–456; II, *An. Phk.*, vol. 18, pp. 457–485, 1933.

162. GIEBE, E., and E. BLECHSCHMIDT: On Torsional Vibrations of Quartz Rods and Their Use as Standards of Frequency, *Hfr. u. El. ak.*, vol. 56, pp. 65–87, 1940.

163. GIEBE, E., and A. SCHEIBE: Luminous Effects of High-frequency Longitudinal Vibrations in Piezoelectric Crystals, *ZS. Ph.*, vol. 33, pp. 335–344, 1925.

164. GIEBE, E., and A. SCHEIBE: A Simple Method for Qualitative Indication of Piezoelectricity of Crystals, *ZS. Ph.*, vol. 33, pp. 760–766, 1925.

165. GIEBE, E., and A. SCHEIBE: Luminous Piezoelectric Resonators as High-frequency Standards, *ETZ*, vol. 47, pp. 380–385, 1926.

166. GIEBE, E., and A. SCHEIBE: Piezoelectric Excitation of Elastic Vibrations, *ZS. Hfr.*, vol. 30, pp. 32–33, 1927.

167. GIEBE, E., and A. SCHEIBE: Activity of the Phys.-tech. Reichsanstalt in the Year 1926, *ZS. Instr.*, vol. 46, pp. 269–297, June, 1927.

168. GIEBE, E. and A. SCHEIBE: Piezoelectric Crystals as Standards of Frequency, *ENT*, vol. 5, pp. 65–82, 1928.

169. GIEBE, E., and A. SCHEIBE: Piezoelectric Excitation of Extensional, Flexural, and Torsional Vibrations of Quartz Rods, *ZS. Ph.*, vol. 46, pp. 607–652, 1928.

170. GIEBE, E., and A. SCHEIBE: Flexurally Vibrating Luminous Resonators as Frequency Standards in the Range from 1000 to 20000 Hertz, *ZS. Hfr.*, vol. 35, pp. 165–177, 1930.

171. GIEBE, E., and A. SCHEIBE: On the Series Relationships of the Natural Elastic Frequencies of Quartz Rods, *An. Phk.*, vol. 9, pp. 93–175, 1931.

172. GIEBE, E., and A. SCHEIBE: On Luminous Resonators as Standards of High Frequency, *Hfr. u. El. ak.*, vol. 41, pp. 83–96, 1933.

173. GOCKEL, H.: Decrement of Damping in Piezoelectric Crystals, *Phys. ZS.*, vol. 37, pp. 657–659, 1936.

174. GOEDECKE, H.: The Dielectric Constant of Rochelle Salt in an Electric Field, as a Function of Time, *ZS. Ph.*, vol. 94, pp. 574–589, 1935.

175. GOENS, E.: Determination of Young's Modulus from Flexural Oscillations, *An. Phk.*, vol. 11, pp. 649–678, 1931.

176. GOENS, E.: On Flexural and Torsional Vibrations of a Thin Crystal Rod of any Crystallographic Orientation, *An. Phk.*, vol. 15, pp. 455–484, 1932.

177. GOENS, E.: On the Calculation of Velocity of Propagation of Elastic Waves in Crystals, *An. Phk.*, vol. 29, pp. 279–285, 1937.

178. GOLAY, M. J. E.: A Rochelle Salt Electrometer, *R.S.I.*, vol. 8, pp. 228–230, July, 1937.

179. GOODMAN, B.: Keying the Crystal Oscillator, *QST*, vol. 25, pp. 10–13, May, 1941.

180. GRAMONT, A. DE: On the Movements of a Quartz Crystal in an Electrostatic Field, *C.R.*, vol. 196, pp. 1705–1707, 1933.

181. GRAMONT, A. DE: On Various Types of Vibration of a Quartz Parallelepiped, *C.R.*, vol. 197, pp. 101–103, 1933.

182. GRAMONT, A. DE: Clock Controlled by Means of Piezoelectric Quartz, *An. fr. chron.*, no. 1, pp. 37–43, 1937.

183. GRAMONT, A. DE, and D. BÉRETZKI: A New Method for Temperature Control of Quartz Crystals, *ETZ*, vol. 53, pp. 1039–1040, 1932.

184. GRAMONT, A. DE, and D. BÉRETZKI: Stabilization of Beat Frequency by Temperature-coefficient Compensation, *C.R.*, vol. 200, pp. 1558–1560, 1935.

185. GRAMONT, A. DE, and D. BÉRETZKI: On the Generation of Acoustic Waves by Means of Piezoelectric Quartz, *C.R.*, vol. 202, pp. 1229–1232, 1936.

186. GRAMONT, A. DE, and D. BÉRETZKI: Determination of the Area of a Piezoelectric Plate as Function of Frequency (optimal ratio of diameter to thickness for high-frequency piezo-oscillators), *C.R.*, vol. 204, pp. 459–462, 1937.

187. GRANT, K.: High-frequency Interruption of Light, *Nature*, vol. 120, p. 586, 1927.

188. GREENIDGE, R. M. C.: The Mounting and Fabrication of Plated Quartz Crystal Units, *Bell Syst. T.J.*, vol. 23, pp. 234–259, 1944.

189. GROSSMANN, E., and M. WIEN: On the Effect of Surroundings on the Frequency of a Quartz Resonator, *Phys. ZS.*, vol. 32, pp. 377–378, 1931.

190. GROTH, E. J., and L. N. LIEBERMANN: Precision Measurement of the Velocity of Sound at Supersonic Frequencies Using a Microphone (abstr.), *Phys. Rev.*, vol. 65, p. 350, 1944.

191. GRUETZMACHER, J.: Piezoelectric Crystal with Very Low Natural Frequency, *ENT*, vol. 12, p. 257, 1935.

192. GRUETZMACHER, J.: Piezoelectric Crystal with Ultrasonic Convergence, *ZS. Ph.*, vol. 96, pp. 342–349, 1935.

193. GRUETZMACHER, J.: Directed Supersonic Radiator, *ZS. tech. Ph.*, vol. 17, pp. 166–167, 1936.

194. GÜNTHER, N.: Investigation of the Effect of Mechanical and Electrical Forces on the Double Refraction of Quartz, *An. Phk.*, vol. 13, pp. 783–801, 1932.

195. GÜNTHER, R.: On a Measurement of the Equivalent Electrical Constants of Piezoelectric Crystals, *Hfr. u. El. ak.*, vol. 45, pp. 185–186, 1935.

196. GÜNTHER, R.: The Equivalent Electrical Constants of Piezoelectric Crystals and Their Measurement, *Hfr. u. El. ak.*, vol. 50, pp. 200–203, 1937.

197. GÜNTHER, R.: The Internal Friction in Quartz Crystals, *ENT*, vol. 16, pp. 53–62, 1939.

198. HABLÜTZEL, J.: Anomalous Expansion of Rochelle Salt, *Helv. Ph. Ac.*, vol. 8, pp. 498–499, 1935.

199. HABLÜTZEL, J.: Dielectric Investigations of Heavy-water Rochelle Salt, *Helv. Ph. Ac.*, vol. 12, pp. 489–510, 1939.

200. HANDEL, P. VON: Investigations of Quartz-controlled Oscillations, *ENT*, vol. 7, pp. 34–40, 1930.

201. HANDEL, P. VON: Investigations of the Behavior of Quartz-controlled Transmitters, *Luftfahrt-F.*, vol. 8, pp. 121–140, 1930.

202. HANDEL, P. VON, K. KRÜGER, and H. PLENDL: Quartz Control for Frequency Stabilization in Short-wave Receivers, *Proc. I.R.E.*, vol. 18, pp. 307–320, 1930; *Hfr. u. El. ak.*, vol. 34, pp. 12–18, 1929.

203. HANKEL, W. G.: Following are references to a few of the more important of Hankel's many papers on pyro- and piezoelectricity. Abstracts of all are in *ZS. Kr.* and *Neues Jahrb. Min.* (a) *Abh. Sächs.*, vol. 10, pp. 345*f.*, 1872. (b) *Abh. Sächs.*, vol. 12, pp. 457–548, 1881. (c) *Abh. Sächs.*, vol. 12, pp. 549–596, 1882. (d) *Abh. Sächs.*, vol. 24, pp. 467–497, 1899. (e) *Ber. Sächs.*, vol. 33, pp. 52–63, 1881. (f) *An. Phk.*, vol. 10, pp. 618*f.*, 1880. (g) *An. Phk.*, vol. 19, pp. 818–844, 1883. It was in papers (b) and (e) that the term "piezoelectricity" was introduced.

204. HARDING, J. W., and F. W. G. WHITE: On the Modes of Vibration of a Quartz Crystal, *Phil. Mag.*, vol. 8, pp. 169–179, 1929.

205. HARRISON, J. R.: Piezoelectric Resonance and Oscillatory Phenomena with Flexural Vibrations in Quartz Plates, *Proc. I.R.E.*, vol. 15, pp. 1040–1054, 1927.

206. HARRISON, J. R.: Piezoelectric Oscillator Circuits with Four-electrode Tubes, *Proc. I.R.E.*, vol. 16, pp. 1455–1467, 1928; discussion, pp. 1467–1470.

207. HARRISON, J. R.: Push-pull Piezoelectric Oscillator Circuits, *Proc. I.R.E.*, vol. 18, pp. 95–100, 1930.

208. HARRISON, J. R., and I. P. HOOPER: The Striated Luminous Glow of the Piezoelectric Quartz Resonator at Flexural Vibration Frequencies, *Phys. Rev.*, vol. 55, p. 674, 1939.

209. HATAKEYAMA, K.: Frequency Variation of Quartz Resonator Due to Heating by Its Vibration, *J.I.T.T.E. Jap.*, no. 109, pp. 522–532, 1932; *R.R.R.W. Jap.*, vol. 2, supp., p. 6, 1932.

210. HAYASHI, F.: Observations on Pyroelectricity, dissertation, Göttingen, 48 pp., 1912.

211. HAYASI, T., and S. AKASI: Quick Building-up of the Electron-coupled Quartz Oscillator, *Electrotech. Jour.* (*Jap.*), vol. 3, pp. 219–222, 1939.

212. HEATON, V. E., and E. G. LAPHAM: Quartz Plate Mountings and Temperature Control for Piezo Oscillators, *Proc. I.R.E.*, vol. 20, pp. 261–271, 1932; discussion, p. 1064; *J. Res. N.B.S.*, vol. 7, pp. 683–690, 1931.

213. HECKMANN, G.: The Lattice Theory of Solids, *Ergeb. exakt. Naturwiss.*, vol. 4, pp. 100–153, 1925.

214. HEEGNER, K.: On Measurements with Piezoelectric Crystals, *ZS. Hfr.*, vol. 29, pp. 177–180, 1927.

215. HEEGNER, K.: On the Pierce Crystal Oscillator, *ENT*, vol. 10, pp. 357–371, 1933.

216. HEEGNER, K.: Coupled Self-excited Circuits and Crystal Oscillators, *ENT*, vol. 15, pp. 359–368, 1938.

217. HEHLGANS, F. W.: On Plates of Piezoelectric Quartz as Transmitters and Receivers of High-frequency Sound-waves, *An. Phk.*, vol. 86, pp. 587–627, 1928.

218. HEIERLE, J.: The Frequency Constancy of Tourmaline-controlled Ultra-short-wave Transmitters, *Helv. Ph. Ac.*, vol. 10, pp. 345–346, 1937.

219. HENDERSON, J. T.: Properties of Tourmaline Crystals Used as Piezoelectric Resonators, *Trans. Roy. Soc. Can.*, vol. 22, pp. 127–131, 1928.

220. HERLINGER, E.: On a New Photogoniometer, *ZS. Kr.*, vol. 66, pp. 282–296, 1927.

221. HETTICH, A.: Piezoelectric Experiments According to the Principle of the Method of Giebe and Scheibe, *ZS. Ph.*, vol. 65, pp. 506–511, 1930.

222. HETTICH, A.: On Ammonium Salts at Low Temperatures, *ZS. ph. Chem. A*, vol. 168, pp. 353–362, 1933.

223. HETTICH, A., and A. SCHLEEDE: Polarity and Piezoelectric Excitation, *ZS. Ph.*, vol. 46, pp. 147–148, 1927.

224. HETTICH, A., and A. SCHLEEDE: Contributions to the Methods for Determining Crystal Classes, *ZS. Ph.*, vol. 50, pp. 249–265, 1928.

225. HIGHT, S. C.: Wind from Quartz Crystals, *Bell Labs. Rec.*, vol. 14, pp. 121–123, 1935.

226. HIGHT, S. C.: Quartz Plates for Frequency Sub-standards, *Bell Labs. Rec.*, vol. 16, pp. 21–25, 1937.

227. HIGHT, S. C., and G. W. WILLARD: A Simplified Circuit for Frequency Sub-standards Employing a New Type of Low-frequency Zero-temperature-coefficient Quartz Crystal, *Proc. I.R.E.*, vol. 25, pp. 549–563, 1937.

228. HILTSCHER, R.: Piezoelectric Vibration Experiments with Rochelle Salt Crystals, *ZS. Ph.*, vol. 104, pp. 672–680, 1937.

229. HINZ, H.: Elastic Deformations of Rochelle Salt, *ZS. Ph.*, vol. 111, pp. 617–632, 1939.

230. HITCHCOCK, R. C.: The Dimensions of Low-frequency Quartz Oscillators, *R.S.I.*, vol. 1, pp. 13–21, 1930.

231. HOLDEN, A. N., and W. P. MASON: Constants of Heavy-water Rochelle Salt, *Phys. Rev.*, vol. 57, pp. 54–56, 1940.

232. HOLMAN, W. F.: Piezoelectric Excitation of Cane Sugar, *An. Phk.*, vol. 29, pp. 160–178, 1909.

233. HOLTON, G. J.: Rodometric Examination of Quartz Crystals, *Electronics*, vol. 17, pp. 114*f.*, 1944. U.S. Pat. No. 2,374,543.

234. HORTON, J. W., and W. A. MARRISON: Precision Determination of Frequency, *Proc. I.R.E.*, vol. 16, pp. 137–154, 1928.

235. HOVGAARD, O. M.: Application of Quartz Plates to Radio Transmitters, *Proc. I.R.E.*, vol. 20, pp. 767–782, 1932.

236. HUBBARD, J. C.: The Acoustic Resonator Interferometer, I, *Phys. Rev.*, vol. 38, pp. 1011–1019, 1931; II, *Phys. Rev.*, vol. 41, pp. 523–535, 1932; *errata*, vol. 46, p. 525, 1934.

237. HUBBARD, J. C.: Ultrasonics—A Survey, *Am. Jour. Phys.*, vol. 8, pp. 207–221, 1940.

238. HUND, A.: Uses and Possibilities of Piezoelectric Oscillators, *Proc. I.R.E.*, vol. 14, pp. 447–469, 1926.

239. HUND, A.: Notes on Quartz Plates, Air Gap Effect and Audio-frequency Generation, *Proc. I.R.E.*, vol. 16, pp. 1072–1078, 1928.

240. HUND, A.: Generator for Audio Currents of Adjustable Frequency with Piezoelectric Stabilization, *Sci. Pap. Bur. St.*, vol. 22, pp. 631–637, 1928 (No. 569); *QST fr.*, vol. 9, pp. 16–19, 1928.

241. HUND, A.: Note on a Piezoelectric Generator for Audiofrequencies, *J. Res. N.B.S.*, vol. 2, pp. 355–358, 1929.

242. HUND, A., and R. B. WRIGHT: New Piezo-oscillations with Quartz Cylinders Cut along the Optical Axis, *Proc. I.R.E.*, vol. 18, pp. 741–761, 1930; *J. Res. N.B.S.*, vol. 4, pp. 383–394, 1930.

243. ISELEY, F. C.: The Relation between the Mechanical and Piezoelectrical Properties of a Rochelle Salt Crystal, *Phys. Rev.*, vol. 24, pp. 569–574, 1924.

244. JACKSON, C. H.: Development of an Improved Crystal Exciter Unit, *Civil Aeronautics Authority (U.S.A.)*, Tech. Development Rept. 26, pp. 1–14, July, 1940.

245. JAFFE, H.: Polymorphism of Rochelle Salt, *Phys. Rev.*, vol. 51, pp. 43–47, 1937.

246. JAFFE, H.: Crystalline Transitions and Dielectric Constant (abst.), *Phys. Rev.*, vol. 53, p. 917, 1938.

247. JEFFERSON, H.: The Pierce Piezoelectric Oscillator, *W.E.*, vol. 18, pp. 232–237, 1941.

248. JIMBO, S.: An International Comparison of Frequency by Means of a Luminous Quartz Resonator, *Proc. I.R.E.*, vol. 18, pp. 1930–1934, 1930; *Elec. Rev. (Jap.)*, vol. 18, pp. 185–194, 1930; *Researches Electrotech. Lab.*, Tokyo, March, 1930.

249. KAMAYACHI, Z., and H. WATANABE: On Ultra-short-wave Quartz Crystal Vibrators, *Electrotech. Jour. (Jap.)*, vol. 5, pp. 19–20, 1941.

250. KAMIENSKI, S.: Spherical Piezoelectric Resonators, *Wiadomosci i Prace (WPPIT)*, vol. 7, pp. 54–58, 1936.

251. KAMMER, E. W., and J. V. ATANASOFF: A Determination of the Elastic Constants of Beta-quartz, *Phys. Rev.*, vol. 62, pp. 395–400, 1942.

252. KAO, P. T.: Relaxation Oscillations Produced by a Quartz Piezoelectric Oscillator, *C.R.*, vol. 191, pp. 932–934, 1930.

253. KAO, P. T.: A Phenomenon Produced in Polarized Light by Quartz in Vibration, *C.R.*, vol. 200, pp. 563–565, 1935.

254. KARCHER, J. C.: A Piezoelectric Method for the Instantaneous Measurement of High Pressures, *Sci. Pap. Bur. St.*, vol. 18, pp. 257–264, 1922 (No. 445); *J. Frank. Inst.*, vol. 194, pp. 815–816 (abst.), 1922.

255. KELLER, H.: Piezoelectric Flexural Strip as an Electromechanical Transducer, *Hfr. u. El. ak.*, vol. 60, pp. 5–10, 1942.

256. KELVIN, LORD: On the Piezoelectric Property of Quartz, *Phil. Mag.*, vol. 36, pp. 331, 342, 384, 453, 1893.

257. KEYS, D. A.: Adiabatic and Isothermal Piezoelectric Constants of Tourmaline, *Phil. Mag.*, vol. 46, pp. 999–1001, 1923.

258. KHOL, F.: A Method for the Measurement of Elastic Constants, *ZS. Ph.*, vol. 108, pp. 225–231, 1938.

259. KHOL, F.: Elastic Constants and Phase Velocities of Transverse and Longitudinal Waves, *ZS. Ph.*, vol. 111, pp. 450–453, 1939.

260. KISHPAUGH, A. W., and R. E. CORAM: Low Power Radio Transmitters for Broadcast Requirements for 100 to 1000 Watts, *Proc. I.R.E.*, vol. 21, pp. 212–227, 1933.

261. KLUGE, M., and H. SCHÖNFELD: Electric Barkhausen Effect in Rochelle Salt Crystals, *Naturwiss.*, vol. 21, p. 194, 1933.

262. KNOL, K. S.: Measurement of the Piezoelectric Modulus of Zinc Blende, *Konink. Akad. Amst.*, vol. 35, pp. 99–106, 1932.

263. KOBEKO, P., and I. KURCHATOV: Dielectric Properties of Rochelle Salt Crystals, *ZS. Ph.*, vol. 66, pp. 192–205, 1930; *J. Russ. Ph.-Chem. Soc.*, vol. 62, p. 251, 1930.

264. KOBEKO, P., and J. G. NELIDOV: The Discontinuity in the Specific Heat of Rochelle Salt, *Phys. ZS. d. Sowjetunion*, vol. 1, pp. 382–386, 1932.

265. KOBZAREV, J.: On the Parameters of Piezoelectric Resonators, *J. Appl. Ph. (Russian)*, vol. 6, pp. 17–37, 1929.

266. KOGA, I.: On the Piezoelectric Oscillator, *Denki Hyoron*, vol. 15, p. 547, 1927.

267. KOGA, I.: Tuning Fork Made of Quartz Crystal, *J.I.E.E. (Japan)*, vol. 48, p. 100, 1928; *Rep. El. Res. Inst. Tokyo*, series 1, pp. 213–221, 1928.

268. KOGA, I.: Characteristics of Piezoelectric Quartz Oscillators, *Proc. I.R.E.*, vol. 18, pp. 1935–1959, 1930.

269. KOGA, I.: Note on the Piezoelectric Quartz Oscillating Crystal Regarded from the Principle of Similitude, *Proc. I.R.E.*, vol. 19, pp. 1022–1023, 1931.

270. KOGA, I.: Thickness Vibrations of Piezoelectric Oscillating Crystals, *Physics*, vol. 3, pp. 70–80, 1932; *R.R.R.W. Jap.*, vol. 2, pp. 157–173, 1932; *J.I.T.T.E. Jap.*, no. 115, pp. 1223–1253, 1932.

271. KOGA, I.: Vibration of Piezoelectric Oscillating Crystal, *Phil. Mag.*, vol. 16, pp. 275–283, 1933.

272. KOGA, I.: Thermal Characteristics of Piezoelectric Oscillating Quartz Plates, *U.R.S.I. Gen. Assembly, Document* 33, *Comm.* I, London, 1934; *R.R.R.W. Jap.*, vol. 4, pp. 61–76, 1934.

273. KOGA, I.: On the Temperature-coefficients of Quartz Plates for Long Waves, *ENT*, vol. 12, pp. 1–2, 1935.

274. KOGA, I.: Notes on Piezoelectric Quartz Crystals, *Proc. I.R.E.*, vol. 24, pp. 510–531, 1936.

275. KOGA, I.: Young's Modulus of a Crystal in any Direction, *Proc. I.R.E.*, vol. 24, pp. 532–533, 1936.

276. KOGA, I.: Vibrating Piezoelectric Quartz Plates without Variation of Frequency with Temperature, *L'Onde élec.*, vol. 15, pp. 457–468, 498–507, 1936.

277. KOGA, I.: A Portable Standard Frequency Oscillator, *R.R.R.W. Jap.*, vol. 7, pp. 219–225, 1937.

278. KOGA, I.: An Ultra-short-wave Quartz Crystal Oscillator, *R.R.R.W. Jap.*, vol. 7, pp. 227–229, 1937.

279. KOGA, I.: Equivalence of Two Piezoelectric Oscillating Quartz Crystals of Symmetrical Outlines with Respect to a Plane Perpendicular to an Electrical Axis, *Phil. Mag.*, vol. 27, pp. 640–643, 1939.

280. KOGA, I.: Variable Resistance Device and Its Application Especially to the Frequency Modulation of Quartz Crystal Oscillator, *Electrotech. Jour. (Jap.)*, vol. 4, no. 5, pp. 99–107, 1940.

281. KOGA, I., and M. SHOYAMA: Contour Vibration of Rectangular X-cut Oscillating Quartz Plate, *J.I.E.E. (Japan)*, vol. 56, p. 852, 1936.

282. KOGA, I., and M. SHOYAMA: Transient Frequency Variation of Crystal Oscillator (abst.), *R.R.R.W. Jap.*, vol. 8, p. 6, 1938; *Electrotech. Jour. (Jap.)*, vol. 2, pp. 199–201, 1938.

283. KOGA, I., and M. TATIBANA: Anomalies of Thickness Vibration of Quartz Plates Due to Non-uniform Thickness, *Electrotech. Jour. (Jap.)*, vol. 3, pp. 81–85, 1939.

284. KOGA, I., and W. YAMAMOTO: Beat-frequency Crystal Oscillator, *Electrotech. Jour. (Jap.)*, vol. 4, pp. 134–137, 1940.

285. KOGA, I., W. YAMAMOTO, H. NISIO, O. HARASIMA, and S. IKEZAWA: 250-Watt Pentode Crystal Oscillator, *Electrotech. Jour. (Jap.)*, vol. 3, pp. 92–94, 1939.

286. KOLENKO, B. VON: Pyroelectricity of Quartz with Respect to Its Crystalline System, *ZS. Kr.*, vol. 9, pp. 1–28, 1884.

287. KÖRNER, H.: Growing Rochelle-salt Crystals for Reproducible Measurements, *ZS. Ph.*, vol. 94, pp. 801–807, 1935.

288. KÖRNER, H.: Dielectric Constant, Conductivity and Piezo-effect of Rochelle-salt Crystals, *ZS. Ph.*, vol. 103, pp. 170–190, 1936.

289. KOTLYAREVSKI, M. L., and E. YA. PUMPER: Investigations of the Oscillations of Piezo-quartz Plates by the Interferometer Method, *J. Ph. U.S.S.R.*, vol. 4, pp. 67–78, 1941.

290. KRISTA, F.: Dependence of the Velocity of Propagation of Flexural Vibrations upon Frequency, *ZS. Ph.*, vol. 112, pp. 326–338, 1939.

291. KÜHNHOLD, W.: The Control by Means of Tourmaline Crystals of Ultra-short Waves Excited in any Type of Circuit, *Hfr. u. El. ak.*, vol. 46, pp. 82–85, 1935.

292. KURCHATOV, B., and M. EREMEEV: On the Electrical Properties of Rochelle-salt Mixed Crystals, *Phys. ZS. d. Sowjetunion*, vol. 1, pp. 140–154, 1932.

293. KURCHATOV, B., and I. KURCHATOV: The Lower Curie-point in Rochelle Salt, *Phys. ZS. d. Sowjetunion*, vol. 3, pp. 321–334, 1933.

294. KURCHATOV, I.: Unipolarity of Polarization in Rochelle-salt Crystals, *Phys. ZS. d. Sowjetunion*, vol. 4, pp. 125–129, 1933.

295. KURCHATOV, I.: Rochelle Salt in the Region of Spontaneous Orientation, *Phys. ZS. d. Sowjetunion*, vol. 5, pp. 200–211, 1934.

296. KURCHATOV, I., and A. SHAKIROV: Inversion Phenomena in the Polarization of Rochelle Salt, *Phys. ZS. d. Sowjetunion*, vol. 7, pp. 631–638, 1935 (in German). KURTSCHATOW—see KURCHATOV.

297. KUSUNOSE, Y., and S. ISHIKAWA: Frequency Stabilization of Radio Transmitters, *Proc. I.R.E.*, vol. 20, pp. 310–339, 1932; *R.R.R.W. Jap.*, vol. 1, pp. 157–183, 1931.

298. LACK, F. R.: Observations on Modes of Vibration and Temperature-coefficients of Quartz Crystal Plates, *Proc. I.R.E.*, vol. 17, pp. 1123–1141, 1929; *Bell Syst. T.J.*, vol. 8, pp. 515–535, 1929.

299. LACK, F. R., G. W. WILLARD, and I. E. FAIR: Some Improvements in Quartz Crystal Circuit Elements, *Bell Syst. T.J.*, vol. 13, pp. 453–463, 1934.

300. LAMB, J. J.: A More Stable Crystal Oscillator of High Harmonic Output, *QST*, vol. 17, pp. 30–32, June, 1933.

301. LAMB, J. J.: Tritet Multi-band Crystal Control, *QST*, vol. 17, pp. 9–15, October, 1933.

302. LAMB, J. J.: A Practical Survey of Pentode and Beam Tube Crystal Oscillators for Fundamental and Second Harmonic Output, *QST*, vol. 21, pp. 31–38, 106, 107, April, 1937.

303. LANE, C. T.: Magnetic Properties of Rochelle Salt, *Phys. Rev.*, vol. 45, p. 66, 1934.

304. LANGEVIN, A.: On the Variation of the Piezoelectric Modulus of Quartz with Temperature, *J. phq.*, vol. 7, pp. 95–100, 1936.

305. LANGEVIN, A.: Absolute Value of the Principal Piezoelectric Modulus of Quartz, *C.R.*, vol. 209, pp. 627–630, 1939.

306. LANGEVIN, A., and A. MOULIN: On the Variation of the Piezoelectric Modulus of Quartz with Temperature, *J. phq.*, vol. 8, pp. 257–259, 1937.

307. LANGEVIN, P., and J. SOLOMON: On the Laws of the Liberation of Electricity by Torsion in Piezoelectric Bodies, *C.R.*, vol. 200, pp. 1257–1260, 1935.

308. LARMOR, J.: Electro-crystalline Properties as Conditioned by Atomic Lattices, *Proc. Roy. Soc.*, vol. 99, pp. 1–10, 1921.

309. LAUE, M. v.: Piezoelectrically Excited Vibrations of Quartz Rods, *ZS. Ph.*, vol. 34, pp. 347–361, 1925.

310. LAWSON, A. W.: The Piezoelectricity of Beta-quartz, *Science*, vol. 92, p. 419, 1940.

311. LAWSON, A. W.: A Determination of the Elastic Modulus s_{13} of Beta-quartz, *Phys. Rev.*, vol. 59, pp. 608–612, 1941.

312. LAWSON, A. W.: Comment on the Elastic Constants of Alpha-quartz, *Phys. Rev.*, vol. 59, p. 838, 1941.

313. LAWSON, A. W.: The Vibration of Piezoelectric Plates, *Phys. Rev.*, vol. 62, pp. 71–76, 1942.

314. LEITHÄUSER, G., and V. PETRZILKA: On Standards for Measurement of Ultra-short Waves, *Funktech. Mon.*, no. 9, 1932.

315. LE QUÉRÉ, H.: An Apparatus Designed for the Determination of the Pyro-electric Effect, *Bull. soc. min. fr.*, vol. 59, pp. 137–142, 1936.

316. LIPPMANN, G.: Principle of the Conservation of Electricity, *C.R.*, vol. 92, pp. 1049–1051, 1149–1152, 1881; *J. phq.*, vol. 10, pp. 381–394, 1881; *An. chim. phys.*, ser. 5, vol. 24, pp. 145–178, 1881 (prediction of the converse piezoelectric effect).

317. LISSÜTIN, A.: The Vibrations of a Quartz Plate, *ZS. Ph.*, vol. 59, pp. 265–273, 1930.

318. LLEWELLYN, F. B.: Constant Frequency Oscillators, *Bell Syst. T.J.*, vol. 11, pp. 67–100, 1932; *Proc. I.R.E.*, vol. 19, pp. 2063–2094, 1931.

319. LONN, E.: Theory of Oscillation of Crystal Plates, *An. Phk.*, vol. 30, pp. 420–432, 1937.

320. LUCAS, H. J.: Some Developments of the Piezoelectric Crystal as a Frequency Standard, *J.I.E.E. (London)*, vol. 68, pp. 855–872, 1930; reprinted in *Wireless Section*, vol. 5, pp. 151–163, 1930; discussion, pp. 163–168.

321. LUCAS, R., and P. BIQUARD: New Optical Properties of Liquids Subjected to Ultra-sonic Waves, *C.R.*, vol. 194, pp. 2132–2134, 1932; more fully in *J. phq.*, vol. 3, pp. 464–477, 1932.

322. LÜDY, W.: The Piezoelectricity of Potassium Phosphate, *ZS. Ph.*, vol. 113, pp. 302–305, 1939; *Helv. Ph. Ac.*, vol. 12, pp. 278–279, 1939.

323. LÜDY, W.: Effect of Temperature on the Dynamic-elastic Behavior of Substances like Rochelle Salt, *Helv. Ph. Ac.*, vol. 15, pp. 527–552, 1942.

324. MACKINNON, K. A.: Crystal Control Applied to the Dynatron Oscillator, *Proc. I.R.E.*, vol. 20, pp. 1689–1714, 1932.

325. MALLETT, E., and V. J. TERRY: The Quartz Oscillator, *W. World*, vol. 16, pp. 630–636, 1925.

326. MANDELL, W.: The Determination of the Elastic Moduli of the Piezoelectric Crystal Rochelle Salt by a Statical Method, *Proc. Roy. Soc.*, vol. 116, pp. 623–636, 1927.

327. MANDELL, W.: The Change in Elastic Properties on Replacing the Potassium Atom of Rochelle Salt by the Ammonium Group, *Proc. Roy. Soc.*, vol. 121, pp. 122–130, 1928.

328. MANDELL, W.: The Determination of the Piezoelectric Moduli of Ammonium Seignette Salt, *Proc. Roy. Soc.*, vol. 121, pp. 130–140, 1928.

329. MANDELL, W.: Resonance in Crystal Beams of Sodium-ammonium Seignette Salt, *Proc. Roy. Soc.*, vol. 165, pp. 414–431, 1938.

330. MARRISON, W. A.: A High Precision Standard of Frequency, *Proc. I.R.E.*, vol. 17, pp. 1103–1122, 1929; *Bell Syst. T.J.*, vol. 8, pp. 493–514, 1929.

331. MARRISON, W. A.: The Crystal Clock, *Proc. Nat. Acad. Sci.*, vol. 16, pp. 496–507, 1930.

332. MASON, W. P.: Electrical Wave Filters Employing Quartz Crystals as Elements, *Bell Syst. T.J.*, vol. 13, pp. 405–452, 1934.

333. MASON, W. P.: The Motion of a Bar Vibrating in Flexure, Including the Effects of Rotary and Lateral Inertia, *J.A.S.A.*, vol. 6, pp. 246–249, 1935.

334. MASON, W. P.: An Electromechanical Representation of a Piezoelectric Crystal Used as a Transducer, *Proc. I.R.E.*, vol. 23, pp. 1252–1263, 1935; *Bell. Syst. T.J.*, vol. 14, pp. 718–723, 1935.

335. MASON, W. P.: A Dynamic Measurement of the Elastic, Electric and Piezoelectric Constants of Rochelle Salt, *Phys. Rev.*, vol. 55, pp. 775–789, 1939.

336. MASON, W. P.: A New Quartz-crystal Plate, Designated the GT, Which Produces a Very Constant Frequency over a Wide Temperature Range, *Proc. I.R.E.*, vol. 28, pp. 220–223, May, 1940.

337. MASON, W. P.: Low Temperature Coefficient Quartz Crystals, *Bell Syst. T.J.*, vol. 19, pp. 74–93, 1940.

338. MASON, W. P.: The Location of Hysteresis Phenomena in Rochelle Salt Crystals, *Phys. Rev.*, vol. 58, pp. 744–756, 1940.

339. MASON, W. P.: Electrical and Mechanical Analogies, *Bell Syst. T.J.*, vol. 20, pp. 405–414, 1941.

340. MASON, W. P.: Quartz Crystal Applications, *Bell Syst. T.J.*, vol. 22, pp. 178–223, 1943.

341. MASON, W. P., and I. E. FAIR: A New Direct Crystal-controlled Oscillator for Ultra-short-wave Frequencies, *Proc. I.R.E.*, vol. 30, pp. 464–472, 1942.

342. MASON, W. P., and R. A. SYKES: Electrical Wave Filters Employing Crystals with Normal and Divided Electrodes, *Bell Syst. T.J.*, vol. 19, pp. 221–248, 1940.

343. MASON, W. P., and R. A. SYKES: Low Frequency Quartz-crystal Cuts Having Low Temperature Coefficients, *Proc. I.R.E.*, vol. 32, pp. 208–215, 1944.

344. MATSUMURA, S., and K. HATAKEYAMA: Comparison between Oscillations of Short Wave Length Produced by Means of Quartz Resonator with Reference to the Effect of the Air Gap, *J.I.T.T.E. Jap.*, no. 87, pp. 575–580, 1930.

345. MATSUMURA, S., and K. HATAKEYAMA: On a Discontinuity in Wave Length of an X-cut Quartz Resonator Depending on the Dimensional Relation, *J.I.T.T.E. Jap.*, no. 91, pp. 946–952, October, 1930.

346. MATSUMURA, S., and K. HATAKEYAMA: On a Discontinuity in Wave Length of an X-cut Quartz Resonator of Rectangular Form and Method of Determining the Most Suitable Dimensions, *J.I.T.T.E. Jap.*, no. 97, pp. 469–477, April, 1931.

347. MATSUMURA, S., and K. HATAKEYAMA: Relation between the Wave Length Constant and Dimension of Rectangular X-cut Quartz Resonators, *J.I.T.T.E. Jap.*, no. 101, pp. 984–989, August, 1931.

348. MATSUMURA, S., and S. ISHIKAWA: On Tourmaline Oscillators, *R.R.R.W. Jap.*, vol. 3, pp. 1–5, 1933.

349. MATSUMURA, S., S ISHIKAWA, and S. KANZAKI: Effect of Temperature on Piezoelectric Vibration of Tourmaline Plate, *J.I.E.E. (Japan)*, vol. 53, p. 199, 1933; *Monthly Bibliographical. Ref. U.R.S.I.*, p. 10, May, 1933.

350. MATSUMURA, S., and S. KANZAKI: On the Temperature Coefficient of Natural Frequency of Y-waves in X-cut Quartz Plates, *R.R.R.W. Jap.*, vol. 2, pp. 35–48, 157–173, 1932.

351. MATSUMURA, S., and S. KANZAKI: On a Method of Reducing the Temperature Coefficient of a Piezo-resonator, *J.I.T.T.E. Jap.*, no. 111, pp. 834–842, 1932; *J.I.E.E. (Japan)*, vol. 52, suppl. issue, pp. 172–174, 929, 1932.

352. MATSUMURA, S., and S. KANZAKI: Quartz Plates with a Very Small Temperature-coefficient of Oscillation Frequency, *U.R.S.I. Gen. Assembly, Document 34*, Comm. I, London, 1934; *Elec. Rev. (Jap.)*, vol. 21, pp. 24f., 1933; *R.R.R.W. Jap.*, vol. 4, pp. 105–108, 1934; abstr. in *J.I.E.E. (Japan)*, vol. 52, p. 932, 1932, vol. 53, p. 201, 1933.

353. MATTHIAS, B.: On the Piezoelectric ΔE-effect in the Seignette-electrics, *Helv. Ph. Ac.*, vol. 16, pp. 99–135, 1943.

354. MATTHIAS, B., and P. SCHERRER: Crystal Band Pass Filters, *Helv. Ph. Ac.*, vol. 16, pp. 432–434, 1943.

355. MATTIAT, O.: On Vibrating Crystals of Rochelle Salt, *Hfr. u. El. ak.*, vol. 50, pp. 115–120, 1937.

356. McSKIMIN, H. J.: Theoretical Analysis of Modes of Vibration for Isotropic Rectangular Plates Having All Surfaces Free, *Bell Syst. T.J.*, vol. 23, pp. 151–177, 1944.

357. MEACHAM, L. A.: The Bridge-stabilized Oscillator, *Proc. I.R.E.*, vol. 26, pp. 1278–1294, 1938; *Bell Syst. T.J.*, vol. 17, pp. 574–591, 1938; short account in *Bell Labs. Rec.*, suppl. to vol. 18, January, 1940.

358. MEAHL, H. R.: Quartz Crystal Controlled Oscillator Circuits, *Proc. I.R.E.*, vol. 22, pp. 732–737, 1934.

359. MEISSNER, A.: Piezoelectric Crystals at High Frequency, *ZS. tech. Ph.*, vol. 7,

pp. 585–592, 1926, vol. 8, pp. 74–77, 1927; *ENT*, vol. 3, pp. 401–408, 1926; *ZS. Hfr.*, vol. 29, pp. 20–24, 1927.

360. MEISSNER, A.: Piezoelectric Crystals at Radio Frequencies, *Proc. I.R.E.*, vol. 15, pp. 281–296, 1927.

361. MEISSNER, A.: Investigations on Quartz, *Phys. ZS.*, vol. 28, pp. 621–625, 1927.

362. MEISSNER, A., and R. BECHMANN: Investigation and Theory of Pyroelectricity, *ZS. tech. Ph.*, vol. 9, pp. 175–186, 1928.

363. MELIKIAN, A. B., and E. K. PIETROVA: On a Method for the Determination of Parameters of Piezo-resonators, *Izv. El. Slab. Toka*, no. 3, pp. 40–51, 1935.

364. MENDELSSOHN, J., and K. MENDELSSOHN: Specific Heat of a Substance Showing Spontaneous Electric Polarization, *Nature*, vol. 144, p. 595, 1939.

365. METSCHL, E. C.: The Nature and Applications of Piezoelectricity, *ETZ*, vol. 59, pp. 819–825, 1938.

366. MIKHAILOV, G.: The Influence of Temperature on the Frequency of Piezo-electric Oscillations in Rochelle Salt, *Tech. Phys. U.S.S.R.*, vol. 3, pp. 511–518, 1936.

367. MIKHAILOV, G.: The Investigations of Elastic Vibration in a Piezocrystal of Rochelle Salt, *Tech. Phys. U.S.S.R.*, vol. 3, pp. 652–661, 1936.

368. MIKHAILOV, G.: Influence of Temperature on the Dynamic Piezo-modulus of Rochelle Salt, *Tech. Phys. U.S.S.R.*, vol. 4, pp. 461–465, 1937.

369. MILLER, J. M.: Quartz Crystal Oscillators, *U.S. Navy Radio Sound Rept.*, issue of Apr. 1, May 1, June 1, 1925, pp. 53–64.

370. MITSUI, H.: Broadcast Frequency Monitor Employing Luminous Quartz Resonator, *Nippon Elec. Comm. Eng.*, no. 1, pp. 86–87, September, 1935.

371. MODRAK, P.: Quartz and Tourmaline, *W.E.*, vol. 14, pp. 127–134 and 175–183, 1937.

372. MOENS, R., and J. E. VERSCHAFFELT: Optical Phenomena Exhibited by Quartz When Vibrating Piezoelectrically, *C.R.*, vol. 185, pp. 1034–1036, 1927.

373. MÖGEL, H.: Control of Operation of Short-wave Transmitters, *ENT*, vol. 7, pp. 333–348, 1930; *Telef.-Z.*, vol. 11, pp. 8–21, 1930.

374. MÖGEL, H.: Monitoring the Operation of Short-wave Transmitters, *Proc. I.R.E.*, vol. 19, pp. 214–232, 1931.

375. MORRISON, J. F.: A New Broadcast Transmitter Circuit Design for Frequency Modulation, *Proc. I.R.E.*, vol. 28, pp. 444–449, 1940.

376. MUELLER, H.: Properties of Rochelle Salt, *Phys. Rev.*, vol. 47, pp. 175–191, 1935.

377. MUELLER, H.: Determination of Elasto-optical Constants with Supersonic Waves, *ZS. Kr.*, vol. 99, pp. 122–141, 1938.

378. MUELLER, H.: Properties of Rochelle Salt, II, *Phys. Rev.*, vol. 57, pp. 829–839, 1940.

379. MUELLER, H.: Influence of Electrostatic Fields on the Elastic Properties of Rochelle Salt, *Phys. Rev.*, vol. 57, pp. 842–843, 1940.

380. MUELLER, H.: Properties of Rochelle Salt, III, *Phys. Rev.*, vol. 58, pp. 565–573, 1940.

381. MUELLER, H.: Properties of Rochelle Salt, IV, *Phys. Rev.*, vol. 58, pp. 805–811, 1940.

382. MUELLER, H.: The Dielectric Anomalies of Rochelle Salt, *Ann. N.Y. Acad. Sci.*, vol. 40, pp. 321–356, 1940.

383. MÜLLER, H., and T. KRAEFFT: Doppler Effect with Piezoelectric Quartz, *Phys. ZS.*, vol. 33, pp. 305–306, 1932.

384. MURPHY, E. J., and S. O. MORGAN: The Dielectric Properties of Insulating Materials, *Bell Syst. T.J.*, vol. 16, pp. 493–512, 1937, vol. 17, pp. 640–669, 1938.

385. MYERS, L. M.: Application of the Electrometer Triode to the Determination of Piezoelectric Constants, *Brit. Rad. Ann.*, pp. 15–20, 1934–5.

386. NACHTIKAL, F.: Proportionality between Piezoelectric Moment and Pressure, *Nachr. Gött.*, pp. 109–118, 1899.

387. NACKEN, R.: Etching Experiments with Spheres of Quartz and α-quartz, *Neues Jahrb. Min.*, vol. 1, pp. 71–82, 1916.

388. NAMBA, S., and S. MATSUMURA: Piezoelectric Properties of Quartz and Its Value as a Frequency Standard, *J.I.T.T.E. Jap.*, no. 70, pp. 817–833, November, 1928; *Researches Electrotech. Lab. (Tokyo)*, no. 248, April, 1929 (in English); also in abbreviated form in *ZS. Hfr.*, vol. 34, pp. 198–200, 1929.

389. NAMBA, S., and S. MATSUMURA: Piezoelectric Quartz Resonator with a Small Temperature Coefficient, *J.I.E.E. (Japan)*, vol. 49, suppl. issue, pp. 9–10, 1929.

390. NELSON, E. L.: Radio Broadcasting Transmitters and Related Transmission Phenomena, *Bell Syst. T.J.*, vol. 9, pp. 121–140, 1930.

391. NICOLSON, A. M.: The Piezoelectric Effect in the Composite Rochelle Salt Crystal, *Trans. A.I.E.E.*, vol. 38, pp. 1467–1485, 1919; *Proc. A.I.E.E.*, vol. 38, pp. 1315–1333, 1919; *Electrician (London)*, vol. 83, pp. 32f., 1919.

392. NIESSEN, K. F.: Frequency-stability of Some Resonators, *Physica*, vol. 8, pp. 1077–1093, 1941.

393. NORGORDEN, O.: The Inverse Piezoelectric Properties of Rochelle Salt at Audio Frequencies, *Phys. Rev.*, vol. 49, pp. 820–828, 1936.

394. NORGORDEN, O.: The Piezoelectric Properties of Rochelle Salt, *Phys. Rev.*, vol. 50, p. 782, 1936 (letter to the editor).

395. NUSSBAUMER, B.: Measurement of the First Piezoelectric Modulus of Quartz, *ZS. Ph.*, vol. 78, pp. 781–790, 1932.

NY TSI-ZE—see TSI-ZE.

396. ONNES, H. K., and A. BECKMAN: Piezoelectric and Pyroelectric Properties of Quartz at Low Temperatures, *Konink. Akad. Amst.*, vol. 15, pp. 1380–1383, 1913; *Communication* 132f *Phys. Lab. Leyden.*

397. OPLATKA, G.: A New Method of Determining the Static Dielectric Constants of Semiconductors, and Measurements of the Dielectric Constant of Rochelle Salt, *Phys. ZS.*, vol. 34, pp. 296–300, 1933.

398. OSTERBERG, H.: An Interferometer Method of Observing the Vibrations of an Oscillating Quartz Plate, *Proc. Nat. Acad. Sci.*, vol. 15, pp. 892–896, 1929.

399. OSTERBERG, H.: An Interferometer Method of Studying the Vibrations of an Oscillating Quartz Plate, *J.O.S.A.*, vol. 22, pp. 19–35, 1932.

400. OSTERBERG, H.: A Triple Interferometer for Distinguishing Flexural and Longitudinal Vibrations in Quartz, *J.O.S.A.*, vol. 23, pp. 30–34, 1933.

401. OSTERBERG, H.: A Multiple Interferometer for Analyzing the Vibrations of a Quartz Plate, *Phys. Rev.*, vol. 43, pp. 819–829, 1933.

402. OSTERBERG, H.: A Refracting Interferometer for Examining Modes of Vibration in Quartz Plates, *R.S.I.*, vol. 5, pp. 183–186, 1934.

403. OSTERBERG, H., and J. W. COOKSON: Piezoelectric Stabilization of High Frequencies, *R.S.I.*, vol. 5, pp. 281–286, 1934.

404. OSTERBERG, H., and J. W. COOKSON: Some Piezoelectric and Elastic Properties of β-quartz, *J. Frank. Inst.*, vol. 220, pp. 361–371, 1935.

405. OSTERBERG, H., and J. W. COOKSON: A Theory of Two-dimensional Longitudinal and Flexural Vibrations in Rectangular Isotropic Plates, *Physics*, vol. 6, pp. 234–246, 1935.

406. OSTERBERG, H., and J. W. COOKSON: Longitudinal, Shear and Transverse Modes of Vibration in Quartz and Tourmaline, *Physics*, vol. 6, pp. 246–256, 1935.

407. OSTERBERG, H., and J. W. COOKSON: An Interference Method for Measuring the Piezoelectric Moduli of Alpha-quartz: The Moduli, *R.S.I.*, vol. 6, pp. 347–356, 1935.

408. PAVLIK, B.: Two Transmitting Circuits with Octode, *ENT*, vol. 12, pp. 53–54, 1935.

409. PAVLIK, B.: Contribution to the Theoretical and Experimental Investigation of Flexural Vibrations in Rectangular Plates with Free Edges, *An. Phk.*, vol. 27, pp. 532–542, 1936.

410. PAVLIK, B.: Contribution to the Investigation of Flexural Vibrations of Plates in the Form of Parallelograms with Free Edges, *An. Phk.*, vol. 28, pp. 353–360, 1937.

411. PAVLIK, B.: The Possibility of Exciting Simple Modes of Vibration in Piezoelectric Crystals of Low Symmetry, *ZS. Kr.*, vol. 100, pp. 414–419, 1938.

412. PERRIER, A.: Hypotheses Concerning Spontaneous Dielectric Polarization, and Some Experimental Results, *Arch. sci. phys. nat.*, vol. 41, pp. 492f., 1916.

413. PERRIER, A., and R. DE MANDROT: Elasticity and Symmetry of Quartz at High Temperatures, *Mém. société vaudoise sci. nat.*, vol. 1, pp. 333–363, 1922–1924; *C.R.*, vol. 175, pp. 622–624, 1006, 1922; abst. in *Arch. sci. phys. nat.*, vol. 4, pp. 367–369, 1922.

414. PETRZILKA, V.: On the Relation between the Optical and Piezoelectric Properties of Vibrating Quartz Crystals, *An. Phk.*, vol. 11, pp. 623–632, 1931.

415. PETRZILKA, V.: Tourmaline Resonators for Short and Ultra-short Waves, *An. Phk.*, vol. 15, pp. 72–88, 1932.

416. PETRZILKA, V.: Longitudinal and Flexural Vibrations of Tourmaline Plates, *An. Phk.*, vol. 15, pp. 881–902, 1932.

417. PETRZILKA, V.: Longitudinal Oscillations of Circular Quartz Plates, *An. Phk.*, vol. 23, pp. 156–168, 1935.

418. PETRZILKA, V.: Longitudinal Vibrations of Rectangular Quartz Plates, *ZS. Ph.*, vol. 97, pp. 436–454, 1935.

419. PETRZILKA, V.: Control of Transmitters by Lengthwise Vibrations of Tourmaline Plates, *Hfr. u. El. ak.*, vol. 50, pp. 1–5, 1937.

420. PETRZILKA, V., and W. FEHR: On Steady-state Oscillating Conditions in Quartz-controlled Single and Two-circuit Transmitters, *ENT*, vol. 9, pp. 283–292, 1932.

421. PETRZILKA, V., and L. ZACHOVAL: Direct Observation of Oscillations of a Quartz Plate by Means of the Schlieren Method, *ZS. Ph.*, vol. 90, pp. 700–702, 1934.

422. PIELEMEIER, W. H.: Acoustical Detection of Electrically Weak Vibrations in Quartz Plates, *J.A.S.A.*, vol. 9, pp. 212–216, 1938.

423. PIERCE, G. W.: Piezoelectric Crystal Resonators and Crystal Oscillators Applied to the Precision Calibration of Wavemeters, *Proc. A.A.A.S.*, vol. 59, pp. 81–106, 1923.

424. PIERCE, G. W.: Piezoelectric Crystal Oscillators Applied to the Precision Measurement of the Velocity of Sound in Air and Carbon Dioxide at High Frequencies, *Proc. A.A.A.S.*, vol. 60, pp. 277–302, 1925.

425. PINCIROLI, A.: On a New Piezoelectric Oscillator, *Alta freq.*, vol. 11, pp. 341–343, 1942.

426. PITT, A., and D. W. R. McKINLEY: Variation with Temperature of the Piezoelectric Effect in Quartz, *Can. J. Res.*, *A*, vol. 14, pp. 57–65, 1936.

427. POCKELS, F.: On the Changes in Optical Behavior and Elastic Deformations of Dielectric Crystals in an Electric Field, *Neues Jahrb. Min.*, vol. 7 (supplementary vol.), pp. 201–231, 1890.

428. POCKELS, F.: On the Effect of an Electrostatic Field on the Optical Behavior

of Piezoelectric Crystals, *Abh. Gött.*, vol. 39, pp. 1–204, 1894 (also in book form[B40]).

429. PONTECORVO, P.: Piezo-oscillators of High Frequency Stability Obtained by the Simultaneous Use of Positive and Negative Feedback, *Alta freq.*, vol. 7, pp. 365–381, 1938.

430. POPPELE, J. R., F. W. CUNNINGHAM, and A. W. KISHPAUGH: Design and Equipment of a Fifty-kilowatt Broadcast Station for WOR, *Proc. I.R.E.*, vol. 24, pp. 1063–1081, 1936.

431. POWERS, W. F.: Temperature Coefficient of Frequency of Quartz Resonators (abst.), *Phys. Rev.*, vol. 23, p. 783, 1924.

432. QUERVAIN, M. DE, and B. ZWICKER: Observations of the Elementary Electric Domains in the Seignette-electrics, *Helv. Ph. Ac.*, vol. 16, pp. 216–218, 1943.

433. RAYNER, E. H.: The Researches of the Late Dr. D. W. Dye on the Vibrations of Quartz, *J.I.E.E. (London)*, vol. 72, pp. 519–527, 1933; *Proc. Wireless Sec., I.E.E.*, vol. 8, pp. 99–107, 1933.

434. RIECKE, E.: Molecular Theory of the Piezoelectricity of Tourmaline, *Phys. ZS.*, vol. 13, pp. 409–415, 1912; *Nachr. Gött.*, pp. 253–266, 1912.

435. RIECKE, E., and W. VOIGT: Piezoelectric Constants of Quartz and Tourmaline, *Nachr. Gött.*, pp. 247–255, 1891; *Wied. An.*, vol. 45, pp. 523–552, 1892.

436. ROHDE, L.: New Types of Quartz Master-oscillators and Filters, *ZS. tech. Phys.*, vol. 20, pp. 75–80, 1939.

437. ROHDE, L.: Audio-frequency Quartz Oscillators and Filters, *ZS. tech. Phys.*, vol. 21, pp. 30–34, 1940.

438. ROHDE, L., and H. HANDREK: The Properties of Quartz Resonators at Audio- and Intermediate Frequencies, *ZS. tech. Phys.*, vol. 21, pp. 401–405, 1940.

439. RÖNTGEN, W. C.: Pyro- and Piezoelectric Investigations, *An. Phk.*, vol. 45, pp. 737–800, 1914.

440. RÖNTGEN, W. C., and A. JOFFÉ: On the Electric Conductivity of Certain Crystals and the Effect of Radiation Thereupon, *An. Phk.*, vol. 41, pp. 449–498, 1913.

441. RUSTERHOLZ, A. A.: Anomaly in the Specific Heat of Rochelle Salt, *Helv. Ph. Ac.*, vol. 7, pp. 643–644, 1934, vol. 8, pp. 39–54, 1935.

442. RZIANKIN, A. G.: Attenuation of Oscillations in Piezoelectric Quartz Crystals, *J. Tech. Phys.*, vol. 4, pp. 1282–1294, 1934.

443. SABAROFF, S.: A Voltage Stabilized High-frequency Crystal Oscillator Circuit, *Proc. I.R.E.*, vol. 25, pp. 623–629, 1937.

444. SABBATINI, A.: Multiple Oscillations of Piezoelectric Crystals and Their Dependence upon Circuit Conditions, *Dati e mem.*, vol. 2, pp. 618–636, 1930.

445. SALISBURY, W. W., and C. W. PORTER: An Efficient Piezoelectric Oscillator, *R.S.I.*, vol. 10, pp. 269–270, 1939.

446. SANDERS, E. W.: Modes of Fracture in Piezoelectric Crystals, *QST*, vol. 21, pp. 17–18, 84, 1937.

447. SANDERS, E. W.: Wave Propagation in Shearing Quartz Oscillators of High Frequency, *J. Appl. Ph.*, vol. 11, pp. 299–300, 1940.

448. SAWYER, C. B.: The Use of Rochelle Salt Crystals for Electrical Reproducers and Microphones, *Proc. I.R.E.*, vol. 19, pp. 2020–2029, 1931.

449. SAWYER, C. B., and C. H. TOWER: Rochelle Salt as a Dielectric, *Phys. Rev.*, vol. 35, pp. 269–273, 1930.

450. SCHAAFFS, W.: A Schlieren Test of the Vibrations of a Thin Quartz Plate, *ZS. Ph.*, vol. 105, pp. 576–578, 1937.

451. SCHERRER, P.: Investigations of the Dielectric Behavior of Rochelle Salt and Related Materials, *ZS. Elektrochem.*, vol. 45, pp. 171–174, 1939.

452. SCHIFFERMÜLLER, R.: On the Multiplicity of Vibrations in Thin Piezoelectric Quartz Plates, *ZS. tech. Ph.*, vol. 19, pp. 469–475, 1938.
SCHUBNIKOW—see SHUBNIKOV
SCHULWAS—see SHULVAS.

453. SCHUMACHER, R. O.: Investigations on Transversally Vibrating Quartz Plates, *Telef.-Z.*, vol. 18, pp. 16–21, 1937.

454. SCHWARTZ, E.: Experimental Investigations of the Piezoelectric and Dielectric Properties of Rochelle Salt, *ENT*, vol. 9, pp. 481–495, 1932.

455. SEIDL, F.: An Interesting Crack in Piezoelectric Quartz, *Naturwiss.*, vol. 17, pp. 781–782, 1929.

456. SEIDL, F.: Conductivity of Loaded Piezoelectric Quartz, *ZS. Ph.*, vol. 75, pp. 488–503, 1932.

457. SEIDL, F.: Action of Radium and X-rays on Piezoelectric Quartz, *Ber. Wien*, vol. 142, pp. 467–469, 1933.

458. SEIDL, F.: The Electrical Behavior of Rochelle Salt Single Crystals Produced from a Saturated Solution in an Electric Field, *Anz. Wien*, no. 11, pp. 92–93, 1936.

459. SEIDL, F.: The Anomalous Charging Current in Rochelle Salt Crystals, *Phys. ZS.*, vol. 39, pp. 714–716, 1938.

460. SEIDL, F., and E. HUBER: Effect of X-rays and Gamma-rays on Piezoelectric Crystals, *ZS. Ph.*, vol. 97, pp. 671–680, 1935.

461. SHAW, H. S.: Oscillating Crystals, *QST*, vol. 7, pp. 30*f.*, July, 1924.

462. SHORE, S. X.: A series of articles on the grading and orientation of quartz crystals and the sawing, lapping, finishing, and testing of quartz plates, *Communications*, vol. 23, October–December, 1943, vol. 24, January, February, 1944.

463. SHUBNIKOV, A.: On Impact-patterns on Quartz, *ZS. Kr.*, vol. 74, pp. 103–104, 1930.

464. SHULVAS-SOROKINA, R. D.: Is It Possible to Determine the Piezoelectric Constant at High Temperature by the Statical Method? *Phys. Rev.*, vol. 34, pp. 1448–1450, 1929.

465. SHULVAS-SOROKINA, R. D.: Piezoelectric Properties of Rochelle Salt Crystals, *ZS. Ph.*, vol. 73, pp. 700–706, 1932.

466. SHULVAS-SOROKINA, R. D.: On a Characteristic Temperature in Rochelle Salt Crystals, *ZS. Ph.*, vol. 77, pp. 541–546, 1932.

467. SHULVAS-SOROKINA, R. D.: Relaxation Time in Rochelle Salt Crystals, II, *J. Exp. Th. Ph. U.S.S.R.*, vol. 7, pp. 1440–1447, 1937; *Phys. ZS. d. Sowjetunion*, vol. 12, pp. 685–700, 1937.

468. SHULVAS-SOROKINA, R. D.: Polarization of Rochelle Salt Crystals at Low Voltages, *J. Tech. Phys.*, vol. 11, pp. 947–958, 1941.

469. SHULVAS-SOROKINA, R. D., and M. V. POSNOV: The Time of Relaxation in Crystals of Rochelle Salt, *Phys. Rev.*, vol. 47, pp. 166–174, 1935.

470. SKELLETT, A. M.: A Visual Method for Studying Modes of Vibration of Quartz Plates, *J.O.S.A.*, vol. 17, pp. 308–317, 1928.

471. SKELLETT, A. M.: Modes of Vibration of a Round Plate Cut from a Quartz Crystal, *J.O.S.A.*, vol. 20, pp. 293–302, 1930.

472. SMIRNOV, V. A.: The Effect of the Parameters of a Piezoelectric Quartz Oscillator on Its Operation, and the Maximum Permissible Power Rating for Such an Oscillator, *J. Tech. Phys.*, vol. 6, pp. 493–513, 1936.

473. SOKOLOV, S. J.: Oscillations of Piezoelectric Quartz Rods in Non-uniform Fields, *ZS. Ph.*, vol. 50, pp. 385–394, 1928.

474. SPEIGHT, J. W.: The Electrodynamic Characteristics of the Quartz Piezoelectric Oscillator, *Can. J. Res.*, vol. 12, pp. 812–819, 1935.

475. STAMFORD, N. C.: The Production of Rochelle Salt Piezoelectric Resonators Having a Pure Longitudinal Mode of Vibration, *Proc. I.R.E.*, vol. 25, pp. 465–471, 1937.

476. STARR, A. T.: Electro-acoustic Reactions, *W. E.*, vol. 17, pp. 247–256, 303–309, 1940.

477. STAUB, H.: Investigation of the Dielectric Properties of Rochelle Salt by Means of X-rays, *Helv. Ph. Ac.*, vol. 7, pp. 3–45, 1934; *Phys. ZS.*, vol. 34, pp. 292–296, 1933; thesis, 1934.

478. STAUB, H.: Evidence for the Internal Electric Field of Rochelle Salt by Means of X-rays, *Helv. Ph. Ac.*, vol. 7, pp. 480–482, 1934; *Phys. ZS.*, vol. 35, pp. 720–725, 1934.

479. STAUB, H.: Dielectric Anomalies of Rochelle Salt, *Naturwiss.*, vol. 23, pp. 728–733, 1935.

480. STEPHENSON, C. C., and H. E. ADAMS: The Heat Capacity of Ammonium Dihydrogen Arsenate from 15 to 300°K. The Anomaly at the Curie Temperature, *J. Am. Chem. Soc.*, vol. 66, pp. 1409–1412, 1944.

481. STEPHENSON, C. C., and J. G. HOOLEY: The Heat Capacity of Potassium Dihydrogen Phosphate from 15 to 300°K. The Anomaly at the Curie Temperature, *J. Am. Chem. Soc.*, vol. 66, pp. 1397–1401, 1944.

482. STEPHENSON, C. C., and A. C. ZETTLEMOYER: The Heat Capacity of Potassium Dihydrogen Arsenate from 15 to 300°K. The Anomaly at the Curie Temperature, *J. Am. Chem. Soc.*, vol. 66, pp. 1402–1405, 1944.

483. STEPHENSON, C. C., and A. C. ZETTLEMOYER: The Heat Capacity of Ammonium Dihydrogen Phosphate from 15 to 300°K. The Anomaly at the Curie Temperature, *J. Am. Chem. Soc.*, vol. 66, pp. 1405–1408, 1944.

484. STRAUBEL, H.: Piezoelectric Quartz Oscillators, *Phys. ZS.*, vol. 32, p. 222, 1931.

485. STRAUBEL, H.: Some Experiments in Supersonics, *Phys. ZS.*, vol. 32, pp. 379–381, 1931.

486. STRAUBEL, H.: Piezoelectric Oscillators, *Phys. ZS.*, vol. 32, pp. 586–587, 1931.

487. STRAUBEL, H.: Direct Crystal Control for Ultra-short Waves, *Phys. ZS.*, vol. 32, pp. 937–941, 1931.

488. STRAUBEL, H.: Oscillation Form and Temperature Coefficient of Quartz Oscillators, *ZS. Hfr.*, vol. 38, pp. 14–27, 1931.

489. STRAUBEL, H.: Crystal Control of Ultra-short Wave Transmitters, *V.D.I.*, vol. 76, pp. 873–874, 1932.

490. STRAUBEL, H.: Modes of Vibration of Piezoelectric Crystals, *Phys. ZS.*, vol. 34, pp. 894–896, 1933.

491. STRAUBEL, H.: Temperature Coefficient, Mode of Vibration, and Amplitude of Piezoelectric Oscillators, *Phys. ZS.*, vol. 35, pp. 179–181, 1934.

492. STRAUBEL, H.: The Temperature Coefficient of Quartz Oscillators, *Phys. ZS.*, vol. 35, pp. 657–658, 1934.

493. STRAUBEL, H.: The Temperature Coefficient of Quartz Oscillators, *ZS. tech. Ph.*, vol. 15, pp. 607–608, 1934.

494. STRAUBEL, H.: Crystal Control of Decimeter Waves, *ZS. tech. Ph.*, vol. 16, pp. 627–629, 1935.

495. STRAUBEL, H.: Crystal Control of Ultra-short Waves, *Hfr. u. El. ak.*, vol. 46, pp. 4–6, 1935.

496. STRAUBEL, H.: Crystal Control of Decimeter Waves, *Hfr. u. El. ak.*, vol. 47, pp. 152–154, 1936.

497. STRONG, J. A.: New Method of Investigating the Modes of Vibration of Quartz Crystals, *Nature*, vol. 129, p. 59, 1932.

498. SYKES, R. A.: Modes of Motion in Quartz Crystals, the Effects of Coupling and Methods of Design, *Bell Syst. T.J.*, vol. 23, pp. 52–96, 1944.

499. SYKES, R. A.: Principles of Mounting Quartz Plates, *Bell Syst. T.J.*, vol. 23, pp. 178–189, 1944.

500. SZÉKELY, A.: A Simple Method for Determining the First Piezoelectric Modulus of Quartz from Measurements on a Quartz Resonator, *ZS. Ph.*, vol. 78, pp. 560–566, 1932.

501. TAKAGI, N., and Y. MIYAKE: Thickness Vibrations of a Rochelle Salt Plate, *Electrotech. Jour. (Jap.)*, vol. 4, p. 120, 1940.

502. TAKAGI, N., and H. NAKASE: New Characteristics of Pentode Quartz Oscillator, *Electrotech. Jour. (Jap.)*, vol. 2, pp. 22–23, 1938.

503. TAMARU, T.: Determination of the Piezoelectric Constants of Tartaric Acid Crystals, *Phys. ZS.*, vol. 6, p. 379, 1905.

504. TASCHEK, R., and H. OSTERBERG: Crystalline Symmetry and Shear Constants of Rochelle Salt, *Phys. Rev.*, vol. 50, p. 572, 1936.

505. TAWIL, E. P.: On the Variations of the Optical Properties of Piezoelectric Quartz under the Action of High-frequency Electric Fields, *C.R.*, vol. 183, pp. 1099–1101, 1926.

506. TAWIL, E. P.: Observations on Piezoelectric Quartz at Resonance, *C.R.*, vol. 185, pp. 114–116, 1927.

507. TAWIL, E. P.: The Vibrations of Piezoelectric Quartz Made Visible by Polarised Light, *Bull. soc. min. fr.*, p. 129S, Nov. 16, 1928.

508. TAWIL, E. P.: New Method for the Development of Electricity by the Torsion of Quartz Crystals, *C.R.*, vol. 187, pp. 1042–1044, 1928.

509. TAWIL, E. P.: The Vibrations of Piezoelectric Quartz Made Visible by Polarized Light, *Rev. gén. de l'élec.*, vol. 25, p. 58, 1929.

510. TAWIL, E. P.: On the Vibrations along the Optical Axis in an Oscillating Piezoelectric Quartz Crystal, *C.R.*, vol. 189, pp. 163–164, 1929.

511. TAWIL, E. P.: Stationary Ultrasonic Waves Made Visible in Gases by the Method of Striations, *C.R.*, vol. 191, pp. 92–95, 1930.

512. TAWIL, E. P.: Liberation of Electricity in Quartz Crystals by Flexure, *C.R.*, vol. 192, pp. 274–277, 1931.

513. TAWIL, E. P.: Laws of the Liberation of Electricity by Torsion in Quartz, *C.R.*, vol. 199, pp. 1025–1026, 1934.

514. TAWIL, E. P.: Remarks on the Liberation of Electricity by Torsion in Quartz, *C.R.*, vol. 200, pp. 1088–1090, 1935.

515. TAWIL, E. P.: Remarks on the Liberation of Electricity by Torsion in Quartz and on the Reciprocal Phenomenon, *C.R.*, vol. 200, pp. 1306–1308, 1935.

516. TAWIL, E. P.: On a Piezoelectric Chronograph *C.R.*, vol. 202, pp. 1016–1018, 1936.

517. TERRY, E. M.: The Dependence of the Frequency of Quartz Piezoelectric Oscillators upon Circuit Constants, *Proc. I.R.E.*, vol. 16, pp. 1486–1506, 1928.

518. THOMSON, W. T.: Effect of Rotary and Lateral Inertia on Flexural Vibration of Prismatic Bars, *J.A.S.A.*, vol. 11, pp. 198–204, 1939.

519. THURSTON, G. M.: Flatness and Parallelism in Quartz Plates, *Bell Labs. Rec.*, vol. 22, pp. 435–439, 1944.

520. THURSTON, G. M.: A Crystal Test Set, *Bell Labs. Rec.*, vol. 22, pp. 477–480, 1944.

521. TOLANSKY, S.: Topography of a Quartz Crystal Face, *Nature*, vol. 153, pp. 195–196, 1944.

522. TOURNIER, M.: History and Applications of Piezoelectricity, *Elec. Comm.*, vol. 15, pp. 312–327, 1937; *ENT*, vol. 15, pp. 320–334, 1937.

523. TSI-ZE, NY: Electric Deformations of Quartz, *C.R.*, vol. 184, pp. 1645–1647, 1927.

524. TSI-ZE, NY: Experimental Study of the Deformations and of the Changes in the Optical Properties of Quartz under the Influence of an Electric Field, *J. phq.*, vol. 9, pp. 13–37, 1928; *C.R.*, vol. 185, pp. 195–197, 1927.

525. TSI-ZE, NY: The Transverse Circular Vibration of a Hollow Quartz Cylinder, *C.R.*, vol. 204, pp. 226–228, 1937.

526. TSI-ZE, NY, and S. KENG-YI: Vibrations in Quartz Plates Cut in Different Planes Around the Optic Axis, *C.R.*, vol. 204, pp. 1059–1060, 1937.

527. TSI-ZE, NY, and CHUNG MING-SAN: States of Vibration of a Hollow Quartz Cylinder, *J. phq.*, vol. 9, pp. 52–56, 1938.

528. TSI-ZE, NY, and F. SUN-HUNG: On the Circumferential Vibration of a Hollow Cylindrical Quartz Oscillator, *Chinese J. of Phys.*, vol. 2, pp. 145–153, 1936.

529. TSI-ZE, NY, and F. SUN-HUNG: On the Transverse Circular Vibrations of a Hollow Quartz Cylinder, *C.R.*, vol. 203, pp. 461–463, 1936.

530. TSI-ZE, NY, and LING-CHAO TSIEN: Oscillations with Hollow Quartz Cylinders Cut along the Optical Axis, *Nature*, vol. 134, pp. 214–215, 1934.

531. TSI-ZE, NY, and LING-CHAO TSIEN: Electrification by Torsion in Quartz Crystals, *C.R.*, vol. 198, pp. 1395–1396, 1934.

532. TSI-ZE, NY, and LING-CHAO TSIEN: The Laws of Liberation of Electricity by Torsion in Quartz Crystals, *C.R.*, vol. 199, pp. 1101–1102, 1934.

533. TSI-ZE, NY, and LING-CHAO TSIEN: Oscillations of a Hollow Quartz Cylinder, *C.R.*, vol. 200, pp. 565–567, 1935.

534. TSI-ZE, NY, and LING-CHAO TSIEN: On the Laws of Production of Electrification by Torsion in Quartz, *C.R.*, vol. 200, pp. 732–733, 1935.

535. TSI-ZE, NY, and LING-CHAO TSIEN: Electrification by Torsion in Quartz Crystal, *Chinese J. of Phys.*, vol. 1, pp. 41–53, October, 1935.

536. TSI-ZE, NY, LING-CHAO TSIEN, and FANG SUN-HUNG: Oscillations of Hollow Quartz Cylinders Cut along the Optic Axis, *Proc. I.R.E.*, vol. 24, pp. 1484–1494, 1936.

537. TYKOCINSKI-TYKOCINER, J., and M. W. WOODRUFF: Flexural Vibrations of Piezoelectric Quartz Bars and Plates, *Univ. Illinois Bull.*, vol. 34, 33 pp., Jan. 8, 1937 (No. 291).

538. UDA, H., and H. WATANABE: Ultra-short-wave Quartz Oscillator, *Electrotech. Jour. (Jap.)*, vol. 2, pp. 94–95, 1938.

539. UST'YANOV, V. I.: On the Effect of a Layer of Gold Deposited on a Quartz Crystal on the Logarithmic Decrement of the Crystal, *Izv. El. Slab. Toka*, no. 4, pp. 44–48, 1938.

540. USUI, R.: The Circle Diagrams of the Quartz Oscillator, *J.I.E.E. (Japan)*, vol. 54, pp. 201–213, 1934; English summary, pp. 21–24.

541. VALASEK, J.: Piezoelectricity and Allied Phenomena in Rochelle Salt, *Phys. Rev.*, vol. 17, pp. 475–481, 1921.

542. VALASEK, J.: Piezoelectric Activity of Rochelle Salt under Various Conditions, *Phys. Rev.*, vol. 19, pp. 478–491, 1922.

543. VALASEK, J.: Properties of Rochelle Salt Related to the Piezoelectric Effect, *Phys. Rev.*, vol. 20, pp. 639–664, 1922.

544. VALASEK, J.: Dielectric Anomalies in Rochelle Salt Crystals, *Phys. Rev.*, vol. 24, pp. 560–568, 1924.

545. VALASEK, J.: Note on the Piezoelectric Effect in Rochelle Salt Crystals, *Science*, vol. 65, pp. 235–236, 1927.

546. VALASEK, J.: Infrared Absorption by Rochelle Salt Crystals, *Phys. Rev.*, vol. 45, pp. 654–655, 1934.

547. VAN DYKE, K. S.: The Electric Network Equivalent of a Piezoelectric Resonator (abst.), *Phys. Rev.*, vol. 25, p. 895, 1925.

548. VAN DYKE, K. S.: The Use of the Cathode Ray Oscillograph in the Study of Resonance Phenomena in Piezoelectric Crystals (abst.), *Phys. Rev.*, vol. 31, p. 303, 1928.

549. VAN DYKE, K. S.: Some Experiments with Vibrating Quartz Spheres (abst.), *Proc. I.R.E.*, vol. 16, pp. 706–707, 1928; *Phys. Rev.*, vol. 31, pp. 1113, 1133, 1928 (absts.).

550. VAN DYKE, K. S.: The Piezoelectric Resonator and Its Equivalent Network, *Proc. I.R.E.*, vol. 16, pp. 742–764, 1928.

551. VAN DYKE, K. S.: The Measurement of the Decrement of Piezoelectric Resonators (abst.), *Proc. I.R.E.*, vol. 18, p. 1989, 1930.

552. VAN DYKE, K. S.: The Electric Network Equivalent of a Piezoelectric Resonator (abst.), *Phys. Rev.*, vol. 40, p. 1026, 1932.

553. VAN DYKE, K. S.: Temperature Variation of Viscosity and of the Piezoelectric Constant of Quartz (abst.), *Phys. Rev.*, vol. 42, p. 587, 1932.

554. VAN DYKE, K. S.: A Determination of Some of the Properties of the Piezoelectric Quartz Resonator, *Proc. I.R.E.*, vol. 23, pp. 386–392, 1935. *Document AG, No. 24, Comm. I., U.R.S.I. Gen. Assem.*, 1934.

555. VAN DYKE, K. S.: Note on a Peculiar Case of Fracture of a Quartz Resonator, *J. Appl. Ph.*, vol. 8, pp. 567–568, 1937.

556. VAN DYKE, K. S.: Some Unusual Demonstrations with Piezoelectric Resonators (abst.), *Phys. Rev.*, vol. 53, p. 686, 1938.

557. VAN DYKE, K. S.: Vibration Modes of Low Decrement for a Quartz Ring (abst.), *Phys. Rev.*, vol. 53, p. 945, 1938.

558. VAN DYKE, K. S.: On the Right- and Left-handedness of Quartz and Its Relation to Elastic and Other Properties, *Proc. I.R.E.*, vol. 28, pp. 399–406, 1940.

559. VAN DYKE, K. S., and A. M. THORNDIKE: The Three-crystal Method of Quartz Resonator Measurement (abst.), *Phys. Rev.*, vol. 57, p. 560, 1940.

560. VECCHIACCHI, F.: Frequency-stability of Piezoelectric Standards, *L'Elettrot.*, vol. 15, pp. 462–468, 1928.

561. VECCHIACCHI, F.: Piezo-oscillators with Great Frequency-stability, *L'Elettrot.*, vol. 18, pp. 79–82, 1931; *Livorno Publication* 55.

562. VECCHIACCHI, F.: Advances in Piezoelectric Frequency Standards and Stabilizers, *Rass. P.T.T.*, vol. 10, pp. 5–8, October 1931.

563. VEEN, A. L. W. E. VAN DER: Symmetry of Diamond, thesis, Delft, 1911. *ZS. Kr.*, vol. 51, pp. 545–590, 1913.

564. VENKOV, M. M.: Principles in Designing a Crystal Holder for a Piezo-quartz Stabilizer, *Iz. El. Slab. Toka*, no. 6, pp. 39–44, no. 7, pp. 35–41, 1935.

565. VIGNESS, I.: Inverse Piezoelectric Properties of Rochelle Salt, *Phys. Rev.*, vol. 46, pp. 255–257, 1934.

566. VIGNESS, I.: Dilatations in Rochelle Salt, *Phys. Rev.*, vol. 48, pp. 198–202, 1935.

567. VIGOUREUX, J. E. P.: Development of Formulas for the Constants of the Equivalent Electrical Circuit of a Quartz Resonator in Terms of Elastic and Piezoelectric Constants, *Phil. Mag.*, vol. 6, pp. 1140–1153, 1928.

568. VIGOUREUX, J. E. P.: The Valve-maintained Quartz Oscillator, *J.I.E.E. (London)*, vol. 68, pp. 265–295, 1930; discussion, pp. 867–872; *Proc. Wireless Section, I.E.E.*, vol. 5, pp. 41–71, 1930; discussion, pp. 163–168.

569. VOIGT, W.: General Theory of the Piezo- and Pyroelectric Properties of Crystals, *Abh. Gött.*, vol. 36, pp. 1–99, 1890.

570. VOIGT, W.: Can the Pyroelectricity of Crystals Be Attributed Entirely to

Piezoelectric Effects? *Nachr. Gött.*, pp. 166–194, 1898; *An. Phk.*, vol. 66, pp. 1030–1060, 1898.

571. Voigt, W.: On Pyroelectricity in Centro-symmetrical Crystals, *Nachr. Gött.*, pp. 394–437, 1905.

572. Voigt, W.: Remarks on Some New Investigations on Pyro- and Piezoelectricity of Tourmaline, *An. Phk.*, vol. 46, pp. 221–230, 1915.

573. Voigt, W.: Theory and Experiments on Piezoelectric Excitation of a Cylinder by Torsion and Bending, *An. Phk.*, vol. 48, pp. 433–448, 1915.

574. Voigt, W.: Questions on the Pyro- and Piezoelectricity of Crystals, *Phys. ZS.*, vol. 17, pp. 287–293, 307–313, 1916.

575. Voigt, W.: Pyro- and Piezoelectricity. Experimental Determination of Permanent Centro-symmetrical Moments, *Phys. ZS.*, vol. 18, pp. 59–67, 1917.

576. Voigt, W., and V. Fréedericksz: Piezoelectric Excitation of a Cylinder by Torsion and Bending, *An. Phk.*, vol. 48, pp. 145–176, 1915.

577. Wachsmuth, R., and H. Auer: Mechanical Vibrations of Piezoelectrically Excited Quartz, *ZS. Ph.*, vol. 47, pp. 323–329, 1928.

578. Wagner, K. W.: Wedge-shaped Piezoelectric Resonators, *Hfr. u. El. ak.*, vol. 47, p. 28, 1936.

579. Warren, B. E., and H. M. Krutter: X-ray Study of Crystal Structure of Rochelle Salt and Effect of Temperature (abst.), *Phys. Rev.*, vol. 43, p. 500, 1933.

580. Wataghin, G., and G. Sacerdote: Optical Examination of the Surface of Piezoelectric Quartz in Vibration; Doppler Effect of Acceleration, *Atti. accad. sci. Torino*, vol. 66, pp. 424–427, 1930–1931.

581. Watanabe, Y.: Piezoelectric Resonator in High-frequency Oscillation Circuits, *Proc. I.R.E.*, vol. 18, pp. 695–717, 862–893, 1930; *ENT*, vol. 5, pp. 45–64, 1928.

582. Wheeler, L. P.: An Analysis of a Piezoelectric Oscillator Circuit, *Proc. I.R.E.*, vol. 19, pp. 627–646, 1931.

583. Wheeler, L. P., and W. E. Bower: A New Type of Standard Frequency Piezoelectric Oscillator, *Proc. I.R.E.*, vol. 16, pp. 1035–1044, 1928.

584. Willard, G. W.: Raw Quartz, Its Imperfections and Inspection, *Bell Syst. T.J.*, vol. 22, pp. 338–361, 1943.

585. Willard, G. W.: Inspecting and Determining the Axis Orientation of Quartz Crystals, *Bell Labs. Rec.*, vol. 22, pp. 320–326, 1944.

586. Willard, G. W.: Use of the Etch Technique for Determining Orientation and Twinning in Quartz Crystals, *Bell Syst. T.J.*, vol. 23, pp. 11–51, 1944.

587. Williams, N. H.: Modes of Vibration of Piezoelectric Crystals, *Proc. I.R.E.*, vol. 21, pp. 990–995, 1933.

588. Wilson, A. J. C.: The Heat Capacity of Rochelle Salt between $-30°$ and $+30°$C., *Phys. Rev.*, vol. 54, pp. 1103–1109, 1938.

589. Wolf, K.: Flexural Oscillations in a Thin Rod, *Ber. Wien*, vol. 143, pp. 79–86, 1934.

590. Wologdin, V.: Frequency Multiplication by the Use of a Condenser with Rochelle Salt Dielectric, *ZS. tech. Ph.*, vol. 13, pp. 82–84, 1932.

591. Wood, R. G., and C. H. McCale: Simple Apparatus for Detecting the Pyroelectric Effect in Crystals, *J. Sci. Instr.*, vol. 17, pp. 225–226, 1940.

592. Worobieff, V. von: Crystallographic Studies of Tourmaline from Ceylon and Several Other Sources, *ZS. Kr.*, vol. 33, pp. 263f., 1900.

593. Wright, J. W.: The Piezoelectric Crystal Oscillator, *Proc. I.R.E.*, vol. 17, pp. 127–142, 1929.

594. Wright, R. B., and D. M. Stuart: Some Experimental Studies of the Vibrations of Quartz Plates, *J. Res. N.B.S.*, vol. 7, pp. 519–553, 1931.

595. YODA, H.: Thermal Characteristics of Piezoelectric Oscillating AT-cut and YT-cut Plates, *R.R.R.W. Jap.*, vol. 5, pp. 77–87, 1935.

596. YODA, H.: YT-cut Quartz Plates, *Electrot. Jour. (Jap.)*, vol. 2, p. 96, 1938.

597. ZACEK, A., and V. PETRZILKA: On Wedge-shaped Piezoelectric Resonators, *Hfr. u. El. ak.*, vol. 46, pp. 157–159, 1935; *Czech. Inst. Elec. Eng.*, vol. 24, 1935.

598. ZACEK, A., and V. PETRZILKA: Radial and Torsional Vibrations of Annular Quartz Plates, *Phil. Mag.*, vol. 25, pp. 164–175, 1938.

599. ZAKS, E. S., and V. P. UFTIUJANINOV: Low-frequency Luminous Piezo-quartz Resonators, *Izv. El. Slab. Toka*, no. 1, pp. 32–40, January–February, 1934.

    ZE, NY TSI—see TSI-ZE.

600. ZELENY, A., and J. VALASEK: Variation of the Dielectric Constant of Rochelle Salt Crystals with Frequency and Applied Field Strength, *Phys. Rev.*, vol. 46, pp. 450–453, 1934.

601. ZELYAKH, E. V., and Y. I. VELIKIN: Equivalent Circuits of the Four-electrode Quartz Resonator, *Izv. El. Slab. Toka*, no. 3, pp. 46–50, 1938.

602. ZWICKER, B., and P. SCHERRER: Electro-optical Behavior of KH_2PO_4 and KD_2PO_4 Crystals, *Helv. Ph. Ac.*, vol. 16, pp. 214–216, 1943.

A few references to publications after 1946 have been inserted here and there in the text. Still other references are given at the end of Appendix II.

NAME INDEX

This index covers both volumes of the work.   Volume One contains pages 1 through 405; Volume Two contains pages 406 through 822.

The following list includes only authors named in the text and footnotes.   For other authors, see the General Bibliography, the special bibliographies at the ends of chapters, and the bibliography at the end of Appendix II, p. 764.

SUBJECT INDEX

This index covers both volumes of the work. Volume One contains pages 1 through 405; Volume Two contains pages 406 through 822.

A

Actino-electricity, 1, 711
Activity of resonator, 298
Adiabatic heating, 42, 641
ADP, 665, 666
Air blast (*see* Quartz wind)
Air gap (*see* Gap)
Alternating current notation, 288
Ammonium arsenate (*see* Arsenates)
Ammonium chloride, 230
Ammonium phosphate (*see* Phosphates)
Ammonium tartrate (*see* Tartrates)
Analogous end, 30
Antilogous end, 30
Antiresonance (*see* Resonance)
Applications, technical, 665–698, 758
Arsenates, 208, 659–666, 740
Asparagine, 483
Atomic theory, 731–744, 757
  (*See also* Unit cell)
Attenuation constant, 89
Axial ratio, 13
  quartz, 27
  Rochelle salt, 21, 737
  tourmaline, 30
Axinite, 709
Axis, Bravais, 16
  crystal, 13, 16, 27
  Millerian, 16
  orthogonal, 15–17
  piezoelectric, 194
    I.R.E. system, 81, 83, 217, 258, 407–410, 458
  polar, 15, 30
  quartz, 406–410, 415–427

B

Bar, composite, 391
  (*See also* Constants, piezoelectric; Resonator; Vibrations, lengthwise)
Barium antimonyl tartrate (*see* Tartrates)
Beet sugar, 483
Bender, 672

Benzil, 225
Bimorph, 239, 672
Body forces, 46, 312
Bonds, chemical, 731
Boracite, 230
Boundary conditions, 262, 265
Bravais-Miller system, 16
Bravais symbols, 28
  system, 16
Brushite, 201

C

Camphor, 232
  patchouli, 225
Capacitance, parallel, of resonator, 333–336, 342–346, 353, 354, 357, 370, 392, 397, 461, 478
Ceramics, 761
Clamped crystal, 161, 262, 264, 270, 276, 279, 311, 328, 397
  Rochelle salt, 512, 513, 589, 590, 597–602, 606, 620–625, 646
Classes, crystal, 13, 17, 19, 53
  piezoelectric, 190–192
  pyroelectric, 700
Cleavage, 27, 410, 525, 705
Click method, 231, 385
Clinohedrite, 233
Constants, dielectric, 44, 160–176
  clamped, 311, 414, 572, 585
  complex, 325–329, 661
  cross-constants, 162
  definitions of, 550, 551, 586, 587
  effective, 329, 437, 473–475
  lengthwise vibrations, 291, 304, 473 475
  mixed tartrates, 655–657
  phosphates and arsenates, 659–662
  piezoelectric contribution, 267
  quartz, 413–415
  resonator, 296, 304, 321
  thickness vibrations, 311
  wave, 458
  elastic, 43, 49, 53
    adiabatic, 63, 120–146, 157, 158, 437, 460, 477

CATALOG OF DOVER BOOKS

BOOKS EXPLAINING SCIENCE AND MATHEMATICS

THE COMMON SENSE OF THE EXACT SCIENCES, W. K. Clifford. Introduction by James Newman, edited by Karl Pearson. For 70 years this has been a guide to classical scientific and mathematical thought. Explains with unusual clarity basic concepts, such as extension of meaning of symbols, characteristics of surface boundaries, properties of plane figures, vectors, Cartesian method of determining position, etc. Long preface by Bertrand Russell. Bibliography of Clifford. Corrected, 130 diagrams redrawn. 249pp. 5⅜ x 8.
T61 Paperbound $1.60

SCIENCE THEORY AND MAN, Erwin Schrödinger. This is a complete and unabridged reissue of SCIENCE AND THE HUMAN TEMPERAMENT plus an additional essay: "What is an Elementary Particle?" Nobel Laureate Schrödinger discusses such topics as nature of scientific method, the nature of science, chance and determinism, science and society, conceptual models for physical entities, elementary particles and wave mechanics. Presentation is popular and may be followed by most people with little or no scientific training. "Fine practical preparation for a time when laws of nature, human institutions . . . are undergoing a critical examination without parallel," Waldemar Kaempffert, N. Y. TIMES. 192pp. 5⅜ x 8.
T428 Paperbound $1.35

PIONEERS OF SCIENCE, O. Lodge. Eminent scientist-expositor's authoritative, yet elementary survey of great scientific theories. Concentrating on individuals—Copernicus, Brahe, Kepler, Galileo, Descartes, Newton, Laplace, Herschel, Lord Kelvin, and other scientists—the author presents their discoveries in historical order adding biographical material on each man and full, specific explanations of their achievements. The clear and complete treatment of the post-Newtonian astronomers is a feature seldom found in other books on the subject. Index. 120 illustrations. xv + 404pp. 5⅜ x 8.
T716 Paperbound $1.50

THE EVOLUTION OF SCIENTIFIC THOUGHT FROM NEWTON TO EINSTEIN, A. d'Abro. Einstein's special and general theories of relativity, with their historical implications, are analyzed in non-technical terms. Excellent accounts of the contributions of Newton, Riemann, Weyl, Planck, Eddington, Maxwell, Lorentz and others are treated in terms of space and time, equations of electromagnetics, finiteness of the universe, methodology of science. 21 diagrams. 482pp. 5⅜ x 8.
T2 Paperound $2.00

THE RISE OF THE NEW PHYSICS, A. d'Abro. A half-million word exposition, formerly titled THE DECLINE OF MECHANISM, for readers not versed in higher mathematics. The only thorough explanation, in everyday language, of the central core of modern mathematical physical theory, treating both classical and modern theoretical physics, and presenting in terms almost anyone can understand the equivalent of 5 years of study of mathematical physics. Scientifically impeccable coverage of mathematical-physical thought from the Newtonian system up through the electronic theories of Dirac and Heisenberg and Fermi's statistics. Combines both history and exposition; provides a broad yet unified and detailed view, with constant comparison of classical and modern views on phenomena and theories. "A must for anyone doing serious study in the physical sciences," JOURNAL OF THE FRANKLIN INSTITUTE. "Extraordinary faculty . . . to explain ideas and theories of theoretical physics in the language of daily life," ISIS. First part of set covers philosophy of science, drawing upon the practice of Newton, Maxwell, Poincaré, Einstein, others, discussing modes of thought, experiment, interpretations of causality, etc. In the second part, 100 pages explain grammar and vocabulary of mathematics, with discussions of functions, groups, series, Fourier series, etc. The remainder is devoted to concrete, detailed coverage of both classical and quantum physics, explaining such topics as analytic mechanics, Hamilton's principle, wave theory of light, electromagnetic waves, groups of transformations, thermodynamics, phase rule, Brownian movement, kinetics, special relativity, Planck's original quantum theory, Bohr's atom, Zeeman effect, Broglie's wave mechanics, Heisenberg's uncertainty, Eigen-values, matrices, scores of other important topics. Discoveries and theories are covered for such men as Alembert, Born, Cantor, Debye, Euler, Foucault, Galois, Gauss, Hadamard, Kelvin, Kepler, Laplace, Maxwell, Pauli, Rayleigh, Volterra, Weyl, Young, more than 180 others. Indexed. 97 illustrations. ix + 982pp. 5⅜ x 8.
T3 Volume 1, Paperbound $2.00
T4 Volume 2, Paperbound $2.00

CONCERNING THE NATURE OF THINGS, Sir William Bragg. Christmas lectures delivered at the Royal Society by Nobel laureate. Why a spinning ball travels in a curved track; how uranium is transmuted to lead, etc. Partial contents: atoms, gases, liquids, crystals, metals, etc. No scientific background needed; wonderful for intelligent child. 32pp. of photos, 57 figures. xii + 232pp. 5⅜ x 8.
T31 Paperbound $1.35

THE UNIVERSE OF LIGHT, Sir William Bragg. No scientific training needed to read Nobel Prize winner's expansion of his Royal Institute Christmas Lectures. Insight into nature of light, methods and philosophy of science. Explains lenses, reflection, color, resonance, polarization, x-rays, the spectrum, Newton's work with prisms, Huygens' with polarization, Crookes' with cathode ray, etc. Leads into clear statement of 2 major historical theories of light, corpuscle and wave. Dozens of experiments you can do. 199 illus., including 2 full-page color plates. 293pp. 5⅜ x 8.
S538 Paperbound $1.85

TABLES OF FUNCTIONS WITH FORMULAE AND CURVES, E. Jahnke & F. Emde. The world's most comprehensive 1-volume English-text collection of tables, formulae, curves of transcendent functions. 4th corrected edition, new 76-page section giving tables, formulae for elementary functions—not in other English editions. Partial contents: sine, cosine, logarithmic integral; factorial function; error integral; theta functions; elliptic integrals, functions; Legendre, Bessel, Riemann, Mathieu, hypergeometric functions, etc. Supplementary books. Bibliography. Indexed. "Out of the way functions for which we know no other source," SCIENTIFIC COMPUTING SERVICE, Ltd. 212 figures. 400pp. 5⅜ x 8. S133 Paperbound **$2.00**

JACOBIAN ELLIPTIC FUNCTION TABLES, L. M. Milne-Thomson. An easy to ᵻollow, practical book which gives not only useful numerical tables, but also a complete elementary sketch of the application of elliptic functions. It covers Jacobian elliptic functions and a description of their principal properties; complete elliptic integrals; Fourier series and power series expansions; periods, zeros, poles, residues, formulas for special values of the argument; transformations, approximations, elliptic integrals, conformal mapping, factorization of cubic and quartic polynomials; application to the pendulum problem; etc. Tables and graphs form the body of the book: Graph, 5 figure table of the elliptic function sn (u m); cn (u m); dn (u m). 8 figure table of complete elliptic integrals K, K′, E, E′, and the nome q. 7 figure table of the Jacobian zeta-function Z(u). 3 figures. xi + 123pp. 5⅜ x 8.
S194 Paperbound **$1.35**

PHYSICS

General physics

FOUNDATIONS OF PHYSICS, R. B. Lindsay & H. Margenau. Excellent bridge between semi-popular works & technical treatiseˢ. A discussion of methods of physical description, construction of theory; valuable for physicist with elementary calculus who is interested in ideas that give meaning to data, tools of modern physics. Contents include symbolism, mathematical equations; space & time foundations of mechanics; probability; physics & continua; electron theory; special & general relativity; quantum mechanics; causality. "Thorough and yet not overdetailed. Unreservedly recommended," NATURE (London). Unabridged, corrected edition. List of recommended readings. 35 illustrations. xi + 537pp. 5⅜ x 8.
S377 Paperbound **$2.45**

FUNDAMENTAL FORMULAS OF PHYSICS, ed. by D. H. Menzel. Highly useful, fully inexpensive reference and study text, ranging from simple to highly sophisticated operations. Mathematics integrated into text—each chapter stands as short textbook of field represented. Vol. 1: Statistics, Physical Constants, Special Theory of Relativity, Hydrodynamics, Aerodynamics, Boundary Value Problems in Math. Physics; Viscosity, Electromagnetic Theory, etc. Vol. 2: Sound, Acoustics; Geometrical Optics, Electron Optics, High-Energy Phenomena, Magnetism, Biophysics, much more. Index. Total of 800pp. 5⅜ x 8.   Vol. 1 S595 Paperbound **$2.00**
Vol. 2 S596 Paperbound **$2.00**

MATHEMATICAL PHYSICS, D. H. Menzel. Thorough one-volume treatment of the mathematical techniques vital for classic mechanics, electromagnetic theory, quantum theory, and relativity. Written by the Harvard Professor of Astrophysics for junior, senior, and graduate courses, it gives clear explanations of all those aspects of function theory, vectors, matrices, dyadics, tensors, partiᵻal differential equations, etc., necessary for the understanding of the various physical theories. Electron theory, relativity, and other topics seldom presented appear here in considerable detail. Scores of definitions, conversion factors, dimensional constants, etc. "More detailed than normal for an advanced text . . . excellent set of sections on Dyadics, Matrices, and Tensors," JOURNAL OF THE FRANKLIN INSTITUTE. Index. 193 problems, with answers. x + 412pp. 5⅜ x 8.   S56 Paperbound **$2.00**

THE SCIENTIFIC PAPERS OF J. WILLARD GIBBS. All the published papers of America's outstanding theoretical scientist (except for "Statistical Mechanics" and "Vector Analysis"). Vol I (thermodynamics) contains one of the most brilliant of all 19th-century scientific papers—the 300-page "On the Equilibrium of Heterogeneous Substances," which founded the science of physical chemistry, and clearly stated a number of highly important natural laws for the first time; 8 other papers complete the first volume. Vol II includes 2 papers on dynamics, 8 on vector analysis and multiple algebra, 5 on the electromagnetic theory of light, and 6 miscellaneous papers. Biographical sketch by H. A. Bumstead. Total of xxxvi + 718pp. 5⅝ x 8⅜.
S721 Vol I Paperbound **$2.00**
S722 Vol II Paperbound **$2.00**
The set **$4.00**

Relativity, quantum theory, nuclear physics

THE PRINCIPLE OF RELATIVITY, A. Einstein, H. Lorentz, M. Minkowski, H. Weyl. These are the 11 basic papers that founded the general and special theories of relativity, all translated into English. Two papers by Lorentz on the Michelson experiment, electromagnetic phenomena. Minkowski's SPACE & TIME, and Weyl's GRAVITATION & ELECTRICITY. 7 epoch-making papers by Einstein: ELECTROMAGNETICS OF MOVING BODIES, INFLUENCE OF GRAVITATION IN PROPAGATION OF LIGHT, COSMOLOGICAL CONSIDERATIONS, GENERAL THEORY, and 3 others. 7 diagrams. Special notes by A. Sommerfeld. 224pp. 5⅜ x 8.
S81 Paperbound **$1.75**

SPACE TIME MATTER, Hermann Weyl. "The standard treatise on the general theory of relativity," (Nature), written by a world-renowned scientist, provides a deep clear discussion of the logical coherence of the general theory, with introduction to all the mathematical tools needed: Maxwell, analytical geometry, non-Euclidean geometry, tensor calculus, etc. Basis is classical space-time, before absorption of relativity. Partial contents: Euclidean space, mathematical form, metrical continuum, relativity of time and space, general theory. 15 diagrams. Bibliography. New preface for this edition. xviii + 330pp. 5⅜ x 8.
S267 Paperbound **$1.85**

PRINCIPLES OF QUANTUM MECHANICS, W. V. Houston. Enables student with working knowledge of elementary mathematical physics to develop facility in use of quantum mechanics, understand published work in field. Formulates quantum mechanics in terms of Schroedinger's wave mechanics. Studies evidence for quantum theory, for inadequacy* of classical mechanics, 2 postulates of quantum mechanics; numerous important, fruitful applications of quantum mechanics in spectroscopy, collision problems, electrons in solids; other topics. "One of the most rewarding features . . . is the interlacing of problems with text," Amer. J. of Physics. Corrected edition. 21 illus. Index. 296pp. 5⅜ x 8.   S524 Paperbound **$1.85**

PHYSICAL PRINCIPLES OF THE QUANTUM THEORY, Werner Heisenberg. A Nobel laureate discusses quantum theory; Heisenberg's own work, Compton, Schroedinger, Wilson, Einstein, many others. Written for physicists, chemists who are not specialists in quantum theory, only elementary formulae are considered in the text; there is a mathematical appendix for specialists. Profound without sacrifice of clarity. Translated by C. Eckart, F. Hoyt. 18 figures. 192pp. 5⅜ x 8.   S113 Paperbound **$1.25**

SELECTED PAPERS ON QUANTUM ELECTRODYNAMICS, edited by J. Schwinger. Facsimiles of papers which established quantum electrodynamics, from initial successes through today's position as part of the larger theory of elementary particles. First book publication in any language of these collected papers of Bethe, Bloch, Dirac, Dyson, Fermi, Feynman, Heisenberg, Kusch, Lamb, Oppenheimer, Pauli, Schwinger, Tomonoga, Weisskopf, Wigner, etc. 34 papers in all, 29 in English, 1 in French, 3 in German, 1 in Italian. Preface and historical commentary by the editor. xvii + 423pp. 6⅛ x 9¼.   S444 Paperbound **$2.45**

THE FUNDAMENTAL PRINCIPLES OF QUANTUM MECHANICS, WITH ELEMENTARY APPLICATIONS, E. C. Kemble. An inductive presentation, for the graduate student or specialist in some other branch of physics. Assumes some acquaintance with advanced math; apparatus necessary beyond differential equations and advanced calculus is developed as needed. Although a general exposition of principles, hundreds of individual problems are fully treated, with applications of theory being interwoven with development of the mathematical structure. The author is the Professor of Physics at Harvard Univ "This excellent book would be of great value to every student . . . a rigorous and detailed mathematical discussion of all of the principal quantum-mechanical methods . . . has succeeded in keeping his presentations clear and understandable," Dr. Linus Pauling, J. of the American Chemical Society. Appendices: calculus of variations, math. notes, etc. Indexes. 611pp. 5⅜ x 8.
S472 Paperbound **$2.95**

ATOMIC SPECTRA AND ATOMIC STRUCTURE, G. Herzberg. Excellent general survey for chemists, physicists specializing in other fields. Partial contents: simplest line spectra and elements of atomic theory, building-up principle and periodic system of elements, hyperfine structure of spectral lines, some experiments and applications. Bibliography. 80 figures. Index. xii + 257pp. 5⅜ x 8.   S115 Paperbound **$1.95**

THE THEORY AND THE PROPERTIES OF METALS AND ALLOYS, N. F. Mott, H. Jones. Quantum methods used to develop mathematical models which show interrelationship of basic chemical phenomena with crystal structure, magnetic susceptibility, electrical, optical properties. Examines thermal properties of crystal lattice, electron motion in applied field, cohesion, electrical resistance, noble metals, para-, dia-, and ferromagnetism, etc. "Exposition . . . clear . . . mathematical treatment . . . simple," Nature. 138 figures. Bibliography. Index. xiii + 320pp. 5⅜ x 8.   S456 Paperbound **$1.85**

FOUNDATIONS OF NUCLEAR PHYSICS, edited by R. T. Beyer. 13 of the most important papers on nuclear physics reproduced in facsimile in the original languages of their authors: the papers most often cited in footnotes, bibliographies. Anderson, Curie, Joliot, Chadwick, Fermi, Lawrence, Cockcroft, Hahn, Yukawa. UNPARALLELED BIBLIOGRAPHY. 122 double-columned, pages, over 4,000 articles, books classified. 57 figures. 288pp. 6⅛ x 9¼.
S19 Paperbound **$1.75**

MESON PHYSICS, R. E. Marshak. Traces the basic theory, and explicitly presents results of experiments with particular emphasis on theoretical significance. Phenomena involving mesons as virtual transitions are avoided, eliminating some of the least satisfactory predictions of meson theory. Includes production and study of π mesons at nonrelativistic nucleon energies, contrasts between π and μ mesons, phenomena associated with nuclear interaction of π mesons, etc. Presents early evidence for new classes of particles and indicates theoretical difficulties created by discovery of heavy mesons and hyperons. Name and subject indices. Unabridged reprint. viii + 378pp. 5⅜ x 8.   S500 Paperbound **$1.95**

See also: STRANGE STORY OF THE QUANTUM, B. Hoffmann; FROM EUCLID TO EDDINGTON, E. Whittaker; MATTER AND LIGHT, THE NEW PHYSICS, L. de Broglie; THE EVOLUTION OF SCIENTIFIC THOUGHT FROM NEWTON TO EINSTEIN, A. d'Abro; THE RISE OF THE NEW PHYSICS, A. d'Abro; THE THEORY OF GROUPS AND QUANTUM MECHANICS, H. Weyl; SUBSTANCE AND FUNCTION, & EINSTEIN'S THEORY OF RELATIVITY, E. Cassirer; FUNDAMENTAL FORMULAS OF PHYSICS, D. H. Menzel.

Hydrodynamics

HYDRODYNAMICS, H. Dryden, F. Murnaghan, Harry Bateman. Published by the National Research Council in 1932 this enormous volume offers a complete coverage of classical hydrodynamics. Encyclopedic in quality. Partial contents: physics of fluids, motion, turbulent flow, compressible fluids, motion in 1, 2, 3 dimensions; viscous fluids rotating, laminar motion, resistance of motion through viscous fluid, eddy viscosity, hydraulic flow in channels of various shapes, discharge of gases, flow past obstacles, etc. Bibliography of over 2,900 items. Indexes. 23 figures. 634pp. 5⅜ x 8.   S303 Paperbound **$2.75**

A TREATISE ON HYDRODYNAMICS, A. B. Basset. Favorite text on hydrodynamics for 2 generations of physicists, hydrodynamical engineers, oceanographers, ship designers, etc. Clear enough for the beginning student, and thorough source for graduate students and engineers on the work of d'Alembert, Euler, Laplace, Lagrange, Poisson, Green, Clebsch, Stokes, Cauchy, Helmholtz, J. J. Thomson, Love, Hicks, Greenhill, Besant, Lamb, etc. Great amount of documentation on entire theory of classical hydrodynamics. Vol I: theory of motion of frictionless liquids, vortex, and cyclic irrotational motion, etc. 132 exercises. Bibliography. 3 Appendixes. xii + 264pp. Vol II: motion in viscous liquids, harmonic analysis, theory of tides, etc. 112 exercises. Bibliography. 4 Appendixes. xv + 328pp. Two volume set. 5⅜ x 8.
S724 Vol I Paperbound **$1.75**
S725 Vol II Paperbound **$1.75**
The set **$3.50**

HYDRODYNAMICS, Horace Lamb. Internationally famous complete coverage of standard reference work on dynamics of liquids & gases. Fundamental theorems, equations, methods, solutions, background, for classical hydrodynamics. Chapters include Equations of Motion, Integration of Equations in Special Gases, Irrotational Motion, Motion of Liquid in 2 Dimensions, Motion of Solids through Liquid-Dynamical Theory, Vortex Motion, Tidal Waves, Surface Waves, Waves of Expansion, Viscosity, Rotating Masses of liquids. Excellently planned, arranged; clear, lucid presentation. 6th enlarged, revised edition. Index. Over 900 footnotes, mostly bibliographical. 119 figures. xv + 738pp. 6⅛ x 9¼.   S256 Paperbound **$2.95**

See also: FUNDAMENTAL FORMULAS OF PHYSICS, D. H. Menzel; THEORY OF FLIGHT, R. von Mises; FUNDAMENTALS OF HYDRO- AND AEROMECHANICS, L. Prandtl and O. G. Tietjens; APPLIED HYDRO- AND AEROMECHANICS, L. Prandtl and O. G. Tietjens; HYDRAULICS AND ITS APPLICATIONS, A. H. Gibson; FLUID MECHANICS FOR HYDRAULIC ENGINEERS, H. Rouse.

Acoustics, optics, electromagnetics

ON THE SENSATIONS OF TONE, Hermann Helmholtz. This is an unmatched coordination of such fields as acoustical physics, physiology, experiment, history of music. It covers the entire gamut of musical tone. Partial contents: relation of musical science to acoustics, physical vs. physiological acoustics, composition of vibration, resonance, analysis of tones by sympathetic resonance, beats, chords, tonality, consonant chords, discords, progression of parts, etc. 33 appendixes discuss various aspects of sound, physics, acoustics, music, etc. Translated by A. J. Ellis. New introduction by Prof. Henry Margenau of Yale. 68 figures. 43 musical passages analyzed. Over 100 tables. Index. xix + 576pp. 6⅛ x 9¼.
S114 Paperbound **$2.95**

THE THEORY OF SOUND, Lord Rayleigh. Most vibrating systems likely to be encountered in practice can be tackled successfully by the methods set forth by the great Nobel laureate, Lord Rayleigh. Complete coverage of experimental, mathematical aspects of sound theory. Partial contents: Harmonic motions, vibrating systems in general, lateral vibrations of bars, curved plates or shells, applications of Laplace's functions to acoustical problems, fluid friction, plane vortex-sheet, vibrations of solid bodies, etc. This is the first inexpensive edition of this great reference and study work. Bibliography. Historical introduction by R. B. Lindsay. Total of 1040pp. 97 figures. 5⅜ x 8.

S292, S293, Two volume set, paperbound, **$4.00**

THE DYNAMICAL THEORY OF SOUND, H. Lamb. Comprehensive mathematical treatment of the physical aspects of sound, covering the theory of vibrations, the general theory of sound, and the equations of motion of strings, bars, membranes, pipes, and resonators. Includes chapters on plane, spherical, and simple harmonic waves, and the Helmholtz Theory of Audition. Complete and self-contained development for student and specialist; all fundamental differential equations solved completely. Specific mathematical details for such important phenomena as harmonics, normal modes, forced vibrations of strings, theory of reed pipes, etc. Index. Bibliography. 86 diagrams. viii + 307pp. 5⅜ x 8. S655 Paperbound **$1.50**

WAVE PROPAGATION IN PERIODIC STRUCTURES, L. Brillouin. A general method and application to different problems: pure physics, such as scattering of X-rays of crystals, thermal vibration in crystal lattices, electronic motion in metals; and also problems of electrical engineering. Partial contents: elastic waves in 1-dimensional lattices of point masses. Propagation of waves along 1-dimensional lattices. Energy flow. 2 dimensional, 3 dimensional lattices. Mathieu's equation. Matrices and propagation of waves along an electric line. Continuous electric lines. 131 illustrations. Bibliography. Index. xii + 253pp. 5⅜ x 8.

S34 Paperbound **$1.85**

THEORY OF VIBRATIONS, N. W. McLachlan. Based on an exceptionally successful graduate course given at Brown University, this discusses linear systems having 1 degree of freedom, forced vibrations of simple linear systems, vibration of flexible strings, transverse vibrations of bars and tubes, transverse vibration of circular plate, sound waves of finite amplitude, etc. Index. 99 diagrams. 160pp. 5⅜ x 8. S190 Paperbound **$1.35**

LOUD SPEAKERS: THEORY, PERFORMANCE, TESTING AND DESIGN, N. W. McLachlan. Most comprehensive coverage of theory, practice of loud speaker design, testing; classic reference, study manual in field. First 12 chapters deal with theory, for readers mainly concerned with math. aspects; last 7 chapters will interest reader concerned with testing, design. Partial contents: principles of sound propagation, fluid pressure on vibrators, theory of moving-coil principle, transients, driving mechanisms, response curves, design of horn type moving coil speakers, electrostatic speakers, much more. Appendix. Bibliography. Index. 165 illustrations, charts. 411pp. 5⅜ x 8. S588 Paperbound **$2.25**

MICROWAVE TRANSMISSION, J. S. Slater. First text dealing exclusively with microwaves, brings together points of view of field, circuit theory, for graduate student in physics, electrical engineering, microwave technician. Offers valuable point of view not in most later studies. Uses Maxwell's equations to study electromagnetic field, important in this area. Partial contents: infinite line with distributed parameters, impedance of terminated line, plane waves, reflections, wave guides, coaxial line, composite transmission lines, impedance matching, etc. Introduction. Index. 76 illus. 319pp. 5⅜ x 8.

S564 Paperbound **$1.50**

THE ANALYSIS OF SENSATIONS, Ernst Mach. Great study of physiology, psychology of perception, shows Mach's ability to see material freshly, his "incorruptible skepticism and independence." (Einstein). Relation of problems of psychological perception to classical physics, supposed dualism of physical and mental, principle of continuity, evolution of senses, will as organic manifestation, scores of experiments, observations in optics, acoustics, music, graphics, etc. New introduction by T. S. Szasz, M. D. 58 illus. 300-item bibliography. Index. 404pp. 5⅜ x 8. S525 Paperbound **$1.75**

APPLIED OPTICS AND OPTICAL DESIGN, A. E. Conrady. With publication of vol. 2, standard work for designers in optics is now complete for first time. Only work of its kind in English; only detailed work for practical designer and self-taught. Requires, for bulk of work, no math above trig. Step-by-step exposition, from fundamental concepts of geometrical, physical optics, to systematic study, design, of almost all types of optical systems. Vol. 1: all ordinary ray-tracing methods; primary aberrations; necessary higher aberration for design of telescopes, low-power microscopes, photographic equipment. Vol. 2: (Completed from author's notes by R. Kingslake, Dir. Optical Design, Eastman Kodak.) Special attention to high-power microscope, anastigmatic photographic objectives. "An indispensable work," J., Optical Soc. of Amer. "As a practical guide this book has no rival," Transactions, Optical Soc. Index. Bibliography. 193 diagrams. 852pp. 6⅛ x 9¼. Vol. 1 T611 Paperbound **$2.95**
Vol. 2 T612 Paperbound **$2.95**

THE THEORY OF OPTICS, Paul Drude. One of finest fundamental texts in physical optics, classic offers thorough coverage, complete mathematical treatment of basic ideas. Includes fullest treatment of application of thermodynamics to optics; sine law in formation of images, transparent crystals, magnetically active substances, velocity of light, apertures, effects depending upon them, polarization, optical instruments, etc. Introduction by A. A. Michelson. Index. 110 illus. 567pp. 5⅜ x 8. S532 Paperbound **$2.45**

OPTICKS, Sir Isaac Newton. In its discussions of light, reflection, color, refraction, theories of wave and corpuscular theories of light, this work is packed with scores of insights and discoveries. In its precise and practical discussion of construction of optical apparatus, contemporary understandings of phenomena it is truly fascinating to modern physicists, astronomers, mathematicians. Foreword by Albert Einstein. Preface by I. B. Cohen of Harvard University. 7 pages of portraits, facsimile pages, letters, etc. cxvi + 414pp. 5⅜ x 8.
S205 Paperbound **$2.00**

OPTICS AND OPTICAL INSTRUMENTS: AN INTRODUCTION WITH SPECIAL REFERENCE TO PRACTICAL APPLICATIONS, B. K. Johnson. An invaluable guide to basic practical applications of optical principles, which shows how to set up inexpensive working models of each of the four main types of optical instruments—telescopes, microscopes, photographic lenses, optical projecting systems. Explains in detail the most important experiments for determining their accuracy, resolving power, angular field of view, amounts of aberration, all other necessary facts about the instruments. Formerly "Practical Optics." Index. 234 diagrams. Appendix. 224pp. 5⅜ x 8.
S642 Paperbound **$1.65**

PRINCIPLES OF PHYSICAL OPTICS, Ernst Mach. This classical examination of the propagation of light, color, polarization, etc. offers an historical and philosophical treatment that has never been surpassed for breadth and easy readability. Contents: Rectilinear propagation of light. Reflection, refraction. Early knowledge of vision. Dioptrics. Composition of light. Theory of color and dispersion. Periodicity. Theory of interference. Polarization. Mathematical representation of properties of light. Propagation of waves, etc. 279 illustrations, 10 portraits. Appendix. Indexes. 324pp. 5⅜ x 8.
S178 Paperbound **$1.75**

FUNDAMENTALS OF ELECTRICITY AND MAGNETISM, L. B. Loeb. For students of physics, chemistry, or engineering who want an introduction to electricity and magnetism on a higher level and in more detail than general elementary physics texts provide. Only elementary differential and integral calculus is assumed. Physical laws developed logically, from magnetism to electric currents, Ohm's law, electrolysis, and on to static electricity, induction, etc. Covers an unusual amount of material; one third of book on modern material: solution of wave equation, photoelectric and thermionic effects, etc. Complete statement of the various electrical systems of units and interrelations. 2 Indexes. 75 pages of problems with answers stated. Over 300 figures and diagrams. xix +669pp. 5⅜ x 8.
S745 Paperbound **$2.75**

THE ELECTROMAGNETIC FIELD, Max Mason & Warren Weaver. Used constantly by graduate engineers. Vector methods exclusively: detailed treatment of electrostatics, expansion methods, with tables converting any quantity into absolute electromagnetic, absolute electrostatic, practical units. Discrete charges, ponderable bodies, Maxwell field equations, etc. Introduction. Indexes. 416pp. 5⅜ x 8.
S185 Paperbound **$2.00**

ELECTRICAL THEORY ON THE GIORGI SYSTEM, P. Cornelius. A new clarification of the fundamental concepts of electricity and magnetism, advocating the convenient m.k.s. system of units that is steadily gaining followers in the sciences. Illustrating the use and effectiveness of his terminology with numerous applications to concrete technical problems, the author here expounds the famous Giorgi system of electrical physics. His lucid presentation and well-reasoned, cogent argument for the universal adoption of this system form one of the finest pieces of scientific exposition in recent years. 28 figures. Index. Conversion tables for translating earlier data into modern units. Translated from 3rd Dutch edition by L. J. Jolley. x + 187pp. 5½ x 8¾.
S909 Clothbound **$6.00**

THEORY OF ELECTRONS AND ITS APPLICATION TO THE PHENOMENA OF LIGHT AND RADIANT HEAT, H. Lorentz. Lectures delivered at Columbia University by Nobel laureate Lorentz. Unabridged, they form a historical coverage of the theory of free electrons, motion, absorption of heat, Zeeman effect, propagation of light in molecular bodies, inverse Zeeman effect, optical phenomena in moving bodies, etc. 109 pages of notes explain the more advanced sections. Index. 9 figures. 352pp. 5⅜ x 8.
S173 Paperbound **$1.85**

TREATISE ON ELECTRICITY AND MAGNETISM, James Clerk Maxwell. For more than 80 years a seemingly inexhaustible source of leads for physicists, mathematicians, engineers. Total of 1082pp. on such topics as Measurement of Quantities, Electrostatics, Elementary Mathematical Theory of Electricity, Electrical Work and Energy in a System of Conductors, General Theorems, Theory of Electrical Images, Electrolysis, Conduction, Polarization, Dielectrics, Resistance, etc. "The greatest mathematical physicist since Newton," Sir James Jeans. 3rd edition. 107 figures, 21 plates. 1082pp. 5⅜ x 8.
S636-7, 2 volume set, paperbound **$4.00**

See also: **FUNDAMENTAL FORMULAS OF PHYSICS, D. H. Menzel; MATHEMATICAL ANALYSIS OF ELECTRICAL & OPTICAL WAVE MOTION, H. Bateman.**

Mechanics, dynamics, thermodynamics, elasticity

MECHANICS VIA THE CALCULUS, P. W. Norris, W. S. Legge. Covers almost everything, from linear motion to vector analysis: equations determining motion, linear methods, compounding of simple harmonic motions, Newton's laws of motion, Hooke's law, the simple pendulum, motion of a particle in 1 plane, centers of gravity, virtual work, friction, kinetic energy of rotating bodies, equilibrium of strings, hydrostatics, sheering stresses, elasticity, etc. 550 problems. 3rd revised edition. xii + 367pp. 6 x 9.
S207 Clothbound **$3.95**

MECHANICS, J. P. Den Hartog. Already a classic among introductory texts, the M.I.T. professor's lively and discursive presentation is equally valuable as a beginner's text, an engineering student's refresher, or a practicing engineer's reference. Emphasis in this highly readable text is on illuminating fundamental principles and showing how they are embodied in a great number of real engineering and design problems: trusses, loaded cables, beams, jacks, hoists, etc. Provides advanced material on relative motion and gyroscopes not usual in introductory texts. "Very thoroughly recommended to all those anxious to improve their real understanding of the principles of mechanics." MECHANICAL WORLD. Index. List of equations. 334 problems, all with answers. Over 550 diagrams and drawings. ix + 462pp. 5⅜ x 8.
S754 Paperbound **$2.00**

THEORETICAL MECHANICS: AN INTRODUCTION TO MATHEMATICAL PHYSICS, J. S. Ames, F. D. Murnaghan. A mathematically rigorous development of theoretical mechanics for the advanced student, with constant practical applications. Used in hundreds of advanced courses. An unusually thorough coverage of gyroscopic and baryscopic material, detailed analyses of the Corilis acceleration, applications of Lagrange's equations, motion of the double pendulum, Hamilton-Jacobi partial differential equations, group velocity and dispersion, etc. Special relativity is also included. 159 problems. 44 figures. ix + 462pp. 5⅜ x 8.
S461 Paperbound **$2.00**

THEORETICAL MECHANICS: STATICS AND THE DYNAMICS OF A PARTICLE, W. D. MacMillan. Used for over 3 decades as a self-contained and extremely comprehensive advanced undergraduate text in mathematical physics, physics, astronomy, and deeper foundations of engineering. Early sections require only a knowledge of geometry; later, a working knowledge of calculus. Hundreds of basic problems, including projectiles to the moon, escape velocity, harmonic motion, ballistics, falling bodies, transmission of power, stress and strain, elasticity, astronomical problems. 340 practice problems plus many fully worked out examples make it possible to test and extend principles developed in the text. 200 figures. xvii + 430pp. 5⅜ x 8.
S467 Paperbound **$2.00**

THEORETICAL MECHANICS: THE THEORY OF THE POTENTIAL, W. D. MacMillan. A comprehensive, well balanced presentation of potential theory, serving both as an introduction and a reference work with regard to specific problems, for physicists and mathematicians. No prior knowledge of integral relations is assumed, and all mathematical material is developed as it becomes necessary. Includes: Attraction of Finite Bodies; Newtonian Potential Function; Vector Fields. Green and Gauss Theorems; Attractions of Surfaces and Lines; Surface Distribution of Matter; Two-Layer Surfaces; Spherical Harmonics; Ellipsoidal Harmonics; etc. "The great number of particular cases . . . should make the book valuable to geophysicists and others actively engaged in practical applications of the potential theory," Review of Scientific Instruments. Index. Bibliography. xiii + 469pp. 5⅜ x 8.
S486 Paperbound **$2.25**

THEORETICAL MECHANICS: DYNAMICS OF RIGID BODIES, W. D. MacMillan. Theory of dynamics of a rigid body is developed, using both the geometrical and analytical methods of instruction. Begins with exposition of algebra of vectors, it goes through momentum principles, motion in space, use of differential equations and infinite series to solve more sophisticated dynamics problems. Partial contents: moments of inertia, systems of free particles, motion parallel to a fixed plane, rolling motion, method of periodic solutions, much more. 82 figs. 199 problems. Bibliography. Indexes. xii + 476pp. 5⅜ x 8.
S641 Paperbound **$2.00**

MATHEMATICAL FOUNDATIONS OF STATISTICAL MECHANICS, A. I. Khinchin. Offering a precise and rigorous formulation of problems, this book supplies a thorough and up-to-date exposition. It provides analytical tools needed to replace cumbersome concepts, and furnishes for the first time a logical step-by-step introduction to the subject. Partial contents: geometry & kinematics of the phase space, ergodic problem, reduction to theory of probability, application of central limit problem, ideal monatomic gas, foundation of thermo-dynamics, dispersion and distribution of sum functions. Key to notations. Index. viii + 179pp. 5⅜ x 8.
S147 Paperbound **$1.35**

ELEMENTARY PRINCIPLES IN STATISTICAL MECHANICS, J. W. Gibbs. Last work of the great Yale mathematical physicist, still one of the most fundamental treatments available for advanced students and workers in the field. Covers the basic principle of conservation of probability of phase, theory of errors in the calculated phases of a system, the contributions of Clausius, Maxwell, Boltzmann, and Gibbs himself, and much more. Includes valuable comparison of statistical mechanics with thermodynamics: Carnot's cycle, mechanical definitions of entropy, etc. xvi + 208pp. 5⅜ x 8.
S707 Paperbound **$1.45**

THE DYNAMICS OF PARTICLES AND OF RIGID, ELASTIC, AND FLUID BODIES; BEING LECTURES ON MATHEMATICAL PHYSICS, A. G. Webster. The reissuing of this classic fills the need for a comprehensive work on dynamics. A wide range of topics is covered in unusually great depth, applying ordinary and partial differential equations. Part I considers laws of motion and methods applicable to systems of all sorts; oscillation, resonance, cyclic systems, etc. Part 2 is a detailed study of the dynamics of rigid bodies. Part 3 introduces the theory of potential; stress and strain, Newtonian potential functions, gyrostatics, wave and vortex motion, etc. Further contents: Kinematics of a point; Lagrange's equations; Hamilton's principle; Systems of vectors; Statics and dynamics of deformable bodies; much more, not easily found together in one volume. Unabridged reprinting of 2nd edition. 20 pages of notes on differential equations and the higher analysis. 203 illustrations. Selected bibliography. Index. xi + 588pp. 5⅜ x 8.
S522 Paperbound **$2.35**

A TREATISE ON DYNAMICS OF A PARTICLE, E. J. Routh. Elementary text on dynamics for beginning mathematics or physics student. Unusually detailed treatment from elementary definitions to motion in 3 dimensions, emphasizing concrete aspects. Much unique material important in recent applications. Covers impulsive forces, rectilinear and constrained motion in 2 dimensions, harmonic and parabolic motion, degrees of freedom, closed orbits, the conical pendulum, the principle of least action, Jacobi's method, and much more. Index. 559 problems, many fully worked out, incorporated into text. xiii + 418pp. 5⅜ x 8.
S696 Paperbound **$2.25**

DYNAMICS OF A SYSTEM OF RIGID BODIES (Elementary Section), E. J. Routh. Revised 7th edition of this standard reference. This volume covers the dynamical principles of the subject, and its more elementary applications: finding moments of inertia by integration, foci of inertia, d'Alembert's principle, impulsive forces, motion in 2 and 3 dimensions, Lagrange's equations, relative indicatrix, Euler's theorem, large tautochronous motions, etc. Index. 55 figures. Scores of problems. xv + 443pp. 5⅜ x 8.
S664 Paperbound **$2.35**

DYNAMICS OF A SYSTEM OF RIGID BODIES (Advanced Section), E. J. Routh. Revised 6th edition of a classic reference aid. Much of its material remains unique. Partial contents: moving axes, relative motion, oscillations about equilibrium, motion. Motion of a body under no forces, any forces. Nature of motion given by linear equations and conditions of stability. Free, forced vibrations, constants of integration, calculus of finite differences, variations, precession and nutation, motion of the moon, motion of string, chain, membranes. 64 figures. 498pp. 5⅜ x 8.
S229 Paperbound **$2.35**

DYNAMICAL THEORY OF GASES, James Jeans. Divided into mathematical and physical chapters for the convenience of those not expert in mathematics, this volume discusses the mathematical theory of gas in a steady state, thermodynamics, Boltzmann and Maxwell, kinetic theory, quantum theory, exponentials, etc. 4th enlarged edition, with new material on quantum theory, quantum dynamics, etc. Indexes. 28 figures. 444pp. 6⅛ x 9¼.
S136 Paperbound **$2.45**

FOUNDATIONS OF POTENTIAL THEORY, O. D. Kellogg. Based on courses given at Harvard this is suitable for both advanced and beginning mathematicians. Proofs are rigorous, and much material not generally avaialable elsewhere is included. Partial contents: forces of gravity, fields of force, divergence theorem, properties of Newtonian potentials at points of free space, potentials as solutions of Laplace's equations, harmonic functions, electrostatics, electric images, logarithmic potential, etc. One of Grundlehren Series. ix + 384pp. 5⅜ x 8.
S144 Paperbound **$1.98**

THERMODYNAMICS, Enrico Fermi. Unabridged reproduction of 1937 edition. Elementary in treatment; remarkable for clarity, organization. Requires no knowledge of advanced math beyond calculus, only familiarity with fundamentals of thermometry, calorimetry. Partial Contents: Thermodynamic systems; First & Second laws of thermodynamics; Entropy; Thermodynamic potentials: phase rule, reversible electric cell; Gaseous reactions: van't Hoff reaction box, principle of LeChatelier; Thermodynamics of dilute solutions: osmotic & vapor pressures, boiling & freezing points; Entropy constant. Index. 25 problems. 24 illustrations. x + 160pp. 5⅜ x 8.
S361 Paperbound **$1.75**

THE THERMODYNAMICS OF ELECTRICAL PHENOMENA IN METALS and A CONDENSED COLLECTION OF THERMODYNAMIC FORMULAS, P. W. Bridgman. Major work by the Nobel Prizewinner: stimulating conceptual introduction to aspects of the electron theory of metals, giving an intuitive understanding of fundamental relationships concealed by the formal systems of Onsager and others. Elementary mathematical formulations show clearly the fundamental thermodynamical relationships of the electric field, and a complete phenomenological theory of metals is created. This is the work in which Bridgman announced his famous "thermomotive force" and his distinction between "driving" and "working" electromotive force. We have added in this Dover edition the author's long unavailable tables of thermodynamic formulas, extremely valuable for the speed of reference they allow. Two works bound as one. Index. 33 figures. Bibliography. xviii + 256pp. 5⅜ x 8. S723 Paperbound **$1.65**

REFLECTIONS ON THE MOTIVE POWER OF FIRE, by Sadi Carnot, and other papers on the 2nd law of thermodynamics by E. Clapeyron and R. Clausius. Carnot's "Reflections" laid the groundwork of modern thermodynamics. Its non-technical, mostly verbal statements examine the relations between heat and the work done by heat in engines, establishing conditions for the economical working of these engines. The papers by Clapeyron and Clausius here reprinted added further refinements to Carnot's work, and led to its final acceptance by physicists. Selections from posthumous manuscripts of Carnot are also included. All papers in English. New introduction by E. Mendoza. 12 illustrations. xxii + 152pp. 5⅜ x 8.
S661 Paperbound **$1.50**

TREATISE ON THERMODYNAMICS, Max Planck. Based on Planck's original papers this offers a uniform point of view for the entire field and has been used as an introduction for students who have studied elementary chemistry, physics, and calculus. Rejecting the earlier approaches of Helmholtz and Maxwell, the author makes no assumptions regarding the nature of heat, but begins with a few empirical facts, and from these deduces new physical and chemical laws. 3rd English edition of this standard text by a Nobel laureate. xvi + 297pp. 5⅜ x 8.
S219 Paperbound **$1.75**

THE THEORY OF HEAT RADIATION, Max Planck. A pioneering work in thermodynamics, providing basis for most later work. Nobel Laureate Planck writes on Deductions from Electrodynamics and Thermodynamics, Entropy and Probability, Irreversible Radiation Processes, etc. Starts with simple experimental laws of optics, advances to problems of spectral distribution of energy and irreversibility. Bibliography. 7 illustrations, xiv + 224pp. 5⅜ x 8.
S546 Paperbound **$1.50**

A HISTORY OF THE THEORY OF ELASTICITY AND THE STRENGTH OF MATERIALS, I. Todhunter and K. Pearson. For over 60 years a basic reference, unsurpassed in scope or authority. Both a history of the mathematical theory of elasticity from Galileo, Hooke, and Mariotte to Saint Venant, Kirchhoff, Clebsch, and Lord Kelvin and a detailed presentation of every important mathematical contribution during this period. Presents proofs of thousands of theorems and laws, summarizes every relevant treatise, many unavailable elsewhere. Practically a book apiece is devoted to modern founders: Saint Venant, Lame; Boussinesq, Rankine, Lord Kelvin, F. Neumann, Kirchhoff, Clebsch. Hundreds of pages of technical and physical treatises on specific applications of elasticity to particular materials. Indispensable for the mathematician, physicist, or engineer working with elasticity. Unabridged, corrected reprint of original 3-volume 1886-1893 edition. Three volume set. Two indexes. Appendix to Vol. I. Total of 2344pp. 5⅜ x 8⅜.
S914-916 The set, Clothbound **$12.50**

THE MATHEMATICAL THEORY OF ELASTICITY, A. E. H. Love. A wealth of practical illustration combined with thorough discussion of fundamentals—theory, application, special problems and solutions. Partial Contents: Analysis of Strain & Stress, Elasticity of Solid Bodies, Elasticity of Crystals, Vibration of Spheres, Cylinders, Propagation of Waves in Elastic Solid Media, Torsion, Theory of Continuous Beams, Plates. Rigorous treatment of Volterra's theory of dislocations, 2-dimensional elastic systems, other topics of modern interest. "For years the standard treatise on elasticity," AMERICAN MATHEMATICAL MONTHLY. 4th revised edition. Index. 76 figures. xviii + 643pp. 6⅛ x 9¼.
S174 Paperbound **$2.95**

RAYLEIGH'S PRINCIPLE AND ITS APPLICATIONS TO ENGINEERING, G. Temple & W. Bickley. Rayleigh's principle developed to provide upper and lower estimates of true value of fundamental period of a vibrating system, or condition of stability of elastic systems. Illustrative examples; rigorous proofs in special chapters. Partial contents: Energy method of discussing vibrations, stability. Perturbation theory, whirling of uniform shafts. Criteria of elastic stability. Application of energy method. Vibrating systems. Proof, accuracy, successive approximations, application of Rayleigh's principle. Synthetic theorems. Numerical, graphical methods. Equilibrium configurations, Ritz's method. Bibliography. Index. 22 figures. ix + 156pp. 5⅜ x 8.
S307 Paperbound **$1.50**

INVESTIGATIONS ON THE THEORY OF THE BROWNIAN MOVEMENT, Albert Einstein. Reprints from rare European journals. 5 basic papers, including the Elementary Theory of the Brownian Movement, written at the request of Lorentz to provide a simple explanation. Translated by A. D. Cowper. Annotated, edited by R. Fürth. 33pp. of notes elucidate, give history of previous investigations. Author, subject indexes. 62 footnotes. 124pp. 5⅜ x 8.
S304 Paperbound **$1.25**

See also: FUNDAMENTAL FORMULAS OF PHYSICS, D. H. Menzel.

ENGINEERING

THEORY OF FLIGHT, Richard von Mises. Remains almost unsurpassed as balanced, well-written account of fundamental fluid dynamics, and situations in which air compressibility effects are unimportant. Stressing equally theory and practice, avoiding formidable mathematical structure, it conveys a full understanding of physical phenomena and mathematical concepts. Contains perhaps the best introduction to general theory of stability. "Outstanding," Scientific, Medical, and Technical Books. New introduction by K. H. Hohenemser. Bibliographical, historical notes. Index. 408 illustrations. xvi + 620pp. 5⅜ x 8⅜.
S541 Paperbound **$2.85**

THEORY OF WING SECTIONS, I. H. Abbott, A. E. von Doenhoff. Concise compilation of subsonic aerodynamic characteristics of modern NASA wing sections, with description of their geometry, associated theory. Primarily reference work for engineers, students, it gives methods, data for using wing-section data to predict characteristics. Particularly valuable: chapters on thin wings, airfoils; complete summary of NACA's experimental observations, system of construction families of airfoils. 350pp. of tables on Basic Thickness Forms, Mean Lines, Airfoil Ordinates, Aerodynamic Characteristics of Wing Sections. Index. Bibliography. 191 illustrations. Appendix. 705pp. 5⅜ x 8.
S558 Paperbound **$2.95**

SUPERSONIC AERODYNAMICS, E. R. C. Miles. Valuable theoretical introduction to the supersonic domain, with emphasis on mathematical tools and principles, for practicing aerodynamicists and advanced students in aeronautical engineering. Covers fundamental theory, divergence theorem and principles of circulation, compressible flow and Helmholtz laws, the Prandtl-Busemann graphic method for 2-dimensional flow, oblique shock waves, the Taylor-Maccoll method for cones in supersonic flow, the Chaplygin method for 2-dimensional flow, etc. Problems range from practical engineering problems to development of theoretical results. "Rendered outstanding by the unprecedented scope of its contents . . . has undoubtedly filled a vital gap," AERONAUTICAL ENGINEERING REVIEW. Index. 173 problems, answers. 106 diagrams. 7 tables. xii + 255pp. 5⅜ x 8.
S214 Paperbound **$1.45**

WEIGHT-STRENGTH ANALYSIS OF AIRCRAFT STRUCTURES, F. R. Shanley. Scientifically sound methods of analyzing and predicting the structural weight of aircraft and missiles. Deals directly with forces and the distances over which they must be transmitted, making it possible to develop methods by which the minimum structural weight can be determined for any material and conditions of loading. Weight equations for wing and fuselage structures. Includes author's original papers on inelastic buckling and creep buckling. "Particularly successful in presenting his analytical methods for investigating various optimum design principles," AERONAUTICAL ENGINEERING REVIEW. Enlarged bibliography. Index. 199 figures. xiv + 404pp. 5⅜ x 8⅜. S660 Paperbound **$2.45**

INTRODUCTION TO THE STATISTICAL DYNAMICS OF AUTOMATIC CONTROL SYSTEMS, V. V. Solodovnikov. First English publication of text-reference covering important branch of automatic control systems—random signals; in its original edition, this was the first comprehensive treatment. Examines frequency characteristics, transfer functions, stationary random processes, determination of minimum mean-squared error, of transfer function for a finite period of observation, much more. Translation edited by J. B. Thomas, L. A. Zadeh. Index. Bibliography. Appendix. xxii + 308pp. 5⅜ x 8. S420 Paperbound **$2.25**

TENSORS FOR CIRCUITS, Gabriel Kron. A boldly original method of analysing engineering problems, at center of sharp discussion since first introduced, now definitely proved useful in such areas as electrical and structural networks on automatic computers. Encompasses a great variety of specific problems by means of a relatively few symbolic equations. "Power and flexibility . . . becoming more widely recognized," Nature. Formerly "A Short Course in Tensor Analysis." New introduction by B. Hoffmann. Index. Over 800 diagrams. xix + 250pp. 5⅜ x 8. S534 Paperbound **$1.85**

DESIGN AND USE OF INSTRUMENTS AND ACCURATE MECHANISM, T. N. Whitehead. For the instrument designer, engineer; how to combine necessary mathematical abstractions with independent observation of actual facts. Partial contents: instruments & their parts, theory of errors, systematic errors, probability, short period errors, erratic errors, design precision, kinematic, semikinematic design, stiffness, planning of an instrument, human factor, etc. Index. 85 photos, diagrams. xii + 288pp. 5⅜ x 8. S270 Paperbound **$1.95**

APPLIED ELASTICITY, J. Prescott. Provides the engineer with the theory of elasticity usually lacking in books on strength of materials, yet concentrates on those portions useful for immediate application. Develops every important type of elasticity problem from theoretical principles. Covers analysis of stress, relations between stress and strain, the empirical basis of elasticity, thin rods under tension or thrust, Saint Venant's theory, transverse oscillations of thin rods, stability of thin plates, cylinders with thin walls, vibrations of rotating disks, elastic bodies in contact, etc. "Excellent and important contribution to the subject, not merely in the old matter which he has presented in new and refreshing form, but also in the many original investigations here published for the first time," NATURE. Index. 3 Appendixes. vi + 672pp. 5⅜ x 8. S726 Paperbound **$2.95**

STRENGTH OF MATERIALS, J. P. Den Hartog. Distinguished text prepared for M.I.T. course, ideal as introduction, refresher, reference, or self-study text. Full clear treatment of elementary material (tension, torsion, bending, compound stresses, deflection of beams, etc.), plus much advanced material on engineering methods of great practical value: full treatment of the Mohr circle, lucid elementary discussions of the theory of the center of shear and the "Myosotis" method of calculating beam deflections, reinforced concrete, plastic deformations, photoelasticity, etc. In all sections, both general principles and concrete applications are given. Index. 186 figures (160 others in problem section). 350 problems, all with answers. List of formulas. viii + 323pp. 5⅜ x 8. S755 Paperbound **$1.95**

PHOTOELASTICITY: PRINCIPLES AND METHODS, H. T. Jessop, F. C. Harris. For the engineer, for specific problems of stress analysis. Latest time-saving methods of checking calculations in 2-dimensional design problems, new techniques for stresses in 3 dimensions, and lucid description of optical systems used in practical photoelasticity. Useful suggestions and hints based on on-the-job experience included. Partial contents: strained and stress-strain relations, circular disc under thrust along diameter, rectangular block with square hole under vertical thrust, simply supported rectangular beam under central concentrated load, etc. Theory held to minimum, no advanced mathematical training needed. Index. 164 illustrations. viii + 184pp. 6⅛ x 9¼. S137 Clothbound **$3.75**

MECHANICS OF THE GYROSCOPE, THE DYNAMICS OF ROTATION, R. F. Deimel, Professor of Mechanical Engineering at Stevens Institute of Technology. Elementary general treatment of dynamics of rotation, with special application of gyroscopic phenomena. No knowledge of vectors needed. Velocity of a moving curve, acceleration to a point, general equations of motion, gyroscopic horizon, free gyro, motion of discs, the damped gyro, 103 similar topics. Exercises. 75 figures. 208pp. 5⅜ x 8. S66 Paperbound **$1.65**
S144 Paperbound **$1.98**

A TREATISE ON GYROSTATICS AND ROTATIONAL MOTION: THEORY AND APPLICATIONS, Andrew Gray. Most detailed, thorough book in English, generally considered definitive study. Many problems of all sorts in full detail, or step-by-step summary. Classical problems of Bour, Lottner, etc.; later ones of great physical interest. Vibrating systems of gyrostats, earth as a top, calculation of path of axis of a top by elliptic integrals, motion of unsymmetrical top, much more. Index. 160 illus. 550pp. 5⅜ x 8. S589 Paperbound **$2.75**

FUNDAMENTALS OF HYDRO- AND AEROMECHANICS, L. Prandtl and O. G. Tietjens. The well-known standard work based upon Prandtl's lectures at Goettingen. Wherever possible hydrodynamics theory is referred to practical considerations in hydraulics, with the view of unifying theory and experience. Presentation is extremely clear and though primarily physical, mathematical proofs are rigorous and use vector analysis to a considerable extent. An Enginering Society Monograph, 1934. 186 figures. Index. xvi + 270pp. 5⅜ x 8.
S374 Paperbound **$1.85**

APPLIED HYDRO- AND AEROMECHANICS, L. Prandtl and O. G. Tietjens. Presents, for the most part, methods which will be valuable to engineers. Covers flow in pipes, boundary layers, airfoil theory, entry conditions, turbulent flow in pipes, and the boundary layer, determining drag from measurements of pressure and velocity, etc. "Will be welcomed by all students of aerodynamics," NATURE. Unabridged, unaltered. An Engineering Society Monograph, 1934. Index. 226 figures, 28 photographic plates illustrating flow patterns. xvi + 311pp. 5⅜ x 8.
S375 Paperbound **$1.85**

HYDRAULICS AND ITS APPLICATIONS, A. H. Gibson. Excellent comprehensive textbook for the student and thorough practical manual for the professional worker, a work of great stature in its area. Half the book is devoted to theory and half to applications and practical problems met in the field. Covers modes of motion of a fluid, critical velocity, viscous flow, eddy formation, Bernoulli's theorem, flow in converging passages, vortex motion, form of effluent streams, notches and weirs, skin friction, losses at valves and elbows, siphons, erosion of channels, jet propulsion, waves of oscillation, and over 100 similar topics. Final chapters (nearly 400 pages) cover more than 100 kinds of hydraulic machinery: Pelton wheel, speed regulators, the hydraulic ram, surge tanks, the scoop wheel, the Venturi meter, etc. A special chapter treats methods of testing theoretical hypotheses: scale models of rivers, tidal estuaries, siphon spillways, etc. 5th revised and enlarged (1952) edition. Index. Appendix. 427 photographs and diagrams. 95 examples, answers. xv + 813pp. 6 x 9.
S791 Clothbound **$8.00**

FLUID MECHANICS FOR HYDRAULIC ENGINEERS, H. Rouse. Standard work that gives a coherent picture of fluid mechanics from the point of view of the hydraulic engineer. Based on courses given to civil and mechanical engineering students at Columbia and the California Institute of Technology, this work covers every basic principle, method, equation, or theory of interest to the hydraulic engineer. Much of the material, diagrams, charts, etc., in this self-contained text are not duplicated elsewhere. Covers irrotational motion, conformal mapping, problems in laminar motion, fluid turbulence, flow around immersed bodies, transportation of sediment, general charcteristics of wave phenomena, gravity waves in open channels, etc. Index. Appendix of physical properties of common fluids. Frontispiece + 245 figures and photographs. xvi + 422pp. 5⅜ x 8.
S729 Paperbound **$2.25**

THE MEASUREMENT OF POWER SPECTRA FROM THE POINT OF VIEW OF COMMUNICATIONS ENGINEERING, R. B. Blackman, J. W. Tukey. This pathfinding work, reprinted from the "Bell System Technical Journal," explains various ways of getting practically useful answers in the measurement of power spectra, using results from both transmission theory and the theory of statistical estimation. Treats: Autocovariance Functions and Power Spectra; Direct Analog Computation; Distortion, Noise, Heterodyne Filtering and Pre-whitening; Aliasing; Rejection Filtering and Separation; Smoothing and Decimation Procedures; Very Low Frequencies; Transversal Filtering; much more. An appendix reviews fundamental Fourier techniques. Index of notation. Glossary of terms. 24 figures. XII tables. Bibliography. General index. 192pp. 5⅜ x 8.
S507 Paperbound **$1.85**

MICROWAVE TRANSMISSION DESIGN DATA, T. Moreno. Originally classified, now rewritten and enlarged (14 new chapters) for public release under auspices of Sperry Corp. Material of immediate value or reference use to radio engineers, systems designers, applied physicists, etc. Ordinary transmission line theory; attenuation; capacity; parameters of coaxial lines; higher modes; flexible cables; obstacles, discontinuities, and injunctions; tuneable wave guide impedance transformers; effects of temperature and humidity; much more. "Enough theoretical discussion is included to allow use of data without previous background," Electronics. 324 circuit diagrams, figures, etc. Tables of dielectrics, flexible cable, etc., data. Index. ix + 248pp. 5⅜ x 8.
S459 Paperbound **$1.50**

GASEOUS CONDUCTORS: THEORY AND ENGINEERING APPLICATIONS, J. D. Cobine. An indispensable text and reference to gaseous conduction phenomena, with the engineering viewpoint prevailing throughout. Studies the kinetic theory of gases, ionization, emission phenomena; gas breakdown, spark characteristics, glow, and discharges; engineering applications in circuit interrupters, rectifiers, light sources, etc. Separate detailed treatment of high pressure arcs (Suits); low pressure arcs (Langmuir and Tonks). Much more. "Well organized, clear, straightforward," Tonks, Review of Scientific Instruments. Index. Bibliography. 83 practice problems. 7 appendices. Over 600 figures. 58 tables. xx + 606pp. 5⅜ x 8.
S442 Paperbound **$2.85**

See also: BRIDGES AND THEIR BUILDERS, D. Steinman, S. R. Watson; A DIDEROT PICTORIAL ENCYCLOPEDIA OF TRADES AND INDUSTRY; MATHEMATICS IN ACTION, O. G. Sutton; THE THEORY OF SOUND, Lord Rayleigh; RAYLEIGH'S PRINCIPLE AND ITS APPLICATION TO ENGINEERING, G. Temple, W. Bickley; APPLIED OPTICS AND OPTICAL DESIGN, A. E. Conrady; HYDRODYNAMICS, Dryden, Murnaghan, Bateman; LOUD SPEAKERS, N. W. McLachlan; HISTORY OF THE THEORY OF ELASTICITY AND OF THE STRENGTH OF MATERIALS, I. Todhunter,

K. Pearson; THEORY AND OPERATION OF THE SLIDE RULE, J. P. Ellis; DIFFERENTIAL EQUATIONS FOR ENGINEERS, P. Franklin; MATHEMATICAL METHODS FOR SCIENTISTS AND ENGINEERS, L. P. Smith; APPLIED MATHEMATICS FOR RADIO AND COMMUNICATIONS ENGINEERS, C. E. Smith; MATHEMATICS OF MODERN ENGINEERING, E. G. Keller, R. E. Doherty; THEORY OF FUNCTIONS AS APPLIED TO ENGINEERING PROBLEMS, R. Rothe, F. Ollendorff, K. Pohlhausen.

CHEMISTRY AND PHYSICAL CHEMISTRY

ORGANIC CHEMISTRY, F. C. Whitmore. The entire subject of organic chemistry for the practicing chemist and the advanced student. Storehouse of facts, theories, processes found elsewhere only in specialized journals. Covers aliphatic compounds (500 pages on the properties and synthetic preparation of hydrocarbons, halides, proteins, ketones, etc.), alicyclic compounds, aromatic compounds, heterocyclic compounds, organophosphorus and organometallic compounds. Methods of synthetic preparation analyzed critically throughout. Includes much of biochemical interest. "The scope of this volume is astonishing," INDUSTRIAL AND ENGINEERING CHEMISTRY. 12,000-reference index. 2387-item bibliography. Total of x + 1005pp. 5⅜ x 8. Two volume set.

S700 Vol I Paperbound **$2.00**
S701 Vol II Paperbound **$2.00**
The set **$4.00**

THE PRINCIPLES OF ELECTROCHEMISTRY, D. A. MacInnes. Basic equations for almost every subfield of electrochemistry from first principles, referring at all times to the soundest and most recent theories and results; unusually useful as text or as reference. Covers coulometers and Faraday's Law, electrolytic conductance, the Debye-Hueckel method for the theoretical calculation of activity coefficients, concentration cells, standard electrode potentials, thermodynamic ionization constants, pH, potentiometric titrations, irreversible phenomena, Planck's equation, and much more. "Excellent treatise," AMERICAN CHEMICAL SOCIETY JOURNAL. "Highly recommended," CHEMICAL AND METALLURGICAL ENGINEERING. 2 Indices. Appendix. 585-item bibliography. 137 figures. 94 tables. ii + 478pp. 5⅝ x 8⅜.

S52 Paperbound **$2.35**

THE CHEMISTRY OF URANIUM: THE ELEMENT, ITS BINARY AND RELATED COMPOUNDS, J. J. Katz and E. Rabinowitch. Vast post-World War II collection and correlation of thousands of AEC reports and published papers in a useful and easily accessible form, still the most complete and up-to-date compilation. Treats "dry uranium chemistry," occurrences, preparation, properties, simple compounds, isotopic composition, extraction from ores, spectra, alloys, etc. Much material available only here. Index. Thousands of evaluated bibliographical references. 324 tables, charts, figures. xxi + 609pp. 5⅜ x 8.

S757 Paperbound **$2.95**

KINETIC THEORY OF LIQUIDS, J. Frenkel. Regarding the kinetic theory of liquids as a generalization and extension of the theory of solid bodies, this volume covers all types of arrangements of solids, thermal displacements of atoms, interstitial atoms and ions, orientational and rotational motion of molecules, and transition between states of matter. Mathematical theory is developed close to the physical subject matter. 216 bibliographical footnotes. 55 figures. xi + 485pp. 5⅜ x 8.

S94 Clothbound **$3.95**
S95 Paperbound **$2.45**

POLAR MOLECULES, Pieter Debye. This work by Nobel laureate Debye offers a complete guide to fundamental electrostatic field relations, polarizability, molecular structure. Partial contents: electric intensity, displacement and force, polarization by orientation, molar polarization and molar refraction, halogen-hydrides, polar liquids, ionic saturation, dielectric constant, etc. Special chapter considers quantum theory. Indexed. 172pp. 5⅜ x 8.

S64 Paperbound **$1.50**

Dover publishes books on art, music, philosophy, literature, languages, history, social sciences, psychology, handcrafts, orientalia, puzzles and entertainments, chess, pets and gardens, books explaining science, intermediate and higher mathematics, mathematical physics, engineering, biological sciences, earth sciences, classics of science, etc. Write to:

Dept. catrr.
Dover Publications, Inc.
180 Varick Street, N. Y. 14, N. Y.